Mack Tyner, Ph.D. University of Cincinnati, is Professor of Chemical Engineering at the University of Florida and a registered engineer. He is author of *Process Engineering Calculations*, published by The Ronald Press Company.

Frank P. May, Ph.D. University of Florida, is Associate Professor of Chemical Engineering at the University of Florida. He is a registered engineer with many years of experience in the process industries. Currently, he is also a consultant to industry on process problems.

PROCESS ENGINEERING CONTROL

- MACK TYNER
- FRANK P. MAY

UNIVERSITY OF FLORIDA

THE RONALD PRESS COMPANY • NEW YORK

To Ray W. Fahien
scholar, educator, and friend, who
helped to make this book possible

Preface

This book is designed as an introduction to process control theory for the engineering student as well as the practicing engineer. The time is past when the process engineer could rely solely on the principles of steady-state analysis to design a stable and economic operating plant. It must be recognized today that the unsteady state is the normal condition in a plant, that plant units interact in operation, and that the whole plant is more than the sum of its parts. Thus the primary objective of this book is to develop those techniques which will facilitate the handling of unsteady-state conditions that will be met in the analysis and design of simple plant systems. The theory is based mainly on college physics and linear differential equations, utilizing Laplace-transform notation, and is suitable for senior and graduate courses in process control.

Through simple process problems the reader becomes acquainted with the techniques of linear systems and such devices as the Nyquist diagram, the Bode plot, and the Nichols chart. He learns early when and how he can linearize nonlinear forms, and studies both the root-locus method of control system analysis and the frequency response method. In text discussion, examples, and problems, emphasis is always on the universality of the control problem as exemplified by the mathematical equation regardless of the specific technological field. Thus, the student develops a "systems engineering viewpoint," which he will carry into further courses in process control and into separate physical and chemical process subject areas.

Attention is given to the use of computers in process engineering—the digital for precise calculation and the analog particularly for simulation study and for nonlinear problems. Today, with increased competition and less process development time, the engineer must make maximum use of these machines in the analysis, design, and operation of process plants.

The authors are grateful to their students for constructive comments on the manuscript, to the typists who assisted in its preparation, and to the publishers who granted permission for use of their material. Comments and suggestions from users of this book will be appreciated.

MACK TYNER
FRANK P. MAY

Gainesville, Florida
January, 1968

v

Contents

List of Symbols, *ix*

1 INTRODUCTION TO PROCESS CONTROL   3
1-1 Process Plant Design, *3*
1-2 The Need for Control, *4*
1-3 The Meaning of Control, *5*
1-4 Controlled Systems, *7*
1-5 Feedback Control System Terminology, *18*
1-6 Block Diagrams or Signal Flow Diagrams, *21*
1-7 Linearization of System Equations, *28*
1-8 Plant Optimization by Computer Control, *32*
1-9 Process System Variables, *34*

2 MATHEMATICS FOR CONTROL THEORY   39
2-1 Complex Numbers and Operations, *39*
2-2 Polynomials and Rational Functions, *44*
2-3 Laplace Transform and Uses, *54*
2-4 Process System Inputs, *71*

3 BASIC PROCESS ELEMENTS   79
3-1 Active Elements, *81*
3-2 Passive Elements, *85*
3-3 Response of Process Elements to Standard Inputs, *111*

4 BASIC PROCESS COMPONENTS   117
4-1 Analysis of Process Components, *117*
4-2 Basic Process Components, *122*
4-3 Interacting Process Components, *171*

5 PROCESS CONTROLLERS   179
5-1 Error-Detecting Component, *179*
5-2 Ideal Controller Components, *181*
5-3 Actual Controller Components, *192*
5-4 Pneumatic Diaphragm—Spring Actuator, *206*

6 SYSTEM RESPONSE AND PERFORMANCE SPECIFICATIONS   212
6-1 Feedback System Equations, *212*
6-2 Feedforward System Equations, *216*

6–3   Response of Simple Systems, *217*

6–4   Control System Performance Criteria, *234*

6–5   Selection of Process Controllers, *241*

6–6   Controller Adjustment, *243*

7   THE ROOT-LOCUS METHOD   **254**

7–1   Root-Locus Method, *254*

7–2   Transient Response from Pole-Zero Map, *270*

7–3   Controllers for Plant Compensation, *280*

7–4   Root Locus of Multiple-Loop Systems, *289*

7–5   Frequency Response from Pole-Zero Map, *294*

8   THE FREQUENCY RESPONSE METHOD   **300**

8–1   Frequency Transfer Functions, *301*

8–2   Frequency Response Plots for Basic Components, *305*

8–3   Construction of Frequency Response Plots, *311*

8–4   Closed-Loop System Frequency Response, *316*

8–5   Stability of Closed-Loop Systems, *321*

8–6   Plant Compensation with Process Controllers, *332*

9   PROCESS MODELS AND CONTROL DESIGN   **346**

9–1   Organization for Computer Control, *347*

9–2   Process Models, *351*

9–3   Process Control Design, *362*

9–4   Comments on Process Systems, *378*

10   ANALOG DATA PROCESSING   **391**

10–1   Operational Amplifiers, *392*

10–2   Plant Data Processing Applications, *409*

10–3   Process Control Computer Applications, *413*

APPENDIX   **423**

A   Complex Functions and Mapping, *423*

B   Liquid-Level Processes, *441*

C   Analog Computer Magnitude and Time Scaling, *442*

D   Nichols Chart for Open-Loop-to-Closed-Loop Transformation, *448*

E   Correlation of Transient and Frequency Response, *450*

F   Frequency Response from Pulse Testing, *454*

G   Analog Computer Simulation of Systems, *460*

Index, *463*

List of Symbols

Since process control applications occur in many different industries, a standard nomenclature is not possible. The most commonly used symbols are given here. Generally, functions of time are represented by lower case symbols and Laplace-transformed variables by capitalized symbols.

a, A	Constant; area; amplifier gain; amplitude of complex quantity
AR	Magnitude or amplitude ratio for frequency response
$b(t), B(s)$	Feedback variable
C	Capacitance; curve
$c(t), C(s)$	Controlled variable; composition of process stream
D	Denominator; diameter; viscous damping coefficient
$e(t), E(s)$	Error; voltage
f	Force
$f(t), F(s)$	General function; function of a complex variable
$G(s)$	General forward transfer function
g, g_c	Gravitational constant; Newton's law conversion factor
GM	Gain margin
$H(s)$	General feedback transfer function
$h(t), H(s)$	Liquid level
$i(t), I(s)$	Current; flow rate for electrons, heat, mass, or materal
$\mathcal{Im}$	Imaginary part of complex number
j	Imaginary operator, $\sqrt{-1}$
k, K	General constant; gain; residue
l, L	Length; displacement; inertance
$\mathcal{L}[\ ]$	Direct Laplace transform
$\mathcal{L}^{-1}[\ ]$	Inverse Laplace transform
m, M	Mass
$m(t), M(s)$	Manipulated variable
M_p	Maximum magnitude ratio of closed-loop frequency response
N	Numerator; number of revolutions
p, P	Pole; number of poles; pressure
$P(s)$	Polynomial in s
PM	Phase margin
R	Resistance; universal gas constant
$r(t), R(s)$	Set-point variable
$\mathcal{Re}$	Real part of imaginary number
Res	Residue
s	Complex frequency variable of Laplace transform
t	Time
t_p, t_z, t_r, t_s	Time to peak; first time to zero error; rise time; settling time
T	Temperature; period of periodic function

u, $u(t)$	Real part of function of complex variable; unit step function
v, V	Imaginary part of function of complex variable; volume
$w(t)$	Impulse response
$x(t)$, $X(s)$	Linear displacement
z, Z	Zero; number of zeros; impedance
α	Constant; phase angle of closed-loop frequency response
β	Scale factor; bulk modulus of fluid; normalized frequency
$\delta(t)$	Unit impulse
Δ	Increment
ζ	Damping ratio of complex pole pair
θ	Angle
μ	Fluid viscosity
ρ	Fluid density
σ	Real part of complex variable s
τ	Time constant of process
ϕ, ϕ_m	Phase angle; phase margin
ψ	Angle
ω	Imaginary part of complex variable s; real frequency
ω_d, ω_n, ω_r	Damped frequency; undamped natural frequency; resonant frequency

PROCESS ENGINEERING CONTROL

1

Introduction to Process Control

Technological progress in the process industries, resulting in increased growth in size and complexity of process plants, has given rise to the need for improved control of such plants. Increasing economic pressures within the industries are forcing managements to look for more effective means to design and operate more efficient process plants. The greatest single recent advance in the process industries has been the widespread application of the techniques of automatic control in the design of new plants and in the improvement of existing ones. This application is popularly known as "automation," which means to control automatically the operation of an apparatus, process, or system through the duplication by mechanical means of the activities of living creatures—in short, control by mechanisms instead of by men. The effects of automation are currently being amplified by the use of computers both as tools in the design of control systems and as integral components of such systems.

The process engineer must expand his experience to include abilities to use modern electronic computers and to handle the complex applications of automatic control principles in process design, operation, and maintenance. In this respect, the primary function of the process engineer is to analyze the dynamic operation of an existing or proposed process and to design or adjust a process system to ensure the economic production of quality product. To fulfill his function, the process engineer must have an understanding of the dynamic behavior of the process units, adequate mathematical background to handle the analytical problems that occur, and the ability to integrate all aspects of plant design and operation which have a bearing on plant production.

1-1. PROCESS PLANT DESIGN

A process plant consists of an arrangement of integrated process equipment which takes raw materials and converts them into finished products.

The processes may range, for example, from the simple preparation and packaging of a raw material for market to the complex processes for converting chemical raw materials into chemical products meeting consumer purity specifications.

The problems of analysis and design of processes and equipment are solved by application of the fundamental concepts of process engineering:

1. Rate laws. The rate laws governing transport phenomena and chemical kinetics form the design equations used for sizing equipment in process plants.

2. Thermodynamic restraints. The conservation and equilibrium laws, studied in thermodynamics, establish the possible operating region for the process variables. Together with the rate laws, they enable the engineer to write equations which describe the process under plant conditions.

3. Control. The uncontrolled process plant is intolerable. Present-day control methods utilize both feedback and feedforward techniques to control the plant performance and to optimize the plant behavior in the operating region.

After the process flow sheet is established, the plant design procedure begins with the properties of matter and the applicable rate laws in order to size the process units according to the process requirements of chemical reaction and of energy and mass transfer. The concepts of control system design must be integrated into the final plant design if a stable and efficient operating plant having a maximum economic advantage is to be achieved. In fact, at the present time, the theory and technology of process control have advanced to the point where complete plants may be placed under computer control and continuously optimized for economic production. *Systems engineering* is the term commonly applied to activities whose purpose is achieved by treating a complex of interrelated components as a single "system." This normally involves the application of the principles of automatic control to the study, design, and control of complex enterprises for optimum results. The systems approach has become practicable only through the availability of electronic computers.

1-2. THE NEED FOR CONTROL

The industrial use of automatic control was not widespread at the turn of this century although the first application, the flyball governor on Watt's steam engine, was more than a century old. Application in the mechanical and process industries began appearing around 1900. The causes of the delay were the common availability of cheap labor and the lack of theoretical understanding of the feedback principle. Maxwell's mathematical discussion of the flyball generator appeared in 1868, but there was no general theory of automatic control until Nyquist's *Regeneration Theory* was published in 1932. This theoretical development was followed by a growing and widespread application of feedback principles in the electronic, mechanical, and process industries. Today automatic devices are used in every industry to control process variables such as temperature, pressure, composition, position, flow rate, speed, power, etc.

The process control engineer analyzes and designs automatic control systems for the process industries. He is indispensable in selecting and designing control equipment for new plants and equally useful in analyzing and adjusting existing plants so that they achieve their optimum performance. To properly perform the latter task he must be able to recognize the existence of a control problem in a plant and be capable of correcting it. Generally, the need for improved process performance is shown by the existence of one or more of the following situations:

1. An appreciable fraction of the production capacity of the unit is not achieved because of poor dynamic performance.

2. The unit, whether controlled automatically or manually, is too sluggish in responding to process disturbances or set-point changes.

3. The unit is too fast in response to disturbances and tends to support oscillations, and therefore requires a long time to settle into a steady-state condition after being disturbed.

4. The important variables in a unit are not held within allowed tolerances during start-up or operation of the unit.

Today automatic control is used in industry to increase productivity and to achieve economic benefits. Some of the many advantages are:

1. Improvement in product quality.

2. Increase in process yield or production rate.

3. Increased safety for personnel and equipment.

4. Economic saving in materials, energy, or time.

5. Improvement of working conditions.

6. Achievement of operation not possible by manual control.

These humanitarian and economic benefits of automatic control applied to the process industries are the indirect results of the technical characteristics achieved by the use of feedback in control systems. Some of these technical advantages of feedback, as an improvement over open-loop control, are the ability to make the process system performance (1) faster in response to commands, (2) less dependent upon the system component parameters, (3) less sensitive to disturbances, and (4) subject to modification by proper choice of controlling components.

1–3. THE MEANING OF CONTROL

Process control engineers are concerned with the flow of material and energy among the parts of a system and the resulting movement of information signals (temperature, pressure, flow rates, product quality, etc.) through the system. On sight, any plant presents the appearance of a large, complex organization; however, on analysis into its component parts, it is found to be made up of simple basic units whose behavior shows a cause-and-effect relationship, as diagrammed in Fig. 1–1.   The

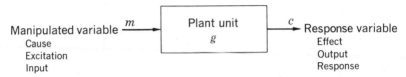

Fig. 1–1. Generalized representation of cause-and-effect relationships in a physical system. The block diagram is a graphical representation of the plant unit as a signal processor.

block represents the plant unit under study, with symbol g representing the functional relationship for the behavior of the unit and arrows m and c (into and out of the block), the information signals of cause (manipulated variable) and effect (response or controlled variable), respectively. The response of the unit is related to the input and, generally, to time by a physical law such that the relationship shown by the block in Fig. 1–1 can be written as

$$c = g(m,t) \qquad\qquad (1\text{–}1a)$$

Later, for purposes of simplifying the analytical procedure for obtaining problem solutions, this equation will be transformed from a function of time to a function of a complex variable s.   The operational form of the equation after transformation may be written as

$$C(s) = G(s)M(s) \qquad\qquad (1\text{–}1b)$$

where $M(s)$ and $C(s)$ are the Laplace transforms of the input and response variables respectively and $G(s)$ is the transfer function of the plant unit, i.e., the Laplace transform of the plant unit process equation with zero initial conditions.   This is a general functional representation which can be applied to single units in a plant or to a whole plant or processing combine.   The terms in the diagram may have various names such as:

Manipulated variable: cause, command, drive, excitation, *input*, forcing function, stimulus.
Response variable: effect, *output*, *response*, result.
Plant unit: apparatus, circuit, device, machine, network, process, *system*.

The italicized terms are those most often used in this book.   The elements in all process control systems are few in number and readily identifiable; only the arrangement and complexity of systems differ; and the process control engineer's first task is to recognize and define the basic elements in a quantitative manner.

1–4. CONTROLLED SYSTEMS

The control of a system means the regulation of the system for some purpose. Generally, the concept of control, as derived from an intuitive feeling for the cause-and-effect relationships operating within a physical system, leads to the conclusion that the output or response of an identified system can be controlled by the proper manipulation of the input to the system. Most process systems suffer from too many known or unknown inputs or disturbances, and the main problem is to stabilize the system so that it can overcome the effects of disturbances occurring at any point in the system.

Process control systems may be open-loop or closed-loop systems. An open-loop system uses an input which is determined from a process calibration and is independent of the actual output. An example of such a system is the automatic washing machine which goes through the calibrated washing cycle without regard to the quality of the washed product. Open-loop control is rarely used in process control since its performance worsens with loss of calibration and it is unable to compensate for process disturbances. A closed-loop system uses a control action that depends upon both the actual output and the desired output. The actual system output is measured and the information signal is fed back and compared with the reference input to make the control action depend upon the desired output. Such a system is able to faithfully follow an input and to correct for process disturbances. Feedforward control is a form of open-loop disturbance control that is sometimes used with a closed-loop control system. Some simple examples will help clarify the many types of control systems.

Open-Loop Systems. For reasons mentioned above, these systems are not commonly used in the process industries; however, some open-loop systems have enormous utilitarian value, e.g., the traffic light and the washing machine.

Continuous Control. Consider the problem of controlling the ventilation in an automobile interior by positioning the glass in the windows. A passenger may position the window glass at his pleasure by turning the window crank in either direction between the extreme limits of open or closed. Provided backlash in the crank gear mechanism is negligible, there is a single-valued relationship between the rotations of the window crank (input) and the position of the window glass (output). This relationship is indicated by the block diagram in Fig. 1–2a. The block symbolically represents the transmission property of the window mechanism. The functional relationship between the crank position and the window position is given in Fig. 1–2b where the window position in percentage open is plotted against the window crank position in number of rotations. In this case, the functional relationship does not include time as a variable.

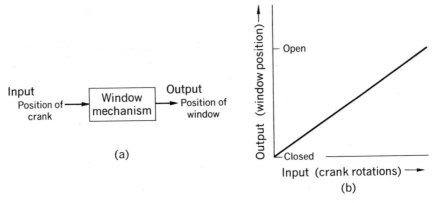

Fig. 1–2. Open-loop window position control. The control is continuous since for each crank position there is a corresponding, definite position of the window. (a) Block diagram of the input-output relationship for crank and window position. (b) Functional relationship between window and crank position.

This example illustrates continuous open-loop control of the window position without amplification, i.e., the input operator supplies all the energy needed for positioning the window glass.

Next consider the quality of ventilation in the car as determined by the window glass position. It is common experience that the amount of air entering a car window per unit time depends upon the position of the other window glasses in the car, the car speed, and the wind speed and direction relative to the car, as well as the window glass position. These causes of car ventilation are all inputs, as shown on the block diagram in Fig. 1–3a. In this case the window position is the primary input, and can be measured and altered by the operator, while the other inputs are secondary, but cannot be conveniently measured or altered. Since these secondary inputs may be detrimental to accurate response of the system, they are called disturbances, upsets, or unwanted inputs. Likewise, there are usually several variables which originate within the system and which are affected by the inputs to the system. These variables are the outputs of the system. The primary output here (the purpose of the control activity) is the car ventilation; the secondary outputs are air drafts and perhaps entrained dust in the car interior. In any circumstance the process control engineer must select the most important cause and effect operating in the system as the primary input and output on which to base the system analysis. The functional relationship between car ventilation and window position shown in Fig. 1–3b holds only for

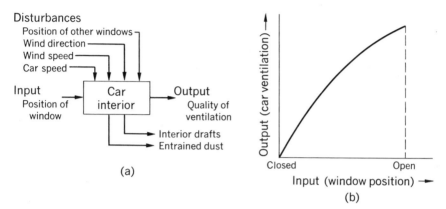

Fig. 1–3. Open-loop car ventilation control. The quality of car ventilation depends upon many inputs. (a) Block diagram of window position-ventilation relationship. (b) Functional relationship between window position and car ventilation.

fixed values of the secondary inputs. Notice that, as the window glass position changes from closed to open, the car ventilation increases from zero to a maximum value in a nonlinear manner, i.e., the output is not directly proportional to the input over the complete range of window glass position.

The overall car-ventilation response to a change in window crank position can be obtained by eliminating the window glass position variable from the diagrams in Figs. 1–2 and 1–3. The results are shown in Fig. 1–4 for constant values of the secondary inputs. This is an example of two units in series, and the overall response is the result of the second unit acting on the output from the first unit of the system. This is open-loop control of car ventilation by manually positioning the window crank mechanism. The passenger quickly learns that a window position which gives comfortable ventilation in low-speed city driving will give too much ventilation in high-speed driving on the freeway. Therefore this open-loop system is unable to maintain comfortable car ventilation at all car speeds since it cannot adjust its input to maintain constant output conditions in the presence of disturbances due to car speed changes. Of course, under normal conditions the car passenger closes the control loop

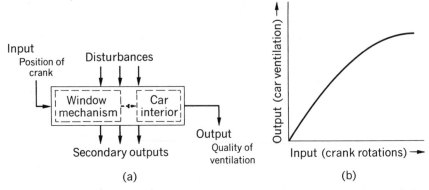

Fig. 1–4. Open-loop control of car ventilation by manipulation of the window crank position. The quality of the car ventilation control also depends upon the disturbances. (a) Block diagram. (b) Functional relationship.

by positioning the window crank to give comfortable car ventilation at any speed.

DISCONTINUOUS CONTROL. In contrast to the foregoing example, in which the input variable can take on continuous values between the two extreme values (open or closed), there is the case of the discontinuous input variable in which the action is either one extreme or the other, i.e., *on* or *off*.

Consider the electric heater with an on-off switch for room heating, shown in Fig. 1–5. The input variable here is the position of a switch: either the contacts are open and no heat is produced in the heater or the contacts are closed and full heat is developed by the heater. Little energy is required to change the switch from either position with the resultant control of kilowatts of power, so that the switch is a power amplifier. The control is discontinuous, since the switch causes either minimum or maximum heat production in the heater and there is no intermediate position of the switch that can given an intermediate heat production. Fig. 1–5 shows the electric wiring connections for the switch and heater and the block diagram for the system. Notice that the block diagram does not show the source of power or the relationship of the heater to the room.

Some of the important disturbances to the system as shown in Fig. 1–5b are: line-voltage fluctuations, ambient temperature outside the room, open doors or windows in the room, and the number of people in the room. The operation of the system is initiated by closing the switch. Flow of current through the heater produces heat which is transferred to the room and its contents by the mechanisms of conduction, convection, and

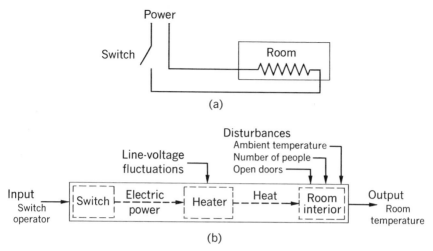

Fig. 1–5. Open-loop discontinuous control with power amplification. The two positions of the switch can produce either maximum or minimum heat production in the room. (a) Wiring diagram for electric heater. (b) Block diagram for room temperature control showing some of the disturbances affecting the system.

radiation. The rates of these transfer processes are proportional to the temperature gradients causing heat transfer; a definite time is needed to transfer finite quantities of heat to the room. The room and its contents have an overall heat capacity, which implies that a certain quantity of heat must be absorbed to increase the room temperature one degree. Therefore, it is natural to expect that the room temperature cannot change instantaneously in response to the heater and that the temperature change will lag in time behind the heat input change resulting from the switch action.

Typical response curves for the switch action and for the resulting room temperature are shown in Fig. 1–6. The on-off switch causes the heat input rate to the room to change from a minimum to a maximum value in a very short time. In response to that change the room temperature increases from an initial steady-state value to a final steady-state value, during a time interval called the *response time*. During this time interval the room temperature is in a transient condition: the temperature is changing with time even though the heat input rate is constant. The final steady-state temperature depends upon the heater wattage, the room parameters (size, room contents, construction materials, etc.), and the magnitude of the secondary inputs (disturbances). Higher heater wattage, of course, will give a higher steady-state temperature if the secondary inputs are constant; a calibration curve of room temperature versus heater wattage could be constructed for constant values of the secondary inputs. Notice, in this case as in the car-ventilation example, that satisfactory performance of the open-loop system depends on selecting the proper value of input (here the heater wattage as determined from the calibration curve) and on maintaining fixed values of the secondary inputs. If the secondary inputs change, the room temperature will change and the system performance may not be satisfactory. The deficiency here is that the action of the open-loop system is not dependent on the output of the system.

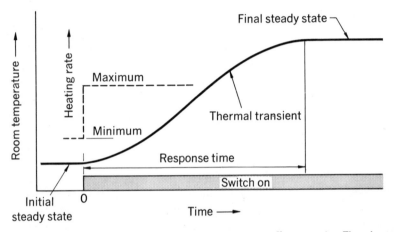

Fig. 1–6. Room temperature response to on-off control. The heater response is instantaneous in time (neglecting thermal capacity of heater and electrical transients). The room temperature response lags in time behind the heat production.

Closed-Loop Systems. In open-loop systems there is a straightforward relationship, obtained by experience or calibration under specific conditions, between the input and output variables. As pointed out above, the system input-output relationship may be modified by disturbances to the system with the result that the specific conditions of calibration no longer apply and the system performance becomes inadequate.

In the case of the open-loop room temperature control system, the temperature produced by a heater of given wattage corresponds to a fixed temperature only if the disturbances are held constant. To make a control system effective in performing a job in spite of normal upsetting disturbances, it is necessary to check the response of the system (i.e., determine its performance) and to modify the input to the system, if necessary, to get the desired performance. One way to improve the performance of the room temperature control system is to install an oversize heater in the room and place an alert operator in the room, who will close the switch when the temperature falls below a desired value and open the switch as the temperature rises above the desired value. The alert operator senses the room temperature, compares this temperature with the desired value, and acts on the basis of the comparison—opens the switch for too high a room temperature and closes it for too low a temperature. This is automatic control by the principle of feedback of information from the output so that the control action is made dependent on the output variable.

The alert operator could be a human being who would read a thermometer in the room and properly manipulate the electric switch according to the value of the room temperature in relation to the desired temperature; the human could also make a decision concerning the switch position on the basis of his psychological reaction to the room temperature. He could perform this task with excellent precision for awhile. However, humans fatigue easily, are subject to errors, and their time is very valuable. Moreover, they can provide greater service to mankind by analyzing and designing better process control systems. In this example the electric switch may be satisfactorily manipulated by an inexpensive bimetallic thermostat (instead of a human), as shown in Fig. 1–7a, with the resulting performance shown in Fig. 1–7c. The desired temperature is set on the thermostat by rotating the input knob until the pointer is opposite the desired value on the temperature scale. If the actual temperature, as measured by the bimetallic thermometer, is below the desired value, the switch will be closed and heat will be added to the room. As the room temperature increases along the heating curve in Fig. 1–7c the force produced by the bimetallic thermal element on the switch contacts will decrease until the switch opens when the temperature reaches the desired value. With the heater switch open and no heat being added to the room, the room temperature begins to decrease along the cooling curve, due to thermal losses to the surroundings. The thermal element responds to the decreasing temperature and closes the switch at a temperature a few degrees below the temperature at which it opened. This temperature difference, called the *differential gap* of the thermostat, is a measure of the sensitivity of the device; it is intentionally made a finite value in practical instruments to avoid the wear and tear accompanying too frequent switching of the device. As illustrated in Fig. 1–7c, the actual room temperature response is cyclic in nature, due to the on-off action of the thermostat. In many applications, the cyclic nature of the controlled variable is not objectionable provided the amplitude of the cycle is not too great and the wear on the devices occasioned by frequent switching from a maximum to a minimum value is not detrimental to the life of the device.

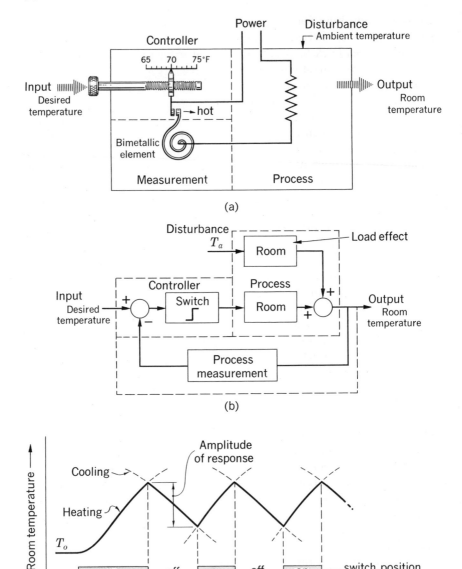

Fig. 1–7. Closed-loop room temperature control system using an on-off controller. (a) Apparatus diagram for room temperature control system. (b) Block diagram of signal flow through the control system. (c) Response of room temperature to switch control action.

The distinguishing feature of this loop as compared to the open-loop systems previously discussed is that information concerning the output of the system is fed back to the input and influences the manipulation of the switch. This is control based on the feedback principle, widely used in automatic devices to improve their behavior in the presence of process disturbances.

The flow of information in the controlled system may be put in block diagram form by recognizing the basic parts of the control system as input, output, disturbance, measurement of controlled variable, controlled process, and controller, as indicated by the lines on the apparatus diagram in Fig. 1–7a. Starting with the input on that figure it is seen that the controller compares the temperature input value to the system with the measured temperature in the process and acts on the resulting information by means of the switch. The controller action is represented by the graph in the switch block in Fig. 1–7b. The switch is closed when the input value to the controller is greater than the process output and open when the reverse condition prevails. The controller output, which is the presence or absence of electric power to the heater, is the input to the process, as represented by the signal leading from the controller to the process. The process responds to the input of thermal energy with an output of room temperature. The thermal element measures the room temperature and its output becomes an input to the summing point in the controller. Thus, the information follows a closed-loop signal path in the control system. Notice that this block diagram (also called *signal flow diagram*) shows neither the source of power used nor the signal amplitudes in the system. The signal amplitudes will be given by the equations used to describe the behavior of each block in the system.

Change in ambient temperature is the largest seasonal disturbance the room temperature control system must withstand. Its effect on the system is to decrease the rate of heat loss from the room ss the ambient temperature increases, with the result that an increase in T_a (ambient temperature) will increase the room temperature if other inputs remain constant. Similarly, a decrease in T_a would decrease the room temperature. This behavior is shown on the block diagram of Fig. 1–7b by adding a second block representing the "room" through which T_a acts to contribute to the room temperature.

Feedforward Control. Feedforward contrlo is used to compensate for specific disturbances to a controlled system. Consider the effect of ambient temperature on the room temperature control problem. When the outside temperature (ambient) increases, the heat losses from the room decrease and as a result the room temperature will increase (Fig. 1–7b). In like manner, a decrease in the outside temperature will cause a decrease in the room temperature unless a control is applied to add heat energy to compensate for the increased heat losses from the room. This can be done by a device which measures the outside temperature and manipulates the heat energy to the room to supply the increased heat losses from the room. This is feedforward control, used in this case to compensate for ambient temperature changes.

Such a device as shown in Fig. 1–8a might use a thermostat to measure the outside temperature and to position a wiper along an autotransformer

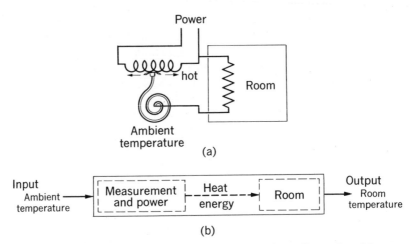

Fig. 1–8. Feedforward control to compensate for effect of ambient temperature on the room temperature. (a) Apparatus diagram. (b) Block diagram for ambient temperature compensation.

winding to provide the needed thermal energy to maintain the room temperature constant for any changes in the outside temperature. Notice that a decrease in ambient temperature causes more heat energy to be added to the room.

This scheme is very similar to the open-loop control of room temperature in Fig. 1–5, except that here the heat energy input is continuously controlled (to make the correction proportional to the need) by the input disturbance of outside temperature instead of by a switch. Notice that proper compensation for an outside temperature change requires measurement of the change and exact balance of increased heat energy to the room for increased heat losses from the room (for decreases in outside temperature). An advantage of this control method over the feedback control in Fig. 1–7a for compensating for changes in the outside temperature is speed of action. Here the correction is instantaneous with the outside temperature change (if the thermostat responds instantaneously) whereas the feedback method can provide no correction until the room temperature has changed enough to give an error signal to the switch.   A disadvantage of the feedforward method is that it cannot correct for unintentional imbalance between heat loss and the controlled heat addition to the room nor can it correct for any other input disturbances unrelated

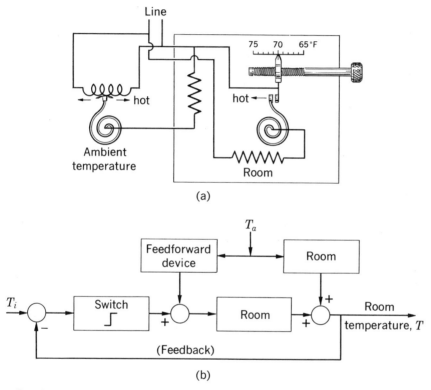

(a)

(b)

Fig. 1–9. Combined feedforward and feedback control of room temperature. (a) Apparatus diagram. (b) Block diagram.

to the outside temperature.   The feedback method, on the other hand, corrects for all system disturbances in an empirical manner, but the time delays needed to overcome the disturbance, the resulting errors in room temperature, and the possible instability of the system must be accepted.

When economically justified, the advantages of both control methods can be had by combining them as shown in Fig. 1–9 for the room temperature control problem.   The feedforward device corrects for changes in a specific input, the outside temperature, and the feedback apparatus responds to changes in one output, the room temperature, to correct for all other disturbances to the system. The system will then respond rapidly, owing to feedforward control, to outside temperature disturbances; and the feedback control will correct for any imbalance in the heat requirements due to any feedforward maladjustment and any other disturbances to the system. Thus, by its empirical nature, feedback control responds to room temperature errors from any disturbance and it alone would be adequate for this application. However, if outside temperature changes were the major disturbances to the system and if near-perfect room temperature control were demanded, then feedforward control would be considered.

In feedforward control the initiation of control action depends upon the variations of specific system disturbances, and the extent of action depends on previous design and adjustment of the components. In feedback control the initiation of control action depends on variation of a system output and the extent of action depends on watching the system output and empirically making adjustments to the input until the output of the system is satisfactory.

1–5. FEEDBACK CONTROL SYSTEM TERMINOLOGY

As mentioned in the discussion of room temperature control, feedback is the system property which permits comparison of the reference input and output quantities, so that the error (which is a function of the output variable) becomes the actuating signal to the control source in the system, telling it what to do to force the output to approach a desired value. A feedback process control system is one whose purpose is to maintain a prescribed relationship between an input-output pair of system variables, using the feedback principle. The input to the system may be a constant, in which case the function of the control is to maintain the system output constant in spite of other inputs or system disturbances (*regulator* operation); or the input may be a function of time (as in the program of inputs for operating a batch system), in which case the control must force the system output to follow the input program (*follower* operation).

Every process control system can be divided into convenient parts or blocks for study purposes. Previous examples made use of block diagrams to show the information signal flow path among the parts of the process control system. The diagram is made up of blocks representing the functional relationship between the block input and output, lines representing the information signal path between blocks, and line intersections representing summing or splitting points for the signal.

The general form of the block diagram for a feedback control system is shown in Fig. 1–10 together with the conventional names and symbols for

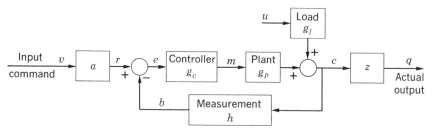

Fig. 1–10. Generalized block diagram for a process control system with feedback. Arrows indicate the direction of information flow within the system.

each signal and functional element in the system. This general block diagram is universally applicable to any type of feedback control system (temperature, pressure, position, etc.) and independent of the physical nature or characteristics of the process units making up the system. Table 1–1 lists the system variables (or information signals), giving the name, symbol and a short description of each variable. The lower case letters used here denote that the variable may be a function of time. Later, capital letters will be used to denote the variables after they are transformed from variables of time to variables of a complex quantity. The same distinction between lower case and capital letters applies to

TABLE 1–1

Information Variables in a Control System

Symbol	Name	Definition
b	Primary feedback	Signal which is a function of the controlled variable.
c	Controlled variable	System variable which is measured and controlled. Control of this variable is the purpose of the control system.
e	Actuating error	Reference input minus feedback signal which is the signal applied to the controller.
m	Manipulated variable	Quantity or condition applied to the controlled process by the controller.
q	Indirectly controlled variable	Quantity or condition, not measured for control, but which is indirectly controlled because of its relationship to the controlled variable.
r	Reference input	Comparison standard derived from the command and used with primary feedback to form the actuating error.
u	Disturbance	Secondary input signal which affects the value of the controlled variable.
v	Command input	External order or input which control system is to duplicate in the indirectly controlled variable.

TABLE 1–2
Functional Elements in a Control System

Symbol	Name	Input to Element	Output from Element
a	Reference input element	Command	Reference input
g_c	Controller	Actuating error	Manipulated variable
g_p	Controlled process	Manipulated variable	Controlled variable
h	Feedback element	Controlled variable	Primary feedback
g_l	Process load element	Load variable	Controlled variable
z	Indirectly controlled element	Controlled variable	Indirectly controlled variable

the functional elements in a control system, listed in Table 1–2. Normally the process variables are functions of time, although for simplification one or more of the variables may be held constant. Likewise, the functional relationship represented by a block is time-dependent since it normally represents the differential equation for that process unit.

Refer again to Fig. 1–10, to follow the information signal through the generalized block diagram of a feedback control system. The command is the input to the system, which may be varied by an external means for the benefit of the plant and is independent of the feedback control system. The reference input element converts the command into a reference input signal that can be summed (usually mechanically or electrically) with the negative of the primary feedback signal to produce the actuating error signal. The signals r, b, and e must have the same physical units. The actuating error signal forces the controller to produce the manipulated variable, which usually has units involving material or energy flow. The manipulated variable acts on the physical process which, in turn, responds to give a part of the controlled variable. A disturbance may also act on the process to make a load contribution to the controlled variable. The feedback element, frequently a measuring device, responds to the controlled variable with an output variable called the primary feedback signal.

The response of the indirectly controlled element to the controlled variable is the actual output. These variables and functional elements are best understood by identifying them in an actual system, as is done in Example 1–1.

Example 1–1. Refer to the temperature control system in Fig. 1–7 and identify the information variables and functional elements used in that system in terms of the symbols on the generalized feedback control system diagram in Fig. 1–10.

Solution. Enter the apparatus diagram (Fig. 1–7a) at the input and identify, step by step, each variable and functional element listed in Fig. 1–10 in terms of specific equipment on Fig. 1–7a. The results are given as:

v, system command, is the angular position of the set-point screw on the thermostat.

a, reference input element, is the set-point screw and the thermostat pointer riding on the screw.

r, reference input is the position of the electric contact on the thermostat pointer.

b, primary feedback, is the position of the electric contact on the free end of the bimetal thermal element.

e, actuating error, is $r - b$, the difference in position of the two electric contacts.

g_c, the controller, is the switch contacts and power connections.

m, manipulated variable is power (on or off) to the heater.

g_p, controlled process, is the room and its contents as they determine the relationship between power and room temperature in the absence of a disturbance.

u, disturbance variable, may be a change in window or door position, voltage on the power line, or change in ambient temperature.

g_l, process load element, is the relationship, as determined by the process, between the load variable and the controlled variable.

c, controlled variable, is room temperature.

h, feedback element, is the bimetal thermal element which provides a relationship between room temperature and the feedback signal.

z, indirectly controlled element, might be the human in the room whose comfort is the indirectly controlled variable.

q, indirectly controlled variable, is the degree of comfort of the human in the room.

From the discussion above, it is seen that a closed-loop feedback process control system must contain the following components: (1) the process to be controlled, (2) a device to measure the controlled process variable and to provide a signal feedback path from the output to the error detector, (3) an input command device to the error detector, (4) an error-detecting mechanism, and (5) a control and power mechanism which can manipulate the output variable in response to the error detector signal.

1–6. BLOCK DIAGRAMS OR SIGNAL FLOW DIAGRAMS

The functional block diagram is a visual means of showing the inter-relationships of significant variables in the system and the dynamic characteristics of the components making up the system. It clarifies the understanding of a system by showing the functional signal or information flow throughout the system rather than the physical equipment handling that signal, i.e., it emphasizes what happens in the system rather than the processing equipment involved. The independent variables in the process system equations are the inputs (the commands, and disturbance signals) and the dependent variables are the output or response signals.

Fig. 1–10 shows a generalized block diagram of a feedback process control system. The blocks represent isolatable, noninteracting sections of the system. The symbols inside a block indicate the dynamic characteristics of the component or group of components making up the blocks. Normally, the dynamic characteristics of a process component will be given by a differential equation, which will be Laplace-transformed for ease in manipulation. Lines connect the blocks, and arrows on the lines indicate the unidirectional signal flow from one block to another. Signal summing points, represented by circles, combine two or more inputs into a single output according to the algebraic signs indicated on the inputs. Signal splitting points, represented by a line branching, transmit the input undiminished in magnitude as an output into both branches of the line. The lower-case letter symbols (a, r, g, h, c, etc.) represent functions of time and the corresponding capital letter symbols (A, R, G, H, C, etc.) represent the Laplace transforms of the functions of time.

TABLE 1–3
Graphic Symbols for Mathematical Operations

Name	Functional Relationship	Graphic Symbol
1. Signal summing	$y = x_1 + x_2 - x_3$	
2. Signal splitting	$y = y$	
3. Signal integration	$y = \int_0^t x \, dt$	
4. Linear system component	$y = Gx$	
5. Signal multiplication General	$y = x_1 x_2$	
By a constant	$y = Kx$	

The basis for drawing the signal flow diagram is found in the algebraic and differential equations representing the functional relationships among the system variables. Standard graphic symbols used to represent common mathematical operations are listed in Table 1–3. Items 1 and 2 in the table have been discussed above. Item 3 is the symbolic representation of signal integration. The linear system component, shown as item 4, represents a linear transformation of input signal x into response signal y as required by the Laplace transform operator G given in the block. In this case, operator G represents a linear functional relationship among input and output signals and time for that component. Item 5 gives the symbols for multiplication of input signal by a constant and by another input signal (a nonlinear operation). The use of these symbols in constructing signal flow diagrams is illustrated in Example 1–2.

Example 1–2. Using the symbols in Table 1–3, construct block diagrams to display the signal flow relationships for these processes:

(a) Single-stage countercurrent extraction process under steady-state operation, as shown in Fig. E1–2a, with x and y as the variables of interest.

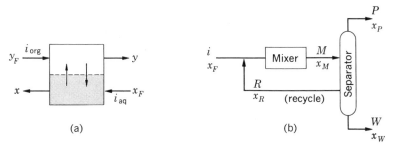

(a)   (b)

Fig. E1–2a, b. Simple extraction and separation processes. (a) Extraction stage. (b) Separation process.

(b) Separation process under steady-state operation, as shown in Fig. E1–2b, with the composition variables x_F, x_R given and variables x_P, x_W to be found.

(c) The first-order differential equation,

$$\tau \frac{dy}{dt} + y = y_i$$

Solution. (a) The single-stage extraction process at steady-state operation can be described by use of algebraic material-balance equations. Let symbols be defined as follows:

i_{org} = Organic solvent flow rate in mass per unit time

i_{aq} = Aqueous carrier flow rate in mass per unit time

y = Concentration of solute in organic phase in mass per mass of solvent

x = Concentration of solute in aqueous phase in mass per mass of solvent.

Assume that the aqueous and organic solvents are not soluble in each other; then the solvent-component material balances at steady state require that the aqueous and organic solvent flow rates into and from the extractor are equal. The material-balance equation for the solute is written as

$$x_F i_{aq} + y_F i_{org} = x i_{aq} + y i_{org}$$

where the subscript F denotes feed stream. When x is the variable of interest this equation can be rearranged to give

$$x = x_F + (y_F - y) i_{org}/i_{aq} \qquad (a)$$

The equilibrium relationship for the extracting component is usually written as

$$y = Kx \qquad (b)$$

If equilibrium is not attained in the extractor, an efficiency factor could be defined for the stage. However, in this example the leaving streams are assumed to be at equilibrium.

The signal flow diagram for Eqs. a and b is shown in Fig. E1–2c. It is constructed stepwise as follows:

1. Assume y_F and y are known and form the signal $(y_F - y)$.
2. Now use Eq. a to obtain x by multiplying $(y_F - y)$ by the flow ratio i_{org}/i_{aq} and adding x_F as required.
3. The diagram is completed by using Eq. b, the equilibrium relationship, to find y from x, as shown in Fig. E1–2c.

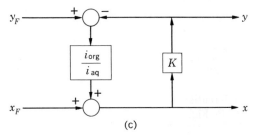

(c)

Fig. E1–2c. Signal flow diagram for single-stage equilibrium extractor.

The signal flow diagram shows the relationships among the x's and y's more clearly than do the algebraic equations.

(b) The separation process in Fig. E1–2b may be described by algebraic material-balance equations for steady-state operating conditions. In this example, let the flow rates i, M, R, P, and W be given in units of mass per time and the composition x be expressed as mass fraction. Then the material-balance equations are written:

Overall balance: $\qquad i + R = M = P + W + R$

Component balance: $\quad x_M M = x_F i + x_R R \qquad (c)$

$$x_W W = x_M M - x_P P - x_R R = x_F i - x_P P \qquad (d)$$

$$x_P P = x_F i - x_W W \qquad (e)$$

The signal flow diagram is constructed from Eqs. c, d, e, assuming that i, P, R, W, x_R, and x_F are known, in the following steps:

1. With signals i, R, x_F, and x_R known, the value of signal $x_M M$ is given by Eq. c and graphed as shown in the sketch in Fig. E1–2d.

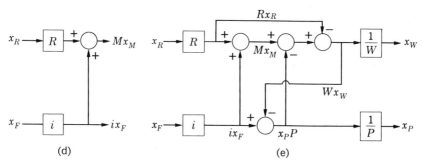

(d)   (e)

Fig. E1–2d, e. Signal flow diagram for separation process. (d) Graph of Eq. c. (e) Complete block diagram.

2. The next step is to form signal $x_W W$ by use of Eq. d. Then x_W is obtained by dividing $x_W W$ by W as shown in Fig. E1–2e.
3. Finally, signal $x_P P$ is formed by use of Eq. e. Signal x_P is obtained by dividing $x_P P$ by P. The finished diagram is shown in Fig. E1–2e.

(c) The differential equation can be rearranged in either of the following equivalent forms:

$$y = \frac{1}{\tau} \int_0^t (y_i - y)\, dt \qquad \text{or} \qquad y = \left[\frac{1}{\tau \dfrac{d}{dt} + 1} \right] y_i \tag{f}$$

where d/dt is the differential operator. The resulting two equivalent signal flow diagrams are given in Fig. E1–2f,g. The diagram on the left is obtained by

(f)   (g)

Fig. E1–2f, g. Block signal flow diagrams for differential equation. (f) Block diagram emphasizng feedback behavior. (g) Block diagram emphasizing feedforward behavior.

forming the signal $(y_i - y)$ and integrating it with respect to time to obtain the signal y that is fed back to the summing point. The diagram on the right is obtained by multiplying signal y_i by the operational characteristics of the equation to produce y in a feedforward manner.

Block Diagram Algebra. Provided that all the system components and operations in a block diagram are linear, a set of graphical theorems or rules may be stated for manipulation and simplification of the block diagram. The basis for these rules is found in the algebra of linear relationships. Some of the rules are listed below.

1. Combining cascaded elements. Two blocks in series may be replaced by a single block whose characteristic is the product of the characteristics of the replaced blocks.

$$g_1 a = b; g_2 b = c \qquad\qquad g_1 g_2 a = c$$

2. Moving a splitting point by a summing point. Signals are not conserved at a splitting point but proceed down both paths undiminished.

$$a \pm b = c \qquad\qquad a \pm b = c$$

3. Moving a summing point by an element.

$$a \pm b = c; gc = d \qquad\qquad ga \pm gb = d$$

4. Moving a splitting point by an element.

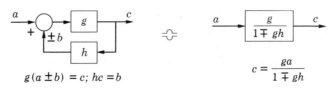

$$a = a; ga = b \qquad\qquad ga = b; b\left(\frac{1}{g}\right) = a$$

5. Eliminating a feedback loop.

$$g(a \pm b) = c; hc = b$$

$$c = \frac{ga}{1 \mp gh}$$

6. Moving an element into a feedback loop.

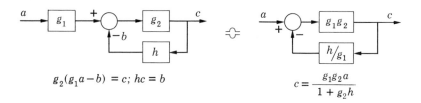

$$g_2(g_1 a - b) = c; \quad hc = b$$

$$c = \frac{g_1 g_2 a}{1 + g_2 h}$$

7. Removing an element from a feedback loop.

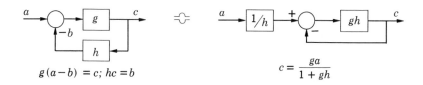

$$g(a - b) = c; \quad hc = b$$

$$c = \frac{ga}{1 + gh}$$

Example 1–3.   Using the rules for block diagram algebra, simplify the two loop systems given in the problem statement of Fig. E1–3 to a single-element system.   Check the results by algebraic manipulation.

Solution.   Graphical theorems: Apply rules 5 and 1, above.

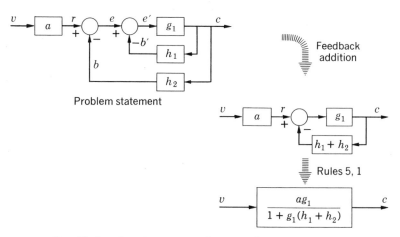

Problem statement

Rules 5, 1

Fig. E1–3.   Graphical simplification of block diagram.

Solution.   Algebraic elimination of r, e, e', b', and b:

(a) $e' = e - b'$ (d) $c = g_1 e'$
(b) $e = r - b$ (e) $b' = h_1 c$
(c) $r = av$ (f) $b = h_2 c$

Starting with Eq. a, substitute for e' the value given by Eq. d, and likewise for e from Eq. b, r from c, b' from e, and b from f.

$$e' = \frac{c}{g_1} = r - b - h_1c = av - h_2c - h_1c = av - (h_1 + h_2)c$$

$$c\left(\frac{1}{g_1} + h_1 + h_2\right) = av$$

$$c = \frac{ag_1v}{1 + g_1(h_1 + h_2)}$$

Thus, the graphical simplification procedure is superior to the algebraic elimination process in obtaining the system equation.

1–7. LINEARIZATION OF SYSTEM EQUATIONS

A linear algebraic equation is one in which all the variables occur to the first power and there are no terms involving products of variables. A linear ordinary differential equation is one in which the dependent variable and its derivatives occur only to the first power and no term in the equation contains either a product of the dependent variable and any of its derivatives or a product of the derivatives of the dependent variable. The coefficients in a linear differential equation may be constants or functions of the independent variable. A linear element or system is one that may be described by linear differential equations. The process control engineer is always interested in the response of systems to various forcing functions. Linear systems obey the principle of superposition, which consists of two parts.

1. Additivity of response. Suppose $c_1(t)$ and $c_2(t)$ are the responses of a linear system to separate manipulations $m_1(t)$ and $m_2(t)$, respectively; then the response of the system to combined manipulation $m_1(t) + m_2(t)$ is $c_1(t) + c_2(t)$. This means that the presence of one manipulation does not affect the responses due to other manipulations in the system, i.e., there is no interaction among responses due to different manipulations within a linear system.

2. Homogeneity of response. Suppose $c(t)$ is the response of a linear system to manipulation $m(t)$; then the response of the system to $km(t)$ will be $kc(t)$, where k is a constant, i.e., in linear systems the effect is always proportional to the cause.

If, in addition, the linear system is described by ordinary linear differential equations with constant coefficients, the steady-state response $c(t)$ (after the initial transient has decayed) to a sinusoidal forcing function with frequency ω will also be sinusoidal with frequency ω, i.e., linear systems with constant parameters generate no new frequencies when manipulated sinusoidally.

Most of the process plant devices and processes show nonlinear behavior. Consider the force required to displace (stretch and/or compress) a spring. Over a wide range of displacements, the force required to effect the displacement is proportional to the spring displacement. However, at the extremes of compression or extension of the spring, the force required to displace the spring by a unit amount becomes proportional to a power of the displacement. Moreover, at small displacements the spring coils approach continuous contact as a limit, and at very large displacements the spring may exceed its elastic limit and take a permanent deformation which would change the spring properties. Both of these extreme conditions lead to nonlinear behavior in the spring. As another example, consider the current-voltage relationship in an electrical resistor. At low values of currents the current is proportional to the voltage producing the current, as predicted by Ohm's law. However, as the current increases, the i^2R energy loss in the resistor produces self-heating which changes its resistance, and the current is no longer linearly proportional to the voltage. Such effects as these occur in all physical systems; it must be realized that restrictions always exist for linear operation in a system. Conversely, when a process engineer states that a system is linear he means that he has neglected (or linearized) the nonlinearities in the system and will restrict the operation of the system to the linear region. Should such a system receive extremely large input signals forcing it into the nonlinear region, the extreme result is that either the system will be physically limited to maximum values of response or the weakest part of the system may fail and the system become inoperative.

It is true that nature is basically nonlinear in behavior and that nonlinear equations are more difficult to handle analytically than linear forms. Since linear control theory is completely developed, there is therefore a strong tendency to force nonlinear problems into a linear form (a technique called "linearization") whenever possible. In most cases the problem solution obtained by linearization of the nonlinear forms is adequate for small signals.

A linear form which approximates the nonlinear form for small signals is obtained by making a Taylor's series expansion of the form around an operating point and taking only the linear terms. Thus, for a function of one variable:

$$z = f(x) \doteq f(x_o) + \frac{\partial f}{\partial x}\bigg|_{x_o} (x - x_o) \qquad (1\text{-}2a)$$

For a function of two variables:

$$z = f(x,y) \doteq f(x_o,y_o) + \frac{\partial f}{\partial x}\bigg|_{x_o,y_o} (x - x_o) + \frac{\partial f}{\partial y}\bigg|_{x_o,y_o} (y - y_o) \qquad (1\text{-}2b)$$

In the usual study of operating systems it is normal to measure system response from a previous steady-state operating point, such as x_o and y_o. Then it is possible to write the Taylor's series terms as

$$z - f(x_o) = \left.\frac{\partial f}{\partial x}\right|_{x_o} (x - x_o)$$

or

$$\tilde{z} = \left.\frac{\partial f}{\partial x}\right|_{x_o} \tilde{x} \qquad (1\text{--}2c)$$

where $\tilde{z} = z - f(x_o)$ and $\tilde{x} = x - x_o$. This result is equivalent to shifting the coordinate origin to the point $(f(x_o), x_o)$ as shown in Fig. 1–11. Like-

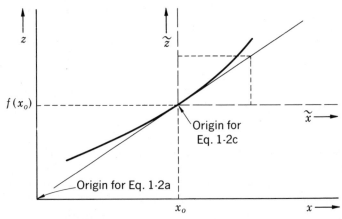

Fig. 1–11. Linearization by use of truncated Taylor's series. The linear function $\tilde{z}$ is written for the origin shifted to a steady-state operating point x_0 as shown.

wise, the linear form of a function of two variables may be written as

$$\tilde{z} = \left.\frac{\partial f}{\partial x}\right|_{x_o,y_o} \tilde{x} + \left.\frac{\partial f}{\partial y}\right|_{x_o,y_o} \tilde{y} \qquad (1\text{--}2d)$$

where $\tilde{z} = z - f(x_o,y_o)$, $\tilde{x} = x - x_o$, and $\tilde{y} = y - y_o$.

The results represented by Eqs. 1–2c and 1–2d may be obtained by an integration process, as shown below for Eq. 1–2d. Let $z = f(x,y)$. Then

$$dz = \frac{\partial f}{\partial x}\,dx + \frac{\partial f}{\partial y}\,dy$$

which is the definition of the total derivative of a function of two variables. Now, in a small operating region around the steady-state point x_o, y_o, the slopes may be considered constant and the equation integrated to give

$$\tilde{z} = z - \text{constant} = \frac{\partial f}{\partial x}\bigg|_{x_o,y_o} \tilde{x} + \frac{\partial f}{\partial y}\bigg|_{x_o,y_o} \tilde{y} = k_x\tilde{x} + k_y\tilde{y}$$

which is of the same form as Eq. 1-2d above. The Taylor's series is not necessarily the best linearization method, but it does ensure that the linearized function has the correct value and slope at the operating point.

In many process systems the position of a lever or a valve is often reversible, so that the average position may be zero. However, the process stream flow rates in a plant always have a non-zero average value, and the process engineer is interested in deviations from this average flow rate. In all cases, the total flow rate is given as

$$i_{\text{total}}(t) = i_{\text{avg}} + \tilde{\imath}(t) \tag{1-3}$$

where $\tilde{\imath}(t)$ is the deviation flow rate. In linear systems analysis it is always possible to write process equations either in terms of total value of variables or in deviations from an average value of variables without changing the form of the system equations. Therefore, in any linearization procedure, it is usual to write the linearized equations in terms of the deviation variables.

Example 1-4. A control valve is a variable-resistance device which regulates flow through the valve by modulating the valve flow area in response to valve stem position signal. Then the flow rate through the control valve is a function of the upstream and downstream pressures p_1 and p_2 and the stem position x, so that

$$i = f(p_1, p_2, x) \tag{a}$$

Linearize the relationship around an operating point p_{o1}, p_{o2}, and x_o and show how the coefficients may be evaluated graphically from experimental data.

Solution. The flow rate relationship on expansion into a Taylor's series retaining only the linear terms becomes

$$i - f(p_{o1}, p_{o2}, x_o) = \frac{\partial f}{\partial p_1}\bigg|_{p_{o1},p_{o2},x_o} (p_1 - p_{o1}) + \frac{\partial f}{\partial p_2}\bigg|_{p_{o1},p_{o2},x_o} (p_2 - p_{o2})$$
$$+ \frac{\partial f}{\partial x}\bigg|_{x_o,p_{o1},p_{o2}} (x - x_o) \tag{b}$$

which may be written in terms of deviation variables as

$$\tilde{\imath} = k_1\tilde{p}_1 + k_2\tilde{p}_2 + k_3\tilde{x} \tag{c}$$

where the coefficients k_1, k_2, k_3 are evaluated at the operating point. As shown in Figs. E1-4a, b, c, the individual coefficients are graphically evaluated as the slopes of the appropriate experimental flow rate curves at the operating point in agreement with the definition of a partial derivative.   The signal flow graph for Eq. c is given in Fig. E1–4d.   The control valve symbol in Fig. E1–4e shows that the stem position x depends upon an input signal p_{in}.

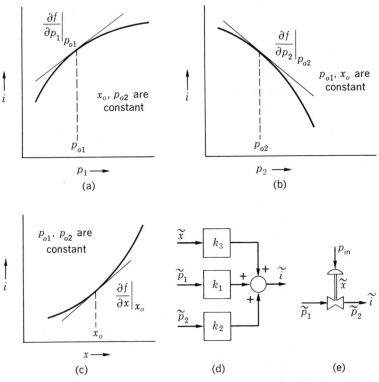

Fig. E1–4.   The coefficients in Eq. c are the partial derivatives of the flow function.   (a) i versus p_1 at constant x, p_2.   (b) i versus p_2 at constant x, p_1. (c) i versus x at constant p_1, p_2.   (d) Signal flow graph.   (e) Valve symbol.

1–8. PLANT OPTIMIZATION BY COMPUTER CONTROL

The overall purpose of process control is to enable a plant to produce the maximum quantity of product meeting specifications at the least cost, despite the normal unavoidable disturbances and upsets occurring in the loads, the feed material flows and properties, and the service supplies to each process unit in the plant.   In the past this goal has been approached by controlling single process units in the plant using a minimum number of controllers on each unit and minimizing the effects of upstream process upsets and load changes by placing surge storage capacity between each plant unit to smooth out changes in concentration, pressure, flow, and temperature between consecutive units. Such an approach does not ensure maximum overall plant operating efficiency, and the large surge capacities slow down the plant response and increase the capital investment and in-plant inventories.

The present trend in process control is toward consideration of a plant as a single system made up of many process units. From this viewpoint the plant may be designed for maximum efficiency and operated at maximum profit since the complete system will be controlled in a coordinated manner from computations and decisions made by a computing machine. In such an installation the computer is given (1) mathematical equations descriptive of the plant operations and costs, (2) a computing program by which the machine may compute the plant costs and profits, (3) instantaneous plant data on the operating variables needed by the computing program, and (4) a decision method by which the computer may optimize plant operation by originating new commands to the individual process controllers in the plant to bring the system to its optimum operating point from either a profit or a cost viewpoint.

A simple diagram for such an application is shown in Fig. 1–12 (also see Chapter 9). The computer is programmed to find the plant optimum

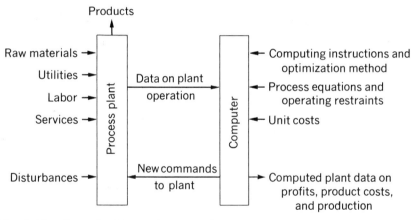

Fig. 1–12. Simplified block diagram of a computer-controlled process plant.

conditions and to operate the plant at those conditions. The computer inputs are (1) the process equations and operating restraints, the unit operating and raw material cost data, and the computation instructions for plant optimization, and (2) plant operating data such as flows, concentrations, pressures, temperatures and product quality, from which plant efficiency may be computed. The computer outputs are computed plant data on production, product costs, and profits and new commands to the process plant for adjustment of inputs on the plant controllers to improve the economic operation of the plant.   Observe here that economics is the basis of plant optimization.   The plant variables are measured by conventional devices, converted to appropriate computer language, and sent to the computer.   The computer takes these plant data and data on unit costs, goes through the computation instructions for optimization using the process equations and restraints and decides what new commands will be sent to the plant to bring the operation to maximum production at best quality and least cost.   The new commands are converted to plant language and sent to the individual controllers.

This is plant optimization by computer control.   It has not been widely used in the past because the processing relations in a plant are often so complex and the calculations so tedious that the human operator could not compute the results fast enough to take full advantage of his knowledge in adjusting the controllers throughout the plant.   The advantage of the computer is speed.   Within a few minutes it can complete plant optimization calculations which the human operator would do in many hours and thus it can keep the plant much closer to a continuous optimum condition than could a human operator.   A few process plants are under computer control at the present time and many more will yield to computer optimization in the years ahead.

1–9. PROCESS SYSTEM VARIABLES

Process engineers are concerned with measuring and controlling the operating states of process equipment and thereby controlling the properties of matter being processed.   A few of the common variables met and controlled in the usual process plant are listed:

Temperature	Density
Pressure	Volume
Flow rate	Liquid level
Composition	Viscosity

Control of a process plant would be a near impossibility if all the variables had to be controlled in each plant unit.   Fortunately many units are inherently self-regulating and, by making use of the feedback principle, it is necessary only to control a few of the variables acting in a process plant.   The controlled variable should be that variable which most directly determines the product quality.   Whenever possible, this variable should be the product quality itself; however, some product qualities such as the flavor of processed foodstuffs, quality of paper sheets, strength of a steel web, etc., are not easily measured directly on a continuous basis; in such cases a measurable variable that is directly related to product quality is selected for process control. This indirect control of product quality is not as satisfactory as direct control would be.

Many process steps far removed from the product finishing operation in a plant must be controlled for best overall plant performance. Frequently, there are several methods available for controlling these units. The process engineer must analyze each unit separately and on the basis of his experience and the technological principles operating within the unit select the controlled variable and the manipulated variable, and devise a logical control loop for that unit.

Independent Process Variables. For purposes of cataloging and discussing system variables, they have been grouped as controlled variable, manipulated variable, load variables, and process disturbances. Now the point is made that not all of the many interrelated variables acting within a process unit are independent. As in any mathematical situation, the number of independent variables in a process unit is the total number of operating variables less the number of independent equations interrelating the variables. Since the number of independent variables is the number of conditions that must be specified to completely describe the system, it is also called the number of "degrees of freedom" of the system. In any one unit it is not possible to control more than the number of independent variables, and by using feedback control it normally is not necessary to control more than one or two of the independent variables to obtain good dynamic performance of the unit. The following example applies these ideas in a discussion of temperature control in a process heat exchanger.

Example 1-5. Heat exchange between a flowing process fluid and low-pressure steam is a common operation in process plants. Consider a heat exchanger supplying a hot fluid at a fixed temperature on demand. List the process variables operating in the exchanger and classify each one by function. Determine the number of independent variables and suggest a method for controlling the exit temperature of the heated fluid.

Solution. The process variables affecting the operation of the heat exchanger are listed below according to the effects they have on the unit (refer to Fig. E1-5):

Controlled variable:	Outlet temperature of fluid, T_{out}
Manipulated variable:	Steam flow to exchanger, i_s
	Steam condensate flow rate, i_c
Load variables:	Flow rate of heated fluid, i
	Heat losses to surroundings, q_{lost}
Disturbance variables:	Inlet temperature of fluid, T_{in}
	Steam quality, x
	Steam pressure, p
	Steam temperature, T

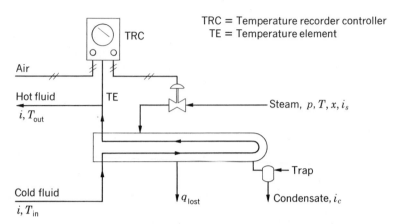

Fig. E1–5. Closed-loop temperature control for fluid heater. Manipulation of steam input is the normal method for control. The process variables are identified.

The number of independent equations relating these variables are three: (a) the conservation-of-energy equation, (b) the vapor pressure equation for steam (assuming the steam is not superheated), and (c) the conservation-of-matter equation applied to the condensate liquid level by the steam-trap device. Therefore the number of independent variables is the total variables (9) less the interrelating equation (3), or $9 - 3 = 6$. Any six of the nine variables might be classed as independent, but normally the manipulated variable is a dependent variable. This conclusion indicates that as many as six controllers or regulators might be used on this heat exchanger, but generally one or two are sufficient as shown in the application in Fig. E1–5.

There are many methods for controlling the exit fluid temperature in a heat exchanger application. The normal method for controlling the fluid temperature is to measure the fluid temperature, compare it with the desired or reference temperature and manipulate the heat input to the exchanger to hold the desired temperature. In the scheme shown here, steam flow to the exchanger is manipulated to overcome any effect of load changes or disturbances to the system. The control system illustrated here uses compressed air for control valve actuation.

PROBLEMS

1–1. Propose a scheme whereby the open-loop control of car ventilation shown in Fig. 1–4 could be made automatic.

1–2. List two examples of open-loop control systems. Draw block diagrams for each example, and identify a possible system disturbance for each.

1–3. Repeat Problem 1–2 for closed-loop control systems.

1–4. Consider the room temperature in a home equipped with an on-off temperature controller. Qualitatively, the heat loss from the home depends on the outside temperature. Discuss the cyclic nature of the room temperature response, considering the switching period and the amplitude of temperature cycles for these cases:

(a) Mild cold weather in autumn
(b) Cold weather in midwinter
(c) Severe cold weather exceeding capacity of the heating system

1–5. List the sequence of actions and responses occurring in an automobile and driver when the road presents these inputs (assume driver observes good practices at all times.):

(a) Curve in road
(b) Steep hill ahead

1–6. Make a list of the variables operating within the following uncontrolled processes and classify them as primary or secondary inputs and outputs. Sketch a block diagram for each process:

(a) Single-effect evaporator at 1 atmosphere.
(b) Household hot water heater

1–7. Use the equations in Example 1–2b and construct a block diagram to display the signal flow relationships for variables x_F, x_P given and variables x_R, x_W to be found.

1–8. Reduce the block diagrams (Fig. P1–8, on page 38) by the use of block diagram algebra and find the output-input equation.

1–9. Classify the following equations as linear or nonlinear equations and suggest ways to linearize the nonlinear ones:

(a) $t\dot{x} + x = f(t)$
(b) $t\ddot{x} + t^2\dot{x} + x = 0$
(c) $\ddot{y} + 2\dot{y}^2 + y = f(t)$
(d) $\ddot{y} + y\dot{y} + y = \sin \omega t$

1–10. Linearize the following functions about an operating point as stated. Write the function in terms of deviations from the operating point.

(a) x^3 about $x = 5$
(b) x^2y^2 about $x = 10$, $y = 5$
(c) $e^{-200/x}$ about $x = 200$
(d) $V = RT/p$ about $p = 1$ atm, $T = 77°F$

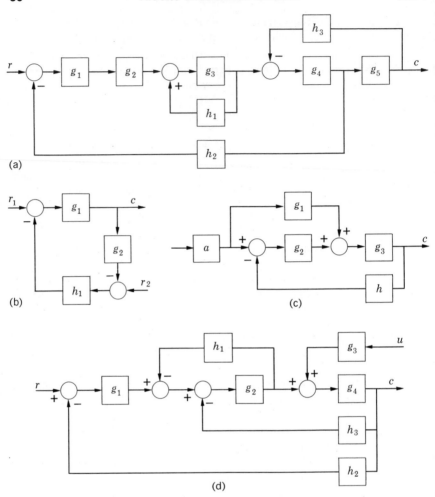

Fig. P1–8

1–11. Make a sketch of a simple closed-loop control system that could be used in the following processes. The sketch should indicate the essential components of a feedback system and show the connections between components.

(a) Control the exit air temperature of an air preheater used to heat air going to a tray dryer. Use steam as the source of heat and assume the dryer air flow rate is constant.

(b) Control the product composition of a single-effect vacuum evaporator concentrating a dilute aqueous sucrose feed solution to a product syrup.

(c) Control the liquid level in an open water tank. Assume the tank outflow is variable and the tank supply is from the plant water mains.

2

Mathematics for Control Theory

Process control engineers are interested in the response of process equipment to the many inputs operating in a plant. In every case the response has a magnitude and a time relationship that are characteristic of the process equipment and the input function. From the analysis viewpoint, knowledge of the equipment response to a known input function is sufficient for the engineer to determine the characteristics of the equipment. Much of the material in this book is devoted to showing how these characteristics may be determined. From the design viewpoint, a knowledge of the plant performance specifications and the system inputs is sufficient to allow the engineer to select or design the needed components and fix their relationship in the process system.

The devices and components in a process system obey the laws of nature in responding to real input quantities by producing real outputs. Much of mathematics that is most convenient in handling magnitudes and time relationships represents real physical quantities by complex mathematical symbols which carry more information than the real physical quantities. These symbols include complex numbers (or complex variables) and functions of complex variables. It must be observed that, even though the equations may involve complex quantities, the ·final useful result of the study of a physical system will be an equation involving real variables.

The purpose of this chapter is to review and extend the reader's knowledge of complex numbers and variables and to present the use of Laplace transformation as a tool for solving linear differential equations.

2–1. COMPLEX NUMBERS AND OPERATIONS*

A complex number s is an ordered pair of real numbers σ, ω that obey certain rules of mathematical operations. The complex number is fre-

* The reader interested in more information on complex variables is referred to R. V. Churchill, *Complex Variables and Applications*, 2nd ed., McGraw-Hill Book Co., Inc., New York, 1960.

quently written as follows, making use of j, the imaginary unit:

$$s = \sigma + j\omega = \Re e\, s + j\, \Im m\, s \qquad (2\text{--}1)$$

where $\sigma = \Re e\, s$ is the first real number in the ordered pair, called the real part of s, and $\omega = \Im m\, s$ is the second real number in the ordered pair, called the imaginary part of s. The ordinary rules of real-number algebra govern algebraic operations with complex numbers, provided $j^2 = -1$. A complex number can be represented as a point on a plane because of the correspondence of the two coordinates of the point on the plane and the pair of real numbers σ, ω. This representation on the complex plane is shown in Fig. 2–1a, where values of σ are plotted along the axis of the

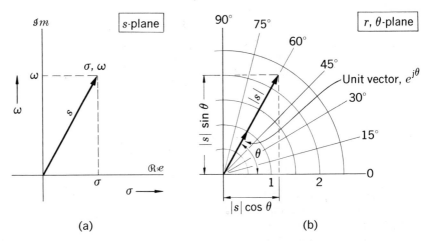

Fig. 2–1. Graphical representation of a complex number on rectangular and polar coordinates. (a) Complex plane representation. (b) Vector and polar representation.

reals $\Re e$ and values of ω are plotted along the axis of the imaginaries $\Im m$. Since a point on the complex plane defines the vector from the origin terminating at the point, it is logical to represent complex numbers by plane vectors, as shown in Fig. 2–1b, where the complex number is represented by the vector length $|s|$ and the direction θ. The vector representation is related to the complex plane representation by the equation

$$s = |s|\angle\theta \qquad (2\text{--}2)$$

where $|s| = \sqrt{\sigma^2 + \omega^2}$, the absolute value of s, and angle $\theta = \tan^{-1} \omega/\sigma$. Read the equation thus: "s equals the absolute value of s at the angle θ." The angle representation can lead to ambiguity since $\tan^{-1} \omega/\sigma$ and $\tan^{-1} -\omega/-\sigma$ differ by π radians. This ambiguity is eliminated by keeping track of the algebraic sign of the real and imaginary parts of the complex number so that the correct quadrant is always known.

The projection of the vector onto the real and imaginary axes leads back to the complex plane representation of complex numbers, since the vector components are given as

Real axis: $\sigma = |s| \cos \theta$
Imaginary axis: $\omega = |s| \sin \theta$

and they may be combined as

$$s = |s| (\cos \theta + j \sin \theta) \qquad (2\text{-}3)$$

Now the exponential function, as defined for a complex variable, provides an exponential representation for a complex number. Euler's relationship for the complex exponential function is

$$e^{j\theta} = \cos \theta + j \sin \theta \qquad \text{where } \theta \text{ is real} \qquad (2\text{-}4)$$

so that

$$|e^{j\theta}| = (\cos^2 \theta + \sin^2 \theta)^{1/2} = 1$$
$$\angle e^{j\theta} = \tan^{-1} \sin \theta / \cos \theta = \theta \pm 2k\pi \qquad k = 0, 1, 2, \ldots$$

From Eqs. 2–2, 2–3, and 2–4 it is clear that $e^{j\theta}$ is a complex number having unit magnitude and an angle whose principal value is θ radians and that it also represents a unit vector having an angle of θ radians from the real axis as shown in Fig. 2–1b. The angle must always be specified in radians, although it is usually converted to degrees for reference in trigonometric tables. In summary, there are four useful forms for representing complex numbers:

$$s = \underset{\text{complex}}{\sigma + j\omega} = \underset{\text{rectangular}}{|s|(\cos \theta + j \sin \theta)} = \underset{\text{polar}}{|s|\angle\theta} = \underset{\text{exponential}}{|s|e^{j\theta}} \qquad (2\text{-}5)$$

The choice of one form over another depends upon the mathematical operation to be performed.

The conjugate of a complex number is a complex number having the magnitude of the original number and the negative of the angle of the original. It is formed by replacing j of the original number by $-j$, with the result that the conjugate is the real-axis mirror image of the original number. For example, the conjugate of $s = \sigma + j\omega$ is $\bar{s} = \sigma - j\omega$.

Several easily verified relationships involving conjugates are:

$$s\bar{s} = (\sigma + j\omega)(\sigma - j\omega) = \sigma^2 + \omega^2 = |s|^2$$
$$\mathcal{R}e\, s = \tfrac{1}{2}(s + \bar{s}) = \tfrac{1}{2}(\sigma + j\omega + \sigma - j\omega) = \sigma$$
$$\mathcal{I}m\, s = \tfrac{1}{2}(s - \bar{s}) = \tfrac{1}{2}(\sigma + j\omega - \sigma + j\omega) = j\omega$$

The algebraic operations of forming sums, products, quotients, and powers of complex numbers may be performed by the usual algebraic rules with the numbers in any form. Certain operations are more easily carried out when the complex numbers are written in particular forms. Algebraic summing is easily done with the numbers in the complex form by taking the algebraic sum of the real parts plus j times the algebraic sum of the imaginary parts:

$$s = s_1 + s_2 = \sigma_1 + j\omega_1 + \sigma_2 + j\omega_2 = (\sigma_1 + \sigma_2) + j(\omega_1 + \omega_2) \quad (2\text{--}6)$$

Addition in the complex plane is shown in Fig. 2–2a.

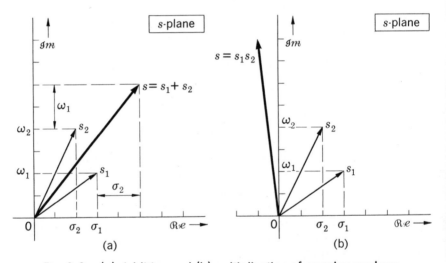

Fig. 2–2. (a) Addition and (b) multiplication of complex numbers.

Products and quotients of complex numbers are best obtained with the numbers expressed in exponential form. The usual rules of exponentials apply, with the result that products of complex numbers are obtained by multiplying their magnitudes and adding their angles and that quotients are obtained by dividing their magnitudes and subtracting their angles, thus:

$$s = s_1 s_2 = |s_1|e^{j\theta_1}|s_2|e^{j\theta_2} = |s_1|\,|s_2|e^{j(\theta_1 + \theta_2)} \quad (2\text{--}7a)$$

and

$$s = s_1/s_2 = |s_1|e^{j\theta_1}/(|s_2|e^{j\theta_2}) = \frac{|s_1|}{|s_2|} e^{j(\theta_1 - \theta_2)} \qquad (2\text{-}8a)$$

Complex multiplication is shown graphically in Fig. 2–2b. These operations can also be performed algebraically, as shown in these examples:

$$s = s_1 s_2 = (\sigma_1 + j\omega_1)(\sigma_2 + j\omega_2) = \sigma_1\sigma_2 - \omega_1\omega_2 + j(\sigma_1\omega_2 + \sigma_2\omega_1) \qquad (2\text{-}7b)$$

$$s = \frac{s_1}{s_2} = \frac{\sigma_1 + j\omega_1}{\sigma_2 + j\omega_2} \frac{\sigma_2 - j\omega_2}{\sigma_2 - j\omega_2} = \frac{(\sigma_1 + j\omega_1)(\sigma_2 - j\omega_2)}{\sigma_2{}^2 + \omega_2{}^2}$$

$$= \frac{\sigma_1\sigma_2 + \omega_1\omega_2 + j(\sigma_2\omega_1 - \sigma_1\omega_2)}{\sigma_2{}^2 + \omega_2{}^2} \qquad (2\text{-}8b)$$

Notice that in forming the quotient by algebraic rules it is convenient to multiply top and bottom terms by the complex conjugate of the denominator, thus making the denominator real and thereby transferring the complex number to the numerator.

Example 2–1. Evaluate the sum, difference, quotient, and product of the two complex numbers, $s_1 = 3 + j5$ and $s_2 = -2 - j3$.
Solution. The results are given as

$$s_1 + s_2 = 3 + j5 + (-2 - j3) = 1 + j2$$
$$s_1 - s_2 = 3 + j5 - (-2 - j3) = 5 + j8$$
$$s_1 s_2 = (3 + j5)(-2 - j3) = 9 - j19$$
$$= \sqrt{34}\, e^{j1.03}\, \sqrt{13}\, e^{j4.12} = 21 e^{j5.15}$$
$$\frac{s_1}{s_2} = \frac{3 + j5}{-2 - j3} \frac{-2 + j3}{-2 + j3} = -1.62 - j0.077$$
$$= \frac{\sqrt{34}\, e^{j1.03}}{\sqrt{13}\, e^{j4.12}} = 1.618 e^{-j3.09}$$

The imaginary unit j is frequently identified as the positive square root of -1, but it is more natural to identify it as the complex number $0 + j1$. These results then follow:

$$j = 0 + j1 = e^{j\pi/2}$$
$$j^2 = -1 + j0 = e^{j\pi}$$
$$j^3 = 0 - j1 = e^{j3\pi/2} = e^{-j\pi/2}$$

From these equations, it is clear that multiplication of a complex number by j rotates the number through an angle of $\pi/2$ radians. Positive rotation is always taken in the counterclockwise direction.

In representing complex numbers in the complex plane (s-plane), there is frequent need to designate areas or regions in the plane. Several regions and their designations are shown in Fig. 2–3; these are listed

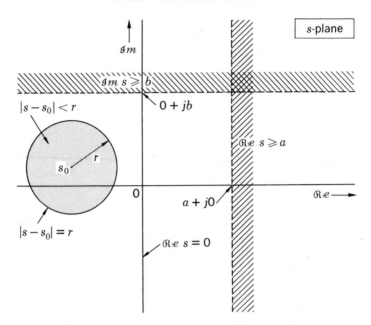

Fig. 2–3. Some designated areas and lines in the s-plane.

below with descriptive statements:

$\Re e\ s \geq a$ Limits σ to values equal to or greater than a while ω takes on all values from $-\infty$ to $+\infty$.

$\Re e\ s = 0$ Limits s to the axis of imaginaries, i.e., $s = \pm j\omega$.

$\Im m\ s \geq b$ Limits ω to values equal to or greater than b while σ takes on all values from $-\infty$ to $+\infty$.

$\Im m\ s = 0$ Limits s to the axis of reals, i.e., $s = \sigma$.

$|s - s_0| = r$ Limits values of s to the boundary of a circle of radius r with center at s_0.   This is shown by finding the absolute value of $(s - s_0)$:
$$|s - s_0| = |\sigma - \sigma_0 + j(\omega - \omega_0)| = [(\sigma - \sigma_0)^2 + (\omega - \omega_0)^2]^{\frac{1}{2}} = r$$

$|s - s_0| < r$ Limits values of s to the interior of the circle of radius r with center at s_0.

2–2. POLYNOMIALS AND RATIONAL FUNCTIONS

The analysis of lumped-parameter process systems leads to polynomial functions having real coefficients.   The general polynomial of degree n is written

$$P(s) = a_n s^n + a_{n-1} s^{n-1} + \cdots + a_2 s^2 + a_1 s + a_0 \qquad (2\text{–}9a)$$

According to the factor theorem of algebra, $P(s)$ can be written in the factored form

$$P(s) = a_n \prod_{i=1}^{n} (s - z_i) \qquad (2\text{–}9b)$$

where z_i are the zeros of the polynomial (roots or values of s which make $P(s) = 0$, i.e., $P(z_i) = 0$). If the factor $(s - z_1)$ is repeated k times, the polynomial has k repeated roots at z_1 and the zero has order k at z_1. A polynomial of degree n has n roots or n zeros when each zero is counted according to its order. The zeros may be real or complex. If they are complex, they must occur in conjugate pairs for polynomials having real coefficients, so that each pair of complex zeros derives from a quadratic factor with real coefficients since

$$(s - \sigma - j\omega)(s - \sigma + j\omega) = (s - \sigma)^2 + \omega^2$$

Therefore it is expected that the polynomials of interest in process engineering systems will have real zeros or zeros occurring in conjugate pairs.

A set of definite relationships exists between the zeros and the coefficients of a polynomial which can be obtained by expanding the factored form of the polynomial. To illustrate such a set, expand the factored form of a third-order polynomial and compare it with the normal form term by term, thus:

$$P(s) = (s - z_1)(s - z_2)(s - z_3) = s^3 - (z_1 + z_2 + z_3)s^2 \\ + (z_1z_2 + z_2z_3 + z_3z_1)s - z_1z_2z_3$$

On equating the coefficients of like powers of s, this set of relations results:

$$\left. \begin{aligned} s^3 &: a_3 = 1 \\ s^2 &: a_2 = -(z_1 + z_2 + z_3) \\ s^1 &: a_1 = z_1z_2 + z_2z_3 + z_3z_1 \\ s^0 &: a_0 = -z_1z_2z_3 \end{aligned} \right\} \qquad (2\text{–}10a)$$

This result can be generalized to give two useful rules concerning the zeros of polynomials. When $a_n = 1$, then

$$\left. \begin{aligned} a_{n-1} &= -(\text{sum of zeros}) \\ a_0 &= (-1)^n(\text{product of zeros}) \end{aligned} \right\} \qquad (2\text{–}10b)$$

Location of the Zeros. The process engineer needs to know the location of the zeros of a polynomial to solve most differential equations. For the solution of a differential equation to remain finite as time increases, it is necessary that the zeros of the characteristic equation have no positive real part.   In other words, the stability of a physical plant depends upon the location of the zeros of certain polynomials: if the zeros all lie to the left of the axis of imaginaries in the s-plane, the physical system is stable. The obvious approach, then, is to find the zeros of the polynomial and determine by inspection if any zero has a positive real part, thereby indicating instability in the system.   Finding the values of the zeros is a tedious and time-consuming task, and a general test is desired to determine if all the zeros of a polynomial lie in the left half of the s-plane. Polynomials having this property are called *Hurwitz polynomials;* there is a simple test for the non-Hurwitz property:

> When any of the coefficients of $P(s)$, a polynomial with real coefficients, vanish or have opposite signs, then the polynomial must have at least one zero with a positive real part.   It may have more than one such zero.

Unfortunately, polynomials may meet this test and yet have zeros with positive real parts, so that a stronger test is needed.   The *Routh-Hurwitz criterion* furnishes such a test.   It is applied to a polynomial of degree n, having real coefficients, by arranging the coefficients in a tabular form and completing the array as indicated below.   Using the polynomial to be examined for roots with positive real parts, Routh writes a series of $n + 1$ polynomials derived from $P(s)$ as shown here:

Polynomial: $P(s) = a_n s^n + a_{n-1} s^{n-1} + \cdots + a_2 s^2 + a_1 s + a_0$
Derived polynomials:

Shorthand representation

$a_n s^n + a_{n-2} s^{n-2} + a_{n-4} s^{n-4} + \cdots$ $s^n: a_n \quad a_{n-2} \quad a_{n-4}\ \cdot\ \cdot$
$a_{n-1} s^{n-1} + a_{n-3} s^{n-3} + a_{n-5} s^{n-5} + \cdots$ $s^{n-1}: a_{n-1} \quad a_{n-3} \quad a_{n-5}\ \cdot\ \cdot$
$b_1 s^{n-2} + b_2 s^{n-4} + \cdots$ $s^{n-2}: b_1 \quad b_2 \qquad\ \cdot \quad \cdot\ \cdot$
$c_1 s^{n-3} + c_2 s^{n-5} + \cdots$ $s^{n-3}: c_1 \quad c_2 \qquad\ \cdot \quad \cdot\ \cdot$

$m_1 s^2 + m_2$ $s^2: m_1 \quad m_2$
$p_1 s$ $s : p_1$
q_1 $s^0: q_1$

The polynomial nature of the derived equations is apparent (each polynomial contains terms of only odd or even powers of s), and the array of coefficients is usually abbreviated to the form shown on the right.   (The indication of the highest power of s in a row is usually dropped from the array after one becomes familiar with the method.)   The first two rows of the array are written in detached coefficient notation directly from the polynomial as indicated. Then the remaining b, c, . . . , m, p, and q rows are developed from the following formulas until tne coefficients become zero.

For the b row, if a_{n-1} does not vanish,

$$b_1 = \frac{a_{n-1}a_{n-2} - a_n a_{n-3}}{a_{n-1}} \qquad b_2 = \frac{a_{n-1}a_{n-4} - a_n a_{n-5}}{a_{n-1}}$$

For the c row, if b_1 does not vanish,

$$c_1 = \frac{b_1 a_{n-3} - a_{n-1}b_2}{b_1} \qquad c_2 = \frac{b_1 a_{n-5} - a_{n-1}b_3}{b_1}$$

Notice that each row is shorter by one coefficient than the preceding row. Zeros may be used in the array to indicate vanishing coefficients. The array is finished when $n + 1$ rows are developed. The first column of the array is called the *Routh series*, and the criterion states that the necessary and sufficient condition for all the roots of the original polynomial to have non-positive real parts is that all coefficients in the Routh series have a positive value. The polynomial then has the Hurwitz property and the physical system it represents is stable. Also, the number of sign changes in the Routh series is the number of roots having positive real parts.

Zeros may develop as coefficients in the array. In one case the first coefficient in a row may be zero; then the next row cannot be developed since division by zero is required. This difficulty is resolved by replacing the zero by a small positive number ϵ and continuing with development of the array.* In the other case which is of great importance in factoring the polynomial, all coefficients of an rth row may be zero, indicating that there are $(n + 2 - r)$ roots occurring as equal and opposite pairs (if $n + 2 - r$ is odd, one root is at the origin); these roots are found by solving the polynomial in the $r - 1$ row of the array. The Routh array is completed by replacing the all-zero row by the coefficients obtained by differentiating the polynomial represented by the preceding row. Frequently, the labor involved in completing an array may be reduced by knowing that any row may be divided by a positive number without changing the sign of the Routh series.

Example 2–2. Determine if the following polynomial has the Hurwitz property and comment on the location of its zeros (or roots).

$$P(s) = s^7 + s^6 + s^5 + s^4 + 4s^3 + 4s^2 + 4s + 4$$

---

* Another approach is to replace s in the original polynomial by $1/r$ and find the number of roots r having positive real parts which is the same as the number of roots s having positive real parts.

Solution. The coefficients of the Routh polynomials are set in an array, as below:

$$
\begin{array}{llllll}
s^7\colon 1 & 1 & 4 & 4 & 0 & \\
s^6\colon 1 & 1 & 4 & 4 & 0 & \\
s^5\colon 0 & 0 & 0 & 0 & & \\
\not{6} & \not{4} & \not{8} & & \text{divide by 2} & \\
s^5\colon 3 & 2 & 4 & 0 & & \\
s^4\colon \frac{1}{3} & \frac{8}{3} & 4 & 0 & & \\
s^3\colon -22 & -24 & 0 & & & \\
s^2\colon 2.3 & 4 & 0 & & & \\
s\colon 14.25 & 0 & & & & \\
s^0\colon 4 & & & & &
\end{array}
$$

In this case the coefficients of the third row vanish, showing that the polynomial has $7 + 2 - 3$, or 6, roots which occur as equal and opposite pairs. They are the solutions of the polynomial

$$s^6 + s^4 + 4s^2 + 4 = 0$$

The array is completed by replacing the zeros of the third row by coefficients obtained by differentiating the polynomial in the second row as shown. These coefficients are divided by 2 (to give smaller numbers to handle), as shown for the third row. The array is completed, and it is noted that the Routh series has two sign changes, indicating that the polynomial has two zeros having positive real parts. Therefore the polynomial does not possess the Hurwitz property: it has two roots in the right half of the s-plane, and it has six roots that occur as equal and opposite pairs. The roots are:

$$
\begin{array}{ll}
s_1 = -1 & s_4, s_5 = 1 \pm j \\
s_2, s_3 = \pm j & s_6, s_7 = -1 \pm j
\end{array}
$$

The numerical location of the zeros of polynomials is essentially an algebraic procedure since it is the same as finding the factors of the polynomial. There is no general equation for the n roots of an nth-degree polynomial, but formulas are given here for polynomials up to the third degree.*

QUADRATIC. The quadratic equation has two convenient forms:

$$s^2 + 2\zeta\omega s + \omega^2 = 0 \qquad \text{(for complex zeros)} \qquad (2\text{--}11\text{a})$$

where ω is the characteristic frequency and ζ is the damping factor; and

$$s^2 + \left(\frac{1}{\tau_1} + \frac{1}{\tau_2}\right)s + \frac{1}{\tau_1\tau_2} = 0 \qquad \text{(for real zeros)} \qquad (2\text{--}11\text{b})$$

* See C. R. Seliger, "Techniques for Finding Roots of Polynomial Equations of Degree Seven and Lower," *Instruments and Control Systems*, **40**(2), 120–124 (1967).

where $1/\tau_1$ and $1/\tau_2$ are the real zeros of the equation. The roots (or zeros) of the quadratic are given by the quadratic formula as

$$s_1, s_2 = -\zeta\omega \pm \omega\sqrt{\zeta^2 - 1} \quad \text{(complex zeros, } \zeta < 1)$$
$$= -1/\tau_1, -1/\tau_2 \quad \text{(real zeros)} \qquad (2\text{–}11c)$$

The physical significance of ω, ζ, and τ will be discussed in Chapters 4 and 7.

CUBIC. A convenient form of the cubic equation, based on Eq. 2–11a, is

$$s^3 + 3\omega s^2 + 3\beta\omega^2 s + \alpha\omega^3 = 0 \qquad \text{(for complex zeros)} \quad (2\text{–}12a)$$

where ω is the characteristic cubic frequency and α,β are parameters. For positive ω the equation will represent a stable plant when $9\beta \geq \alpha \geq 0$ and the cubic can be factored into a linear term and a quadratic term, as,

$$[s^2 + 2\zeta(\mu\omega)s + (\mu\omega)^2][s + (3 - 2\zeta\mu)\omega] = 0 \qquad (2\text{–}12b)$$

where $\alpha = (3 - 2\zeta\mu)\omega^2$ and $3\beta = \mu^2 + 2\zeta\mu(3 - 2\zeta\mu)$. Now, ω can be obtained from the coefficient of s^2 in Eq. 2–12a and ζ and μ obtained by solving the above equations that define α and β. The solution for ζ and μ is greatly simplified by the use of the graph in Fig. 2–4. When $\zeta > 1$

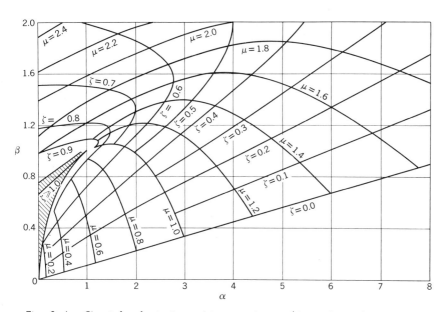

Fig. 2-4. Chart for factoring cubic equations. (From *Control Engineering*, 6(6), 111, 1959; by permission.)

the zeros are all real and the quadratic can be factored into two real terms by Eq. 2–11c.

Example 2–3. Find the zeros of the polynomial

$$P(s) = s^3 + 5s^2 + 10s + 8$$

Solution. On comparison of the polynomial with Eq. 2–12a, it is seen that $\omega = 1.67$ and β and α are found as

$$3\beta\omega^2 = 10 \qquad \beta = 1.2$$
$$\alpha\omega^3 = 8 \qquad \alpha = 1.73$$

For these values of α and β, Fig. 2–4 gives values of $\zeta = 0.75$ and $\mu = 1.2$ and the polynomial has one real root, $1/\tau = [3 - 2(0.75)(1.2)]1.67 = 2$, and a pair of complex roots having $\zeta = 0.75$ and $\mu\omega = 1.2(1.67) = 2$. The factored polynomial is

$$P(s) = (s^2 + 3s + 4)(s + 2)$$

HIGHER-ORDER POLYNOMIALS. In any polynomial factoring procedure it is best to first find any repeated roots and remove them by division before searching for the other roots. A polynomial having k repeated roots and its derivative may be written as

$$P(s) = (s + a)^k Q(s) \qquad (2\text{–}13a)$$
$$P'(s) = k(s + a)^{k-1}Q(s) + (s + a)^k Q'(s)$$
$$= (s + a)^{k-1}[kQ(s) + (s + a)Q'(s)] \qquad (2\text{–}13b)$$

from which it is seen that the derivative $P'(s)$ will contain the root repeated $k - 1$ times and therefore the factor $(s + a)^{k-1}$ becomes a common factor between the two polynomials, $P(s)$ and $P'(s)$.

The highest common factor between two polynomials can be found by application of the same Routh array which was previously used to test for polynomial roots having positive real parts. In this application, the procedure is to use the two polynomials to begin the array and continue it in the usual manner. The presence of a common factor between the two polynomials is shown by the development of a row of zeros in the array. The value of the highest common factor is the polynomial represented by the penultimate row of coefficients. Repeated roots in a polynomial are found by using the derivative $P'(s)$ as the second polynomial in the above procedure.

Example 2–4. By use of the Routh array, find any repeated roots in the following polynomial:

$$P(s) = s^4 + 7s^3 + 18s^2 + 20s + 8$$

Solution. The highest common factor between this polynomial and its derivative, if one exists, will be $(s + a)^{k-1}$ and therefore the repeated roots in the polynomial are $(s + a)^k$. The Routh array is formed from $P(s)$ and its derivative $P'(s)$ in the usual manner.

$$P'(s) = 4s^3 + 21s^2 + 36s + 20$$

The array becomes

$$
\begin{array}{llll}
s^4\!: 1 & 7 & 18 & 20 & 8 \\
 4 & 21 & 36 & 20 \\
s^3\!: \frac{7}{4} & 9 & 15 & 8 \\
 \frac{3}{7} & \frac{12}{7} & \frac{12}{7} \\
s^2\!: 2 & 8 & 8 & \leftarrow \text{This is the common factor.} \\
 0 & 0 & 0 & \leftarrow \text{This shows that a common factor exists.}
\end{array}
$$

Because a row of zeros developed in the array, the polynomial and its derivative has the highest common factor given by the penultimate row of coefficients in the array as

$$2s^2 + 8s + 8 = 2(s^2 + 4s + 4) = 2(s + 2)^2$$

and the polynomial has three repeated roots, $(s + 2)^3$.

After the repeated roots have been removed from the polynomial (by division) work can begin on finding the remaining roots or zeros. An elementary approach to finding a real zero of a function is to plot a graph of $P(s)$ against s and find the values of s for which $P(s) = 0$. An exact value need not be found since an approximate value of a zero can be improved by use of Newton's approximation formula,

$$r_2 = r_1 - \frac{P(r_1)}{P'(r_1)} \tag{2-14}$$

where r_2 is a better approximation to the zero than r_1, the first estimate, and $P'(r_1)$ is the derivative of the polynomial at r_1.

Other methods for finding the roots of polynomials of any order are Lin's method and Graeffe's root-squaring process, which are described in advanced engineering mathematics textbooks.

Rational Functions. A rational function is one that may be reduced to the ratio of two polynomials, $N(s)/D(s)$. Since any polynomial may be expressed in factored form, a rational function can be expressed as a ratio of factors

$$G(s) = \frac{N(s)}{D(s)} = K \frac{(s - z_1)(s - z_2) \cdots (s - z_m)}{(s - p_1)(s - p_2) \cdots (s - p_n)} = K \frac{\displaystyle\prod_1^m (s - z_i)}{\displaystyle\prod_1^n (s - p_i)} \tag{2-15}$$

where K is a constant, the z_i's are zeros of $N(s)$, and the p_i's are zeros of $D(s)$ or poles of $G(s)$. When $s = z_i$, the value of the function $G(s)$ is zero, and when $s \to p_i$ the value of the function $G(s)$ increases without limit but is not defined when $s = p_i$. In general, for real physical systems $n > m$ and $G(s) \to 0$ as $s \to \infty$.

As can be seen from Eq. 2–15, a rational function is determined by the gain multiplier K and the location of its zeros and poles. The factors $(s - z_i)$ and $(s - p_i)$ for any particular value of s are complex numbers which can be represented graphically as shown in Fig. 2–5. Let s have

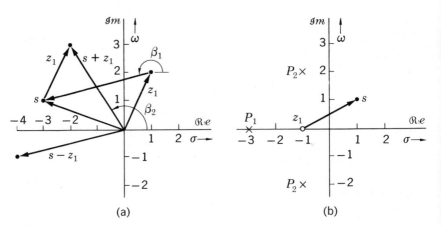

(a)   (b)

Fig. 2–5. Graphical display of vector algebra on the complex plane. (a) Display of vectors s, $(s - z_1)$, $(s + z_1)$. (b) Pole-zero map of rational function, $G(s) = (s + 1)/(s + 3)(s + 1 + j2)(s + 1 - j2)$.

the value $-3 + j$, and z_1 have the value $1 + j2$ as shown. Then the factors $(s - z_1)$ and $(s + z_1)$ are computed algebraically as

$$s - z_1 = -3 + j - (1 + j2) = -4 - j$$
$$s + z_1 = -3 + j + (1 + j2) = -2 + j3$$

The results are shown graphically in Fig. 2–5a, where it is noted that the factor $(s - z_1)$ is the directed line segment beginning at z_1 and terminating at s (its angle is β_1 measured from horizontal at z_1 and its length is measured from z_1 to s). The factor $(s + z_1)$ is the directed line segment from the origin to the end of z_1 after vector z_1 has been vectorially added to s (its angle β_2 is measured at the origin and its length is measured from the origin to the tip of z_1 after it is added to s). Since the $(s - z)$ terms always arise in the factored form of a rational function, this is the most important construction, and the result is given as the directed line segment starting at z and terminating at s.

A complete geometrical representation of a rational function, except for the gain K, is obtained by plotting its zeros and poles on the complex plane. An illustration is given in Fig. 2–5b for the function

$$G(s) = \frac{s + 1}{(s + 3)(s + 1 - j2)(s + 1 + j2)} \qquad (2\text{--}16)$$

The function has a zero at $s = -1$ which is designated on the complex plane by a circle ($\bigcirc$). The poles at $s = -3$, $-1 + j2$, and $-1 - j2$ are designated by crosses ($\times$) on the complex plane. The pole-zero representation on the complex plane is referred to as the *pole-zero map of the function*. In addition to the visual significance which the representation conveys, it is useful in making graphical calculations since for a particular value of s each factor of the rational function can be graphically evaluated from the plot as a magnitude and angle. Then the value of the function at a given s is found by combining the complex factors in the usual manner.

Example 2–5. Evaluate graphically the function given by Eq. 2–16 for a value $s = 1 + j$ and compare the value with that given by analytical methods.

Solution. The problem is to find the magnitude and angle of the function

$$G(1 + j) = \frac{(1 + j + 1)}{(1 + j + 3)(1 + j + 1 - j2)(1 + j + 1 + j2)}$$

$$= \frac{(2 + j)}{(4 + j)(2 - j)(2 + j3)}$$

Usually one would analytically evaluate each factor in polar form and combine the factors. Thus for the zero, the polar value of the $(s - z_1)$ term is

$$(s - z_1) = (1 + j + 1) = 2 + j = \sqrt{4 + 1} \, \angle \tan^{-1} \tfrac{1}{2} = 2.23 \angle 26.5°$$

However, this term may be graphically evaluated as shown in Fig. 2–5b by measuring the length from z_1 to s and the angle from the horizontal. The result is $2.25 \angle 26°$, in good agreement with the actual value. In like manner, the other factors are evaluated and tabulated:

	graphical	analytical
$s - p_1 =$	$4.10 \underline{/14°}$	$4.13 \underline{/14°}$
$s - p_2 =$	$2.25 \underline{/334°}$	$2.24 \underline{/334.5°}$
$s - p_3 =$	$3.60 \underline{/56°}$	$3.61 \underline{/56.3°}$

Finally, the value of the function found by graphical measurements is

$$G(1 + j) = \frac{2.25 \underline{/26°}}{4.10 \underline{/14°} \; 2.25 \underline{/334°} \; 3.60 \underline{/56°}} = 0.0678 \underline{/-378°}$$

The analytical calculation gives $0.0672 \underline{/-377.8°}$. The difference is due to measurement errors in the graphical evaluation of the factors from Fig. 2–5b.

2-3. LAPLACE TRANSFORM AND USES

Much of the mathematical summary in this chapter and Appendix A was selected as a background for the Laplace transformation introduced by P. S. de Laplace in 1779. Today the Laplace transformation finds widespread use in all branches of engineering for solving linear differential equations since it provides a simple way to obtain both the transient and steady-state terms in the solutions. In a few words, it is an operational method that transforms the differential equation into an algebraic equation. The algebraic equation is solved for the transformed variable, and the solution of the original differential equation is obtained by inverting the transformed variable back to the original independent variable (usually time).

A most important use of the Laplace transform in linear control theory is the transformation of a process system linear differential equation to the operational form called the *system transfer function*. The system transfer function is the ratio of the Laplace transform of the system output to the Laplace transform of the system input with all the initial conditions assumed to be zero. The system transfer function is obtained from system equations such as Eq. 1–1a and is normally written as $G(s)$ in the form of Eq. 1–1b, thus:

$$G(s) = \frac{C(s)}{M(s)} \tag{1-1b}$$

Continual use of $G(s)$ is made throughout this book.

The Laplace transformation transforms a function of a real variable $f(t)$ into $F(s)$, a function of a complex variable s, by the integration defined as

$$\mathcal{L}[f(t)] = \int_{0^+}^{\infty} f(t)e^{-st}\, dt = F(s) \tag{2-17}$$

where $\mathcal{L}[\ \ ]$ is the symbol for the Laplace transformation.* The lower limit is usually designated as zero in most texts on Laplace transform, but here it is used as 0^+ (zero approached from the positive side) to avoid ambiguity at $t = 0$. For the Laplace integral to have meaning, $f(t)$ must be defined for $t \geq 0$ and the integral must converge. The value of $f(t)$ for negative values of time is assumed to be zero and is of no consequence in evaluating the Laplace transform of $f(t)$. A function $f(t)$ is Laplace-transformable if it is piecewise-continuous and single-valued and if the integral

$$\int_{0^+}^{\infty} |f(t)|e^{-at}\, dt$$

* The symbol $\mathcal{L}^{-1}[\ \ ]$ represents the inverse operation.

converges. This imposes the restriction that the real part of s must be greater than the lower bound for some sufficiently large positive constant a for which the integral converges, i.e., $\Re e\ s > a$. The physical signifi- cance of t depends on the problem at hand, but in this book it represents time and is restricted to $t \geq 0$. Therefore, since s and t have reciprocal dimensions, the variable s represents reciprocal time.

The Laplace transformation is a linear operation and, of course, the principle of superposition holds for its use. These statements mean that if $f_1(t)$ and $f_2(t)$ are Laplace-transformable and if a and b are independent of s and t, then

$$\mathcal{L}[af_1(t) \pm bf_2(t)] = aF_1(s) \pm bF_2(s)$$

Laplace-Transform Function Pairs. The derivation of Laplace trans- forms for a few simple functions will illustrate the formation of a table of transform pairs.

STEP FUNCTION. Let $f(t) = u(t)$, which is the unit step function, defined as

$$u(t) = 0 \qquad \text{for } t \leq 0$$
$$u(t) = 1 \qquad \text{for } t > 0$$

The Laplace transform of the unit step function is

$$\mathcal{L}[u(t)] = \int_{0^+}^{\infty} 1 \cdot e^{-st}\, dt = -\frac{1}{s} e^{-st} \Big|_{0^+}^{\infty} = \frac{1}{s} \qquad \text{if } \Re e\ s = \sigma > 0 \quad (2\text{–}18)$$

In case of difficulty in substituting the integral limits, it should be remem- bered that the integral is defined by a limit process. In the problem at hand, the value of the step function is undefined at $t = 0$ but it is clear from the nature of the function (unity for all positive time and zero for all other time) that the limiting value at zero time is zero. The functions $u(t)$ and $1/s$ constitute a Laplace-transform pair which may be listed in a table for ready reference. The functions $1/s$ is the Laplace transform of $u(t)$, while $u(t)$ is the inverse transform of $1/s$. Table 2–1 lists a few transform pairs with graphs showing plots of $f(t)$ in the t-plane and of the zero-pole map of $F(s)$ in the s-plane. Table 2–2 lists some commonly used Laplace-transform pairs. Any transform pair in the table will reduce to a simpler pair by setting the appropriate constants to zero. More extensive tabulations are available.*

---

* M. Abramowitz and I. A. Stegun (eds.), *Handbook of Mathematical Functions*, AMS 55, Government Printing Office, Washington, D.C., 1964. See also G. E. Roberts and H. Kaufman, *Table of Laplace Transforms*, W. B. Saunders Co., Phila- delphia, 1965.

TABLE 2–1
Laplace-Transform Function Pairs

$f(t)$	Graph	$F(s)$	Pole-Zero Map
1. $u(t)$		$\dfrac{1}{s}$	
2. t		$\dfrac{1}{s^2}$	
3. $\dfrac{t^{n-1}}{(n-1)!}$	—	$\dfrac{1}{s^n}$	$n = 1, 2, 3, \ldots$
4. e^{-at}		$\dfrac{1}{s+a}$	$-a$
5. $\sin \omega t$		$\dfrac{\omega}{s^2+\omega^2}$	
6. $\cos \omega t$		$\dfrac{s}{s^2+\omega^2}$	
7. $e^{-at}\cos \omega t$		$\dfrac{s+a}{(s+a)^2+\omega^2}$	$-a$
8. $1 - e^{-at}$		$\dfrac{a}{s(s+a)}$	$-a$
9. te^{-at}		$\dfrac{1}{(s+a)^2}$	$-a$
10. $\dfrac{t^{n-1}e^{-at}}{(n-1)!}$		$\dfrac{1}{(s+a)^n}$	$n = 1, 2, 3, \ldots$

RAMP FUNCTION. Let $f(t) = t$, the unit ramp function. The Laplace transform is

$$\mathcal{L}[t] = \int_{0^+}^{\infty} te^{-st}\, dt = -\left(\frac{t}{s} + \frac{1}{s^2}\right) e^{-st} \Big|_{0^+}^{\infty}$$

$$= 0 - \left(-\frac{1}{s^2}\right) = \frac{1}{s^2} \quad \text{for } \sigma > 0 \quad (2\text{--}19)$$

TABLE 2–2
Simple Table of Laplace-Transform Pairs*

No.	$F(s)$	$f(t)$
1.	$\dfrac{1}{\tau s + 1}$	$\dfrac{1}{\tau} e^{-t/\tau}$
2.	$\dfrac{1 + as}{s(\tau s + 1)}$	$1 + \dfrac{a - \tau}{\tau} e^{-t/\tau}$
3.	$\dfrac{1 + as}{(\tau_1 s + 1)(\tau_2 s + 1)}$	$\dfrac{\tau_1 - a}{(\tau_1 - \tau_2)\tau_1} e^{-t/\tau_1} - \dfrac{\tau_2 - a}{(\tau_1 - \tau_2)\tau_2} e^{-t/\tau_2}$
4.	$\dfrac{1 + as}{s(\tau_1 s + 1)(\tau_2 s + 1)}$	$1 + \dfrac{\tau_1 - a}{\tau_2 - \tau_1} e^{-t/\tau_1} - \dfrac{\tau_2 - a}{\tau_2 - \tau_1} e^{-t/\tau_2}$
5.	$\dfrac{\omega_n^2 (1 + as)}{s^2 + 2\zeta\omega_n s + \omega_n^2}$	$\left[\dfrac{a^2\omega_n^2 - 2a\zeta\omega_n + 1}{1 - \zeta^2} \right]^{1/2} \omega_n e^{-\zeta\omega_n t}$ $\sin(\omega_n \sqrt{1 - \zeta^2}\, t + \psi)$ $\psi = \tan^{-1} a\omega_n \sqrt{1 - \zeta^2}/(1 - a\zeta\omega_n)$
6.	$\dfrac{\omega_n^2 (1 + as)}{s(s^2 + 2\zeta\omega_n s + \omega_n^2)}$	$1 + \left[\dfrac{a^2\omega_n^2 - 2a\zeta\omega_n + 1}{1 - \zeta^2} \right]^{1/2} e^{-\zeta\omega_n t}$ $\sin(\omega_n \sqrt{1 - \zeta^2}\, t + \psi)$ $\psi = \tan^{-1} \dfrac{a\omega_n \sqrt{1 - \zeta^2}}{1 - a\zeta\omega_n} - \tan^{-1} \dfrac{\sqrt{1 - \zeta^2}}{-\zeta}$
7.	$\dfrac{1 + as}{(\tau s + 1)^2}$	$\left(\dfrac{a}{\tau^2} + \dfrac{\tau - a}{\tau^3} t \right) e^{-t/\tau}$
8.	$\dfrac{1 + as}{s(\tau s + 1)^2}$	$1 + \left(\dfrac{a - \tau}{\tau^2} t - 1 \right) e^{-t/\tau}$
9.	$\dfrac{1 + as}{(\tau_1 s + 1)(\tau_2 s + 1)(\tau_3 s + 1)}$	$\dfrac{(\tau_1 - a)e^{-t/\tau_1}}{(\tau_1 - \tau_2)(\tau_1 - \tau_3)} + \dfrac{(\tau_2 - a)e^{-t/\tau_2}}{(\tau_2 - \tau_1)(\tau_2 - \tau_3)}$ $+ \dfrac{(\tau_3 - a)e^{-t/\tau_3}}{(\tau_3 - \tau_1)(\tau_3 - \tau_2)}$
10.	$\dfrac{1 + as}{s(\tau_1 s + 1)(\tau_2 s + 1)(\tau_3 s + 1)}$	$1 - \dfrac{\tau_1(\tau_1 - a)e^{-t/\tau_1}}{(\tau_1 - \tau_2)(\tau_1 - \tau_3)} - \dfrac{\tau_2(\tau_2 - a)e^{-t/\tau_2}}{(\tau_2 - \tau_1)(\tau_2 - \tau_3)}$ $- \dfrac{\tau_3(\tau_3 - a)e^{-t/\tau_3}}{(\tau_3 - \tau_1)(\tau_3 - \tau_2)}$

* From F. E. Nixon, *Handbook of Laplace Transformation*, Prentice-Hall, Inc., Englewood Cliffs, N.J., 1960. By permission.

The integration may be performed either by use of a table of integrals or by use of the formula for integration by parts. The transform has two poles at zero.

DECAYING EXPONENTIAL. Let $f(t) = e^{-at}$, where a is real and positive. The Laplace transform is

$$\mathcal{L}[e^{-at}] = \int_{0^+}^{\infty} e^{-at} e^{-st}\, dt = \dfrac{-1}{s + a} e^{-(s+a)t} \Big|_{0^+}^{\infty} = \dfrac{1}{s + a} \qquad \text{if } \sigma > -a \quad (2\text{-}20)$$

As shown in Table 2–1, the transform has a pole at $-a$.

DAMPED COSINUSOIDAL.   Let $f(t) = e^{-at} \cos \omega t$.   Expressing $\cos \omega t$ in exponential form gives the Laplace transform as

$$\mathscr{L}[e^{-at} \cos \omega t] = \frac{1}{2} \int_{0^+}^{\infty} [e^{-(a-j\omega)t} + e^{-(a+j\omega)t}]e^{-st}\, dt$$

$$= \frac{1}{2} \left\{ \frac{-e^{-(s+a-j\omega)t}}{s+a-j\omega} - \frac{e^{-(s+a+j\omega)t}}{s+a+j\omega} \right\} \Big|_{0^+}^{\infty}$$

$$= \frac{1}{2} \left\{ 0 - \left[\frac{-1}{s+a-j\omega} - \frac{1}{s+a+j\omega} \right] \right\}$$

$$= \frac{s+a}{(s+a)^2 + \omega^2} \qquad \text{for } \sigma > 0 \qquad (2\text{-}21)$$

The transform has a zero at $-a$ and a pair of complex poles at $-a + j\omega$ and $-a - j\omega$.

Laplace-Transform Operation Pairs.   Laplace transformation ordinarily does not separate functions from operations, e.g., $1/s$ is the transform of the unit step, $u(t)$ and also of the integration operation.   A function transforms numbers into other numbers, that is, for each t there is assigned the number $f(t)$.   An operator transforms functions into other functions as the differential operator changes the function $\ln x$ into the function $1/x$; and the Laplace-transform operator changes the function $f(t)$ to the corresponding function $F(s)$.   Transform function pairs are listed in Tables 2–1 and 2–2.   Transform operation pairs useful in process system studies are listed in Table 2–3.   Some of these are derived below.

DERIVATIVE OF TIME FUNCTION.   The Laplace transform of the differentiation operation is defined as

$$\mathscr{L}\left[\frac{df}{dt}\right] = \int_{0^+}^{\infty} \frac{df}{dt} e^{-st}\, dt$$

Now let $u = e^{-st}$, $du = -se^{-st}\, dt$ and $dv = (df/dt)\, dt$, $v = f(t)$; using integration by parts, the integral becomes

$$\mathscr{L}\left[\frac{df}{dt}\right] = f(t)e^{-st} \Big|_{0^+}^{\infty} + s \int_{0^+}^{\infty} f(t)e^{-st}\, dt = -f(0^+) + sF(s) \qquad (2\text{-}22)$$

where $f(0^+)$ is the value of the time function at "zero plus" time, i.e., the initial condition.   Thus, the Laplace-transform real differentiation theorem changes the differentiation operation into that of multiplication by s.

Eq. 2–22 can be applied to higher derivatives, giving the corresponding Laplace-transform equations.   The result for the second derivative is obtained as

$$\mathscr{L}\left[\frac{d}{dt} f'(t)\right] = s[sF(s) - f(0^+)] - f'(0^+)$$

$$= s^2 F(s) - sf(0^+) - f'(0^+)$$

where $f'(0^+)$ is the initial value of the first derivative. This inclusion of the initial conditions in the transformation operation is a significant advantage of the Laplace-transform method over the classical method of solving integrodifferential equations.

INTEGRAL OF TIME FUNCTION. To find the Laplace transform of the integral of a function of time, return to the definition of the Laplace integral (Eq. 2–17),

$$F(s) = \int_{0^+}^{\infty} f(t)e^{-st}\, dt$$

and let

$$u = e^{-st}$$

Then

$$du = -se^{-st}\, dt$$

and

$$dv = f(t)\, dt$$

so that

$$v = \int f(t)\, dt \equiv f^{-1}(t)$$

where $f^{-1}(t)$ is the symbol for the indefinite integral. Using the formula for integration by parts, the Laplace integral becomes

$$F(s) = e^{-st}f^{-1}(t)\Big|_{0^+}^{\infty} - \int_{0^+}^{\infty} f^{-1}(t)(-se^{-st}\, dt)$$

$$= 0 - f^{-1}(0^+) + s\int_{0^+}^{\infty} f^{-1}(t)e^{-st}\, dt$$

where the symbol $f^{-1}(0^+)$ represents the value of the indefinite integral as t approaches zero from the positive side. Thus the Laplace transform of the integral of a time function, known as the *real integration theorem*, is

$$\mathcal{L}\left[\int f(t)\, dt\right] = \frac{F(s)}{s} + \frac{f^{-1}(0^+)}{s} \tag{2–23}$$

which shows that the transformation changes time integration into division by s in the complex plane. Again, the initial conditions of the problem are included in the transformation step.

The Laplace transform of higher-order integrals can be written from Eq. 2–23. For the double integral the transform is

$$\mathcal{L}\left[\iint f(t)\, dt\right] = \frac{1}{s}\left[\frac{F(s)}{s} + \frac{f^{-1}(0^+)}{s}\right] + \frac{f^{-2}(0^+)}{s}$$

$$= \frac{F(s)}{s^2} + \frac{f^{-1}(0^+)}{s^2} + \frac{f^{-2}(0^+)}{s}$$

REAL AND COMPLEX TRANSLATION. The process control engineer frequently meets process time delays in the plant; he treats these time delays by using functions of time displacement $f(t - \tau)$ instead of $f(t)$, where τ is the delay time and has the same dimensions as t. And to avoid ambiguity in the function for $t < \tau$, he stipulates that the new function shall be zero for $t < \tau$. The new function of time displacement can be written with the aid of the unit step notation as

$$f(t - \tau)u(t - \tau)$$

where

$$u(t - \tau) = 0 \qquad \text{for } t < \tau$$
$$u(t - \tau) = 1 \qquad \text{for } t \geq \tau$$

The plots in Fig. 2–6 show how the time displacement shifts the function in the positive time direction an amount τ and the delayed function is

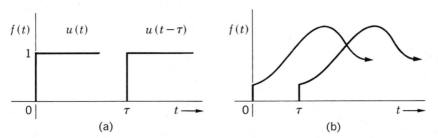

Fig. 2–6. (a) Graphs of unit step function, $u(t)$, and delayed unit step function, $u(t - \tau)$. (b) Graphs of function of time, $f(t)$, and function of time displacement, $f(t - \tau)u(t - \tau)$. The delayed unit step notation ensures that $f(t - \tau)$ is zero for $t < \tau$.

zero for time $t < \tau$. The delayed unit step function $u(t - \tau)$ can be omitted when it is understood that the notation $f(t - \tau)$ means that the function is zero for $t < \tau$. The Laplace transform of the time-displacement function is

$$\mathcal{L}[f(t - \tau)u(t - \tau)] = \int_{0^+}^{\infty} f(t - \tau)u(t - \tau)e^{-st}\,dt = \int_{\tau}^{\infty} f(t - \tau)e^{-st}\,dt$$

where $u(t - \tau)$ is removed as unity and the lower limit changed to τ. If the variable is changed so that $x = t - \tau$, then

$$\mathcal{L}[f(t - \tau)u(t - \tau)] = e^{-\tau s} \int_{0^+}^{\infty} f(x)e^{-sx}\,dx = e^{-\tau s}F(s) \qquad (2\text{--}24)$$

The result is that time displacement in real time corresponds to multiplication by $e^{-\tau s}$ in the complex plane, that is, in simple notation,

$$\mathcal{L}[f(t - \tau)] = e^{-\tau s}F(s)$$

where $\mathcal{L}[f(t)] = F(s)$.

The effect of an s-displacement in the complex plane upon the time function $f(t)$, known as the *complex translation theorem*, is

$$\mathcal{L}[e^{-at}f(t)] = F(s + a) \qquad (2\text{-}25)$$

where $F(s)$ is the Laplace transform of $f(t)$ and a may be real or complex. This theorem points out that the Laplace transform of a function multiplied by an exponential is obtained from the transform of the function by a simple change in variable.

Example 2-6. The time-displacement function (or time-delay function) is very useful in dealing with delayed and displaced functions. By use of the unit step and the time-displacement functions, find the Laplace transform of the functions shown in Fig. E2-6.

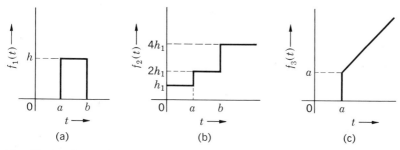

Fig. E2-6. Some functions that are easily defined by using the time-displacement function.

Solution. The functions sketched may be described, using time delay, as follows:

(a) The function in Fig. E2-6a consists of an h-unit step function delayed a time units plus a step function of $-h$ units delayed b time units, written as

$$f_1(t) = hu(t - a) - hu(t - b)$$

Then the Laplace transform of $f_1(t)$ becomes

$$\mathcal{L}[f_1(t)] = \frac{h}{s} e^{-as} - \frac{h}{s} e^{-bs} = \frac{h}{s}(e^{-as} - e^{-bs})$$

(b) The function in Fig. E2-6b consists of an h_1-unit step function plus an h_1-unit step delay of a time units plus a $2h_1$-unit step function delayed b time units, written as

$$f_2(t) = h_1 u(t) + h_1 u(t - a) + 2h_1 u(t - b)$$

Then the Laplace transform of $f_2(t)$ becomes

$$\mathcal{L}[f_2(t)] = \frac{h_1}{s} + \frac{h_1}{s} e^{-as} + \frac{2h_1}{s} e^{-bs} = \frac{h_1}{s}(1 + e^{-as} + 2e^{-bs})$$

(c) The function in Fig. E2–6c consists of a unit ramp function delayed a time units plus a step function of a units delayed a time units. Alternately, it may be viewed as the unit ramp function multiplied by the unit step function, delayed a time units. In either case the function becomes $f_3(t) = tu(t - a)$, and its Laplace transform becomes

$$\mathcal{L}[f_3(t)] = \frac{1}{s^2} e^{-as}$$

Additional Laplace-Transform Theorems. A number of additional theorems are available to aid the process control engineer in using transforms. They are listed here without proofs. A summary of the Laplace-transform operation pairs is given in Table 2–3.

TABLE 2–3
Laplace-Transform Operation Pairs

Theorems	$f(t)$	$F(s)$
1. Linearity	$af(t) + bg(t)$	$aF(s) + bG(s)$
2. Differentiation	$\dfrac{df}{dt}$	$sF(s) - f(0^+)$
	$\dfrac{d^2f}{dt^2}$	$s^2F(s) - sf(0^+) - f^{(1)}(0^+)$
	$\dfrac{d^nf}{dt^n}$	$s^nF(s) - s^{n-1}f^{(1)}(0^+)$ $-s^{n-2}f^{(2)}(0^+) - \cdots$ $-f^{(n-1)}(0^+)$
3. Integration	$\int f(\tau)\, d\tau$	$\dfrac{1}{s}F(s) + \dfrac{1}{s}f^{-1}(0^+)$
	$\int\int(\tau)\, d\tau$	$\dfrac{1}{s^2}F(s) + \dfrac{1}{s^2}f^{-1}(0^+) + \dfrac{1}{s}f^{-2}(0^+)$
4. Time delay	$f(t - \tau)u(t - \tau)$	$e^{-\tau s}F(s)$
5. Complex translation	$e^{-at}f(t)$	$F(s + a)$
6. Initial value	$\lim_{t \to 0} f(t) \qquad =$	$\lim_{s \to \infty} sF(s)$
7. Final value	$\lim_{t \to \infty} f(t) \qquad =$	$\lim_{s \to 0} sF(s)$
8. Convolution	$\displaystyle\int_0^t f(t - \tau)g(\tau)\, d\tau$	$F(s) \cdot G(s)$
9. Time-scale change	$f(at)$	$\dfrac{1}{a}F\left(\dfrac{s}{a}\right)$
10. Periodic function	$f(t + a) = f(t)$	$\dfrac{1}{1 - e^{-as}}\displaystyle\int_0^a e^{-st}f(t)\, dt$
11. Inversion	$f(t) = \dfrac{1}{2\pi j}\displaystyle\int_{a-j\infty}^{a+j\infty} e^{ts}F(s)\, ds$	$F(s)$

Initial Value. If the time function $f(t)$ and its first derivative $f'(t)$ are Laplace-transformable, and if the $\lim_{s \to \infty} sF(s)$ exists, then

$$\lim_{t \to 0} f(t) = \lim_{s \to \infty} sF(s) \qquad (2\text{-}26)$$

where $F(s)$ is the transform of $f(t)$. Then the behavior of $f(t)$ as time approaches zero (the initial value of the function) is related to the behavior of $sF(s)$ as s approaches infinity.

Final Value. If the time function $f(t)$ and its first derivative $f'(t)$ are Laplace-transformable, and if the $\lim_{t \to \infty} f(t)$ exists, then

$$\lim_{t \to \infty} f(t) = \lim_{s \to 0} sF(s) \qquad (2\text{-}27)$$

where $F(s)$ is the transform of $f(t)$. When $sF(s)$ has poles on the imaginary axis or in the right-half s plane, there is no final value of $f(t)$; the theorem does not apply to such cases. In the case of sinusoidal forcing functions, the $\lim_{t \to \infty} \sin \omega t$ does not exist and the theorem does not apply.

Convolution in the Time Plane. This theorem is useful for obtaining the inverse transform of any function of s which is a product of two functions of s whose inverse transforms are known. Thus, when

$$\mathcal{L}[f_1(t)] = F_1(s) \qquad \text{and} \qquad \mathcal{L}[f_2(t)] = F_2(s)$$

are known transform pairs, then

$$\mathcal{L}\left[\int_0^t f_1(\tau) f_2(t - \tau) \, d\tau\right] = F_1(s) F_2(s) \qquad (2\text{-}28a)$$

and also

$$\mathcal{L}\left[\int_0^t f_1(t - \tau) f_2(\tau) \, d\tau\right] = F_1(s) F_2(s) \qquad (2\text{-}28b)$$

Time-Scale Change. This theorem finds frequent usage in analog computer work when the time scale must be changed to fit the problem to the computer. When $\mathcal{L}[f(t)] = F(s)$, the transform of the function with time scale changed is

$$\mathcal{L}[f(at)] = \frac{1}{a} F\left(\frac{s}{a}\right) \qquad (2\text{-}29)$$

which is to say, if the time function is stretched in the ratio $1:a$, then the corresponding transform function is uniformly shrunk in the ratio $a:1$. For $a > 1$, the time scale is compressed; and for $a < 1$ the time scale is expanded. This is demonstrated by taking an example. Let $f(t) = t$, then to compress the time scale take $a = 2$ and then $f(2t) = 2t$. Now, the second function will have identical values to the first function at values of time equal to $1/2$ (or $1/a$) the t values used in the first function; thus, the time scale of the first function has been compressed and the time response will be slowed down.

Example 2–7. The utility of a transform function table can be extended by application of the transform operation pair. Find the Laplace transform of $f(t) = \cos \omega t \cos mt$, using item 5 in Table 2–3, and the transform of $\cos \omega t$ from Table 2–1.

Solution. From Euler's relationship,

$$\mathcal{Re}\ (e^{i\omega t}) = \cos \omega t$$

and item 5 of Table 2–3,

$$\mathcal{L}[e^{-at}f(t)] = F(s + a)$$

the following relationship is obtained,

$$\mathcal{Re}\ \mathcal{L}[e^{i\omega t}f(t)] = \mathcal{L}[\cos \omega t\ f(t)] = \mathcal{Re}\ F(s - j\omega)$$

Now, $f(t) = \cos mt$ and $\mathcal{L}[f(t)] = F(s) = s/(s^2 + m^2)$ so that the required transform is found as

$$\mathcal{L}[\cos \omega t \cos mt] = \mathcal{Re}\ \frac{s - j\omega}{(s - j\omega)^2 + m^2} = \frac{s(s^2 + \omega^2 + m^2)}{[s^2 + (m - \omega)^2][s^2 + (m + \omega)^2]}$$

Laplace Inverse Transformation. The Laplace transform method for solving linear differential equations involves three steps: (1) transforming the functions of time to functions of s and substitution of initial conditions; (2) algebraic solution of the transformed equation for the transformed function, $F(s)$; (3) determination of the inverse transforms to find $f(t)$, the response of the equation. The inverse transform of a function of s, designated $\mathcal{L}^{-1}[F(s)]$, can be found by the method of partial fraction expansion, using a general table of Laplace-transform pairs, as shown in Example 2–8 or by use of the method of residues.

Example 2–8. Solve the following equation with the initial condition that $f(0) = 10$.

$$f'(t) + f(t) = 5$$

Solution. Laplace transformation of the equation, term by term, gives

$$sF(s) - 10 + F(s) = 5/s$$

Algebraic solution of this equation for $F(s)$, the transform of $f(t)$, gives

$$F(s) = \frac{10}{s + 1} + \frac{5}{s(s + 1)}$$

Now the $f(t)$ is found by inversion of $F(s)$ by use of a table of transform pairs or by the method of residues which is discussed in the next section. The inversion is obtained here by use of the transform pairs 4 and 8 in Table 2–1, with the result

$$f(t) = 10e^{-t} + 5(1 - e^{-t}) = 5(1 + e^{-t})$$

METHOD OF PARTIAL FRACTION EXPANSION.   This method uses a table of known transform pairs.   The approach is to algebraically decompose the transform into a sum of elementary terms whose inverse transforms are available in the table.   Then the inverse transform of the function of s is the sum of the inverse transforms of the elementary terms.

When the transform is a rational fraction (ratio of polynomials) it can be written in factored form as

$$F(s) = \frac{N(s)}{D(s)} = \frac{N(s)}{\displaystyle\prod_{i=1}^{n} (s - p_i)} \tag{2-30}$$

where p_i are the zeros of $D(s)$, called *poles* of $F(s)$, and may be real or complex.   Two cases occur; either the poles of $F(s)$ are unequal, and they are called *single-order* poles; or some poles are equal, and they are called *repeated* poles.

Unequal Poles of $F(s)$.   In this case the partial fraction expansion of $F(s)$ can be written as

$$F(s) = \frac{K_1}{s - p_1} + \frac{K_2}{s - p_2} + \cdots + \frac{K_i}{s - p_i} + \cdots$$
$$+ \frac{K_{n-1}}{s - p_{n-1}} + \frac{K_n}{s - p_n} \tag{2-31}$$

and the problem is to evaluate the coefficients $K_1, \ldots, K_n$.   Each K_i can be found by multiplying both sides of Eq. 2-31 by the factor $(s - p_i)$ and then letting s approach p_i as a limit, thus:

$$(s - p_i)F(s) = K_1 \frac{(s - p_i)}{(s - p_1)} + K_2 \frac{(s - p_i)}{(s - p_2)} + \cdots K_i + \cdots$$

and the value of K_i is given as

$$K_i = \lim_{s \to p_i} (s - p_i)F(s) \tag{2-32}$$

The form of the time response is then

$$f(t) = K_1 e^{-p_1 t} + \cdots + K_i e^{-p_i t} + \cdots K_n e^{-p_n t}$$

As an illustration, consider the transform in Example 2-8,

$$F(s) = \frac{10}{s + 1} + \frac{5}{s(s + 1)} = \frac{10}{s + 1} + \frac{K_1}{s} + \frac{K_2}{s + 1}$$

In this case only the second term in $F(s)$ has to be decomposed into partial fractions as indicated. The coefficients K_1, K_2 are found as

$$K_1 = s\left[\frac{5}{s(s+1)}\right]_{s\to 0} = 5$$

$$K_2 = (s+1)\left[\frac{5}{s(s+1)}\right]_{s\to -1} = -5$$

Then the partial fraction expansion of $F(s)$ becomes

$$F(s) = \frac{10}{s+1} + \frac{5}{s} - \frac{5}{s+1} = \frac{5}{s+1} + \frac{5}{s}$$

and

$$f(t) = 5(e^{-t} + 1)$$

The same procedure applies when the poles occur as complex pairs and the corresponding K's will be complex conjugates. However, in order to avoid the manipulation of complex numbers, it is best to keep factors of complex pairs together as a unit, as

$$\frac{as + b}{s^2 + 2\zeta\omega s + \omega^2}$$

Repeated Poles of $F(s)$. When the transform $F(s)$ has repeated poles, the partial fraction expansion can be written as

$$F(s) = \frac{N(s)}{D(s)} = \frac{N(s)}{(s - p_1)^k \prod\limits_{i=k+1}^{n} (s - p_i)} = \frac{K_{11}}{s - p_1} + \cdots$$

$$+ \frac{K_{1(k-1)}}{(s - p_1)^{k-1}} + \frac{K_{1k}}{(s - p_1)^k} + \frac{K_2}{s - p_2} + \cdots \quad (2\text{--}33)$$

where p_1 is a kth-order pole and may be real or complex. The problem is to evaluate the coefficients $K_{11}, \ldots, K_{1k}$; the other coefficients $K_2\ K_3, \ldots, K_n$ may be evaluated by Eq. 2–32. Now the coefficient K_{1k} is obtained from Eq. 2–32 by multiplying both sides of Eq. 2–33 by $(s - p_1)^k$ and taking the limit as $s \to p_1$, as shown in

$$(s - p_1)^k F(s) = \frac{K_{11}}{(s - p_1)^{1-k}} + \cdots + K_{1(k-1)}(s - p_1) + K_{1k}$$

$$+ K_2 \frac{(s - p_1)^k}{s - p_2} + \cdots \quad (2\text{--}34a)$$

and

$$K_{1k} = \lim_{s\to p_1} (s - p_1)^k F(s) = \lim_{s\to p_1} \frac{N(s)}{\prod\limits_{i=k+1}^{n} (s - p_i)} \quad (2\text{--}34b)$$

The coefficients K_{11}, K_{12}, . . . , $K_{1(k-1)}$ of the other terms arising from the kth-order pole are obtained by repeated differentiation of Eq. 2-34a; taking the limit as $s \to p_1$, the first differentiation thus gives

$$\frac{d}{ds}[(s - p_1)^k F(s)] = (k - 1)(s - p_1)^{k-2}K_{11} + \cdots$$

$$+ K_{1(k-1)} + 0 + \cdots$$

and taking the limit as $s \to p_1$, the coefficient $K_{1(k-1)}$ is found to be

$$K_{1(k-1)} = \lim_{s \to p_1} \frac{d}{ds}[(s - p_1)^k F(s)] \qquad (2\text{-}34c)$$

The second differentiation gives $K_{1(k-2)}$ as

$$K_{1(k-2)} = \lim_{s \to p_1} \frac{1}{2!} \frac{d^2}{ds^2}[(s - p_1)^k F(s)] \qquad (2\text{-}34d)$$

and, finally, the $(k - 1)$th differentiation gives K_{11} as

$$K_{11} = \lim_{s \to p_1} \frac{1}{(k - 1)!} \frac{d^{k-1}}{ds^{k-1}}[(s - p_1)^k F(s)] \qquad (2\text{-}34e)$$

Now the coefficients of the terms in the partial fraction expansion, Eq. 2-33, are known and the inverse transform of $F(s)$ is the sum of the inverse transforms of each term in the expansion. The inverse of each term can be read from the table or, since the terms are similar, their inverses may be found from the general relationship

$$\mathcal{L}^{-1}\left[\frac{1}{(s - p_1)^n}\right] = \frac{1}{(n - 1)!} t^{n-1} e^{p_1 t} \qquad (2\text{-}35)$$

An application is given below.

Example 2-9. Find the inverse of the following function of s by partial fraction expansion.

$$F(s) = \frac{(s + 2)^2}{s^2(s + 3)(s - 1)}$$

Solution. The partial fraction expansion is

$$F(s) = \frac{K_{11}}{s} + \frac{K_{12}}{s^2} + \frac{K_2}{s + 3} + \frac{K_3}{s - 1}$$

The coefficients are evaluated as follows: Eq. 2-34b gives

$$K_{12} = \lim_{s \to 0} s^2 F(s) = \lim_{s \to 0} \frac{(s + 2)^2}{(s + 3)(s - 1)} = \frac{4}{3(-1)} = -\frac{4}{3}$$

Eq. 2-34c gives

$$K_{11} = \lim_{s \to 0} \frac{d}{ds}\left[\frac{(s + 2)^2}{(s + 3)(s - 1)}\right]$$

$$= \lim_{s \to 0} \frac{(s + 3)(s - 1)(2)(s + 2) - (s + 2)^2[s + 3 + s - 1]}{[(s + 3)(s - 1)]^2} = -\frac{20}{9}$$

Eq. 2–32 gives

$$K_2 = \lim_{s \to -3} \frac{(s+2)^2}{s^2(s-1)} = \frac{(-1)^2}{9(-4)} = -\frac{1}{36}$$

Eq. 2–32 gives

$$K_3 = \lim_{s \to 1} \frac{(s+2)^2}{s^2(s+3)} = \frac{(3)^2}{1(4)} = \frac{9}{4}$$

The partial fraction expansion of $F(s)$ is

$$F(s) = -\frac{20}{9}\frac{1}{s} - \frac{4}{3}\frac{1}{s^2} - \frac{1}{36}\frac{1}{(s+3)} + \frac{9}{4}\frac{1}{(s-1)}$$

and the inverse transform is found by inverting the separate terms as

$$f(t) = -\tfrac{20}{9} - \tfrac{4}{3}t - \tfrac{1}{36}e^{-3t} + \tfrac{9}{4}e^{t}$$

Notice that the zero of $D(s)$, having a positive real part $(s-1)$, gives rise to the exponential e^t, whose magnitude increases without limit as $t \to \infty$ and causes the system represented by $F(s)$ to be classified as unstable.

Complex Conjugate Poles of $F(s)$. Complex poles of $F(s)$ always occur in conjugate pairs whose real parts may be positive or negative. When the partial fraction expansion is carried out the coefficients for the complex pole terms will be complex. Let $F(s)$ have a pair of complex poles at $s = -\sigma \pm j\omega$, then the transform is written as

$$F(s) = \frac{N(s)}{(s+\sigma-j\omega)(s+\sigma+j\omega)\displaystyle\prod_{i=3}^{n}(s-p_i)}$$

$$= \frac{K_{11}}{s+\sigma+j\omega} + \frac{K_{12}}{s+\sigma-j\omega} + \frac{K_2}{s-p_2} + \cdots \qquad (2\text{–}36)$$

and the coefficients K_{11}, K_{12} will have complex conjugate values given by Eq. 2–32 as

$$K_{11} = \alpha + j\beta \qquad K_{12} = \alpha - j\beta$$

Then the inverse transforms of these terms will contribute damped sinusoids to time response, such as,

$$\begin{aligned}
f(t) &= (\alpha + j\beta)e^{-(\sigma+j\omega)t} + (\alpha - j\beta)e^{-(\sigma-j\omega)t} + \cdots \\
&= \alpha e^{-\sigma t}(e^{-j\omega t} + e^{j\omega t}) - j\beta e^{-\sigma t}(e^{j\omega t} - e^{-j\omega t}) + \cdots \\
&= 2e^{-\sigma t}(\alpha \cos \omega t + \beta \sin \omega t) + \cdots \\
&= 2\sqrt{\alpha^2 + \beta^2}\, e^{-\sigma t} \sin(\omega t + \phi) + \cdots \qquad (2\text{–}37)
\end{aligned}$$

where $\phi = \tan^{-1} \alpha/\beta$ and $\alpha + j\beta$ is the coefficient with the positive imaginary part. The form of Eq. 2–37 is particularly convenient to use since it does not contain any complex quantities. Also, it can be evaluated directly from the value of K_{11}.

METHOD OF RESIDUES. The Laplace transform was defined for a value of

$$\mathcal{L}[f(t)] = \int_{0^+}^{\infty} f(t)e^{-st}\,dt = F(s) \qquad (2\text{–}17)$$

$\mathcal{Re}\ s = \sigma > a$ where a is a positive number that ensures convergence of the integral. The inversion formula is

$$\mathcal{L}^{-1}[F(s)] = \frac{1}{2\pi j}\oint_{\sigma-j\infty}^{\sigma+j\infty} F(s)e^{st}\,ds = f(t) \qquad (2\text{–}38a)$$

where the value of σ must be large enough to include all poles of $F(s)$ to the left of $s = \sigma$. Now, if $F(s)$ has only a finite number of poles in any finite region of the s-plane and no branch point, and if $\lim_{s\to\infty} |s|\,|F(s)|$ exists, then Cauchy's residue theorem (Eq. A–10) may be used to evaluate the line integral in Eq. 2–38a, and the inverse Laplace transform is given for $t > 0$ as

$$f(t) = \mathcal{L}^{-1}[F(s)] = \sum_{j=1}^{k} \text{Res}\ [F(s)e^{st};\ s_j] \qquad \text{in the } s\text{-plane} \quad (2\text{–}38b)$$

$$f(t) = 0 \qquad\qquad\qquad\qquad \text{for } t < 0$$

The summation is made for all poles of $F(s)e^{st}$. Since e^{st} has no poles, the poles of $F(s)e^{st}$ are the poles of $F(s)$. The residues are given by Eqs. A–9a, b, c.

The partial fraction expansion method of inverting Laplace transforms is equivalent to the method of residues when $F(s)$ is a ratio of polynomials. The method of residues for inverting Laplace transforms is more general than the partial fraction expansion method.

Example 2–10. Invert the Laplace transform given in Example 2–9 by the method of residues.

Solution. The problem is to invert the function

$$F(s) = \frac{(s+2)^2}{s^2(s+3)(s-1)}$$

The method of residues applies here since the number of poles is finite and the $\lim_{s\to\infty} |s|\,|F(s)|$ exists. The inverse of $F(s)$ is the sum of the residues listed below.

(a) Second-order pole at $s = 0$ (Eq. A-9a).

$$\text{Res } [F(s)e^{st}; 0] = \frac{1}{1!} \left\{ \frac{d}{ds} \left[s^2 \frac{(s+2)^2 e^{ts}}{s^2(s+3)(s-1)} \right] \right\}_{s=0} = \frac{d}{ds} \left[\frac{(s+2)^2 e^{ts}}{(s+3)(s-1)} \right]_{s=0}$$

$$= \left[\frac{(s+3)(s-1)[ts(s+2)^2 e^{ts} + 2e^{ts}(s+2)] - (s+2)^2 e^{ts}[(s+3) + (s-1)]}{[(s+3)(s-1)]^2} \right]_{s=0}$$

$$= \frac{-3[(4t+4)] - 8}{9} = -\frac{4t}{3} - \frac{20}{9}$$

(b) Pole at $s = -3$ (Eq. A-9b).

$$\text{Res } [F(s)e^{ts}; -3] = \lim_{s \to -3} \frac{(s+2)^2 e^{ts}}{s^2(s-1)} = \frac{-e^{-3t}}{36}$$

(c) Pole at $s = 1$ (Eq. A-9b).

$$\text{Res } [F(s)e^{ts}; 1] = \lim_{s \to 1} \frac{e^{ts}(s+2)^2}{s^2(s+3)} = \frac{9}{4} e^t$$

The inversion of the original $F(s)$ becomes

$$f(t) = \frac{9}{4} e^t - \frac{1}{36} e^{-3t} - \frac{4t}{3} - \frac{20}{9}$$

These operations are equivalent to expanding $F(s)$ into partial fractions and using the Cauchy integral formulas, Eq. A-7, on each term.

COMPARISON OF OPERATIONAL METHOD AND CLASSICAL METHOD. It is interesting to contrast the Laplace-transform operational method with the classical method of solving linear differential equations with constant coefficients. As an illustration, consider the Laplace-transform solution of a linear second-order equation,

$$\ddot{f}(t) + (\alpha + \beta)\dot{f}(t) + \alpha\beta f(t) = q(t) \qquad (2\text{-}39)$$

with initial conditions of $\dot{f}(0^+)$ and $f(0^+)$, where α and β are unequal constants. Laplace transformation of the equation gives

$$F(s)[s^2 + (\alpha + \beta)s + \alpha\beta] = \mathcal{L}[q(t)] + f(0^+)[s + \alpha + \beta] + \dot{f}(0^+)$$

The solution is obtained by solving the equation for $F(s)$ and finding the inverse transforms as shown below, where

$$D(s) = (s^2 + (\alpha + \beta)s + \alpha\beta) = (s + \alpha)(s + \beta)$$

$$f(t) = \mathcal{L}^{-1}[F(s)] = \mathcal{L}^{-1} \left\{ \frac{L[q(t)]}{D(s)} \right\} + \mathcal{L}^{-1} \left\{ \frac{f(0^+)(s + \alpha + \beta)}{D(s)} \right\}$$

$$+ \mathcal{L}^{-1} \left\{ \frac{\dot{f}(0^+)}{D(s)} \right\}$$

and

$$f(t) = \mathcal{L}^{-1} \left\{ \frac{L[q(t)]}{D(s)} \right\} + \frac{e^{-\alpha t}}{(\beta - \alpha)} [\beta f(0^+) + \dot{f}(0^+)]$$

$$- \frac{e^{-\beta t}}{(\beta - \alpha)} [\alpha f(0^+) + \dot{f}(0^+)] \qquad (2\text{-}40)$$

This is the solution to the linear equation, provided the indicated direct and inverse Laplace transformations can be obtained. The response $f(t)$ consists of two parts: the first part is the response to $q(t)$ with the system relaxed $(f(0^+) = \dot{f}(0^+) = 0)$, and the second part, containing two terms, is the system response to the initial conditions alone $(q(t) = 0)$. Thus, the Laplace-transform method gives the response as the sum of the solution to the non-homogeneous equation with zero initial conditions plus the solution to the homogeneous equation with given initial conditions. This is contrasted with the classical method, which gives the response as the sum of the solution of the homogeneous equation with no excitation (complementary function which is the transient response) plus the particular integral which represents the steady-state response of the system and depends on both the system and the forcing function.

The first term of the system response in Eq. 2-40 can be written by use of the convolution theorem (Eq. 2-28a) as

$$\mathcal{L}^{-1}\left\{\frac{1}{D(s)}\,\mathcal{L}[q(t)]\right\} = \int_0^t w(\tau)q(t-\tau)\,d\tau \qquad (2\text{-}41)$$

where $w(\tau)$ is the response of the relaxed system to a unit impulse at $\tau = 0$ and τ is a dummy variable.

$$w(\tau) = \mathcal{L}^{-1}[1/D(s)]$$

is called the weighting function of the system. Thus it can be stated that the response of a relaxed linear system at any time t is the sum (integral) of the weighted values of the forcing function at times $(t - \tau)$ from $\tau = 0$ to $\tau = t$. The weighting is determined by the value of $w(t)$. Generally, the response of a relaxed linear system to any Laplace-transformable forcing function is the convolution of its impulse response and the forcing function; in other words, the impulse response contains the input-output characteristics of the linear system.

2-4. PROCESS SYSTEM INPUTS

The input to a process control system may be (1) a preset program which changes the reference input to the system in a predetermined manner (as in batch processing operations); (2) a change in load variable in the system (as the electrical load on a turbine generator or the enthalpy demand of colder feed to a distillation unit); or (3) a change in ambient conditions or random signals generated outside the system. All these different types of inputs are important but they cannot all be investigated, and it is usual in a first course to develop process control system responses to a few standard inputs. In principle, the response of an initially

TABLE 2–4
Test Inputs for Theoretical and Practical Results

Input Signal	Symbol	$f(t)$ Graph	Laplace Transform	Pole-Zero Chart
Doublet	$\delta'(t)$		s	
Impulse	$\delta(t)$		1	
Pulse	$u(t) - u(t - a)$		$\dfrac{1 - e^{-as}}{s}$	
Step	$u(t)$		$\dfrac{1}{s}$	
Ramp	t		$\dfrac{1}{s^2}$	
Sine	$\sin \omega t$		$\dfrac{\omega}{s^2 + \omega^2}$	

relaxed system to any input can be found from the response of that system to a known input.

The typical test signals used in experimental work for checking the response of a process system are listed in Table 2–4 in terms of unit functions. Any experimental input may be a multiple of the unit functions given.

Unit step function. The step function is an easy input signal to generate experimentally since it represents the closing of a switch, the positioning of a quick-opening valve, or other sudden displacement of input applied to a system at zero time. The Laplace transform is given for this function in Table 2–4, on input test signals.

Unit ramp function. The integral of a step function is a ramp function. The unit ramp function, also called the *unit step velocity function*, is shown in Table 2–4. It is not convenient to use as a test signal since some part of the system under test is likely to saturate or limit as the input becomes large as time increases.

Unit impulse function. The derivative of a step function is an impulse function. It is usually said that a discontinuous function has a left-hand and a right-hand derivative at a point of discontinuity and that the derivative is not defined at the point. The impulse function can extend the concept of differentiation at a point of discontinuity. The impulse function is developed by a limiting process as shown in Fig. 2–7. The

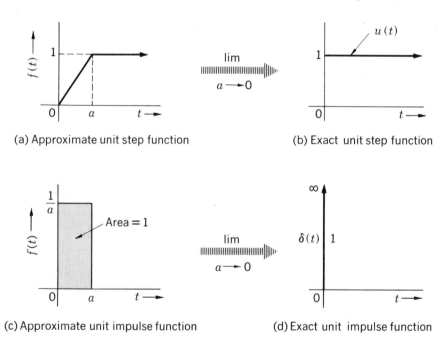

(a) Approximate unit step function   (b) Exact unit step function

(c) Approximate unit impulse function   (d) Exact unit impulse function

Fig. 2–7.   Relationship between unit step and unit impulse functions.

function $f(t)$ sketched in Fig. 2–7a consists of a ramp of duration a terminating in a unit function and it approaches the unit step function as a approaches zero, as shown in Fig. 2–7b. The derivative of this function, $f'(t)$, is a pulse (Fig. 2–7c) with magnitude $1/a$, duration a, and unit area. Now the pulse and its Laplace transform are written in terms of the time-displacement function as

$$\text{pulse} = \frac{1}{a}[u(t) - u(t - a)] \qquad \mathcal{L}[\text{pulse}] = \frac{1}{as}(1 - e^{-as}) \qquad (2\text{-}42)$$

In the limit, as $a \to 0$, both expressions become indeterminate, but the limiting value is found by L'Hôpital's rule; the result is a singular function called a *unit impulse function*, $\delta(t)$. The unit impulse function and its Laplace transform are written

$$\text{unit impulse} = \delta(t) = \frac{d}{dt}u(t) \qquad \mathcal{L}[\delta(t)] = \lim_{a \to 0}\frac{1}{as}(1 - e^{-as}) = 1 \qquad (2\text{-}43\text{a})$$

and the integral of the unit impulse is the step function,

$$\int_0^t \delta(t)\,dt = u(t) \qquad (2\text{-}43\text{b})$$

A convenient graphical symbol for the unit impulse, as shown in Fig. 2-7d, is a vertical spike of infinite magnitude, no time duration, and unit area. This function is physically unrealizable, but it can be approximated by letting a have a very small value. The impulse function gives meaning to the derivative of a function at a point of discontinuity and thereby allows regeneration of the function by integration of its derivative (see Example 2-11).

Unit doublet function. Another singular function, called the *unit doublet impulse*, can be developed in a manner similar to that of the impulse by consideration of the derivative of the triangular pulse shown in Fig. 2-8a. When the value of a is finite, the derivative of the tri-

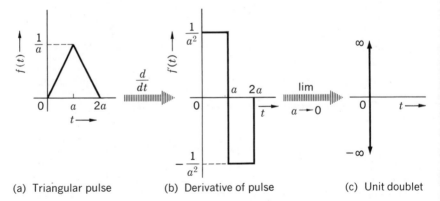

(a) Triangular pulse   (b) Derivative of pulse   (c) Unit doublet

Fig. 2-8. Development of the unit doublet from the double rectangular pulse.

angular pulse is a double rectangular pulse sketched in Fig. 2–8b and written as

$$\text{double rectangular pulse} = \frac{1}{a^2}\left[u(t) - 2u(t - a) + u(t - 2a)\right]$$

$$= \frac{d}{dt}\left(\delta(t)\right) \tag{2-44}$$

In the limit, as $a \to 0$, it can be shown that the triangular pulse approaches the unit impulse and therefore the double rectangular pulse in the limit approaches the derivative of the impulse function, as indicated by Eq. 2–44. The transform of the unit doublet is found by transforming Eq. 2–44 and taking the limit as $a \to 0$, formally,

$$\mathcal{L}\left[\frac{d}{dt}\,\delta(t)\right] = \lim_{a \to 0} \frac{1}{a^2 s}\left[1 - 2e^{-as} + e^{-2as}\right] = s \tag{2-45}$$

Now the inversion of improper rational fractions (which give rise to terms such as 1, s, etc.) will include singular functions such as the impulse, doublet, etc. Like the impulse, the doublet is physically unrealizable but is of interest in theoretical calculations.

Unit rectangular function. A rectangular pulse is generated by switch action as described for a unit step function followed by a delayed switch action in the opposite direction. The unit rectangular pulse function and its transform are given in terms of the time-displacement function as

$$\text{pulse} = u(t) - u(t - a) \qquad \mathcal{L}[\text{pulse}] = \frac{1}{s}\,(1 - e^{-as}) \tag{2-46}$$

Unit sine function. Any sinusoidal function test signal is especially useful in experimental process work since the steady-state ratio of output to input for this forcing function at various frequencies gives a relationship called *frequency response* that is characteristic of the system. Frequency response testing of process equipment is common practice and sinusoidal function generators are commercially available. The Laplace transform of the unit sine function is given in Tables 2–1 and 2–4. The transform has a pair of conjugate poles on the imaginary axis.

A summary of the common test signals and their transforms is given in Table 2–4. The time functions and the pole-zero map of the transforms are shown.

Example 2–11. The unit impulse concept enables functions containing discontinuities to be differentiated. Find the derivative of the function given in Fig. E2–11a and also its Laplace transform.

Solution. The derivative of $f(t)$ is shown in Fig. E2–11b, where the impulses of magnitude one and 0.865 are the derivatives of $f(t)$ at $t = 0$ and $t = 2, 4$, etc.,

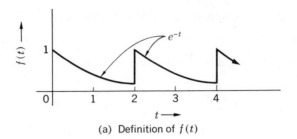

(a) Definition of $f(t)$

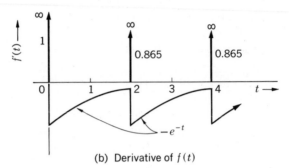

(b) Derivative of $f(t)$

Fig. E2–11. Graph of $f(t)$ and its derivative.

and $-e^{-t}$ is the derivative of $f(t)$ between the discontinuities. Since the derivative of $e^{-t} = -e^{-t}$, the derivative of the original $f(t)$ becomes

$$f'(t) = -f(t) + \Sigma \text{ (impulses)} \qquad \text{(a)}$$

Notice that the original function can be obtained by integrating Eq. a and summing the impulses as shown:

$$
\begin{aligned}
f(t) &= 1 + (e^{-t} - 1) & \text{for } 0 < t < 2 \\
&= 1 + (e^{-2} - 1) = 0.135 \text{ and } = 0.135 + 0.865 = 1 & \text{for } t = 2 \\
&= 1 + (e^{-(t-2)} - 1) & \text{for } 2 < t < 4
\end{aligned}
$$

and so on.

Now, Eq. a is also the differential equation whose solution is $f(t)$. Therefore the transform of $f(t)$ can be obtained by transforming Eq. a term by term as shown:

$$sF(s) - 1 = -F(s) + 0.865e^{-2s}/(1 - e^{-2s})$$

so that

$$F(s) = \frac{1 - 0.135e^{-2s}}{(s + 1)(1 - e^{-2s})}$$

The transform $F(s)$ is also obtainable by writing $f(t)$ from Fig. E2–11a in terms of time-displacement functions and transforming the equation term by term.

PROBLEMS

For Problems 2–9 through 2–14, refer to Appendix A for help.

2–1. Write the following quantities in the $u + jv$ form where u and v are real:

(a) $\dfrac{1 + j2}{(1 + j)^2}$

(b) $e^{j\pi/2}$

(c) $\ln(3 + j2)$

2–2. Use Routh's criterion to determine if any of the following polynomials have roots with positive real parts, and then factor the polynomials to check your conclusion.

(a) $s^3 + 4s^2 + 3s + 3$

(b) $s^4 + 3s^2 + 4s + 2$

(c) $s^4 + 5s^3 + 2s^2 + 3s + 1$

2–3. Find values of these rational functions when $s = 2 + j3$ both analytically and graphically.

(a) $\dfrac{s}{(s + 2)(s^2 + 1)}$

(b) $\dfrac{s + 5}{s(s + 4)}$

2–4. Find the Laplace transform of the following functions:

(a) $f(t) = t$ $0 < t \le 4$
    $f(t) = 4$ $t \ge 4$
    $f(t) = 0$ $t \le 0$

(b) $f(t) = t^2$ $0 < t \le 10$
    $f(t) = 110 - t$ $10 \le t \le 110$
    $f(t) = 0$ $t \le 0$ and $t \ge 110$

2–5. Solve the second-order differential equation

$$\ddot{y}(t) + 5\dot{y}(t) + 4y(t) = f(t)$$

when (a) $y(0) = 2, \dot{y}(0) = 2, f(t) = 0$; and when (b) $y(0) = 0; \dot{y}(0) = 0; f(t) = 2$.

2–6. Solve the second-order differential equation

$$\ddot{y}(t) + 2\dot{y}(t) + 2y(t) = f(t)$$

for the conditions in Problem 2–5 above.

2–7. Solve the third-order equation

$$\dddot{y}(t) + 6\ddot{y}(t) + 11\dot{y}(t) + 6y = f(t)$$

(a) when all initial conditions are zero and $f(t) = 2t$

(b) when all initial conditions are zero and $f(t) = 2$

What is the relationship between the answers in parts a and b?

2-8. Solve the first-order equation

$$\dot{y}(t) + 2y(t) = f(t)$$

when $\dot{y}(0) = 5$ and $f(t) = \sin \omega t$. After the transient fades away, compare the values of $y(t)$ and $f(t)$ and show how they are related for various values of ω. Hint: Use the magnitude ratio and phase angles for comparison.

2-9. Demonstrate the mapping properties of the given function by finding values of u and v in terms of σ and ω.

$$G(s) = s^2$$

Map the lines $\sigma + j2$ and $2 + j\omega$; $\sigma + j3$ and $3 + j\omega$ from the s-plane into the $G(s)$ plane.

2-10. Plot magnitude and phase angle loci on the $G(j\omega)$ plane for the following functions when $s = j\omega$ and $0 < \omega < \infty$:

(a) $\dfrac{1}{(s + 1)(s + 2)}$

(b) $\dfrac{1}{s^2 + 2s + 2}$

(c) $\dfrac{1}{2} e^{-s}$

2-11. Determine if the following functions are analytic in a region of the s-plane:

(a) $\dfrac{1}{s}$

(b) s^2

(c) s^{-2}

(d) $s^2 + 3s + 2$

2-12. Determine if the following functions are analytic in a region of the s-plane:

(a) $s^2 - 1$

(b) $3\sigma\omega^2 + j\omega^3$

(c) $s + s^{-1}$

2-13. Find the singular points and classify them for the following functions:

(a) $\dfrac{1}{(s^2 + a)}$

(b) $\ln (s + 1)$

(c) $e^{-\tau s}$

2-14. To illustrate Cauchy's argument principle graphically, take $G(s) = s + 2 + j$ and plot $G(s)$ for any closed curve C encircling the zero in the s-plane. Then repeat the plotting with $F(s) = [G(s)]^{-1}$ and for the same closed curve C used before.

3

Basic Process Elements

Every industrial process consists of a sequence of operations that convert, shape, transform, react, or otherwise manipulate and change the process raw materials into the desired product. The types of operation are many and varied, depending on the product and the method of making it; but the natural laws governing these operations are few and well known. To be effective in control work, the process engineer must be able to analyze the process operations in the light of the applicable natural laws and thereby to write a quantitative description of the dynamic nature of all the process operations. The synthesis problem in control is more challenging since it involves an integration of the analysis of process operations and the selection of feedback and/or feedforward devices and process controllers to give the design for an operable process plant which maximizes the economic return on the allowed investment.

The present chapter seeks to prepare the student for process analysis by describing in a quantitative manner the basic process elements of resistance, capacitance, and inertance. The following chapter introduces process analysis and shows that these basic process elements are the building blocks for the components which make up the complex process units in a plant. The analogy principle is used to show the similarities in variables and parameters in process systems, making it possible to discuss several different systems in a minimum of space.

The basis of analogous elements and components is found in the similar form of the mathematical equations that characterize physical systems. With this in mind, many types of systems such as electrical, mechanical, hydraulic, pneumatic, and analog computers can be treated as having certain analogies between them. There are several possible analogies for use with process variables, but the one used here is the voltage-force-temperature analogy, shown in Table 3–1 for several systems. Everyday experiences give one an intuitive feel for the ability of potentials of voltage, force, pressure, and temperature to overcome the appropriate resistances and produce proportional flows of electricity, motion, matter,

TABLE 3-1
Analogies Between Process Variables

System	Potential	Quantity	Flow Rate
Electrical	Voltage e (volts)	Charge q (coulombs)	Current i (amperes)
Mechanical translation	Force f (lb$_f$)	Displacement x (ft)	Velocity u (ft/time)
Fluid	Pressure p (ft of fluid) (or lb$_f$/ft^2)	Volume q (ft^3) Mass m (lb$_m$)	Quantity/time, i
Thermal or thermochemical	Temperature T (degrees)	Thermal units q (Btu or cal)	Quantity/time, i

or thermal energy. Some of the quantitative advantages obtained by use of analogies are: (1) an immediate application of knowledge in one field to problems in another field, e.g., the use of electrical network theorems in solving hydraulic and thermal circuit problems, and (2) the use of easily constructed electric analog circuits to study the behavior of hydraulic and thermal systems.

Most industrial process operations consist of complex arrangements of a few basic process elements. A process element in a system defines a distinct activity for that part of the system. These elements are classified as either active or passive elements. The active elements are material or energy sources which can give rise to corresponding material or energy flows in the system. The passive elements are resistance, capacitance, and inertance in the system.

In reality all physical bodies occupy space and their properties are therefore distributed in space. For example, the thermal energy in a body is distributed throughout the body but for many purposes the energy in that body may be treated as if it were concentrated or "lumped" at a point. This lumped-parameter assumption, whenever applicable to a system under study, simplifies the analytical treatment by reducing the space variables from one or two variables of position to none. In this book, the properties of a system are assumed to be lumped unless otherwise designated.

The discussion is limited to the basic elements in electrical, mechanical, fluid, and thermochemical processes. The common electrical units of volt, ampere, ohm, etc. are used for electric elements and the English engineering units of pound mass, foot, and pound force are generally adopted for process variables and elements. Laplace transformation is used to obtain the system transfer function from the system differential equation since this technique is widely used and it simplifies the mechanics of writing, manipulating, and solving linear differential equations.

Unless otherwise noted, the initial conditions for Laplace transformation are zero as required by the definition of the transfer function.

3-1. ACTIVE ELEMENTS

The active elements in process systems are material or energy sources and are classified as potential sources or flow sources, depending upon whether they are designed to provide constant potentials or constant flow rates in the process. An actual device usually contains some properties of the passive elements, e.g., a pressure pump has some flow resistance, capacitance, and inertance characteristics and the importance of these secondary characteristics will depend on the pump application. Since potential forces have polarity and flow rates have direction, it is always necessary to indicate these properties on any graphical symbols used to represent the elements. Table 3–2 gives a summary of the ideal active process elements together with graphical symbols and suggested units for engineering use.

In electric systems the active elements are tubes, transistors, batteries, or generators whose output is a driving voltage $e(t)$ (voltage source) or a driving current $i(t)$ (current source) which may be time-dependent as

TABLE 3–2
Analogous Ideal Active Elements of Process Systems

System	Element	Symbol	Unit
Electrical	Voltage source	$e(t)$	volt
	Current source	$i(t)$	amp (coulomb/sec)
Mechanical	Force source	$f(t)$	lb_f
	Velocity source	$u(t)$	ft/sec
Fluid and chemical	Pressure source	$p(t)$	lb_f/ft^2 or ft of fluid
	Concentration source		lb moles/ft^3
	Fluid flow source	$i(t)$	lb_m/min or ft^3/min
Thermal	Temperature source	$T(t)$	°C, °K, °F, or °R
	Heat flow source	$i(t)$	Btu/min or Chu/min

indicated.   The ideal active element has no passive element characteristics such as resistance and capacitance.

In mechanical systems the active elements are energy sources whose output is either a driving force $f(t)$ acting in the system (force source) or a driving velocity $u(t)$ acting in the system (velocity source).   These ideal elements produce forces or velocities that are independent of the mechanical connections made to them.

In fluid and chemical systems the active elements are mechanically or electrically driven pumps, conveyors, or the like whose output is either a fluid pressure $p(t)$ acting in the system (potential source) or a fluid flow rate $i(t)$ acting in the system (flow source).   Actual pumps and devices usually have resistance which is related to fluid leakage in the pump, capacitance which is related to the pump volume and to the compressibility of the fluid, and inertance which is related to the acceleration of the device and of the material moving through the device.

An empirical analysis of the steady-state characteristics of a given pump may be made from the pressure-head–flow-rate–speed curves furnished by the pump manufacturer.   The curves in Fig. 3–1 are typical of the usual performance curves of a centrifugal pump, which show that the pressure head developed by the pump is a function of the flow rate and the pump speed.   For linearization purposes, the pump equation can be expanded in a Taylor's series and the nonlinear terms neglected to give

$$p_2 - p_1 = f(i,n) = f(i_o,n_o) + \frac{\partial f}{\partial i}\bigg|_{i_o,n_o}(i - i_o) + \frac{\partial f}{\partial n}\bigg|_{i_o,n_o}(n - n_o) \quad (3\text{–}1)$$

where the subscript denotes average operating conditions.   This equation can be rearranged to give the linearized pump equation as

$$(p_2 - p_{o2}) - (p_1 - p_{o1}) = \tilde{p}_2 - \tilde{p}_1 = \frac{\partial f}{\partial i}\bigg|_{i_o,n_o}\tilde{\imath} + \frac{\partial f}{\partial n}\bigg|_{i_o,n_o}\tilde{n} \quad (3\text{–}1a)$$

where the tildes indicate deviation of the variable from an average operating point i_o, n_o, p_{o2}, p_{o1}, and $\partial f/\partial i$ and $\partial f/\partial n$ are the slopes of the $(p_2 - p_1)$ vs. i curve at $n = n_o$ and of the $p_2 - p_1$ vs. n curve at $i = i_o$, respectively.   Laplace transformation of Eq. 3–1a yields the pump equation

$$\tilde{P}_2(s) - \tilde{P}_1(s) = \frac{\partial f}{\partial i}\bigg|_{i_o}\tilde{I}(s) + \frac{\partial f}{\partial n}\bigg|_{n_o}\tilde{N}(s) \quad (3\text{–}1b)$$

where $P(s)$, $I(s)$, and $N(s)$ are the transformed deviation variables of pressure head, flow rate, and pump speed from the operating point i_o, n_o. The linearization of pump characteristics and the signal flow diagram are shown in Fig. 3–1.   The steady state characteristics of a centrifugal pump are analyzed in Example 3–1.

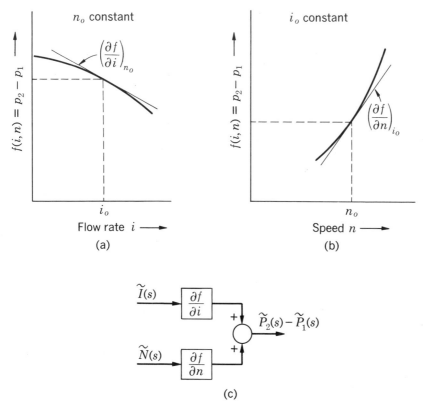

Fig. 3–1. General steady-state operating characteristics of process pump and linearized signal flow graph. (a) Effect of flow rate. (b) Effect of pump speed. (c) Signal flow graph.

Example 3–1. The actual head–flow rate characteristics of a centrifugal pump under steady-state conditions are shown in Fig. E3-1. The pressure head is that developed across the pump from suction to discharge. The decrease of output potential with increase of flow rate is characteristic of potential sources having internal resistance. Effects of capacitance and inertance in the pump are not shown by steady-state tests. Find an equation for the pump pressure head–flow rate characteristic at 1750 rpm and linearize it at about the operating point $p_o = 81$ ft of fluid head and $i_o = 10$ ft³/min flow rate.

Solution. Study of the curve for 1750 rpm indicates that the pump discharge pressure decreases at an increasing rate as the flow rate increases. This is to be expected since the fluid in the pump is in a turbulent condition and the pressure drop in such condition is expected to be proportional to the square of the flow rate. Using this assumption, the problem is to fit an equation of the form

$$p_2 - p_1 = a + ki^2$$

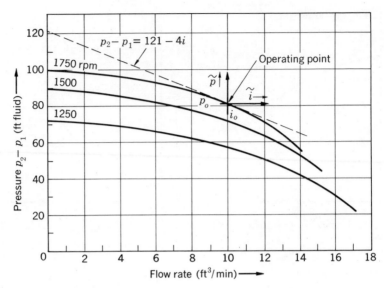

Fig. E3–1. Centrifugal pump steady-state operating characteristic curves.

to the curves in Fig. E3–1. A satisfactory fit for the data at 1750 rpm and for flow rates less than 14 ft³/min is obtained by making $a = 100.0$ and $k = -0.2$.

A linearized head–flow rate equation at the operating point (81 ft, 10 ft³/min) may be obtained either by graphical evaluation of the slope or by differentiation of the nonlinear equation. Using the latter method, the linear relationship is

$$\tilde{p}_2 - \tilde{p}_1 = \frac{\partial f}{\partial i}\bigg|_{i_o} \tilde{\imath}$$

and $\dfrac{\partial f}{\partial i}\bigg|_{i_o} = 2ki_o = 2(-0.2)10 = -4$, so that

$$\tilde{p}_2 - \tilde{p}_1 = \tilde{p} = -4\tilde{\imath} \qquad \text{or} \qquad (p - 81) = -4(i - 10)$$

where $\tilde{p}$ and $\tilde{\imath}$ are deviations from the operating-point values of 81-ft fluid pressure and 10 ft³/min flow rate.

Centrifugal pumps are usually operated at constant speed and are low-impedance constant-potential fluid sources. Positive-displacement pumps handling incompressible fluids have very high internal resistance and are high-impedance constant flow rate sources. They provide a flow rate that is proportional to the pump speed.

In fluid systems the variables are generally pressure and flow rate. Chemical systems have these variables too but, in addition, they have the variable of fluid composition since most chemical processes involve the addition, removal, or transformation of a chemical material in the processed fluid. A simple example of a chemical system is a process in which changes in concentration of a fluid stream are effected by a dilution or a concentration step.

In thermal systems the active elements are sources of thermal energy derived from heaters or refrigerators, heat effects of chemical reactions, or other process heat sources or sinks.

3-2. PASSIVE ELEMENTS

The three kinds of passive process elements are resistance, capacitance, and inertance. They are characterized by the fact that they are either reservoirs or dissipators of energy or material and never energy or material sources. It will be seen that in terms of the ratio of potential across the elements to the material or energy flow through the element, the ideal devices involve proportionality, integration, or differentiation. The parameter value of an ideal linear element does not vary with potential across or flow rate through the element; but for actual elements linearity must be shown by experiment, since many physical properties of the materials from which actual elements are made depend upon the process temperature, pressure, voltage, etc.

Resistance. The resistance of an element is a measure of the frictional effects that degrade any form of energy in the element into heat. The resistance of a process element may be generally defined as the rate of change of an applied potential force across the element with respect to the material or energy flow rate through the element at an operating point; thus

$$\text{Resistance, } R = d(\text{potential force})/d(\text{flow rate})$$

or in more definite terms

$$-d(p_2 - p_1) = R\,di$$

where $p_1 - p_2$ is the potential across the resistance, i is the material or energy flow rate through the resistance, and p_1 and p_2 are the upstream and downstream pressures under the particular set of operating conditions. The Laplace-transformed resistance equation is

$$P_1(s) - P_2(s) = RI(s) \qquad (3-2)$$

The reciprocal of resistance, called *conductance*, is sometimes used in process analysis.

The parameter value of a linear resistance is independent of the magnitude of process variables, and the material or energy flow rate through the resistance. The properties of actual resistances depend to some extent upon the process variables but, for simplicity in process analysis, they may be assumed constant as a first approximation. The signal flow graph for a resistance element is derived from the defining equations and shown in Fig. 3–2. The graph is constructed by viewing the resist-

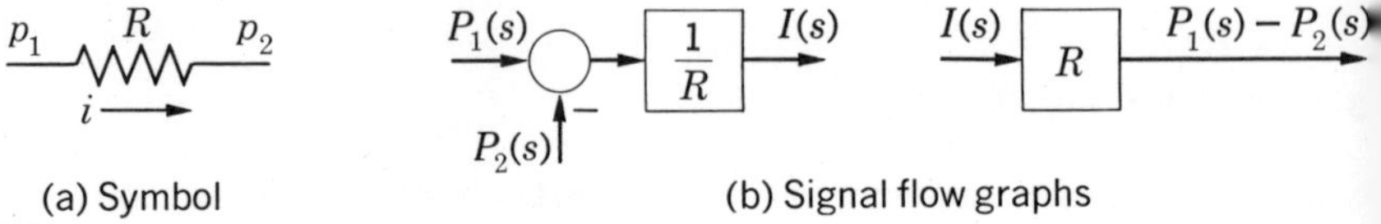

(a) Symbol   (b) Signal flow graphs

Fig. 3–2. Signal flow graph for linear resistance.

ance either as a device that transforms flow rate into potential across the element or as a device whose reciprocal transforms potential across to flow rate through the element. It must be remembered that the potential across is a difference between two process variables whose values may change independently of each other. As an example, observe that the effect of an upstream change in potential is not the same as that for a downstream change in potential, since

$$d(p_1 - p_2) = R\,di = dp_1 - dp_2$$

so that

$$R = \left(\frac{\partial p_1}{\partial i}\right)_{p_2} = -\left(\frac{\partial p_2}{\partial i}\right)_{p_1}$$

These are general relationships and must be used in process analysis whenever both potentials can change independently.

From physics it is known that for resistances in series the total resistance is the sum of the individual resistances, or

$$R_{\text{total}} = \sum_k R_k$$

and that for resistances in parallel the total resistance is the reciprocal of the sum of the reciprocals of the individual resistances, or

$$R_{\text{total}} = \left[\sum_k R_k^{-1}\right]^{-1}$$

A process resistance always dissipates the energy flowing through it.

Equations for resistances in several systems are developed below. Table 3–3 gives a summary of analogous resistances in process systems with appropriate graphical symbols, defining relationships, and engineering units.

ELECTRICAL. Electrical resistance is a measure of the ability of an element to oppose the movement of electrons. Electrical energy used to move electrons through a resistor is converted into heat during the process. The heat generation is due to some of the ordered motion of the electrons (accelerated by the applied voltage) being converted to disordered motion (heat) by collision of the electrons with the atoms of the resistor. The resistance in ohms is given as $R = d(e_1 - e_2)/di$, where $e_1 - e_2$ is the voltage across the resistance in volts and i is the current through the resistance in amperes (coulombs/sec). When the resistance is independent of the voltage, the voltage across the resistance is given as

$$e_1 - e_2 = Ri = R\, dq/dt$$

which, after Laplace transformation, becomes

$$E_1(s) - E_2(s) = RI(s) \tag{3–2a}$$

MECHANICAL. Mechanical motion in linear systems is opposed or damped by viscous friction that degrades the energy into heat. Dry friction and other forms of mechanical resistance exhibit non-linear behavior. In linear systems the viscous damping force for translational motion is proportional to the net velocity u and is given as

$$f_1 - f_2 = D_x u = D_x \frac{d(x_1 - x_2)}{dt}$$

where $f_1 - f_2 = f$ is the damping force across the component in lb_f,

$$\frac{d(x_1 - x_2)}{dt} = u$$

is the net velocity in ft/sec, and $x_1 - x_2 = x$ is the net displacement across the component. The viscous damping coefficient D_x (the resistance) has units of lb_f-sec/ft.

In Laplace-transform notation with zero initial conditions, the force equation becomes

$$F(s) = D_x U(s) = D_x s X(s) \tag{3–2b}$$

A viscous damping element is called a dashpot and is represented by the dashpot symbol in Table 3–3.

FLUID OR CHEMICAL. Liquid and gaseous substances are transported in pipelines, metered through orifices, and controlled by valves. From a network viewpoint these devices have resistances that oppose the flow of fluids. Flow in conduits is characterized as viscous when the flow occurs in streamlines with absence of turbulence, and non-viscous when the flow is accompanied by turbulent or swirling motion resulting in back

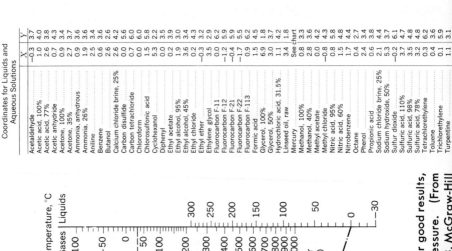

Pressure Drop Due to Friction

Turbulent Region

Coordinates for Liquids and Aqueous Solutions

	X	Y
Acetaldehyde	-0.3	3.7
Acetic acid, 100%	1.0	4.0
Acetic acid, 77%	2.6	3.8
Acetic anhydride	0.7	4.3
Acetone, 100%	0.9	3.4
Acetone, 35%	2.7	3.7
Ammonia, anhydrous	0.9	3.6
Ammonia, 26%	1.9	3.6
Aniline	2.5	3.4
Benzene	0.6	3.6
Butanol	2.6	2.6
Calcium chloride brine, 25%	2.6	4.2
Carbon disulfide	0.0	5.6
Carbon tetrachloride	0.7	6.0
Chloroform	0.0	6.0
Chlorosulfonic acid	1.5	5.8
Cyclohexanol	5.3	2.2
Diphenyl	0.0	3.5
Ethyl acetate	0.2	3.9
Ethyl alcohol, 95%	1.9	3.0
Ethyl alcohol, 45%	3.6	3.4
Ethyl chloride	0.2	4.3
Ethyl ether	-0.3	3.2
Ethylene glycol	3.5	2.9
Fluorocarbon F-11	0.0	6.2
Fluorocarbon F-12	-1.2	5.9
Fluorocarbon F-21	-0.4	5.9
Fluorocarbon F-22	-1.7	5.5
Fluorocarbon F-113	0.9	6.2
Formic acid	1.5	4.5
Glycerol, 100%	6.9	1.8
Glycerol, 50%	3.0	3.7
Hydrochloric acid, 31.5%	1.1	4.2
Linseed oil, raw	3.4	1.8
Mercury	See chart	
Methanol, 100%	0.8	3.3
Methanol, 40%	2.8	3.6
Methyl acetate	0.0	4.2
Methyl chloride	-0.8	4.3
Nitric acid, 95%	0.8	5.8
Nitric acid, 60%	1.5	4.8
Nitrobenzene	1.7	4.4
Octane	0.4	2.7
Phenol	2.4	3.4
Propionic acid	0.6	3.8
Sodium chloride brine, 25%	2.1	4.4
Sodium hydroxide, 50%	5.3	3.7
Sulfur dioxide	-0.2	6.1
Sulfuric acid, 110%	3.7	4.7
Sulfuric acid, 98%	3.5	4.8
Sulfuric acid, 78%	3.2	4.8
Tetrachloroethylene	0.3	6.2
Toluene	0.4	3.6
Trichlorethylene	0.1	5.9
Turpentine	1.1	3.1

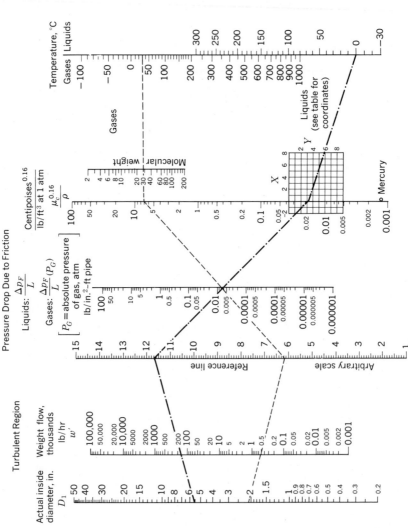

Fig. 3–3. Nomogram for turbulent flow of gases and liquids in clean steel pipe. For good results, the pressure drop for any problem of gas flow should be less than 10% of the inlet pressure. (From Chemical Engineer's Handbook, 4th ed., edited by R. H. Perry et al. Copyright © 1963. McGraw-Hill

88

mixing of the fluid. The magnitude of the dimensionless Reynolds number (average velocity $\times$ pipe diameter/kinematic viscosity) characterizes the type of flow and a Reynolds number greater than 2200 denotes non-viscous flow conditions.

Pipelines. Most fluid flow in process plants is of the non-viscous or turbulent type with the pressure drop across the pipeline being proportional to a power of the flow rate (nonlinear).* For isothermal turbulent flow in circular pipes, the Fanning flow equation is usually written as

$$p_1 - p_2 = ki^2 \tag{3-2c}$$

where p_1 and p_2 are the upstream and downstream pressures in lb_f/in^2, i is the flow rate in lb_m/min, and k is a constant which depends upon the flow conditions in the pipe. A nomographic solution of this equation for turbulent flow of liquids and gases through clean steel pipe over a wide range of temperatures and pressures is shown in Fig. 3-3. For gases, the temperature and molecular weight scales determine the density and viscosity data needed in the equation and, for liquids, the x-y grid and the temperature scale for liquids give the necessary data. The use of the pipe flow chart is illustrated by the construction lines shown. For example, the dashed line shows that air (molecular weight of 29) at 30°C and 134.7 psia flowing through a 2-in. pipe (i.d., 2.067 in.) at a rate of 500 lb_m/hr experiences a pressure drop per ft of pipe of $0.008/(134.7/14.7) = 0.00087$ $lb/in.^2$-ft of pipe. Note that the chart value of $\Delta p/L$ for gases must be divided by the process pressure in atmospheres. As another example, the dot-dash line shows that the pumping of a 25 wt % aqueous $CaCl_2$ brine ($x = 2.6$, $y = 4.2$) at 0°C at the rate of 250 gal/min (147,000 lb_m/hr) in a clean steel pipe requires the use of a 6-in. pipe if the allowable pressure drop is less than 0.006 $lb_f/in.^2$-ft pipe. This chart is useful for both liquid and gas flows when the pressure drop is less than 10% of the upstream pressure. If the pressure drop for a pipeline exceeds this value, the chart may be used for a fraction of the pipeline length and repeated until the full length has been reached.

The nonlinear flow equation can be linearized around an average operating point in the usual manner to show the effects of pressures p_1 and p_2, thus:

$$\bar{\imath} = \left(\frac{\partial i}{\partial p_1}\right)_{p_2} \bar{p}_1 + \left(\frac{\partial i}{\partial p_2}\right)_{p_1} \bar{p}_2$$

* Viscous flow obeys a linear flow rate equation given as

$$p_1 - p_2 = \frac{46.8\, l\mu i}{\rho A^2} = ki$$

where $p_1 - p_2$ is the pressure across the pipeline in $lb_f/in.^2$, l is the length in ft, μ is the viscosity of the fluid in lb_m/ft-sec, ρ is the fluid density in lb_m/ft^3, A is the cross-sectional area of the circular pipe in ft^2, i is the flow rate in lb_m/min, and k is the total resistance of the pipeline in lb_f-min/lb_m-in.^{2}.

where $\tilde{\imath}$, $\tilde{p}_1$, and $\tilde{p}_2$ are deviations from the operating point. The derivatives are the pipe conductances (reciprocal of resistance) and are found from Eq. 3–2c by differentiation as

$$\left(\frac{\partial i}{\partial p_1}\right)_{p_2} = \frac{1}{R} = \frac{1}{2ki} = \frac{1}{2}\left[\frac{i}{p_1 - p_2}\right]_{avg} = -\left(\frac{\partial i}{\partial p_2}\right)_{p_1}$$

Magnitudes of the pipe conductances must be evaluated at the average operating conditions in the pipeline. The Laplace transform of the linearized equation is

$$\tilde{I}(s) = \frac{1}{R}[\tilde{P}_1(s) - \tilde{P}_2(s)] \tag{3–2d}$$

The derivative is easily approximated from the pipe chart in Fig. 3–3 for any operating condition. The linearized resistance of the pipeline carrying air as discussed above is found to be

$$R_{air} = \left(\frac{\partial p_1}{\partial i}\right)_{p_2} = 2\left[\frac{p_1 - p_2}{i}\right]_{avg} = \frac{2(0.00087 \times 144)}{500}(60)(0.667)$$
$$= 0.0201 \; lb_f\text{-min/ft}^5\text{-ft pipe}$$

where the pressure is converted to lb_f/ft^2, the time to min and 0.667 lb_m/ft^3 is the air density at 30°C and 134.7 lb_f/in^2. The resistance for an increase of downstream pressure p_2 is -0.0201 since an increase in p_2 would decrease the air flows.

Example 3–2. Experimental calibration data for an orifice meter measuring air at 70°F, 10 psig are given in Fig. E3–2a as a plot of pressure across the meter

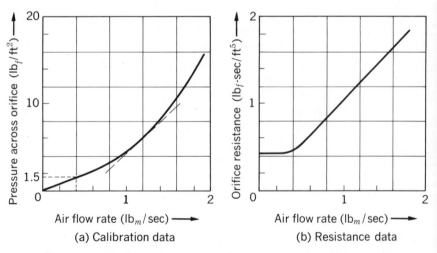

(a) Calibration data   (b) Resistance data

Fig. E3–2. (a) Head–flow rate and (b) resistance–flow rate characteristics of an orifice meter measuring air flow rate.

in lb_f/ft^2 against flow rate in lb_m/sec. Compute the instantaneous resistance of the orifice and plot the values as a function of the flow rate.

Solution. Viscous-flow conditions prevail in the meter at low flow rates and the pressure across the meter is linear with flow rate, giving a constant meter resistance. This is the case in Fig. E3–2 for flow rates less than about 0.4 lb_m/sec. The resistance is constant at

$$R = \rho \, \frac{\partial(p_1 - p_2)}{\partial i} = \frac{(29)(24.7)(1.5)}{(10.73)(530)(0.4)} = 0.473 \, \frac{lb_f\text{-sec}}{ft^5}$$

The density ($\rho = Mp/RT$) is used to eliminate the mass unit from the resistance units.

The linearized turbulent resistance is found by use of the equation

$$R = \rho \, \frac{\partial p_R}{\partial i} = 2\rho \left[\frac{p_R}{i} \right]_{avg}$$

where $p_R = p_1 - p_2$ and the density is evaluated at the inlet conditions. Thus the resistance is obtained either from the slope of the p-vs.-i plot or, more easily, by taking twice the p_R/i ratio at the desired point, as was used here. The results are shown in Fig. E3–2b.

Restrictions in Line. Fluid flow through restrictions in pipelines such as orifice plates, lengths of pipe, hand valves, and control valves is usually in the turbulent region and the flow rate relationships are similar to Eq. 3–2c. A simple method of estimating fluid flow rates through different devices is based on a flow capacity index called C_v, the valve flow coefficient or valve conductance. It is defined as the number of gallons per minute of water that will pass through a flow restriction with a 1 psi pressure drop across the restriction. This definition of C_v is based on Bernoulli's theorem and does not involve any specific restrictions on flow. When C_v is known for a device, the flow through that device under any operating conditions can be found from the relations given below for control valves.

A control valve (see Fig. 3–4) is designed to have the properties of a variable resistance by manipulation of the valve stem position and in addition the valve trim (plug and seat) may be selected for a specific relationship between valve stem position and flow rate. Some manufacturers rate control valves in terms of $C_{v,max}$ the flow capacity of the valve in its wide-open position (full lift). This rating is determined by test in view of the complex relationship between flow capacity and valve area, flow pattern, and body design. Universal agreement upon control valve flow formulas does not exist; however, the following formulas*

---

* G. K. Tucker and D. M. Wills, *A Simplified Technique of Control System Engineering*, Minneapolis-Honeywell Regulator Co., Philadelphia, 1958.

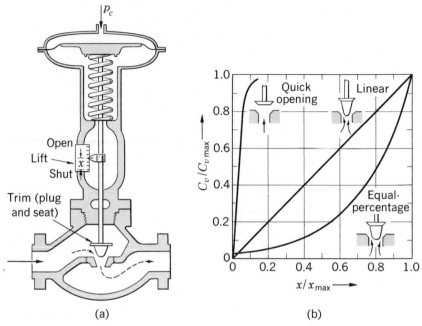

(a)   (b)

Fig. 3–4. (a) A single-seat pneumatic control valve and (b) some control valve trim characteristics. The equal-percentage valve has a rangeability of 40.

are widely used for sizing process control valves.

For non-flashing liquids: $\qquad i = C_v \sqrt{\dfrac{p_1 - p_2}{\rho}} \qquad$ gal/min $\qquad$ (3–2e)

where ρ is the specific gravity of the flowing liquid (water = 1) and the pressures are in $lb_f/in.^2$ and the fluid viscosity is below about 100 SSU.

For gases:

$$\left.\begin{array}{l} \text{Subsonic flow:} \qquad i = 22.7 C_v \sqrt{\dfrac{(p_1 - p_2)p_2}{\rho T}} \qquad \text{scfm, for } p_2 > \dfrac{1}{2} p_1 \\[4mm] \text{Sonic flow:} \qquad i = 11.3 C_v \dfrac{p_1}{\sqrt{\rho T}} \qquad \text{scfm, for } p_2 < \dfrac{1}{2} p_1 \end{array}\right\}$$

(3–2f)

where ρ is the specific gravity of the gas (air = 1), T is the upstream temperature in °R, the pressures are in $lb_f/in.^2$ absolute and the flow rate is ft^3/min at 14.7 psia and 60°F.

For steam:

Subsonic flow: $i = 0.05C_v \dfrac{\sqrt{(p_1 - p_2)p_2}}{K}$ lb/min $\left.\vphantom{\begin{array}{c}a\\b\\c\\d\end{array}}\right\}$

Sonic flow: $i = 0.025C_v \dfrac{p_1}{K}$ lb/min

$$(3\text{-}2\text{g})$$

where $K = 1 + 0.0007(\Delta°F$ steam superheat) and the pressures are in $\text{lb}_f/\text{in.}^2$ absolute. These formulas assume that the pressure drop across the valve is constant, that turbulent flow conditions exist in the valve, and that the value of C_v used is determined by the valve trim and stem position, i.e., if $C_v = C_{v,\max}$ for the valve, then $i = i_{\max}$ for the valve. Reliable methods are not available for estimating valve flow rates under unusual conditions such as high pressure drop across the valve, flashing liquids, and high-viscosity liquids and, in such cases, individual manufacturers should be consulted for advice on the applicability of their valves.

The control valve flow equations above may be linearized in the usual manner. The technique will be illustrated by linearizing Eq. 3-2f for subsonic flow conditions about an average operating point. Since the flow rate is a function of C_v, p_1, and p_2 (T and ρ are constant), the equation may be written

$$\tilde{\imath} = \left(\frac{\partial i}{\partial p_1}\right)_{p_2,C_v} \tilde{p}_1 + \left(\frac{\partial i}{\partial p_2}\right)_{p_1,C_v} \tilde{p}_2 + \left(\frac{\partial i}{\partial C_v}\right)_{p_1,p_2} \tilde{C}_v \qquad (3\text{-}2\text{h})$$

and the partial derivatives are found from the original equation as

$$\left(\frac{\partial i}{\partial p_1}\right)_{p_2,C_v} = \frac{257.6}{\rho T}\left[\frac{C_v{}^2 p_2}{i}\right]_{\text{avg}}$$

$$\left(\frac{\partial i}{\partial p_2}\right)_{p_1,C_v} = \frac{257.6}{\rho T}\left[\frac{C_v{}^2(p_1 - 2p_2)}{i}\right]_{\text{avg}}$$

$$\left(\frac{\partial i}{\partial C_v}\right)_{p_1,p_2} = \left[\frac{i}{C_v}\right]_{\text{avg}}$$

Remember that $C_{v,\max}$ is constant for a given control valve and that the actual C_v is determined by the valve stem position.

An automatic control valve is the final control element in many process control systems and its function is to manipulate the flow of material or energy to the process in response to the controller signal. The control valve shown in Fig. 3-4a uses air in the range of 3-15 psig acting on the diaphragm motor and spring to position the valve stem and thereby control the fluid flow through the valve. The valve stem position is measured in inches from the fully seated position, so, for the air-to-close valve and the air-to-open valve, the stem positions are given in terms of the controller signal as:

Air-to-close valve:

$$x = x_{max}(15 - p_c)/12 \qquad \partial x/\partial p_c = -x_{max}/12, \text{ in/psi}$$

Air-to-open valve:

$$x = x_{max}(p_c - 3)/12 \qquad \partial x/\partial p_c = +x_{max}/12, \text{ in/psi}$$

$$(3-2i)$$

where p_c is the air pressure signal to the valve diaphragm motor. Control valves have a safety function in a process plant, and the valve type is selected for the "fail-safe" valve position needed if the valve signal fails. Values of x_{max} and $C_{v,max}$ for a valve are given by the manufacturer. The valve plug and valve port are matched and referred to as "trim."

Control valve trim is available with linear, equal percentage, and other characteristics, depending on the relationship between C_v and valve stem position. The valve stem position x is usually measured in inches from a closed position (plug seated). For this convention, when $x = 0$, $C_v = C_{v,min}$, the minimum valve flow, and when $x = x_{max}$, $C_v = C_{v,max}$, the maximum valve flow. Assuming a constant pressure drop across the control valve, the valve flow coefficient equations for linear and equal percentage trim are:

Linear:
$$C_v = \frac{C_{v,max}}{x_{max}} x$$

Equal-percentage:
$$C_v = C_{v,min} \left[\frac{C_{v,max}}{C_{v,min}} \right]^{\frac{x}{x_{max}}}$$

$$(3-2j)$$

The value $C_{v,max}/C_{v,min}$ is the rangeability of the control valve, the ratio of the maximum controllable flow to the minimum. For equal-percentage valves the rangeability is often 40–50:1. For a rangeability of 50:1, the valve flow coefficient becomes

$$C_v = 0.02 C_{v,max}(50)^{\frac{x}{x_{max}}}$$

which is a nonlinear relationship. A valve with nonlinear characteristics may be selected to compensate for nonlinear gain in the process. These two valve trim characteristics are contrasted with the quick-opening valve characteristic in Fig. 3–4b.

The linear valve trim increases the flow area directly with lift, so that a 30% flow is obtained with 30% of the valve stroke. The equal percentage valve opens at a much slower rate, so that a 30% valve lift gives only about 11% of maximum flow and the change in flow per unit change in stroke is proportional to the quantity flowing. In other words, when the flow is large, a unit change in stroke produces a large change in flow and when the flow is small a unit change in stroke produces a small flow change. The equal-percentage (also called "logarithmic") valve is the most commonly used valve in the process industries. However, for simplicity, most of the work in this book will assume linear values. Fig. 3–5 is a rating chart for selecting equal-percentage valves from

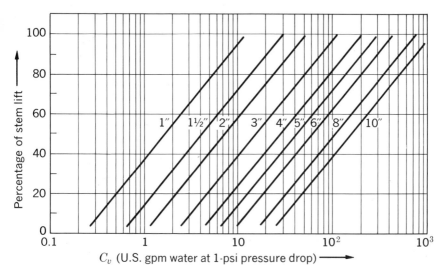

Fig. 3–5. Valve rating chart for equal-percentage valves. The valve sizes correspond to the size of pipe used. (Courtesy of The Foxboro Company)

which it is seen that a $1\frac{1}{2}$-inch control valve has $C_{v,\max} = 30$. Notice that the actual valve C_v varies logarithmically with the valve travel (Eq. 3–2j).

Example 3–3. Determine a linearized fluid resistance for these problems:

(a) Using the nomogram in Fig. 3–3, estimate the resistance per foot of pipe of a 2-in. (2.067-in. i.d.) pipeline carrying 500 gal/hr of raw linseed oil at 100°F ($d = 0.93$ gm/cm³).

(b) An equal-percentage control valve (rangeability of 40) with stem at 50% of maximum value and controlling liquid water flow rate. The pressure drop across the valve is 20 psia and $C_{v,\max}$ for the valve is 20.

Solution. (a) Resistance of pipeline. The linseed oil flow rate is

$$\text{flow rate} = 500(8.34 \times 0.93) = 3870 \text{ lb}_m/\text{hr}$$

Refer to Fig. 3–3 and locate a value of $D_i = 2.067$ in. on the D_i-line and a value of $w = 3.87$ on the w-line. Draw a straight line through these two points and locate its intersection on the reference line (at a value of 9.2). Next locate linseed oil on the x-y coordinates at $x = 3.4$, $y = 1.8$, and from the 100°F point through the linseed oil point find a value of 0.022 on the viscosity-density line. Connecting this point and the point on the reference line gives $\Delta p/L = 0.0006$ $lb_f/in.^2$-ft. The linearized resistance becomes

$$R = 2 \left[\frac{p_1 - p_2}{i} \right]_{avg} p = \frac{2(0.0006)(144)(60)(62.4 \times 0.93)}{3870} = 0.155 \frac{lb_f\text{-min}}{ft^5}$$

(b) The equal-percentage control valve having a rangeability of 40 and 50% open has a value $C_v/C_{v,max} = 0.16$ from Fig. 3–4, so that the instantaneous flow rate is found from Eq. 3–2e

$$i = 0.16(20) \sqrt{20} = 14.3 \text{ gal/min}$$

The linearized resistance is given

$$R = \left(\frac{\partial p}{\partial i} \right)_{avg} = 2 \left[\frac{p}{i} \right]_{avg} = 2 \frac{(20)(144)(7.48)}{14.3} = 3,020 \frac{lb_f\text{-min}}{ft^5}$$

This resistance value shows that to increase the flow rate through this valve at 50% open position one gallon per minute would require a pressure drop increase of $3,020/(7.48 \times 144) = 2.80$ $lb_1/in.^2$ On the other hand, this 7.0% flow rate increase could be obtained by increasing $C_v/C_{v,max}$ to $0.16(1.07) = 0.17$ which requires an $x/x_{max} = 0.52$ (Fig. 3–4b), or a 4.0% change.

Control valves are usually installed in pipelines giving a series combination of pipeline and valve resistances. With a constant pressure fluid source, the pressure drop across the valve will vary with the flow rate due to the pressure drop in the pipeline. Under these conditions the total pressure drop, Δp_t, is the sum of the individual pressure drops, or

$$\Delta p_t = \Delta p_{valve} + \Delta p_{line}$$

where

$$\Delta p_{line} = i^2 \rho / C_l^2$$

The individual pressure drops may be written in terms of a C_v, C_l and C_t from Eq. 3–2e for liquid flow, to give

$$\Delta p_t = \frac{i^2 \rho}{C_t^2} = \frac{i^2 \rho}{C_v^2} + \frac{i^2 \rho}{C_l^2} \quad \text{or} \quad C_t = \left[\frac{1}{C_v^2} + \frac{1}{C_l^2} \right]^{-1/2} \quad (3\text{–}2k)$$

where C_t is the effective flow coefficient in gpm at 1.0-psi pressure drop and C_l is the pipeline flow coefficient not including the valve. The effective flow characteristics of this series combination is shown by finding i/i_{max} in terms of x/x_{max}, the fraction of valve lift, for various ratios of $C_{v,max}/C_l$. From Eq. 3–2k the flow through the combination is found to be

$$i = \frac{1}{\sqrt{\dfrac{1}{C_v^2} + \dfrac{1}{C_l^2}}} \sqrt{\dfrac{\Delta p_t}{\rho}}$$

The maximum flow occurs when $C_v = C_{v,\text{max}}$ for the valve so that for a constant $(\Delta p_l/\rho)$ the flow ratio becomes

$$\frac{i}{i_{\text{max}}} = \frac{\sqrt{\dfrac{1}{C_{v,\text{max}}^2} + \dfrac{1}{C_l^2}}}{\sqrt{\dfrac{1}{C_v^2} + \dfrac{1}{C_l^2}}} = \frac{C_v}{C_{v,\text{max}}} \sqrt{\frac{1 + (C_{v,\text{max}}/C_l)^2}{1 + (C_v/C_l)^2}} \qquad (3\text{–}21)$$

For a linear valve the trim equation is $C_v/C_{v,\text{max}} = x/x_{\text{max}}$, and the system flow ratio becomes

$$\frac{i}{i_{\text{max}}} = \frac{x}{x_{\text{max}}} \sqrt{\frac{1 + (C_{v,\text{max}}/C_l)^2}{1 + (x/x_{\text{max}})^2(C_{v,\text{max}}/C_l)^2}} \qquad (3\text{–}2m)$$

A similar equation can be obtained for other valves by using the proper trim equation for $C_v/C_{v,\text{max}}$.

Results are shown in Fig. 3–6 for the flow characteristics of a linear valve (Eq. 3–2m) and an equal-percentage valve for constant value of

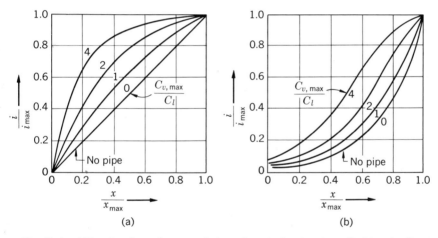

Fig. 3–6. Effective flow characteristics of control valve installed in pipeline. (a) Plot of Eq. 3–21 for linear valve. (b) Equal-percentage valve in pipeline.

$\Delta p_l/\rho$, as the ratio $C_{v,\text{max}}/C_l$ increases from 0 to 4. The curves show that the pipeline destroys the linearity of the linear valve when $C_{v,\text{max}}/C_l > 1$, and as the ratio increases the combination tends to approach the quick-opening valve characteristics. On the other hand, the equal-percentage valve combination tends to approach a linear flow characteristic for high ratios of $C_{v,\text{max}}/C_l$. The usual practice is to size a control valve for about 150% of normal flow at the normal pressure drop of $\frac{1}{3}$ to $\frac{1}{4}$ of the total pressure drop. For example, if a liquid-level system normally requires 100 gpm of water with a total pressure drop of 30 psia, then using the factors of 1.5 for flow and $\frac{1}{3}$ for pressure drop, the estimated C_v would be

$$C_v = i \sqrt{\frac{\rho}{\Delta p}} = \frac{100(1.5)}{\sqrt{\frac{1}{3}(30)}} = 47.5$$

The chart in Fig. 3–5 indicates that a 2-in. equal-percentage valve would be selected.

Turbulent fluid flow through nozzles, orifices, and other restrictions can be estimated from the Fanning flow equation (Eq. 3–2c) or by the use of the C_v-factor and Eqs. 3–2e, f, and g. In using the C_v-factor for a system whose components and conductances are known, the flow rate should be expressed in mass or "standard condition" units because the factor contains corrections for pressure, density, and temperature.

Example 3–4. Find the complete linearized valve flow equation for an equal-percentage valve with a rangeability of 50 and $C_{v,\text{max}} = 30$ controlling a liquid flow. Consider the upstream and downstream pressures, the C_v-factor, and the pneumatic controller signal to the air-to-open valve.

Solution. The equations of interest are:

Valve position: $\quad\quad\quad\quad x = x_{\text{max}}(p_c - 3)/12 \quad\quad$ (linear) $\quad\quad\quad$ (a)

Valve characteristic: $\quad C_v = 0.6(50)^{x/x_{\text{max}}} \quad\quad$ (nonlinear) $\quad\quad$ (b)

Valve flow: $\quad\quad\quad\quad i = C_v \sqrt{\dfrac{p_1 - p_2}{\rho}} \quad\quad$ (nonlinear)

$$= 0.6(50)^{x/x_{\text{max}}} \sqrt{\frac{p_1 - p_2}{\rho}} \quad\quad\quad\quad\quad\quad \text{(c)}$$

The flow rate through the valve may be written in terms of deviations from a normal operating point as

$$\tilde{i} = \frac{\partial i}{\partial x} \tilde{x} + \frac{\partial i}{\partial p_1} \tilde{p}_1 + \frac{\partial i}{\partial p_2} \tilde{p}_2$$

If the valve position responds instantly to a change in controller signal p_c, then the deviation in valve position is given by $\tilde{x} = (\partial x / \partial p_c)\tilde{p}_c$.

The differential coefficients are found to be:

$$\frac{\partial i}{\partial x} = \frac{\ln(50)}{x_{\text{max}}} i_o \quad\quad \frac{\partial i}{\partial p_1} = \frac{i_o}{2(p_1 - p_2)_o}$$

$$\frac{\partial i}{\partial p_2} = -\frac{i_o}{2(p_1 - p_2)_o} \quad\quad \frac{\partial x}{\partial p_c} = \frac{x_{\text{max}}}{12}$$

and the valve flow equation for transformed deviation variables is

$$\tilde{I}(s) = \left[\frac{\ln(50)}{12} i_o\right] \tilde{P}_c(s) + \left[\frac{i_o}{2(p_1 - p_2)_o}\right] [\tilde{P}_1(s) - \tilde{P}_2(s)]$$

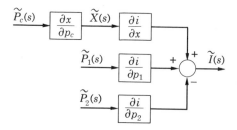

Fig. E3–4. Signal flow diagram for pneumatic control valve.

The signal flow diagram for the valve as drawn from the equations is shown in Fig. E3–4.

Example 3–5. The performance of a control valve depends upon the flow source and the installed valve characteristics. A centrifugal pump feeds a distillation unit through a heat exchanger and a control valve. Consider the dynamic and static pressure losses due to pipe friction, the heat exchanger, elevation above the pump, and discharge pressure and make a sketch which shows the interrelationships among these factors, the pump head characteristic and the pressure drop across the control valve.

Solution. The flow control plant is shown in Fig. E3–5a. Under all conditions the flow rate must be such that the centrifugal pump discharge pressure p_2 must equal the dynamic and static pressure drops in the system, thus

$$p_2 = \Delta p_o + \Delta p_v + \Delta p_e + \Delta p_f + h + p_d$$

where the terms in the equation represent the pressure drops across the orifice, the control valve, the heat exchanger, the equivalent pipe length, the elevation change, and the discharge pressure (static), respectively. The chart in Fig. E3–5b shows the pump characteristic curve and the static and dynamic pressure

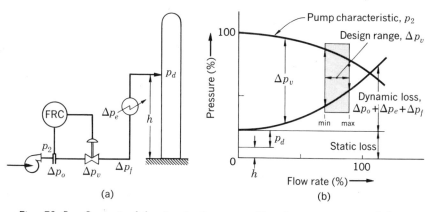

Fig. E3–5. Control of feed rate from centrifugal pump source. (a) Feed control plant. (b) Pressure–flow rate relationships.

drops in the system with the control valve pressure drop Δp_v being the difference between p_2 and the other dynamic and static losses as sketched. It is clear that Δp_v varses with the throttling action of the control valve. A design range for flow rate (or Δp_v) between minimum and maximum flow rates is indicated in the chart. The valve pressure drop Δp_v for good control is determined from an analysis of the installed control valve and is normally 30–50% of the total dynamic pressure drop in process systems. Since the throttling effect of control valves represents an economic loss, certain applications such as pipelines may normally operate with the control valves as wide open as possible.

THERMAL. Thermal energy flows from a higher temperature to a lower temperature by three mechanisms, viz., conduction, convection, and radiation. The thermal resistance in any case may be found as

$$R = \frac{d(\text{temperature})}{d(\text{heat flow})} = \frac{d(T_1 - T_2)}{di}$$

where i is the heat flow rate and $(T_1 - T_2)$ is the temperature across the resistance. Unsteady heat flow by conduction is always associated with heat storage and should be discussed as a distributed-parameter problem but, for the present purpose, assume that the heat storage and thermal resistance are lumped parameters of the element. This problem of heat storage does not occur in the convection and radiation mechanisms since in the first case the thermal resistance is assumed to reside in a thin film having negligible thermal capacity and in the latter case the intervening space between the hot and cold bodies does not absorb appreciable radiant energy.

The familiar Fourier heat conduction law for a lumped-parameter element can be rearranged to give

$$(T_1 - T_2) = \frac{\Delta x}{kA} i = Ri \qquad (3\text{--}2\text{i})$$

or in Laplace-transform notation

$$T_1(s) - T_2(s) = RI(s)$$

where $(T_1 - T_2)$ is the temperature across the element (°F), Δx is the thickness (ft), A is the area perpendicular to heat flow (ft^2), k is the thermal conductivity of the material (Btu/ft-min-°F), i is the heat flow rate (Btu/min), and R is the thermal resistance (°F-min/Btu), given as

$$R = \frac{\Delta x}{kA} \qquad °\text{F-min/Btu}$$

Heat transfer by convection follows a similar law,

$$(T_1 - T_2) = \frac{1}{hA} i = Ri \qquad (3\text{--}2\text{j})$$

where h is the convection heat transfer coefficient (Btu/ft²-min-°F), and A is the area normal to heat flow, (ft²). Heat transfer by these two mechanisms approximate linear relationships since the thermal conductivity k and heat transfer coefficient h are slowly varying functions of temperature and for practical purposes may be considered constant at an average temperature of the element.

In a process plant when the heat transfer rate may change because of changes in T_1, T_2, and h, the deviation in the heat transfer rate may be linearized as

$$\tilde{\imath} = \left(\frac{\partial i}{\partial h}\right)_{T_1,T_2} \tilde{h} + \left(\frac{\partial i}{\partial T_1}\right)_{T_2,h} \tilde{T}_1 + \left(\frac{\partial i}{\partial T_2}\right)_{T_1,h} \tilde{T}_2$$

When the derivatives are evaluated and the equation is transformed the result expressed as deviations from a normal operating condition is

$$\tilde{I}(s) = A(T_1 - T_2)_o \tilde{H}(s) + (hA)_o[\tilde{T}_1(s) - \tilde{T}_2(s)] \qquad (3\text{--}2k)$$

Heat transfer by radiation follows the Stefan-Boltzmann law, which may be written for a surface receiving radiation as

$$i = KAE(T_1{}^4 - T_2{}^4) = KAE(T_1 - T_2)(T_1{}^3 + T_1{}^2T_2 + T_1T_2{}^2 + T_2{}^3)$$

This equation may be forced into the usual form as

$$(T_1 - T_2) = [(KAE)(T_1{}^3 + T_1{}^2T_2 + T_2{}^2T_1 + T_2{}^3)]^{-1}i = Ri \qquad (3\text{--}2l)$$

where T_1 and T_2 are the temperatures of the radiation source and receiver, in °R, K is a constant, 2.87×10^{-11}, Btu/ft²-min-°R⁴, A is the area of receiver, ft², E is the surface emissivity, i is the heat flow Btu/min, and R is the resistance, °R-min/Btu, found from

$$R = [KAE(T_1{}^3 + T_1{}^2T_2 + T_2{}^2T_1 + T_3{}^3)]^{-1}$$

or

$$R \cong \frac{8.71 \times 10^9}{AET_o{}^3} \qquad \text{°R-min/Btu} \qquad (3\text{--}2m)$$

Example 3–6. Estimate a lumped-parameter resistance value for the following conditions:

(a) Conductive heat transfer along an insulated steel rod of 1 ft² cross-sectional area, 6 in. long. Use $k = 28$ Btu/hr-ft²-(°F/ft).
(b) Radiative heat transfer to a body at 600°F in a furnace with wall temperatures of 1000°F. Assume black-body conditions ($E = 1$) and a unit area of the heated body.
(c) Convective heating of process fluid in a steam jacketed stirred vessel of unit area. Assume the overall heat transfer coefficient is 250 Btu/hr-ft²-°F.

Solution. (a) The conductive thermal resistance of a material is found to be $\Delta x/kA$. Then the resistance for the steel rod becomes

$$R = \frac{\Delta x}{kA} = \left(\frac{6}{12}\right)\left(\frac{1}{28 \times 1}\right) 60 = 1.07°\text{F-min/Btu}$$

(b) The radiative thermal resistance is approximately (for $T_o = 1260°R$)

$$R = \frac{8.71(10^9)}{AET_o{}^3} = \frac{8.71(10^9)}{(1)(1)(1260)^3} = 4.35°\text{R-min/Btu}$$

(c) The convective thermal resistance for the jacketed vessel is

$$R = \frac{1}{hA} = \frac{(1)60}{250(1)} = 0.24°\text{F-min/Btu}$$

It is expected that thermal resistances will vary widely depending upon the heat transfer mechanism and the process equipment involved.

Heat transfer coefficients are best obtained under plant operating conditions. Frequently, the needed plant measurements are not available and then it is necessary to seek information on the heat transfer coefficient from the heat transfer correlations in the literature.[*] A summary of analogous resistances in process systems is given in Table 3–3. Notice that the defining equations for the various resistances are of identical form and that the resistance units are potential/flow rate in all cases.

TABLE 3–3

Analogous Resistances in Process Systems

Equation: d(potential) = (resistance) d(flow rate)

System	Symbol	Equation	Resistance Unit	Device
Electric	e_1 -⋀⋀⋀- e_2 $i \rightarrow$	$R = d(e_1 - e_2)/di$	ohms, or volt-sec coulomb	Resistor
Mechanical translation	$x \rightarrow$ f_1 —▯— f_2	$D_x = d(f_1 - f_2)/du$	$\dfrac{\text{lb}_f\text{-min}}{\text{ft}}$	Dashpot
Fluid and chemical	p_1 -▷◁- p_2 $i \rightarrow$	$R = d(p_1 - p_2)/di$	$\dfrac{\text{lb}_f\text{-min}}{\text{ft}^5}$	Pipeline, orifice valve, *or* restriction
Thermal, or thermo- chemical	T_1 -⋀⋀⋀- T_2 $i \rightarrow$	$R = \dfrac{d(T_1 - T_2)}{di}$	$\dfrac{°\text{F-min}}{\text{Btu}}$	Insulator, film resistance

---

[*] R. H. Perry and S. D. Kirkpatrick, eds., *Chemical Engineers' Handbook*, 4th ed., Section 10, McGraw-Hill Book Co., Inc., New York, 1963.

Capacitance. The capacitance of an element is a measure of its ability to hold or store material or energy. The capacity is the ratio of the quantity of material or energy stored to the potential force across the element, thus,

$$\text{Capacitance, } C = \frac{d(\text{quantity})}{d(\text{potential force})} \qquad (3\text{–}3)$$

An ideal capacitance is able to return all the material or energy stored in it, therefore it does not dissipate energy or lose material. In terms of net flow rate the capacitance of an element is

$$C = \frac{i_1 - i_2}{dp_C/dt} = \frac{i_C}{dp_C/dt} \qquad \text{or} \qquad i_C = C\frac{dp_C}{dt}$$

where p_C is the potential across the capacitance and $i_1 - i_2 = i_C$ is the net flow rate through the element. The signal flow graphs may be drawn

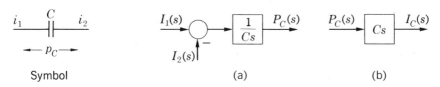

Symbol   (a)   (b)

Fig. 3–7. Signal flow graph for linear capacitance with zero initial conditions.

as shown in Fig. 3–7a,b, since the Laplace transformation of the basic equation is

$$I_1(s) - I_2(s) = I_C(s) = C[sP_C(s) - p_C(0^+)]$$

The total capacitance of several capacitors in parallel is the sum of the individual capacitances:

$$C_{\text{total}} = \sum_k C_k$$

The total capacitance of several capacitors in series is

$$C_{\text{total}} = \left[\sum_k C_k{}^{-1}\right]^{-1}$$

ELECTRICAL. Electrical capacitance is the ability of an element to store electrostatic energy as separated positive and negative charges. A pure capacitance C stores electrostatic energy of amount $\frac{1}{2}Ce_C{}^2$ which gives rise to a voltage across its terminals given as

$$e_C = \frac{1}{C}\int_0^t i\,dt = \frac{q}{C} + e_C(0^+) \qquad (3\text{–}3a)$$

or in Laplace-transform notation

$$E_C(s) = \frac{1}{Cs} I(s) + \frac{e_C(0^+)}{s}$$

where e_C is the potential across the capacitance in volts, i is the current in amperes, q is the charge in coulombs, C is the capacitance in farads (ampere-sec/volt), and $e_C(0^+) = q_0/C$ is the initial voltage across the capacitor.

MECHANICAL. In a mechanical system, potential energy can be stored by extension or compression of a spring. In the case of translational mechanical energy the force on the spring increases as the spring is extended or compressed and is given as

$$f_C = \frac{1}{C_x} \int_0^t u \, dt = \frac{x}{C_x} + f_C(0^+) \qquad (3\text{-}3b)$$

or in Laplace-transform notation

$$F_C(s) = \frac{1}{C_x s} U(s) + \frac{f_C(0^+)}{s}$$

$$= \frac{1}{C_x} X(s)$$

where f_C is the force across the spring in lb_f, C_x is the translational compliance of the spring, ft/lb_f, and x is the spring displacement from equilibrium in ft. The sign convention is taken so that a positive force gives a positive displacement.

FLUID OR CHEMICAL. Fluid capacitance is the ability of an element to store additional fluid as the pressure increases. With incompressible fluids (liquids at low pressure) this can occur by raising the interface in an unfilled container or by increasing the volume of a filled container due to the elastance of the container walls. The latter case is important for high pressure process equipment and for specially constructed vessels such as bellows and gas holders.

The Laplace-transformed relationship for pressure across a fluid capacitance is

$$P_C(s) = \frac{1}{Cs} I_C(s) + \frac{p_C(0^+)}{s}$$

where $I(s)$ is the transformed flow rate, ft^3/sec.

Constant-Volume Vessel. The capacitance of a filled vessel of fixed volume, V, is found from the definition of capacitance as

$$C = \frac{i_C}{dp_C/dt} = \frac{i_C dt}{dp_C} = \frac{dV}{dp_C} \qquad (3\text{-}3c)$$

where dV is the additional volume of fluid added to the vessel to increase the pressure by an amount dp_C. From physics, the bulk modulus* of a fluid is defined as

$$\beta = -\frac{V\,dp_C}{dV} \qquad \text{lb}_f/ft^2$$

and it has two values, isothermal or adiabatic, depending upon the plant operating conditions. Now the capacitance of any fixed volume vessel filled with fluid of bulk modulus β is found after eliminating dV/dp_C in the above equations to be

$$C = \frac{V}{\beta} \qquad ft^5/lb_f$$

For the polytropic compression of ideal gases the pressure-volume relationship is assumed to be

$$pV^n = \text{constant}$$

from which the dp/dV coefficient is obtained by differentiation:

$$p(nV^{n-1}) + V^n\,dp/dV = 0 \qquad \text{or} \qquad -\frac{dp}{dV} = \frac{np}{V}$$

and

$$\beta = np$$

Therefore, the capacitance of a gas-filled vessel is

$$C = \left[\frac{V}{np}\right]_o \tag{3–3d}$$

where the values are taken at average operating conditions. The polytropic exponent is unity ($n = 1$) for isothermal conditions, it is the heat capacity ratio ($n = C_p/C_V$) for adiabatic conditions, and for actual plant conditions it is between these two extremes. Plant responses to slow changes in pressure and flow rate will occur under isothermal conditions; whereas, plant responses to rapid fluctuations in pressure and flow rate will tend to occur adiabatically.

The capacitance of hydraulic fluid filled vessels will usually be negligible since the bulk moduli of these fluids are large. A typical value for hydraulic fluids is $20–40(10^6)$ lb_f/ft^2. Of course, the capacitance may not be negligible when the fluid volume in the system is large or the pressure very great. In such cases the capacitance of a fixed volume system is given as V/β.

Elastic Vessel. When the vessel has elastic walls, as in the case of an extensible bellows or a rubber tube, the capacitance must be increased to

* Bulk modulus is the reciprocal of compressibility. The values listed in tables are usually isothermal values.

take this effect into account by adding a term $[dV/dp_C]_{\text{vessel}}$ to Eq. 3–3c for vessel capacitance due to vessel elasticity. Then the total capacitance of an elastic container is

$$C_{\text{total}} = \left[\frac{dV}{dp_C}\right]_{\text{fluid}} + \left[\frac{dV}{dp_C}\right]_{\text{vessel}} \tag{3–3e}$$

Consider the capacitance of an extensible bellows due to the elasticity of the bellows itself. Let the cross-sectional area of the bellows be A (ft²), the spring constant of the bellows be k (lb$_f$/ft), the bellows pressure be p (lb$_f$/ft²), and the position of the free end be x (ft) from the zero reference position where the element volume is V_o. Then the force required to extend the bellows x ft is

$$pA = kx$$

and the volume of the bellows becomes

$$V = V_o + Ax = V_o + pA^2/k$$

so that the coefficient dV/dp for the bellows is found by differentiation to be

$$\left(\frac{dV}{dp}\right)_{\text{vessel}} = \frac{A^2}{k}$$

and the total capacitance of the extensible bellows becomes

$$\begin{aligned} C_{\text{total}} &= \left[\frac{V}{\beta} + \frac{A^2}{k}\right]_o \quad \text{for hydraulic fluids} \\ &= \left[\frac{V}{np} + \frac{A^2}{k}\right]_o \quad \text{for ideal gases} \end{aligned} \left.\rule{0pt}{40pt}\right\} \tag{3–3f}$$

where the values are taken at average operating conditions.

Example 3–7. Find the capacitance of an elastic spherical balloon of diameter D, ft, at pressure p, lb$_f$/ft². The bulk modulus of the balloon fabric is k, lb$_f$/ft².

Solution. The capacitance of any elastic element is given by Eq. 3–3e. The volume of the balloon is $\pi D^3/6$ and, therefore, the change of volume with a change in diameter D is found as

$$dV/dD = \pi D^2/2 = 3V/D$$

The balloon construction material is elastic, having a modulus of k lb$_f$/ft² and thickness x, ft. The pressure-diameter relationship is given by a differential force balance on a great circle, thus

$$d\left(\frac{\pi D^2 p}{4}\right) = d\left(\frac{k\pi x D}{2}\right) \quad \text{or} \quad \frac{dD}{dp} = \frac{D^2}{2kx}$$

Then the capacitance of the balloon due to its elasticity is found

$$\left[\frac{dV}{dp}\right]_{\text{balloon}} = \frac{dV}{dD}\cdot\frac{dD}{dp} = \frac{3V}{D}\cdot\frac{D^2}{2kx} = \frac{3VD}{2kx}$$

and the total capacitance of the balloon at the operating condition equals

$$C_{\text{total}} = \left[\frac{V}{\beta} + \frac{3VD}{2kx}\right]_o$$

Example 3-8. Compute the fluid capacitance for the following process vessels:

(a) A 1-cubic foot storage tank filled with hydraulic fluid having a bulk modulus of $25(10^6)$ lb_f/ft^2.

(b) Repeat (a) with tank filled with air at 70°F and 50 psig for adiabatic conditions, i.e., $n = 1.4$.

(c) A bellows having 1-ft^2 area and a spring constant of $5(10^4)$ lb_f/ft filled with air at 70°F and 50 psig. Assume that the unextended bellows volume is 1 ft^3 and that the operation is isothermal.

Solution. The fluid capacitance of any vessel is given by Eq. 3-3e.

(a) For hydraulic-fluid-filled tank (assuming an inelastic tank) the capacitance is

$$C = \left[\frac{dV}{dp_c}\right]_{\text{fluid}} = \frac{V}{\beta} = \frac{1}{25(10^6)} = 4.0(10^{-8}) \text{ ft}^5/lb_f$$

(b) For the air-filled tank (assuming an inelastic tank) the capacitance is

$$C = \left[\frac{V}{np}\right]_o = \frac{1}{1.4(64.7)(144)} = 7.64(10^{-5}) \text{ ft}^5/lb_f$$

(c) The bellows at 50 psig is extended a distance $x = 50(144)(1)/(5 \times 10^4) = 0.144$ ft. The extended volume is 1.14 ft^3 and the capacitance of the bellows at the average operating condition is found from Eq. 3-3f to be

$$C = \left[\frac{V}{p} + \frac{A^2}{k}\right]_o = \frac{1.14}{64.7(144)} + \frac{(1)^2}{5(10^4)} = 1.42(10^{-4}) \text{ ft}^5/lb_f$$

These process capacitances as used here are independent of the fluid density because they are defined in terms of volume in Eq. 3-3c.

THERMAL. Thermal capacitance is the ability of an element to store thermal energy as the temperature increases. Process thermal energy may be added either at constant volume or at constant pressure with most industrial applications occurring at constant pressure. Generally, the thermal capacitance is defined as

$$C = \frac{d(\text{thermal energy})}{d(\text{temperature})} \quad \text{Btu/°F}$$

The thermal energy of the element is its enthalpy per degree of temperature change and therefore the capacitance is found for constant pressure operation as

$$C = mC_p \quad \text{Btu/°F}$$

where m is the mass in lb_m and C_p is the average constant pressure heat capacity in Btu/lb_m-°F. Care should be exercised in applying this lumped-parameter technique to furnaces and large thermal equipment since in such cases the capacitance is actually distributed in space and the lumped-parameter assumption may be a poor approximation to the actual behavior. The thermal potential across a capacitance is

$$T_C(s) = \frac{I(s)}{Cs} + \frac{T_C(0^+)}{s} \qquad (3\text{-}3g)$$

TABLE 3–4
Analogous Capacitances in Process Systems

Equation: Potential $= \dfrac{1}{Cs}$ (flow rate)

System	Symbol	Rate Equation	Capacitance Unit	Device
Electric		$C = i \Big/ \dfrac{de_C}{dt}$	$\text{farad} = \dfrac{\text{coulomb}}{\text{volt}}$	Capacitor
Mechanical translation		$C_x = u \Big/ \dfrac{df_C}{dt}$	$\dfrac{\text{ft}}{\text{lb}_f}$	Spring
Fluid and chemical		$C = i \Big/ \dfrac{dp_C}{dt}$	$\dfrac{\text{ft}^5}{\text{lb}_f}$	Filled tank
Thermal		$C = i \Big/ \dfrac{dT_C}{dt}$	$\dfrac{\text{Btu}}{{}^\circ\text{F}}$	Thermal recuperator

Inertance. The inertia of an element is the property by which it opposes change in the rate of material or energy flow through the component. As based on Newton's law, the inertance of a component is the ratio of potential force to the rate of change of the resulting flow rate, thus

$$\text{Inertance, } L, = \frac{\text{potential force}}{\dfrac{d}{dt} \text{(flow rate)}} = \frac{\text{potential force}}{\dfrac{d^2}{dt^2} \text{(quantity)}} \qquad (3\text{-}4)$$

In terms of symbols, the potential across the inertance is given

$$p_L = L \frac{di_L}{dt} = L \frac{d^2q}{dt^2}$$

where i_L is the flow rate through the inertance and q is the quantity. Laplace transformation of the equation with initial conditions gives

$$P_L(s) = Ls I_L(s) - Li(0^+) = Ls^2 Q(s) - Lsq(0^+) - L\dot{q}(0^+)$$

which can be represented by signal flow graphs as shown in Fig. 3-8. An ideal inertance does not dissipate energy but stores it in an attempt to keep the flow rate of energy or material through the component at a constant value. Under steady-state conditions there will be no potential force across an ideal inertance.

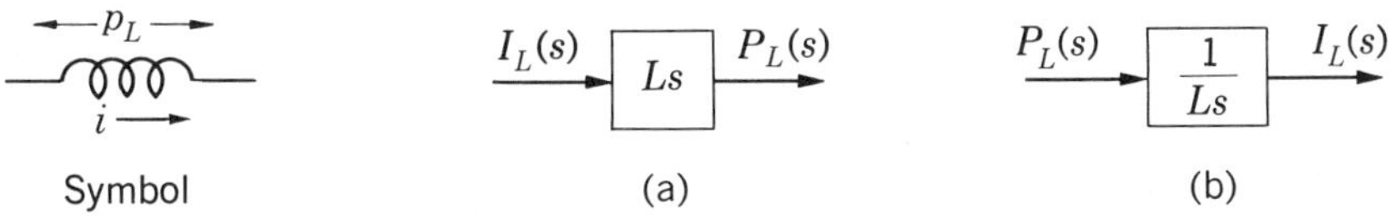

Fig. 3-8. Signal flow graph for linear inertance with zero initial conditions.

ELECTRICAL. Electric inductance is the property of a circuit element that opposes a change in current. It is associated with the storage of electromagnetic energy. The voltage across the inductance is proportional to the value of inductance in henries and the rate of change of current. When the current flow is constant, the voltage across the inductance is zero. The Laplace-transformed equation may be written

$$E_L(s) = LsI_L(s) - Li(0^+) \tag{3-4a}$$

where $E_L(s)$ is the transform of the voltage across the inductance and L is the inductance in henries, $I_L(s)$ is the transform of the current in the inductance in amperes.

MECHANICAL. Inertia is the mechanical parameter that opposes a change in velocity of an element. It is associated with the mass of the element. For translation motion the force through the element is proportional to the mass and the rate of change of linear velocity, thus:

$$f_L = \frac{m}{g_c}\frac{du}{dt} = \frac{m}{g_c}\frac{d^2x}{dt^2} \quad \text{or} \quad F_L(s) = \frac{ms}{g_c}U(s) - \frac{mu(0^+)}{g_c}$$

$$= \frac{ms^2}{g_c}X(s) - \frac{msx(0^+)}{g_c} - \frac{m\dot{x}(0^+)}{g_c} \tag{3-4b}$$

where f_L is the force in lb_f, m is the inertia in lb_m, u is the linear velocity in ft/sec, and x is the linear displacement in ft.

FLUID OR CHEMICAL. Fluid inertance is the mass or inertia effect associated with fluids in motion in pipes, tanks, and other containers. The pressure across a pipeline due to fluid motion (not including resistance) is given from Newton's law as

$$p_L = \frac{f_L}{A} = \frac{m}{g_c A}\frac{du}{dt}$$

where A is the cross-sectional area of pipeline in ft^2, u is the fluid velocity in the pipe in ft/sec, m is the mass of fluid in lb$_m$ and g_c is the constant in Newton's law in lb$_m$-ft/lb$_f$-sec^2. The mass of fluid having density, ρ lb$_m$/ft^3, contained in a pipe of length, l ft, and cross-sectional area, A ft^2 is $l\rho A$. Similarly the flow rate, i ft^3/sec, is the product of pipe area and velocity u, thus: $i = Au$. Making these substitutions in the pressure equation gives

$$p_L = \frac{l\rho A}{g_c A}\frac{du}{dt} = \frac{l\rho}{g_c A}\frac{di}{dt}$$

or, in transform notation,

$$P_L(s) = LsI(s) - Li(0^+)$$

where $L = l\rho/g_c A$ is the fluid inertia in lb$_f$-sec^2/ft^5, p_L is the pressure in lb$_f$/ft^2 due to inertia across the pipe of length l, and i is the flow rate in ft^3/min. The inertance of a fluid is a distributed parameter, but it may be considered as lumped in many applications. From the definition, the inertance is proportional to the fluid density and pipe length and inversely proportional to the pipe cross-sectional area. Therefore for low-density fluids and short pipelines, the inertia may be negligible.

THERMAL. In the inertance component, considered above, the flow of matter or energy is always coupled to another transport process. For example, the flow of electric charge in a circuit results in a magnetomotive force (causing displacement of magnetic charges) which gives rise to a magnetic current in a magnetic circuit and a magnetic current in turn produces an electromotive force. Thus, the electric charge flow and the magnetic current flow are coupled. In mechanical systems, the translational force and momentum change (inertial force) are coupled phenomena giving rise to the inductive behavior.

The flow of heat by pure conduction has no coupled transport phenomena and therefore, the flow is non-inductive. When heat flow is coupled with an associated transport as the mass transport accompanying convective heat transfer then the heat flow has an inductive behavior. The treatment of such circuits is beyond the aim of the present book.

Example 3–9. Compute the inertance of the following process elements:

(a) A mass that is accelerated 3 ft/sec^2 by a force of 18 lb$_f$.
(b) A 4-in. (i.d.) pipeline 100 ft long, filled with CCl$_4$ liquid ($d = 1.58$ gm/cm^3).
(c) An exhaust gas stack 18-in. (i.d.) 30-ft high filled with gas at 325°F and 14.5 psia. The average molecular weight of the gas is 30.8.

Solution. (a) Newton's law relates inertia to force and acceleration so that the inertia of the mass is

$$m = g_c F/a = 32.2(18)/3 = 193.2 \text{ lb}_m$$

(b) The inertance of an element is directly related to its mass; thus, for the liquid-filled pipeline,

$$L = \frac{l\rho}{g_c A} = \frac{100(1.58 \times 62.4)4}{32.2(\pi)(\frac{4}{12})^2} = 3500 \text{ lb}_f\text{-sec}^2/\text{ft}^5$$

(c) The inertance of the gas-filled stack is

$$L = \frac{lp}{g_c A} = \frac{30(30.8 \times 14.5)4}{32.2(10.73 \times 785)(\pi \times 1.5^2)} = 0.028 \text{ lb}_f\text{-sec}^2/\text{ft}^5$$

TABLE 3-5
Analogous Inertances in Process Systems

Equation: Potential $= Ls$(flow rate)

System	Symbol	Rate Equation	Inertance Units	Device
Electric	e_L $i \to$	$L = e_L \Big/ \dfrac{di}{dt}$	henry $= \dfrac{\text{volt-sec}^2}{\text{coulomb}}$	Inductor
Mechanical translation	f_L $\boxed{M}$	$M = f_L \Big/ \dfrac{du}{dt}$	$\text{lb}_m = \dfrac{\text{lb}_f\text{-sec}^2}{\text{ft}}$	Mass
Fluid and chemical (liquid and gas)	p_L $i \to$	$L = p_L \Big/ \dfrac{di}{dt}$	$\dfrac{\text{lb}_f\text{-sec}^2}{\text{ft}^5}$	Mass of fluid
Thermal	None			

3-3. RESPONSE OF PROCESS ELEMENTS TO STANDARD INPUTS

Process engineers study the response of physical systems for the purposes of understanding the system (analysis) or of improving the system performance (design). The test input for study is generally selected as the impulse, step, ramp, or steady-state sinusoidal input. A discussion of these system inputs may be found at the end of Chapter 2. The standard potential responses of the ideal process resistance, capacitance, and inertance elements to the standard flow rate inputs are derived below and tabulated graphically in Table 3-6.

Resistance Element. The equation to be solved for this element is

$$p_R = Ri$$

It is clear that the resistance is a proportional element, so that the response in $p_R(t)$ is equal to the input $i(t)$ multiplied by R, as shown in Table 3-6.

TABLE 3-6
Response of Ideal Process Elements to Standard Inputs

	Impulse	Step	Ramp	Sinusoidal (Steady-State)
Standard inputs				
1. Resistance $p_R = Ri$				
2. Capacitance $p_C = \dfrac{1}{C}\displaystyle\int_0^t i\,dt$				
3. Inertance $p_L = L\dfrac{di}{dt}$				

Capacitance Element. The integral equation to be solved for this element is

$$p_C = \frac{1}{C}\int_0^t i\,dt$$

from which it is seen that the ideal element is an integrator with the proportional factor $1/C$ multiplying the value of the integral. Graphical plots of the responses are shown in Table 3-6.

Inertance Element. The equation to be solved for this element is

$$p_L = L\frac{di}{dt}$$

which shows that the response $p_L(t)$ is equal to the inertance of the element multiplied by the derivative of the input $i(t)$. The responses are shown in Table 3-6. In studying this table, remember that the integral of the impulse and sine functions are the step and negative cosine functions and that the derivative of the impulse and sine functions are the doublet and cosine functions respectively.

Example 3-10. Find the flow rate responses of these ideal process elements to the indicated changes:

BASIC PROCESS ELEMENTS

(a) Resistance. Let the potential across a resistance R change from $+10$ to -15 units of potential at $t = 0^+$.
(b) Capacitance. Let the potential across a capacitance C change from $+10$ to -15 units of potential at $t = 0^+$.
(c) Inertance. Let the potential across an inductance change from zero to $+5$ units of potential at $t = 0^+$. (It is physically impossible to have a non-zero potential across an ideal inductance under steady-state conditions.)

Solution. (a) The Laplace-transformed equation for the resistance element is

$$E_R(s) = RI(s)$$

Note that initial condition terms do not appear, since flow rate and potential variables can change instantaneously. In this problem the forcing function is a step of -15 units; therefore,

$$E_R(s) = -15/s$$

from which the flow rate response is

$$I(s) = \frac{1}{R} E_R(s) = -\frac{15}{Rs}$$

The inverse transformation gives

$$i(t) = -15/R$$

so that the total change is from $10/R$ to $-15/R$ units of flow rate.
(b) The transformed capacitance equation is

$$I(s) = C[sE_C(s) - e_C(0^+)]$$

where $e_C(0^+) = 10$, the initial condition potential and $E_C(s) = -15/s$ as before. The flow rate response is

$$I(s) = C[s(-15/s) - 10] = -25C$$
$$i(t) = -25C\delta(t)$$

since the inverse transformation of a constant is the impulse function.
(c) The transformed inertance equation is

$$E_L(s) = L[sI(s) - i(0^+)]$$

where $i(0^+) = 0$, the initial condition flow rate and $E_L(s) = 5/s$. Then the flow rate response is

$$I(s) = \frac{E_L(s)}{Ls} = \frac{5}{Ls^2}$$
$$i(t) = 5t/L$$

The flow rate must increase $5/L$ units every unit of time to maintain a 5-unit potential across the inertance.

The resistance, capacitance, and inertance elements of electric, mechanical, fluid, and thermal systems have been defined in basic terms so that the differential equations for flow circuits containing these elements may be written on the basis of the analogy principle. Table 3–7 lists mathematically analogous variables in summary form. These analogies are not the only ones possible but they do appeal to our physical intuition and also satisfy the mathematical analogy requirement. Any set of consistent units may be used; those listed are from the English engineering system.

TABLE 3–7
Mathematical Analogies in Process Systems

	Equation	Electric	Mechanical Translation	Fluid	Thermal
Potential		e, volts	f, lb$_f$	$p, \dfrac{\text{lb}_f}{\text{ft}^2}$	T, °F
Quantity		q, coulomb	x, ft	q, ft^3	q, Btu
Flow rate		i, amperes	u, ft/sec	$i, \dfrac{\text{ft}^3}{\text{min}}$	$i, \dfrac{\text{Btu}}{\text{min}}$
Resistance	$e_R = Ri$	R, ohms	$D, \dfrac{\text{lb}_f\text{-sec}}{\text{ft}}$	$R, \dfrac{\text{lb}_f\text{-min}}{\text{ft}^5}$	$R, \dfrac{°\text{F-min}}{\text{Btu}}$
Capacitance	$e_C = \dfrac{1}{C}\displaystyle\int_0^t i\, dt$	C, farads	$C_x, \dfrac{\text{ft}}{\text{lb}_f}$	C, ft^5/lb$_f$	$C, \dfrac{\text{Btu}}{°\text{F}}$
Inertance	$e_L = \dfrac{L\, di}{dt}$	L, henries	m, lb$_m$	$L, \dfrac{\text{lb}_f\text{-min}^2}{\text{ft}^5}$	None

PROBLEMS

3–1. Find the linearized effect of speed and flow rate on the pressure developed by the centrifugal pump described in Fig. E3–1 when the flow rate is 10 ft^3/min and the speed is 1500 rpm.

3–2. The electrical resistance of a body is given by

$$dR = \frac{k}{A}\, dl$$

where k is the electrical characteristic of the material, A is the cross-sectional area of the body, and l is the length. Find a general formula for the electrical resistance between the inside and outside radial surfaces of a flat circular washer of thickness t, inside radius r_i, and outside radius r_o.

3–3. A dashpot consists of a freely movable piston in an oil-filled case. The piston is pierced by a capillary tube through which the oil flows in viscous motion as the piston is moved. Derive an equation for the damping coefficient of a dashpot with piston radius r_p, capillary radius r_o, and capillary length l. The oil has density ρ and viscosity μ.

3–4. Find the linearized equation for air flow through an equal-percentage control valve having $C_{v,\max} = 52$ and rangeability of 40 with the stem at 50% travel. The upstream and downstream pressures are 50 and 30 psig, respectively, and the fluid is air at 80°F.

3-5. A bypass line with hand valve and a flow control valve are connected in parallel. Assume that the bypass line and hand valve are equivalent to 250 ft of 2-in. pipe and that the installed control valve has a $C_{v,max}$ of 50. Make a plot of the flow rate of water at 25°C through the combination against fraction of control valve stem position for a 25-psi constant pressure drop across the combination. Use an equal-percentage control valve with rangeability of 40 (data given in Fig. 3–4b).

3-6. Estimate the thermal resistance of the following devices:

(a) Flat magnesia insulation 4 in. in thickness and 1 ft² in area
(b) Surface film of 1 ft² in boiling-water evaporator
(c) A body at 300°F, having 10 ft² surface area, placed in an enclosed furnace at 700°F

3-7. Estimate the capacitance of the following items:

(a) A circular lake with 1 mile of shore line (fluid capacitance)
(b) A spherical air tank 10 ft in diameter at 70°F when the pressure in the tank is 5 psig (gas capacitance)
(c) A spring which deflects 0.3 in. under load of 75 lb$_f$
(d) A 150-lb$_m$ steel tank containing 50 gal water (thermal capacitance); assume that the tank and water have the same temperature

3-8. Estimate the inertance of the following items (for the fluids, compute the inertance per 100 ft of pipeline):

(a) A mechanical lever 5 ft long having a mass of 200 lb$_m$ in linear motion
(b) The water in a 12-in. pipeline with a velocity of 50 ft/sec
(c) Air at 100°F, 50 psig, in a 12-in. pipeline with a velocity of 50 ft/sec

3-9. A linear control valve is used to manipulate the liquid flow of a constant-speed centrifugal pump by throttling the flow into a pipeline (Fig. P3–9). The

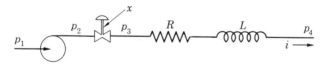

Fig. P3–9

pipeline has lumped R and L parameters (C is negligible). Using linearized approximations, write the separate equations for pump, valve, and pipeline, and draw the signal flow diagram for the system. The system variables producing flow are p_1, p_4, and x, the position of the control valve.

3-10. Compute the current response of a 1 μf capacitor charged to 50 volts at zero time when connected to a sinusoidal voltage input of 10 sin t.

3–11. Find the liquid-level response of a water tank which discharges 5 gal/min constantly and has an input flow rate of $10 - 8 \sin t$ gal/min. The liquid level at zero time is 20 ft, and the upright cylindrical tank is 3 ft in diameter.

3–12. Repeat Problem 3–11 for a tank whose fluid capacity is $1 + 0.01h$ ft³/ft.

3–13. Find response equations for a resistance R, a capacitance C, and an inductance L elements with a ramp flow rate input $\tilde{\imath}(t) = t$ and initial conditions of $i(0^+)$.

3–14. Repeat Problem 3–13 for an input exponential flow rate $\tilde{\imath}(t) = e^{-at}$ and initial conditions of $i(0^+)$.

4

Basic Process Components

The process control engineer has responsibility for the performance of complete plants. However, a whole plant is too complex to study as a unit, so the engineer breaks it down into its basic components for detailed analysis. It is found that the basic components in lumped-parameter systems are a few simple network combinations of the process elements R, C, L, having distinct dynamic characteristics. Experience has shown that a process unit generally consists of a relatively few of the basic components and that the best way to prepare for process analysis is to study the basic components. Thus, process analysis enables the engineer to convert the conventional flowsheet into a dynamic flowsheet from which dynamic responses of the plant may be found.* This chapter outlines an approach to the analysis of dynamic processes in electrical, mechanical, fluid, and thermal systems and then analyzes the basic process components, showing examples of each in the four technologies. Again the analog principle is applied in the simulation of the basic components, using an analog computer.

4–1. ANALYSIS OF PROCESS COMPONENTS

The mathematical analysis of a process system† is the quantitative statement of the cause-and-effect relationships operating in the system. These relationships are usually given as differential equations obtained from application of the appropriate physical and chemical laws to the process under study. The analysis of simple process systems may be accomplished by the application of specific laws, such as Kirchhoff's laws

* R. H. Luecke, M. L. McGuire, and O. K. Crosser, "Dynamic Flowsheeting," *Chemical Engineering Progress*, **63**, pp. 60–66, 1967.

† A "process system" is an assembly of process elements organized for a specific purpose and having definite performance characteristics. Systems vary in size from a simple RC component to an organized industry such as a telephone system. In this book, "system" refers to the thing being studied at the moment, whether a single block in a process control application or the whole process control unit.

for electric circuits, and of the material- and energy-balance principle, to fluid and chemical process systems. The present article lists the key natural laws for electric, mechanical, fluid, and thermal systems and shows their application to the basic process components.

Construction of Mathematical Model. The purpose in making an analysis of a physical system is to obtain a practical mathematical expression that represents the behavior of the system. Most physical systems are so complex that they cannot be rigorously analyzed in mathematical terms, so the general approach is to construct and analyze a reasonable model of the system based on a logical set of assumptions. If the mathematical description of the simple model does not result in useful relationships, the model is improved and the analysis is repeated until useful engineering results are obtained. The working assumptions must be kept in mind throughout an analysis since nonlinearities and neglected effects may become significant in different operating regions. Also, the exactness of the mathematical work tends to give the engineer a false feeling that the analysis is better than the assumptions upon which it is based. The method may be outlined in these steps:

1. Construct a model for the system. This involves (a) sketching the process model, (b) listing all assumptions to be made in the analysis, and identifying the dependent and independent variables operating in the system, (c) selecting units of measurement for the system variables and determining the magnitude and range of the variables, and (d) recognizing, from experience, the individual process components. Any interacting components must be analyzed together, as a unit. Signal flow diagrams aid in the study and analysis of the model. Designation of cause (input or manipulated variable), effect (output or controlled variable), and load variables will be helpful. The construction of analogous circuits will improve understanding of the system.

2. Apply the appropriate physical and chemical principles governing the behavior of each process element and component in the system. This step gives one or more equations that describe the model in a quantitative manner.

3. Study the behavior of the physical system and compare its experimental response with the predicted response. Serious disagreement between the two responses in the operating range of the system indicates a need to improve the system model. Generally, the experimental data obtained from the system are used to evaluate parameters in the system equations.

This chapter is concerned with combining the process elements into the basic process components and showing that, based on the mathematical equations, the components in one system may be considered analogs of similar components in another system. Simulation of engineering systems based on this principle of mathematical analogy is now widely practiced with the use of the analog computer.

Natural Laws Applicable to Model. All physical equipment and processes obey the laws of nature. These laws have a common origin in material and energy balances, the laws of thermodynamics, and the rate equation; but for convenience in application these general laws are restated in specific terms below.

PROCESSES INVOLVING MATERIAL AND ENERGY BALANCES. Matter and energy are universally conserved. They may be changed in form but they cannot be created or destroyed. Then it may be written for a convenient quantity of matter or energy that

$$\text{Input} = \text{output} + \text{accumulation} \qquad (4\text{--}1)$$

The steps in making such an analysis of a process model are outlined:

For material balance
Apply Eq. 4–1 directly to the process, using consistent units for the material entering and leaving in the process streams and that accumulating in the system.

For energy balance
Study the model and determine the forms of energy present (heat, work, and so on) and the potential and kinetic energies and the enthalpy terms, including heats of chemical reaction.
Then select a suitable datum temperature and datum condition for the enthalpy terms for all the process streams and apply Eq. 4–1 directly to the process, using consistent units for all the terms.

PROCESSES INVOLVING ELECTRIC, FLUID, AND THERMAL CIRCUITS. The principles of conservation of material and energy, when restated in terms of conservation of charge and energy as applied to electric circuits, are known as Kirchhoff's current and potential laws.

Kirchhoff's Current Law. At any junction in an electric circuit the algebraic sum of the currents is zero, i.e., at any junction in a circuit,

$$\sum_{k} i_k(t) = 0 \qquad (4\text{--}2)$$

where $i_k(t)$ denotes the kth current as a function of time. The nodal method of circuit analysis based on Kirchhoff's current law requires that the algebraic sum of the currents flowing out of a circuit node or junction be zero. The usual steps in an analysis are:

1. Select one node or junction point as ground potential, then assume voltages referred to ground for all the other nodes in the circuit.

2. Write Eq. 4–2 for each node, thus obtaining a number of equations equal to the number of node voltages.
3. Solve the equations for the desired circuit relationship.

Kirchhoff's Potential Law. The algebraic sum of the potential drops e_k around a closed circuit is zero, i.e., for any closed loop in a circuit,

$$\sum_k e_k(t) = 0 \qquad (4\text{–}3)$$

The method of analysis based on Kirchhoff's potential law is called the loop method since it consists of summing the potential drops around each loop of a circuit and setting each loop equation to zero. The application of this method in solving a circuit problem may be outlined as:

1. Assume currents flowing in a clockwise direction in all loops, being certain that a current flows through every circuit component.
2. Write Eq. 4–3 for each loop. This procedure gives an equation for each assumed current in the circuit.
3. Solve the equations for the desired loop currents and obtain the circuit equation in the desired final form.

These laws are applicable to electric, fluid, and thermal circuits for potentials and flows (currents).

Processes Involving Mechanical Circuits. Newton's law for mechanical systems can be stated for translational motion as: The algebraic sum of the forces acting on a body is equal to the product of the mass and acceleration of the body; or,

$$\sum_k f_k(t) = \frac{ma}{g_c} \qquad (4\text{–}4)$$

where m is the body mass in lb_m, a is the body acceleration in ft/sec², and g_c is a constant in lb_m-ft/lb_f-sec². Both action and reaction forces act at a point, and Newton's law is a statement that the summation of the action forces on a mass is the reaction force ma/g_c. The summation of action forces on a dashpot is the reaction force $D\dot{x}$ and that on a spring is the reaction force Kx. The analysis of translational motion is similar to that for electric circuits and may be outlined thus:

1. Assume displacements and directions in a coordinate system for each mass in the circuit. Take the same positive direction for the displacement, velocity, and acceleration of each mass. The forces are the driving potentials and the displacements are the dependent variables.
2. Draw a "free-body diagram" for each mass in order to isolate the forces on each mass. Then write Newton's law for each mass and eliminate the variables of no interest in the analysis.

PROCESSES INVOLVING ANALOG COMPUTERS. The analog computer is used to implement the analog concept on a computational basis. It is an electronic device which uses d-c operational amplifiers (see Chapter 10) and resistors and capacitors to perform mathematical operations. If the computer equations describe a process system then the analog computer simulates the process system. Corresponding measurements of process variables can be made from the computer network to give answers to process problems which otherwise would have to be measured on the process itself or be computed by other means. Thus, it is clear that process simulation by means of analog computation is a rapid method for obtaining dynamic information on existing or planned process systems when descriptive equations for these systems are available.

An analog computer amplifier consists of coupled electronic devices with a high-impedance grid input and a cathode-follower output. The schematic connections for the single-ended computer amplifier are shown in Fig. 4–1. Blocks Z_i and Z_f represent input and feedback impedances

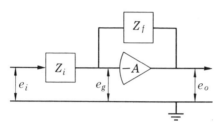

Fig. 4–1. Schematic analog computer circuit.

which may be pure resistance or combined resistance and capacitance circuits, function-generation circuits, or diode circuits. The circular segment represents the high-gain d-c operational amplifier with gain of $-A$, since the amplifier output is negative with respect to the input. The amplifier grid current is usually negligible, and therefore the currents through Z_i and Z_f are identical; hence

$$i = \frac{e_i - e_g}{Z_i} = \frac{e_g - e_o}{Z_f}$$

and

$$e_o = -A e_g$$

Therefore

$$\frac{e_i}{Z_i} + \frac{e_o}{Z_f} = e_g \left(\frac{1}{Z_f} + \frac{1}{Z_i} \right)$$

Normally, the equipment is designed so that $e_o < 100$ volts and $A > 10^5$ to 10^7; then e_g is of the order of millivolts or less and may be neglected for large values of input and feedback impedances.   Under these conditions the amplifier equation becomes

$$e_o = - \frac{Z_f}{Z_i} e_i \qquad (4\text{--}5)$$

This circuit may be used for multiplying by a constant (when Z_f and Z_i are pure resistances) and for integration or differentiation when Z_f/Z_i is complex.   Examples of simulation using the amplifier will be discussed with the process components.

PROCESSES INVOLVING MIXED CIRCUITS.   Many devices for measuring and controlling variables in the process industries are not purely electrical, mechanical, etc., but are a combination of various kinds of elements. In these applications the various elements are coupled by levers and electric or other forces, and the coupled elements must be analyzed as a single unit.   Examples of such units are moving-coil electric meters, electric machinery, electro-fluid devices, mechanical-fluid devices, and so on.

The method of derivation of equations for mixed systems is similar to those already covered.   For any case, the basic laws applicable to each element in the unit are written and the variables of no interest are eliminated.   Analogous electric circuits for the complete unit may be written by using the analogies tabulated in Table 3–7.

4–2. BASIC PROCESS COMPONENTS

Experience has shown that many processes are found after analysis to be made up of a few basic process components which have analogies in electric, mechanical, fluid, and thermal systems.   The transfer functions of the basic process components are listed below:

1. Proportional component, K
2. Integration or differentiation component, $s^{\pm 1}$
3. First-order lead or lag component, $(\tau s + 1)^{\pm 1}$
4. Second-order lead or lag component, $\left(\dfrac{s^2}{\omega_n{}^2} + \dfrac{2\zeta s}{\omega_n} + 1 \right)^{\pm 1}$
5. Transportation lag component, $e^{-\tau s}$
6. Distributed parameter component, $e^{-\sqrt{\tau s}}$
7. Exothermic component, $(\tau s - 1)^{-1}$
8. Inverse response component

Several examples of these components from electric, mechanical, fluid, and thermal systems are discussed below for each of the basic process components.   Some analogous components for each group are listed in tables along with the analog simulation circuit.

Proportional Component (Gain), K. The proportional component gives an output that is proportional to the input to that component and is independent of time; therefore, the input-output relationship is instantaneous. The proportional components, such as ideal transformers, levers, and gear trains, are frequently used to couple two circuits, and in such cases they are coupling components. Several analogous proportional components are tabulated in Table 4–1. Only the potentiometer, the pneumatic nozzle-flapper device, and the analog computer simulation of this group will be discussed. The proportionality constant is normally called the *gain;* it is the ratio of change in output to change in input, $\Delta c/\Delta m$, for the device.

POTENTIOMETER. The potentiometer is an electrical resistance, usually formed in a circular arc or a helix, along which a slider may move. The input voltage is applied across the full resistance and the output voltage is selected by moving the slider along the resistance, usually by rotation of a shaft. Commonly the resistance is linear, but nonlinear potentiometers are available. The schematic diagram of the unloaded potentiometer is shown in Table 4–1. If the slider contact draws no current then the same current flows in resistance r, the resistance between the slider and ground, and R, the total potentiometer resistance. Using Ohm's law, the voltages across the input and the output are

$$e_i = iR \qquad e_o = ir$$

so that

$$e_o = \frac{r}{R} e_i = Ke_i \tag{4–6}$$

where K is the fraction of the total resistance engaged by the slider. The constant $K \leq 1$, so that $e_o \leq e_i$.

Normally the potentiometer is loaded by a load resistance R_L in the output which draws current i_2, as indicated in Fig. 4–2. This circuit may be analyzed, using Kirchhoff's current law, by writing a current balance at the potentiometer slider tap, thus:

$$i_1 - i_2 - i_3 = 0$$

The voltages at the input and at the slider top are e_i and e_o, respectively, and current i_1 may be found as

$$i_1 = \frac{e_i - e_o}{R - r}$$

where $R - r$ is the resistance between the tap and the ungrounded potentiometer terminal. Currents i_2 and i_3 are given as e_o/R_L and e_o/r, respec-

TABLE 4–1
Analogous Proportional Components for Process Systems

Device	Relationship and Remarks
Input $\boxed{K}$ Output	1. Signal flow diagram. General equation: $$K = \text{output/input}$$
e_i R r e_o — $\boxed{K}$ — Symbol	2. Unloaded potentiometer. $$K = r/R \leq 1$$
n_i turns e_i e_o n_o	3. Ideal transformer. For voltage: $$K = n_o/n_i$$ Can have any reasonable value.
f_i a b f_o	4. First-class lever. For force: $$K = a/b$$ Rigid, frictionless lever having no mass.
n_i, teeth θ_o θ_i n_o	5. Gear train; also friction drive. For angle: $$K = -n_i/n_o$$ Neglect backlash and slippage.
p_i A_i p_o A_o	6. Pressure intensifier. For pressure: $$K = A_i/A_o$$ Neglects friction and piston masses.
$\tilde{l}$ p_s Pilot relay $\tilde{p}_o$	7. Pneumatic nozzle-baffle and pilot relay. $$K = \frac{\tilde{p}_o}{\tilde{l}}$$ (See Eq. 4–8b.)
R_f R_i e_i e_o (a) Circuit e_i K e_o (b) Symbol	8. Analog simulation. $$K = -R_f/R_i$$ Can have any reasonable value. The symbol is used to simplify program writing.

tively, so that the loaded-potentiometer equation is

$$\frac{e_i - e_o}{R - r} - \frac{e_o}{R_L} - \frac{e_o}{r} = 0$$

and

$$\frac{e_o}{e_i} = \frac{K}{K\beta(1 - K) + 1} \tag{4-7}$$

where $K = r/R$, and $\beta = R/R_L$. The result is that the behavior of the loaded potentiometer is nonlinear and the output voltage depends on both the load resistance and the potentiometer setting. In computer

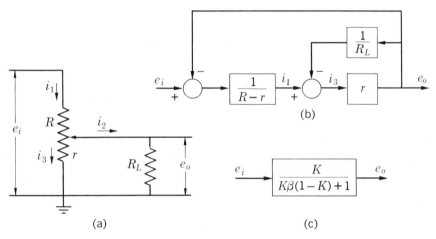

Fig. 4–2. Circuit for a loaded potentiometer. (a) Electric circuit. (b) Signal flow diagram. (c) Block diagram representation.

work this nonlinear characteristic is of no importance since the potentiometers are set under loaded conditions. The signal flow diagram for the loaded potentiometer is shown in Fig. 4–2b. The feedback loops have no particular significance in this device since the resistances have no time-dependent characteristics.

PNEUMATIC NOZZLE-FLAPPER AND PILOT RELAY. The basic device in a pneumatic control system is the nozzle-flapper mechanism that converts a small motion into a proportional pneumatic signal. The simple nozzle-flapper shown in Fig. 4–3a consists of a tube containing a fixed restriction R_1, and terminating in a nozzle-flapper variable restriction R_2 whose resistance depends upon the nozzle-flapper clearance x.

The nozzle tube receives a constant-pressure air supply p_s (usually about 20 psig) and produces an output nozzle pressure p_n that is propor-

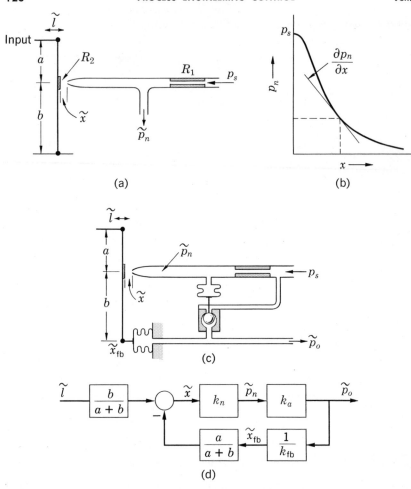

Fig. 4-3. Simple pneumatic nozzle-flapper device. (a) Pneumatic nozzle-flapper. (b) Nonlinear nozzle-flapper relationship. (c) Practical nozzle-baffle device using feedback. (d) Signal flow diagram of nozzle-baffle device.

tional to the clearance x. The area of the fixed restriction is about one-fourth the nozzle area, and the flapper movement may be a few thousandths of an inch. The simple nozzle-flapper device is very sensitive to flapper movement, has an extremely nonlinear response as shown in Fig. 4-3b, and has a low volumetric flow capacity. Most of the limitations of the device can be overcome by using a pilot relay to amplify the nozzle pressure and provide more flow capacity and by using a feedback positioning system to reposition the flapper.

The nonlinear characteristic shown in Fig. 4–3b can be minimized by limiting the nozzle pressure p_n to small changes about an operating point, thus linearizing the nozzle-flapper position relationship for a constant-pressure air supply as

$$\tilde{p}_n = \left(\frac{\partial p_n}{\partial x}\right)\tilde{x} = k_n\tilde{x}$$

where $\tilde{p}_n$ and $\tilde{x}$ are changes in nozzle pressure and clearance from an operating point and k_n is the nozzle-flapper gain constant. The clearance is related to the motion of the input element $\tilde{l}$ by the lever-arm rule as

$$\tilde{x} = \frac{b}{a+b}\tilde{l}$$

and the nozzle-flapper relationship becomes

$$\tilde{p}_n = \frac{k_nb}{a+b}\tilde{l} \tag{4–8a}$$

where $\tilde{l}$ is input position element change, $(a+b)$ is the pivoted lever length, and b is the distance of the nozzle from the lever pivot. Lever-arm motion to the left in the diagram increases $\tilde{x}$ and decreases $\tilde{p}_n$ since k_n is negative. This device is very sensitive to flapper clearance and tends to give an on-off signal response to small changes of input signal.

The practical nozzle-flapper device in Fig. 4–3c uses feedback to overcome the sensitivity of the basic nozzle-flapper and to linearize its characteristics and a pilot relay to amplify the air pressure to furnish useful signal volume. The nozzle pressure acts on a low-capacity bellows in the pilot relay to give a 3–15-psig output pressure that is directly proportional to the nozzle pressure (direct-acting relay). A reverse-acting relay would give a proportional 15–3-psig output. Now the output pressure of the direct-acting device in Fig. 4–3c is applied to the feedback bellows, giving a feedback position effect $\tilde{x}_{fb}$ to the lower end of the flapper lever. The flapper-lever and the flapper-nozzle equations are:

Lever: $\tilde{x}(a+b) = b\tilde{l} + a\tilde{x}_{fb}$ (I)
Nozzle: $\tilde{p}_n = k_n\tilde{x}$ (II)

where the symbols have their usual meaning. The feedback bellows equation is

Feedback bellows: $\tilde{p}_o = k_{fb}\tilde{x}_{fb}$ (III)

where k_{fb} is the bellows spring constant and $\tilde{x}_{fb}$ is the change in feedback bellows position. The pilot relay equation for direct action is

Pilot relay: $\tilde{p}_o = k_a\tilde{p}_n$ (IV)

where k_a is the gain of the pilot relay. The signal flow diagram based upon the above equations is drawn in Fig. 4–3d and it shows how the pilot relay output depends upon the flapper input l. When the variables $\tilde{x}$, $\tilde{p}_n$, and $\tilde{x}_{fb}$ are eliminated from Eqs. I, II, III, and IV either by the signal flow rules in Chapter 1 or by algebra, the equation for the practical nozzle-flapper device with a direct acting pilot relay becomes

$$\tilde{p}_o = \frac{bk_ak_nl}{(a + b)[1 + ak_ak_n/(k_{fb}(a + b))]} \cong \frac{bk_{fb}}{a} l \qquad (4\text{–}8b)$$

provided that $1 \ll ak_ak_n/k_{fb}(a + b)$. Notice that the output pressure change depends upon the input l, the feedback bellows spring constant k_{fb}, and the lever-arm ratio b/a. This lever-arm ratio is normally used to adjust the gain of the device, and the product k_ak_n is always large, so that the approximation is justified. Feedback has made the behavior of this device independent of the nozzle-baffle and pilot relay characteristics. In Chapter 5 it will be seen that this device is the basis of motion-balance pneumatic controllers. This equation contains no time-dependent terms because the capacitance of the bellows and the resistance to flow in the lines have been neglected.

Analog Computer. The high-gain amplifier of the analog computer may be used as a proportional element by making the feedback and input impedances pure resistances, as indicated in Table 4–1. In this application the resistance values can be selected so that the proportionality constant K normally has values between 0.01 and 100, thus:

$$e_o = -\frac{R_f}{R_i} e_i = -Ke_i$$

where R_f and R_i are the amplifier feedback and input resistances, respectively. The computer resistances are precision components and normally have values in the range of 0.1 to 5 megohms. They are not adjustable for obtaining continuously variable values of K at will, but by the use of an input potentiometer (as shown in Fig. 4–4a) fractional values of gain may be obtained. The equation for the circuit shown in Fig. 4–4a is

$$e_o = -aKe_i \qquad (4\text{–}9a)$$

where a is the load-compensated potentiometer setting. Most computing potentiometers are set under loaded conditions in order to obtain highest accuracy in analog computation.

The symbols in Fig. 4–4 are used for writing analog computer programs since they are easy to draw and require less space than the complete wiring program. The potentiometer is represented by a circle with the gain shown within. The computer amplifier with gain K is represented

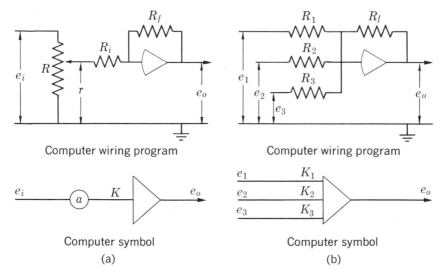

Fig. 4-4. (a) Computer circuit for multiplication by a non-integer constant. (b) Computer circuit for simultaneous multiplication by constant and algebraic summing.

by a triangle with the gain symbolized on the amplifier input as shown.

Simultaneous multiplication by a constant and algebraic summing of several inputs is achieved by the program in Fig. 4-4b, as shown by the circuit equation:

$$e_o = -R_f\left(\frac{e_1}{R_1} + \frac{e_2}{R_2} + \frac{e_3}{R_3}\right) = -(K_1 e_1 + K_2 e_2 + K_3 e_3) \quad (4\text{-}9b)$$

This practice is useful in minimizing the number of amplifiers needed for a given problem.

RESPONSE. The response of a proportional device is instantaneous and proportional to the input signal. In an actual device, linearity may be limited to small-amplitude and low-frequency signals because of the simplifying assumptions made in the analysis and the inherent nonlinear nature of many physical phenomena. The response of the resistance in Table 3-6 applies to all proportional linear devices.

Integration or Differentiation Component, $s^{\pm 1}$. These components may be any of the appropriate process elements treated in Tables 3-4 and 3-5. Usually, there will in practice be a gain value K associated with the component, and frequently the integrator or differentiator is an integral part of a device, not recognizable as a separate component. The transfer function of the integration component has a first-order pole at the origin and that of the differentiator has a zero at the origin.

ANALOG COMPUTER. The analog computer components used for integration and differentiation are shown in Fig. 4–5. Their actions may be found by use of the analog computer equation (Eq. 4–5). For

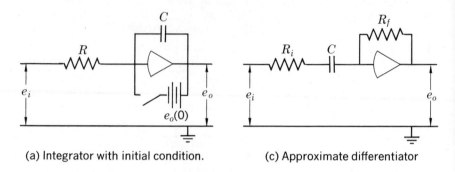

(a) Integrator with initial condition.   (c) Approximate differentiator

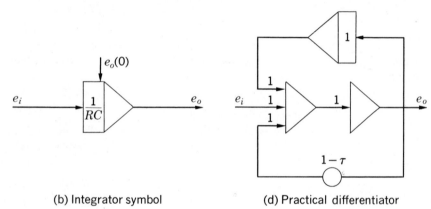

(b) Integrator symbol   (d) Practical differentiator

Fig. 4–5. Analog computer components for integration and differentiation.

the integrator, the feedback and input impedances in transform notation are

$$Z_f = \frac{1}{Cs} \qquad Z_i = R$$

and the integrator equation becomes

$$E_o(s) = -\frac{Z_f}{Z_i} E_i(s) = -\frac{1}{RCs} E_i(s) + e_o(0)$$

or
$$e_o = -\frac{1}{RC} \int_o^t e_i \, dt + e_o(0) \qquad (4\text{–}10a)$$

where $1/RC$ is the gain of the integrator and $e_o(0)$ is the value of its output at zero time.   When values of R and C are given in megohms and microfarads, the units of RC are seconds. The integrating amplifier in a computer must provide for initial-condition output voltage and for over-load signal in case $e_o(t)$ exceeds the linear range of the amplifier. The circuit shown obtains the amplifier initial condition by momentarily switching a battery of voltage $e_o(0)$ across the amplifier at zero time, thus charging the capacitor to the proper-initial value as computation begins. In order to conserve equipment a single amplifier can sum several inputs and integrate at the same time by making input connections like those in Fig. 4–4b with Z_f as an integrating capacitor. The integrator symbol in Fig. 4–5b shows the amplifier gain, $1/RC$, and the initial condition, $e_o(0)$ of the output variable.

An approximate analog differentiator is shown in Fig. 4–5c, where the computing impedances are

$$Z_i = R_i + 1/Cs \qquad Z_f = R_f$$

and its behavior in transform notation is given as

$$E_o(s) = \frac{-R_f Cs}{R_i Cs + 1} E_i(s) \cong -R_f Cs E_i(s) \qquad \text{when } R_i \cong 0 \quad (4\text{–}10b)$$

When R_i is very small, the behavior of the device approaches true different-tiation. Normally, differentiation should be avoided in analog computa-tion because (1) the signals always contain extraneous erratic signals (called *noise*) and differentiation tends to amplify this noise and (2) differentiation of rapidly changing signals can easily overload the ampli-fier. Therefore, never use analog differentiation unless it is absolutely necessary.

The approximate differentiator in Fig. 4–5c requires an external capaci-tor (inconvenient on many computers) and a variable resistor R_i to adjust the desired response characteristics. The circuit in Fig. 4–5d has the same response characteristics as that in Fig. 4–5c with the advantages that the response characteristics can be quickly changed to suit the problem by adjusting the feedback $1 - \tau$, and the derivative has the correct sign. The output of the differentiator in transform notation is obtained as

$$E_o(s) = -\frac{1}{s} E_o(s) + E_i(s) + (1 - \tau)E_o(s)$$

which reduces to the tranfer function

$$\frac{E_o(s)}{E_i(s)} = \frac{s}{\tau s + 1} \qquad (4\text{–}10c)$$

which is the negative of Eq. 4–10b. The derivative response is filtered by the first-order lag whose time constant can be adjusted to remove any high-frequency noise in the signal $sE_i(s)$.

TABLE 4–2
Analogous First-Order Lag Components in Process Systems

Device	Relationship and Remark
$M(s) \rightarrow \boxed{\dfrac{1}{\tau s + 1}} \rightarrow C(s)$ Symbol Pole-zero map	1. Signal flow diagram. General equation: Output/input $= (\tau s + 1)^{-1}$
	2. (a) Electric RC circuit. Filter circuit. $\tau = RC$ Can have any reasonable value. (b) Electric RL circuit. $\tau = L/R$
	3. Mechanical damper. $\tau = D/K$
	4. Liquid level. $\tau = RC$ and unity gain when input is Ri_i.
	5. Thermometer. $\tau = RC$
(a) Circuit (b) Symbol	6. Analog simulation. $\tau = R_f C$ and the gain $= R_f/R_i = K$. $\dfrac{E_o(s)}{E_i(s)} = \dfrac{-K}{\tau s + 1}$
	7. Feedback around an ideal integrator. $\tau = 1/K$ and the gain is unity.

RESPONSE. The response of these ideal devices is discussed in the previous chapter and listed in Table 3–6 for the usual test input signals.

First-Order Lag or Lead Component, $(\tau s + 1)^{\pm 1}$. The first-order lag component is typically a capacitance element receiving or losing material or energy through a resistance. Many examples are given in Table 4–2 together with the parameter value in the transfer function. The first-order lead component is usually a part of a more complex system and does not occur separately except as an ideal component; hence it will not be discussed in this section. The first-order lag component is frequently called a single time-constant element because its time response to various inputs may be characterized by a single constant having the dimension of time. Its transfer function has a first-order pole at $s = -1/\tau$, as shown on the pole-zero map in Table 4–2.

ELECTRIC RC CIRCUIT. The electric RC circuit is used for smoothing rectified voltages and filtering noise from signals. The typical RC circuit

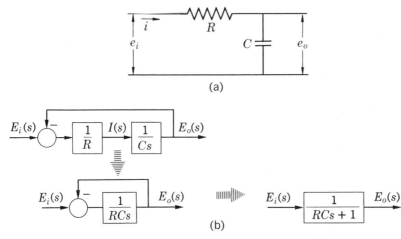

(a)

(b)

Fig. 4–6. First-order lag or time-constant component. (a) The RC electric circuit. (b) Steps in reduction of the signal flow diagram.

in Fig. 4–6a may be analyzed on the basis of Kirchhoff's voltage law. The algebraic sum of voltages around the circuit must be zero, therefore

$$e_i - iR - e_o = 0$$

and the condenser current law requires that

$$i = C \frac{de_o}{dt}$$

Elimination of the current between the two equations gives the circuit equation,

$$RC \frac{de_o}{dt} + e_o = e_i$$

Laplace transformation of the circuit equation with zero initial conditions leads to the RC circuit transfer function as

$$\frac{E_o(s)}{E_i(s)} = \frac{1}{(RCs + 1)} = \frac{1}{\tau s + 1} \qquad (4\text{–}11a)$$

where $\tau = RC$ is the time constant for the circuit. The signal flow diagram in Fig. 4–6b is constructed from the above equations by forming the difference $E_i(s) - E_o(s)$, which equals $I(s)R$. If $I(s)R$ is multiplied by $1/R$ and the resulting current $I(s)$ integrated, the result is the output voltage $E_o(s)$, which signal is fed back as $-E_o(s)$, and the diagram is complete. The diagram is simplified by noting that elements in series may be combined by multiplication and that a unity feedback loop may be replaced by its equivalent $G/(1 + G)$. Observe that a negative feedback loop around an integrator gives a first-order lag component.

There are other ways to characterize this circuit, e.g., by relating the voltage across the resistance to the input voltage. In this case the voltage across the resistance is the difference voltage $e_R = e_i - e_o$; therefore

$$e_R = e_i \left(1 - \frac{e_o}{e_i} \right)$$

so that the transfer function $E_R(s)/E_i(s)$ becomes

$$\frac{E_R(s)}{E_i(s)} = 1 - \frac{E_o(s)}{E_i(s)} = \frac{RCs}{RCs + 1} = \frac{\tau s}{\tau s + 1} \qquad (4\text{–}11b)$$

Notice that this equation is made up of three components: a gain RC, a differentiator s, and a first-order lag component $(RCs + 1)^{-1}$.

The same circuit can be characterized by relating the current in the circuit to the input voltage. In this instance the voltage across the resistance becomes $e_R = iR$, and when this equation is transformed and substituted in Eq. 4–11b the resulting transfer function is

$$\frac{I(s)}{E_i(s)} = \frac{Cs}{RCs + 1} = \frac{1}{R} \frac{\tau s}{\tau s + 1} \qquad (4\text{–}11c)$$

which again consists of three components: a gain C or τ/R, differentiator s, and a first-order lag component. Each of the three equations, 4–11a, b, and c, describes the filter circuit; the process engineer's choice would be determined by his interest in either i, e_o, or e_R as a response to the input voltage e_i.

LIQUID LEVEL. The control of liquid level in open process tanks is a common application. The analysis of the open-tank liquid-level process in Table 4–2 (item 4) is based on the material-balance principle and use of the RC units for liquid level given in Appendix B. The process input signal is flow rate into the tank, i_i, in ft³/min, and the output signal might be the outflow rate from the tank, i_o, in ft³/min. Normally the liquid level or hydraulic pressure in the tank is of more interest as the output signal. The capacity of the tank is a constant value, C, in ft³/ft of tank. The differential material-balance principle requires that

$$d(\text{volume in}) = d(\text{volume out}) + d(\text{accumulation})$$

But the incremental volumes are the products of flow rate and time increment and the incremental accumulation is the product of capacity and liquid level increment, so that the total material-balance equation becomes

$$i_i\, dt = i_o\, dt + C\, dp \qquad (4\text{–}12\text{a})$$

where p is the tank liquid level, in feet of fluid. If the flow condition in the outlet pipe is laminar, the outflow rate i_o will be linearly related to the liquid level p in the tank by Ohm's law for linear fluid flow circuits.

$$p = i_o R$$

Substituting for i_o and converting to Laplace-transform notation, the response equation or the transfer function for the liquid-level process becomes

$$\frac{P(s)}{R I_i(s)} = \frac{1}{(RCs + 1)} = \frac{1}{\tau s + 1} \qquad (4\text{–}12\text{b})$$

as given in the table where $\tau = RC$. The input signal $R i_i$ may be interpreted as a hypothetical liquid level, $p_i = R i_i$, which would be realized in the tank at steady-state conditions at the inflow rate i_i, giving a transfer function of the system as

$$\frac{P(s)}{P_i(s)} = \frac{1}{(\tau s + 1)} \qquad (4\text{–}12\text{c})$$

which is analogous to Eq. 4–11a above for the electric circuit.

FLUID CONCENTRATION. The problem of controlling solute concentration in a process fluid stream is very common in the process industries. Basically, the analysis of a concentration process consists of writing one or more chemical component material balances for the process. Consider the continuous-stirred mixing vessel in Fig. 4–7a, with inlet flow rate of i_i ft³/min of fluid containing component A at a concentration c_{Ai} moles/ft³. The fluid in the vessel is perfectly mixed at all times so that the concentration c_{A1} moles A/ft³ is the same throughout the vessel and is also the concentration of component A in the outlet stream. If volume changes on mixing the fluids of different concentrations are neglected, then the inlet and outlet flow rates must be equal ($i_i = i_1$). A differential material balance for component A in the mixing vessel may be written as follows:

Input rate of A = output rate of A + accumulation rate of A

or, in terms of symbols,

$$i_i c_{Ai} = i_1 c_{A1} + \frac{d(V c_{A1})}{dt} = i_1 c_{A1} + V \frac{dc_{A1}}{dt} \qquad (4\text{-}13a)$$

assuming the vessel volume, V ft³, remains constant. If the flow rates i_i and i_1 are constant and if the initial concentration of A in the vessel

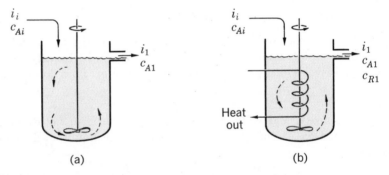

Fig. 4–7. Continuous-stirred process vessels. (a) Mixing vessel. (b) Chemical reactor with internal cooling coil.

is zero ($c_{A1}(0) = 0$), this equation may be transformed to give the transfer function of the mixing vessel as

$$\frac{C_{A1}(s)}{C_{Ai}(s)} = \frac{1}{\tau s + 1} \qquad (4\text{-}13b)$$

where $\tau = V/i_i$, the vessel holding time, or time constant. For n mixing vessels of the same volume, in series, it can be shown that the transfer function for the response of the concentration c_{An} in the nth vessel to the inlet concentration c_{Ai} is given by

$$\frac{C_{An}(s)}{C_{Ai}(s)} = \frac{1}{(\tau s + 1)^n} \qquad (4\text{-}13c)$$

Next consider an irreversible isomerization chemical reaction occurring in the perfectly mixed vessel as shown in Fig. 4–7b under isothermal conditions. The chemical reaction and its rate equation are written as

$$A \xrightarrow{k} R$$

$$\frac{dc_{R1}}{dt} = -\frac{dc_{A1}}{dt} = kVc_{A1} \quad \text{moles/min}$$

where k is the chemical reaction rate constant. The cooling coil removes heat from the reactor, and this effect must be considered in making an energy balance on the reactor. The material-balance equation for component A will include the rate of reaction of A as an output item, then Eq. 4–13a becomes

$$i_i c_{Ai} = i_1 c_{A1} + kV c_{A1} + V\frac{dc_{A1}}{dt}$$

As before, if $i_i = i_1$ and $c_{A1}(0) = 0$, the transformation of this equation gives the transfer function for the stirred reaction vessel as

$$\frac{C_{A1}(s)}{C_{Ai}(s)} = \frac{i_i}{Vs + kV + i_i} = \left(\frac{i_i}{kV + i_i}\right)\frac{1}{\tau s + 1} \quad (4\text{–}13\text{d})$$

where $\tau = V/(kV + i_i)$, the time constant for the reactor. Notice that the chemical reaction term kV decreases the reactor time constant and also the reactor system gain: i.e., other things being equal, the reactor will respond faster to process disturbances than will the mixer and the steady-state outlet concentration will always be less than the inlet concentration.

SIMPLE THERMOMETER. Measuring instruments may be analyzed in the same manner as processes. The simple mercury-in-glass thermometer responds to temperature signals because of thermal energy gained or lost by the mercury. The mercury is enclosed in the thermometer bulb and the capillary stem. Heat is transferred to the mercury through the glass bulb wall and the fluid film surrounding the bulb. The energy balance is stated as

Heat input rate = heat output rate + accumulation rate

Assuming that the resistance to heat transfer is a lumped parameter residing in the fluid film and that the mercury is at uniform temperature T_o, the heat input rate is given

Input rate = $hA(T_i - T_o)$ Btu/sec

where A is the area of thermometer bulb available for heat transfer, h is the transfer cofficient, and T_i is the input temperature signal. The heat output rate is zero if the heat conducted along the stem is negligible. The heat accumulation rate is the product of the effective mass, M, times the mean heat capacity, C, times the rate of change of T_o with time. Substitution of values in the energy-balance equation gives

$$hA(T_i - T_o) = 0 + \frac{d}{dt}(MCT_o) = MC\frac{dT_o}{dt}$$

which can be Laplace-transformed with zero initial conditions and rearranged to give the transfer function listed in Table 4-2,

$$\frac{T_o(s)}{T_i(s)} = \frac{1}{\tau s + 1} \tag{4-14}$$

where $\tau = MC/hA$, the time constant for the thermometer. To exhibit rapid response the thermometer should have a small time constant. Minimum τ requires maximum values of film coefficient and area and minimum mass and heat capacity. It is clear that a practical thermometer will have a finite time constant and therefore cannot be instantaneous in response to an input signal.

ANALOG COMPUTER. The analog computer simulation of a first-order lag is shown in Table 4-2 (item 6). Analysis of the circuit shows that

Feedback impedance: $Z_f = \dfrac{1}{\dfrac{1}{R_f} + Cs} = \dfrac{R_f}{R_f Cs + 1}$

Input impedance: $Z_i = R_i$

Therefore, the transfer function of the computer circuit is

$$\frac{E_o(s)}{E_i(s)} = -\frac{Z_f}{Z_i} = -\frac{R_f}{R_i}\frac{1}{R_f Cs + 1} \tag{4-15}$$

which clearly shows that for computational purposes this circuit is the equivalent of a first-order lag component in any system. For unity gain select $R_f = R_i$.

RESPONSE. The first-order lag component can arise from forward feed through a resistance-capacitance network or from various combinations of feedback around an integrator component, as shown in Table 4-2. It is characterized by a gain value K and a time-constant parameter, τ. The transfer function has a singularity (pole) at $s = -1/\tau$.

The responses of this component with zero initial conditions to a few test inputs are shown graphically in Table 4-3. The response can be written generally as

$$C(s) = \frac{K}{\tau s + 1}M(s) \tag{4-16a}$$

where $C(s)$ and $M(s)$ represent the controlled variable and manipulated variable respectively.

Unit Impulse Response. The Laplace transform of the unit impulse is unity ($M(s) = 1$) so that the impulse response is found by inverting

TABLE 4–3
Responses of First-Order System for $K = 1$

Input $M(s)$	Output $C(s)$	Pole-Zero Chart	Time Response $c(t)$ Equation	Graph
1. Impulse 1	$\dfrac{1}{\tau s + 1}$		$\dfrac{1}{\tau} e^{-t/\tau}$	
2. Step $\dfrac{1}{s}$	$\dfrac{1}{s(\tau s + 1)}$		$1 - e^{-t/\tau}$	
3. Ramp $\dfrac{1}{s^2}$	$\dfrac{1}{s^2(\tau s + 1)}$		$t - \tau + \tau e^{-t/\tau}$	
4. Sinusoidal $\dfrac{\omega}{s^2 + \omega^2}$	$\dfrac{\omega}{(\tau s + 1)(s^2 + \omega^2)}$		$\dfrac{\sin(\omega t - \phi)}{\sqrt{1 + \omega^2\tau^2}}$ (steady-state)	

the expression

$$w(t) = \mathcal{L}^{-1}\left[\frac{K}{\tau s + 1}\right] = \frac{K}{\tau} e^{-t/\tau} \qquad (4\text{-}16b)$$

where $w(t)$ represents the response to the unit impulse functions. The impulse response is a fundamental characteristic of the component and is the residence time distribution* for perfectly mixed vessels such as described by Eq. 4–13b, where $K = 1$.

* The residence time distribution for imperfectly mixed vessels can be measured by impulse testing and compared with the impulse response to characterize the actual mixing obtained. In both cases $K = 1$ and the fraction of material in the leaving stream with age between t and $t + dt$ is $w(t)\, dt$. Due to material-balance requirements, the following relationships hold for unit impulse response of mixing vessels:

Unit impulse: $\displaystyle \int_0^\infty w(t)\, dt = 1$

Average residence time: $\displaystyle \tau = \int_0^\infty t w(t)\, dt$

The impulse response may be used to obtain other time responses by integration as shown under the unit step response. In another approach, the convolution integral (Chapter 2) gives the response of a constant coefficient linear system $c(t)$ to the impulse response $w(t)$ of the system and any arbitrary input $m(t)$ as

$$c(t) = \int_0^t w(\lambda)m(t - \lambda)\, d\lambda \quad \text{or} \quad c(t) = \int_0^t w(t - \lambda)m(\lambda)\, d\lambda$$

where λ is a dummy variable. Of course, the Laplace-transform method will also give the system response for any input by inversion of Eq. 4–16a.

Example 4–1. Use the convolution integral to find the response of a first-order system to a unit square pulse. Find also the response by use of the Laplace transform.

Solution. The unit square pulse may be written in terms of unit step functions as

$$m(t) = u(t) - u(t - 1)$$

(a) Convolution integral method. The impulse response of the system with unit gain ($K = 1$) is given by Eq. 4–16b, and the convolution integral gives the response to $m(t)$ as

$$c(t) = \int_0^t \frac{1}{\tau} e^{-(t-\lambda)/\tau} \left[u(\lambda) - u(\lambda - 1) \right] d\lambda$$

$$= \frac{1}{\tau} \int_0^t e^{-(t-\lambda)/\tau} u(\lambda)\, d\lambda - \frac{1}{\tau} \int_1^t e^{-(t-\lambda)/\tau} u(\lambda - 1)\, d\lambda$$

Integration gives the response by convolution as

$$c(t) = (1 - e^{-t/\tau})u(t) - (1 - e^{-(t-1)/\tau})u(t - 1)$$

(b) Laplace-transform method. The transform of the unit square pulse is

$$M(s) = \frac{1}{s} - \frac{e^{-s}}{s}$$

and the transform of the response becomes

$$C(s) = \frac{1}{s(\tau s + 1)} - \frac{e^{-s}}{s(\tau s + 1)}$$

The inverse of this transform is the same unit pulse response given above by convolution. In a particular case, the choice of method would depend upon the ease of performing the respective mathematical steps.

Unit Step Response. The unit step response is the integral of the impulse response since the step input is the integral of the impulse input. Then the time response $c(t)$ is given by

$$c(t) = \int_0^t w(t)\, dt = \int_0^t \frac{K}{\tau} e^{-t/\tau}\, dt = K(1 - e^{-t/\tau}) \qquad (4\text{–}16c)$$

Of course, the response is also given by inverting the transform expression

$$c(t) = \mathcal{L}^{-1}\left[\frac{K}{s(\tau s + 1)}\right] = K(1 - e^{-t/\tau})$$

Since the step response is often used for testing components, it should be pointed out that the time-constant parameter τ can easily be found by rearranging the equation in the form

$$\ln\left[1 - \frac{c(t)}{K}\right] = -t/\tau$$

Then a plot of the experimental response data expressed as $\ln(1 - c(t)/K)$, the logarithm of the fraction of the change remaining, plotted against the time, will give a straight line with a slope of $-1/\tau$. In addition, it should be noted that (1) when $t = \tau$, the fraction of the change remaining is $e^{-1} = 0.368$ or the fraction of the change accomplished is $1 - e^{-1} = 0.632$ and (2) when $t = 0$, the rate of change of the response, $(dx/dt)_{t=0} = 1/\tau$; in other words, if the rate of response were kept constant at the value when $t = 0$, then the complete response would be accomplished in a time equal to the time constant of the component.

One must remember that the superposition principle applied to linear systems allows shifting the response origin as well as changing the response scale factor without altering the functional behavior of the response. The step response of two cascaded lags is discussed in Example 4–2.

Example 4–2. The NaCl in two continuous-stirred constant-volume brine-filled tanks operated in series is to be washed out of both tanks by a freshwater stream which enters and is uniformly mixed with the contents of the first tank. The overflow from the first tank enters the second tank and is uniformly mixed with the contents before it is discharged to waste. The following transient data were obtained on the concentration of NaCl in the two tanks when the freshwater flow rate to the first was 20 gal/min:

| | lb NaCl/gal solution | |
Time, min	Tank 1	Tank 2
0	0.250	0.250
8	0.180	0.223
16	0.130	0.195
32	0.065	0.145
64	0.015	0.085
128	–	0.017
200	–	0.003

Find the volume of each tank.

Solution. The purging process from the first tank is described by a differential material balance for NaCl such as that given by Eq. 4–13a, with $c_{Ai} = 0$, thus:

$$V\frac{dc_{A1}}{dt} + i_1 c_{A1} = 0$$

Laplace-transformation of this equation with $c_{A1}(0) = 0.25$ gives

$$\tau_1 s C_{A1}(s) - 0.25\tau_1 + C_{A1}(s) = 0$$

and

$$C_{A1}(s) = 0.25\tau_1/(\tau_1 s + 1) \qquad\qquad (a)$$

where $\tau_1 = V/i_1$, the tank time constant.   Inversion of this form yields

$$c_{A1}(t) = 0.25e^{-t/\tau_1} \qquad \text{or} \qquad \ln[c_{A1}(t)/0.25] = -t/\tau_1$$

from which it can be seen that a semilog plot of $c_{A1}(t)/0.25$, the fraction of the concentration change remaining at any time, against the time gives a straight line, as shown in Fig. E4–2.   The slope of the line is $-1/\tau$.   When $\tau_1 = t$, the

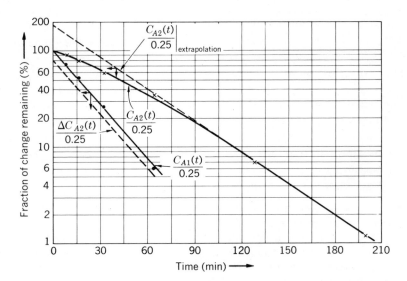

Fig. E4–2. Treatment of experimental data for stirred tanks in series.

fraction of the change remaining is $e^{-1} = 0.368$, and in this case it occurs when $t = 23$ min is read from the chart.   Therefore, the volume of the first tank is $V = i_1\tau_1 = 20(23) = 460$ gal.

The application of Eq. 4–13a to the second tank gives

$$V\frac{dc_{A2}}{dt} + i_1 c_{A2} = i_1 c_{A1}$$

Laplace-transformation of this equation with $c_{A2}(0) = 0.25$ gives

$$\tau_2 s C_{A2}(s) - 0.25\tau_2 + C_{A2}(s) = C_{A1}(s) = 0.25\tau_1/(\tau_1 s + 1)$$

where $\tau_2 = V_2/i_1$ and $C_{A1}(s)$ has been eliminated by Eq. a above.   Simplification and inversion of this equation take the following steps:

$$C_{A2}(s) = \frac{0.25\tau_1}{(\tau_1 s + 1)(\tau_2 s + 1)} + \frac{0.25\tau_2}{(\tau_2 s + 1)}$$

and

$$c_{A2}(t) = 0.25 \left(\frac{\tau_1}{\tau_1 - \tau_2} \right) e^{-t/\tau_1} + \frac{0.25\tau_2}{\tau_2 - \tau_1} e^{-t/\tau_2} \tag{b}$$

Notice that the response of the second tank contains information on both tanks. The time constants τ_1 and τ_2 are easily obtained from the data when $\tau_2 > \tau_1$, for then the term e^{-t/τ_1} will decay faster than e^{-t/τ_2}, and, for large values of time, Eq. b becomes

$$c_{A2}(t) \simeq \frac{0.25\tau_2}{\tau_2 - \tau_1} e^{-t/\tau_2} \quad \text{(by extrapolation)} \tag{c}$$

or

$$\ln [c_{A2}(t)/0.25] = \ln \left[\frac{\tau_2}{\tau_2 - \tau_1} \right] - \frac{t}{\tau_2}$$

Under these conditions, a semilog plot of the fraction of the change remaining $(c_{A2}(t)/0.25)$ against time will approach a straight line, as is the case in Fig. E4–2 for $t > 90$ min. In this region, the tank behaves like a first-order component responding to a fictitious fraction of change remaining at zero time, equal to $\tau_2/(\tau_2 - \tau_1)$. Now, as before, the slope of this line is $-1/\tau_2$, where τ_2 is the largest time constant, and, when $t = \tau$, the tank time constant, the fraction of the change remaining is 0.368 times its initial value. In this case the initial value is 180%, and, when the fraction of the change remaining is $0.368(180) = 66.3\%$, the time is 38 min; therefore, the time constant for the tank is 38 min, and its volume is $38(20) = 760$ gal.

The time constant for the first tank can be found from the data on the second tank, since, by subtracting Eq. b from Eq. c above, an expression that depends only on $e^{-\frac{t}{\tau_1}}$ is found as

$$[c_{A2}(t)]_{\text{extrap.}} - [c_{A2}(t)]_{\text{true}} = \Delta c_{A2}(t) = 0.25 \left(\frac{\tau_1}{\tau_2 - \tau_1} \right) e^{-t/\tau_1}$$

Now a semilog plot of $[\Delta c_{A2}(t)/0.25]$ against time gives a straight line whose slope is $-1/\tau_1$. Or, as before, $\tau_1 = t$ when the fraction of the change remaining is 0.368 times its initial value. This difference line is the lower dashed line on Fig. E4–2. The first tank time constant obtained from this plot is 23 min, in agreement with the first evaluation.

Unit Ramp Response. Since the unit ramp is the integral of the unit step, the unit ramp response is the integral of the unit step response and is given by

$$c(t) = \int_0^t K(1 - e^{-t/\tau}) \, dt = K(t - \tau + \tau e^{-t/\tau}) \tag{4–16d}$$

Of course, the response is also given by inverting the transform expression:

$$c(t) = \mathcal{L}^{-1} \left[\frac{1}{s^2} \frac{K}{(\tau s + 1)} \right] = K(t - \tau + \tau e^{-t/\tau})$$

where $M(s) = 1/s^2$, the transform of the manipulated variable. The response consists of a steady-state part, $K(t - \tau)$, and a transient part, $K\tau e^{-t/\tau}$.

Unit Sine Response. The unit sine response is best obtained by inverting the Laplace transform, where $\mathcal{L}[\sin \omega t] = M(s) = \omega/(s^2 + \omega^2)$, thus:

$$c(t) = \mathcal{L}^{-1}\left[\frac{K}{\tau s + 1}\left(\frac{\omega}{s^2 + \omega^2}\right)\right]$$

$$c(t) = \frac{K\omega\tau}{1 + \omega^2\tau^2} e^{-t/\tau} + \frac{K}{\sqrt{1 + \omega^2\tau^2}} \sin (\omega t - \phi) \qquad (4\text{--}16e)$$

where $\phi = $ arc tan $\omega\tau$. This response includes the transient response term $e^{-t/\tau}$ (which decays to zero as time increases) and the steady-state response term (which lags the input and is attenuated as shown in Table 4–3 but does not decay with time). The steady state is the condition obtained when all transients have decayed to zero.

Frequency Response. The steady-state response of a linear component to a sinusoidal signal is a sinusoidal output of the same frequency but generally decreased in magnitude and retarded in phase, as indicated in Table 4–3 (item 4). The frequency response of a component consists of the steady-state magnitude ratio and the phase difference of the output with respect to the input sinusoid. Since the Laplace transform of a sinusoid has poles at $s = \pm j\omega$, it is found that s may be replaced by $j\omega$ in a system transfer function to give the system frequency response. From the steady-state sine response given above, the frequency response of a first-order lag component is

Magnitude ratio: $\quad \mathrm{AR} = \left[\dfrac{\text{amplitude of } c(t)}{\text{amplitude of } \sin \omega t}\right]_{t \gg \tau} = \dfrac{K}{\sqrt{1 + \omega^2\tau^2}}$

Phase angle: $\qquad \phi = -$ arc tan $\omega\tau$

The frequency response is also obtained from the transfer function as

$$G(j\omega) = G(s)\Big|_{s=j\omega} = \frac{K}{j\omega\tau + 1} = \mathrm{AR}\angle\phi \qquad (4\text{--}16f)$$

with the results given above for AR and ϕ.

The frequency response is simply related to the system impulse response. Let a system at rest having a transfer function $G(s)$ be stimulated by a unit impulse, $M(s) = 1$, to produce the system impulse response $w(t)$. Then the definition of transfer function requires that

$$G(s) = \frac{C(s)}{M(s)} = \frac{\displaystyle\int_0^\infty w(t)e^{-st}\, dt}{1}$$

Now if s is replaced by $j\omega$, the frequency response is given as the integral of the impulse response multiplied by $e^{-j\omega t}$, which for the first-order lag system gives

$$G(j\omega) = \int_0^\infty w(t)e^{-j\omega t}\,dt = \int_0^\infty \frac{K}{\tau}\,e^{-t/\tau}e^{-j\omega t}\,dt = \frac{K}{j\omega\tau + 1}$$

$$= \frac{K}{\sqrt{1 + \omega^2\tau^2}}\angle\phi \qquad \text{where } \phi = -\text{arc tan } \omega\tau \qquad (4\text{-}16g)$$

There are three established ways of graphically presenting the magnitude ratio and phase lag data of frequency response tests: (1) Nyquist polar plot, (2) Bode logarithmic plot, and (3) Nichols semilog plot.

1. The Nyquist polar plot is a plot of magnitude versus phase angle on polar coordinates. The frequency ω is a parameter on the plot. Fig. 4–8a is such a plot for the first-order lag system. Notice that the magnitude ratio varies from unity to zero and the phase lag varies from zero to $-90°$ as the frequency changes from zero to infinity. Values of the parameter $\omega\tau$ are noted on the plot.

2. The Bode plot consists of separate plots of magnitude and phase angle against frequency. The magnitude plot is made on log-log coordinates, since, for a first-order lag system,

$$\log \text{AR} = -\tfrac{1}{2}\log (1 + \omega^2\tau^2)$$

This relationship has simple approximations when $\omega\tau \ll 1$ and when $\omega\tau \gg 1$. When $\omega\tau$ is very small, $(1 + \omega^2\tau^2) \cong 1$, and the log magnitude ratio becomes

$$\log \text{AR} \cong 0 \qquad (\text{when } \omega\tau \to 0)$$

When $\omega\tau$ is very large, $(1 + \omega^2\tau^2) \cong \omega^2\tau^2$, and the log magnitude ratio becomes

$$\log \text{AR} \cong -\log \omega\tau \qquad (\text{when } \omega\tau \gg 1)$$

The maximum error resulting from using these approximations occurs when $\omega\tau = 1$. The correct magnitude for that frequency is

$$\text{AR} = 1/\sqrt{2} = 0.707$$

The Bode magnitude ratio plot for a first-order lag system is shown in Fig. 4–8b along with the straight-line approximations. The phase angle–frequency plot is made on semilog coordinates. For ease in making graphical calculations, these magnitude and phase-angle curves may be formed on plastic templates and used whenever Bode plots of first-order transfer functions are needed. The Bode plots show the frequency variable directly.

3. The Nichols plot is a plot of log magnitude versus phase angle, with the frequency as a parameter on the curve, as shown in Fig. 4–8c for the

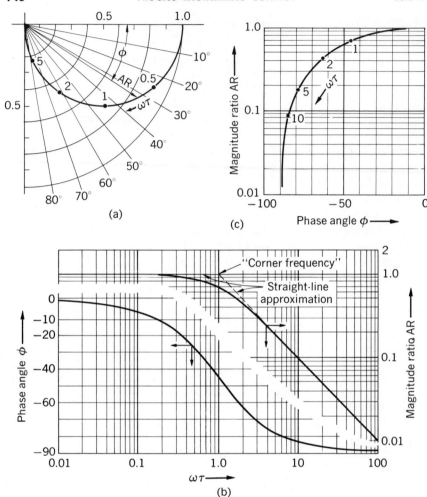

Fig. 4–8. Frequency response plots for a first-order lag transfer function. (a) Nyquist polar plot. (b) Bode plot. (c) Nichols plot.

first-order lag system. The graphical plot selected for presenting frequency response data depends upon the technique used for analysis and design of the control system. This will be discussed in Chapter 8.

Second-Order Lead or Lag Component, $\left(\dfrac{s^2}{\omega_n{}^2} + 2\zeta\,\dfrac{s}{\omega_n} + 1 \right)^{\pm 1}$.

Second-order differential equations are needed to describe any dynamic system having two material or energy storage components. Common examples of such devices are pressure gages, RLC electric circuits, and inertia devices. A second-order system may be characterized by two system parameters related to the three coefficients in the differential equation; thus, the constants in the equation

$$a_2\ddot{x} + a_1\dot{x} + a_0 x = f(t)$$

may be variously arranged, using the following definitions of system parameters:

$$\tau = \sqrt{\frac{a_2}{a_0}} \qquad \zeta = \frac{a_1}{2\sqrt{a_0 a_2}} \qquad \omega_n = \sqrt{a_0/a_2}$$

With these definitions the Laplace transform of the second-order equation with zero initial conditions is usually written either as

$$(\tau^2 s^2 + 2\tau\zeta s + 1)X(s) = \frac{1}{a_0} F(s) \qquad (4\text{--}17a)$$

or

$$\left(\frac{s^2}{\omega_n{}^2} + \frac{2\zeta s}{\omega_n} + 1\right) X(s) = \frac{1}{a_0} F(s) \qquad (4\text{--}17b)$$

The characteristic equation for this system may be factored into a product of two first-order terms, so that

$$(s + p_a)(s + p_b)X(s) = 0$$

where

$$p_a, \ p_b = -\zeta\omega_n \pm \omega_n \sqrt{\zeta^2 - 1} \qquad (4\text{--}17c)$$

Depending upon the magnitude of ζ, the factors p_a and p_b may be: (1) real and equal ($\zeta = 1$), classifying the system as critically damped; (2) real and unequal ($\zeta > 1$), classifying the system as overdamped; or (3) complex ($\zeta < 1$), classifying the system as underdamped. In the first two cases, the factors are real and the response of the system is like that of two first-order lag components in series. In the third case the factors are complex and the response is of an oscillatory nature corresponding in many respects to the response of a properly operating closed-loop control system. The first-order lag components have been discussed; this section will consider only the oscillatory second-order lag component. An isolated system may be oscillatory if inertance and capacitance are simultaneously present and the resistance is not too great. This combination gives rise to the opportunity for repeated interconversion of potential and kinetic energy which occurs in an oscillating system. Resistance in the system dissipates the energy and thereby provides damping.

Since inertance of process fluids is frequently negligible compared to other process effects and thermal processes normally have no inertance effect, it is expected that fluid and thermal processes seldom become

TABLE 4–4

Analogous Second-Order Oscillatory Components for Process Systems

Device	Relationship and Remarks
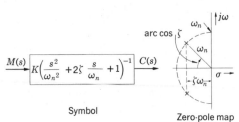 Symbol Zero-pole map	1. Signal flow diagram. K = Component gain ω_n = Component natural frequency ζ = Component damping ratio
	2. RLC electric circuit. $K = 1$ $\omega_n = (LC)^{-1/2}$ $\zeta = \dfrac{R}{2}\sqrt{\dfrac{C}{L}}$
	3. Fluid manometer. $K = 1$ $\omega_n = \sqrt{2g/L}$ $\zeta = 8\mu L\omega_n/D^2 g\rho$
	4. Mechanical damper. $K = 1/K_x$ $\omega_n = \sqrt{K_x/M}$ $\zeta = D/(2\sqrt{MK_x})$
	5. Thermal component does not exist since all thermal systems are overdamped.
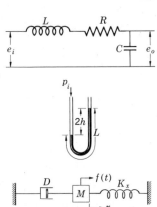	6. Analog computer. $K = -R_3/R_1$ $\omega_n = (R_2R_3C_1C_2)^{-1/2}$ $\zeta = (R_1R_3 + R_1R_2 + R_2R_3)$ $\times\sqrt{\dfrac{C_2}{4R_1^2R_2R_3C_1}}$
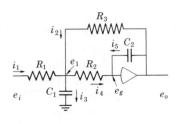	7. Feedback control system. $K = \omega_n^2$ $\omega_n = (\tau\tau_i)^{-1/2}$ $\zeta = \dfrac{1}{2}\sqrt{\tau_i/\tau}$

The symbol box shows:

$$M(s) \quad K\left(\frac{s^2}{\omega_n^2} + 2\zeta\,\frac{s}{\omega_n} + 1\right)^{-1} \quad C(s)$$

oscillatory except through feedback in a closed-loop system. (The fluid manometer and flow in large pipelines are obvious exceptions.)

Table 4-4 lists a few of these lag components in electric, mechanical, fluid, and computer systems. The analysis of the RLC electric circuit is straightforward and presents no difficulties; its analysis is therefore left to the reader as an exercise.

MECHANICAL DAMPER. The analysis of a mechanical system to find the equation of motion in a translational case is illustrated by the forced vibration in one dimension of a damped spring-mass system in Table 4-4 (item 4). Consider the application of a force $f(t)$ to the mass M whose motion in the x-direction is restrained by the viscous damper on the left and the spring on the right. The method of analysis begins with the "free-body diagram" shown in Fig. 4-9a. Let a force $f(t)$ be applied to

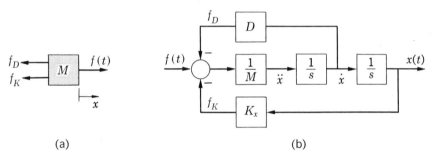

(a)   (b)

Fig. 4-9. Second-order oscillatory mechanical system. (a) Free-body diagram for damped spring-mass system. (b) Signal flow diagram for system.

the mass which tends to move it to the right. Displacement, velocity, and acceleration of the mass are positive in the right-hand direction, i.e., in the direction of the applied force. The algebraic summation of forces includes the following:

Applied force: $f(t)$
Viscous-damping force: $f_D = -D\dot{x}$
Spring force: $f_K = -K_x x$
Inertia force: $f_M = M\ddot{x}$

Newton's law for translational systems applies to this case, so

$$\Sigma(\text{forces}) = M\ddot{x} \qquad (4\text{-}18a)$$

and

$$f(t) - D\dot{x} - K_x x = M\ddot{x}$$

Thus the Laplace-transformed equation of motion for the mass when the initial conditions are zero is

$$(Ms^2 + Ds + K_x)X(s) = F(s)$$

which can be put in standard form as

$$\frac{X(s)}{F(s)} = \frac{1/K_x}{\dfrac{M}{K_x}s^2 + \dfrac{D}{K_x}s + 1} \tag{4–18b}$$

The dissipative element in this system is the viscous damper with constant D. If this term is zero or absent, the component response will be simple harmonic motion when it is forced by a unit step displacement.

The signal flow diagram in Fig. 4–9b is developed directly from Eq. 4–18a for the forces acting in the system. The forces acting on the body, $(f(t) - f_D - f_K)$ are summed and multiplied by $(1/M)$, giving the acceleration of the body, $\ddot{x}$, which can be integrated once to give $\dot{x}$ (useful in forming f_D) and a second time to give x (useful in forming f_K). This diagram gives a visual description of the signals operating in the system, and it can be simplified by the rules of block diagram algebra to give Eq. 4–18b.

FLUID MANOMETER. The fluid manometer is a common laboratory instrument for measuring pressure differences. As normally used it has the characteristics of an oscillatory second-order lag component. The analysis of the manometer parallels that of the damped spring-mass mechanical component. At every instant a force balance must be satisfied, and when the manometer tubing is of uniform diameter this implies a dynamic pressure balance. Refer to the diagram in Table 4–4 and assume that p_i increases from an equilibrium condition producing manometer displacement $2h$, that the flow is laminar, and that the fluid accelerates uniformly. Then the pressures acting in the manometer in English engineering units are:

Driving pressure: $\qquad\qquad p_i = \dfrac{2h_i \rho g}{g_c}$

Flow resistance pressure: $\quad p_R = Ri = RA\,\dfrac{dh}{dt} = \dfrac{128\mu L}{\pi D^4 g_c} \cdot \dfrac{\pi D^2}{4}\,\dfrac{dh}{dt}$

$$\qquad\qquad\qquad\qquad\qquad = \dfrac{32\mu L}{D^2 g_c}\,\dfrac{dh}{dt}$$

Inertance pressure: $\qquad\quad p_L = \dfrac{L\rho}{g_c A}\,\dfrac{di}{dt} = \dfrac{L\rho}{g_c}\,\dfrac{d^2 h}{dt^2}$

Displacement pressure: $\qquad p = \dfrac{2h\rho g}{g_c}$

where D, L are diameter of manometer tubing and length of manometer fluid column; ρ, μ are density and viscosity of the manometer fluid; and R is the laminar resistance of the fluid column given by Poiseuille's law as $128\mu L/\pi D^4 g_c$, in consistent units. The pressure-balance equation is

$$\frac{L\rho}{g_c}\frac{d^2h}{dt^2} + \frac{32\mu L}{D^2 g_c}\frac{dh}{dt} + \frac{2h\rho g}{g_c} = p_i = \frac{2h_i\rho g}{g_c}$$

which can be simplified to give the manometer equation

$$\frac{L}{2g}\frac{d^2h}{dt^2} + \frac{16\mu L}{D^2 g\rho}\frac{dh}{dt} + h = h_i \qquad (4\text{-}19)$$

The equation may be transformed and put in the standard oscillatory form of Table 4-4, where $\omega_n = \sqrt{2g/L}$ and $\zeta = 8\mu L\omega_n/D^2 g\rho$ have the usual significance of the natural frequency and the damping ratio. A variable resistance (such as a needle valve or restriction) may be intentionally placed in the manometer so that the damping ratio ζ may be varied by the operator to suit circumstances.

ANALOG COMPUTER. There are two different methods for building up the analog computer program to simulate a system or solve a differential equation. One method, based on the component equation or transfer function, uses complex input and feedback impedances and Eq. 4-5. In this method Z_f and Z_i are selected so that the problem equation and Eq. 4-5 are identical. This method is economical in the number of amplifiers needed for a given problem but generally the equation parameters are not simply related to the computer input and feedback impedances; thus there is a loss of one-to-one correspondence between equation parameters and computer elements, which is inconvenient from an experimental viewpoint.

The second method, based on the system differential equation, provides simple correspondence of each system parameter with a computer resistor or capacitor. This method yields a computer program in which it is possible to vary each system parameter at will in a systematic manner to show the effect of each parameter on system response. This method is illustrated here by preparing a computer program for the general second-order differential equation with constant coefficients, as shown in Fig. 4-10a. The first step is to solve the equation for the highest derivative, in this case $\ddot{x}$, thus:

$$\ddot{x} = -\frac{a_1}{a_2}\dot{x} - \frac{a_0}{a_2}x + \frac{1}{a_2}f(t)$$

Now, successive integrations of $\ddot{x}(t)$ will yield, in order, the first derivative $-\dot{x}(t)$ and then the dependent variable $+x(t)$. With these functions available the $\ddot{x}(t)$ function can be formed as the equation requires by multiplying $-\dot{x}(t)$ by $+a_1/a_2$, $x(t)$ by $-a_0/a_2$, $f(t)$ by $1/a_2$, and summing these terms to give $\ddot{x}(t)$. The computer program begins by assuming $\ddot{x}(t)$ is available at the start position marked by an arrow. Amplifier 1 integrates $\ddot{x}(t)$ to give $-\dot{x}(t)$ and amplifier 2 integrates $-\dot{x}(t)$ to give the function $x(t)$. Of course, in an actual problem initial conditions must

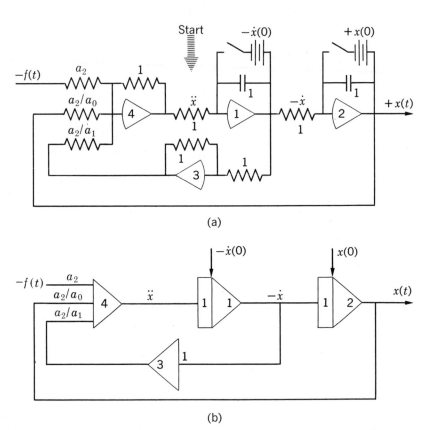

(a)

(b)

Fig. 4–10. Computer diagram for solution of the general linear second-order differential equation with constant coefficients. (a) Circuit program. (b) Symbolic program.

be applied to the integrators as shown. The next step is to form $\ddot{x}(t)$ as required by the given equation. In this case $+\dot{x}(t)$, needed for the summation, is obtained from the sign-changing amplifier 3; and amplifier 4 multiplies $+\dot{x}(t)$ by a_1/a_2, $+x(t)$ by a_0/a_2, and $-f(t)$ by $1/a_2$ and sums the terms as required by the equation to give $\ddot{x}(t)$ (note the sign change). The final connection is made from amplifier 4 to amplifier 1, and the computer program is complete. A function generator may be needed. to provide $-f(t)$ for a particular problem. The solution to the equation is obtained by switching, by means of auxiliary equipment, initial condition voltages to integrating amplifiers 1 and 2 and providing $-f(t)$ from a voltage source. The answer $x(t)$ appears as a voltage at the point shown; it may be displayed on an oscilloscope or recorded on an oscillograph or other recorder. It is clear that this method produces a program in which the circuit parameters have a direct correspondence to the coefficients in the differential equation. The same program, using computer symbols, is given in Fig. 4–10b.

Example 4–3. A single amplifier can be used to simulate a second-order oscillatory component, using the computer diagram given in Table 4–4 (item 6). Analyze the circuit and determine relationships for ζ, ω_n, and K in terms of the computer components.

Solution. The currents in each branch of the circuit are labeled for direction and circuit branch. The voltage at the first node is e_1, that at the amplifier input is $e_g \cong 0$. The current equations are written as follows, assuming i_g and e_g are negligible. The current summation at the amplifier input gives

$$i_4 + i_5 = 0$$

and, therefore, in terms of the transformed variables, it becomes

$$\frac{E_1(s)}{R_2} + C_2 s E_o(s) = 0 \qquad \text{or} \qquad E_1(s) = -R_2 C_2 s E_o(s)$$

The current summation at the input node gives

$$i_1 + i_2 = i_3 + i_4$$

and, therefore,

$$\frac{E_i(s) - E_1(s)}{R_1} + \frac{E_o(s) - E_1(s)}{R_3} = C_1 s E_1(s) + \frac{E_1(s)}{R_2}$$

Elimination of $E_1(s)$ from this equation gives the computer equation as

$$\frac{E_o(s)}{E_i(s)} = -\frac{R_3/R_1}{R_3 C_1 R_2 C_2 s^2 + (R_3 C_2 + R_2 C_2 + R_3 R_2 C_2/R_1)s + 1}$$

which fits the standard form of the second-order equation when

$$\omega_n = (R_3 C_1 R_2 C_2)^{-1/2}, \quad 2\zeta = \sqrt{\frac{R_3 C_2}{R_2 C_1}} + \sqrt{\frac{R_2 C_2}{R_3 C_1}} + \sqrt{\frac{R_3 R_2 C_2}{R_1{}^2 C_1}}$$

In these expressions, if the resistors are in megohms and the capacitors are in microfarads, the RC products have the units of seconds. This programming approach provides economy in the use of amplifiers but sacrifices direct comparison with a physical system, since the system parameters are hidden in the circuit constants. It also requires increased labor in setting up the computer circuit.

RESPONSE. The second-order lag component is a two-parameter device which can arise from forward feed through a resistance-inertia-capacity network (such as a manometer) or from various combinations of feedback in a closed-loop system. The response of this component with zero initial conditions to the various test inputs is found by inverting either of the equivalent equations

$$C(s) = \frac{1}{\tau^2 s^2 + 2\tau \zeta s + 1} M(s) \qquad \text{or} \qquad C(s) = \frac{\omega_n{}^2}{s^2 + 2\zeta \omega_n s + \omega_n{}^2} M(s)$$

$$(4\text{--}20a)$$

where ζ is the damping ratio, ω_n is the natural frequency of the system and τ is the system-characteristic time ($\tau \omega_n = 1$).

Unit Impulse Response: $M(s) = 1$. The unit impulse transform is unity; the impulse response is obtained by inverting the expression

$$w(t) = \mathcal{L}^{-1} \left[\frac{\omega_n{}^2}{s^2 + 2\zeta \omega_n s + \omega_n{}^2} \right] \qquad (4\text{--}20b)$$

In terms of the parameters ω_n and ζ, the results are given as follows by use of a table of Laplace transforms: For $0 < \zeta < 1$,

$$w(t) = \frac{\omega_n}{\sqrt{1 - \zeta^2}} e^{-\zeta \omega_n t} \sin \left(\omega_n \sqrt{1 - \zeta^2}\, t \right) \qquad (4\text{--}20c)$$

For $\zeta = 1$, by using L'Hôpital's rule, the equation reduces to the form

$$w(t) = \omega_n{}^2 t e^{-\omega_n t} \qquad (4\text{--}20d)$$

For $\zeta > 1$, the response is non-oscillatory and given as

$$w(t) = \frac{\omega_n}{\sqrt{\zeta^2 - 1}} e^{-\zeta \omega_n t} \sinh \left(\omega_n \sqrt{\zeta^2 - 1}\, t \right) \qquad (4\text{--}20e)$$

Graphical plots of these equations on dimensionless coordinates are shown in Fig. 4–11.

Unit Step Response: $M(s) = 1/s$. The unit step response is the integral of the impulse response and could be obtained by the integration of Eqs. 4–20c, d, or e. However, in this case it is probably easier to use a table of Laplace transforms to obtain the response equations by inverting

$$c(t) = \mathcal{L}^{-1} \left[\frac{\omega_n{}^2}{s(s^2 + 2\zeta \omega_n s + \omega_n{}^2)} \right]$$

The response equations are found from transform tables: For $0 < \zeta < 1$,

$$c(t) = 1 + \frac{1}{\sqrt{1 - \zeta^2}} e^{-\zeta \omega_n t} \sin \left(\omega_d t - \phi \right) \qquad (4\text{--}21a)$$

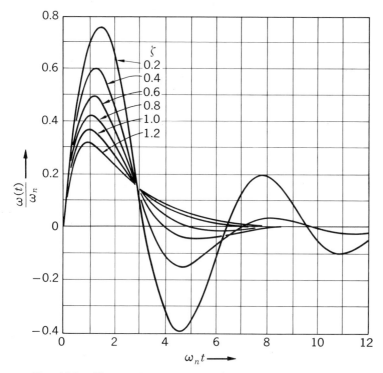

Fig. 4-11. The impulse response of a second-order system.

where $\omega_d = \omega_n \sqrt{1 - \zeta^2}$, the damped frequency of oscillation, and $\phi = \tan^{-1} \sqrt{1 - \zeta^2}/-\zeta = -\cos^{-1} \zeta$. For $\zeta = 1$, by using L'Hôpital's rule, the response equation is

$$c(t) = 1 - (1 + \omega_n t)e^{-\omega_n t} \qquad (4\text{-}21\text{b})$$

For $\zeta > 1$, the response is non-oscillatory and given as

$$c(t) = 1 + \frac{1}{\sqrt{\zeta^2 - 1}} e^{-\zeta \omega_n t} \sinh (\omega_d t - \phi) \qquad (4\text{-}21\text{c})$$

where $\omega_d = \omega_n \sqrt{\zeta^2 - 1}$ and $\phi = -\cosh^{-1} \zeta$.

These equations are shown in Fig. 4–12, where the output is plotted as a function of the normalized time $\omega_n t$ for various values of ζ, the damping ratio. Observe that the control system becomes more oscillatory and that the amount of overshoot increases as ζ decreases toward zero and that there is no overshoot in response for $\zeta > 1$.

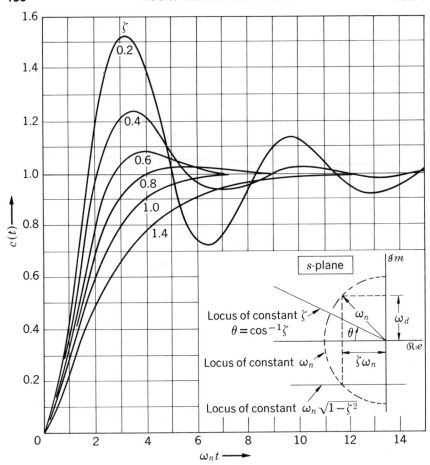

Fig. 4–12. The unit step response of the second-order system. The inset sketch shows the system parameters as they are related to the location of the poles of the transfer function.

Example 4–4.   A laboratory manometer has a natural frequency of 2 rad/sec and a damping ratio of 0.4.   A step increase of pressure of 0.3 ft of fluid is applied to the manometer.   Find the response of the manometer.

Solution.   The unit step response of a second-order oscillatory device is given by Eq. 4–21a.   The parameters of the manometer are

$$\omega_n = 2 \qquad\qquad \zeta\omega_n = 0.8$$
$$\zeta = 0.4 \qquad\qquad \omega_d = \omega_n \sqrt{1 - \zeta^2} = 1.83$$
$$\sqrt{1 - \zeta^2} = 0.916 \qquad\qquad \phi = -\cos^{-1} \zeta = 1.16 \text{ rad}$$

Therefore, the response of the manometer is found from Eq. 4–21a to be

$$c(t) = 0.3[1 + 1.09e^{-0.8t} \sin (1.83t - 1.16)]$$

Properties of Step Response Related to ζ. The relationship of ζ to the step response of a second-order component has considerable use in specifying component performance and in experimentally measuring ~~component parameters~~. For the case of $\zeta < 1$, the maxima and minima nd by differentiating Eq. 4–21a and simplify-

:os $(\omega_d t - \phi) - \zeta\omega_n \sin (\omega_d t - \phi)$

$= \omega_d/\zeta\omega_n = \sqrt{1 - \zeta^2}/\zeta = \tan \phi.$ Values of on are

$$\omega_d t = n\pi \qquad \text{for} \qquad n = 0, 1, 2, 3, \ldots$$

s in the response curve occur when the time is

$$= \frac{n\pi}{\omega_d} = \frac{n\pi}{\omega_n \sqrt{1 - \zeta^2}} \tag{4–21d}$$

m or maximum) is

$$1 - (-1)^n e^{-\zeta n\pi/\sqrt{1-\zeta^2}} \tag{4–21e}$$

ot, occurs for $n = 1$ at time $\pi/(\omega_n \sqrt{1 - \zeta^2})$ l as percentage:

$$= 100[c(t)_{n=1} - 1] = 100 e^{-\zeta\pi/\sqrt{1-\zeta^2}} \tag{4–21f}$$

he damping ratio. The ratio of consecutive peaks is useful in finding the damping ratio from a step response curve and is found as the ratio of the $(n + 2)$th peak to the nth peak where $n = 1, 3, 5$, etc. The ratio, called *peak attenuation*, is

$$\text{Peak attenuation:} \quad \text{PA} = \frac{e^{-\zeta(n+2)\pi/\sqrt{1-\zeta^2}}}{e^{-\zeta n\pi/\sqrt{1-\zeta^2}}} = e^{-2\zeta\pi/\sqrt{1-\zeta^2}} = (\text{overshoot})^2 \tag{4–21g}$$

and is independent of n, the peak designation, i.e., the ratio is the same for all consecutive peaks.

The time to first zero error t_z is the time when the response first equals the final value of response; for the present case it is the least time when $c(t) = 1$. From Eq. 4–21a, it is seen that $c(t) = 1$ when

$$\sin (\omega_d t + \cos^{-1} \zeta) = 0$$

which requires that $\omega_d t + \cos^{-1} \zeta = 0, \pi, 2\pi, \ldots$. The time to first zero error is found as

$$\omega_d t_z = \pi - \cos^{-1} \zeta = \omega_n \sqrt{1 - \zeta^2}\, t_z$$

or

$$\omega_n t_z = \frac{1}{\sqrt{1 - \zeta^2}} (\pi - \cos^{-1} \zeta) \qquad (4\text{--}21\text{h})$$

which depends only upon ζ. Fig. 4–13 shows a plot of overshoot (as fraction), peak attenuation, and time to first zero error as a function of

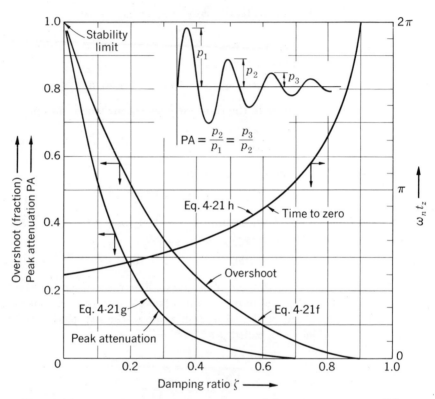

Fig. 4–13. The effect of damping ratio on (a) peak attenuation, (b) overshoot, and (c) time to zero error in unit step response of a second-order system.

the damping ratio. It is clear that there is no "best zeta" for a second-order device and that the choice of zeta is a compromise between the allowable overshoot (or required peak attenuation) and the specified time to first zero error. Frequently an "optimum zeta" is specified in the range of 0.3 to 0.5. One must remember that all three coefficients in the second-order equation may be adjusted for optimum operation and that ζ is involved in each case. For example, $\omega_n t_z$ is related to zeta as shown in Fig. 4–13: for a given zeta, the larger ω_n is, the faster will be the response, because the time to first zero error will be smaller. In Chapter 2 it is emphasized that the location of the poles and zeros (the singularities) of a complex function and its gain multiplier determine the function, and also that the poles and zeros may be plotted on the complex plane and the residues at each pole (which are the coefficients in the Laplace-transform partial fraction expansion) may be found by a graphical procedure. The object here is to show how the values of the parameters ζ and ω_n (also properties R, L, C or D, M, K) fix the locus of the poles of the oscillatory second-order component.

The poles of the second-order component are the roots of the characteristic equation given by Eq. 4–17c as a complex conjugate pair,

$$p_1, \; p_2 \; = \; -\zeta\omega_n \pm j\omega_n \sqrt{1 - \zeta^2} \; = \; |\omega_n| \angle \pm \theta \qquad (4\text{–}17c)$$

where ω_n is the absolute value of the pole and θ is its angle, given as arc tan $\sqrt{1 - \zeta^2}/\zeta$ or arc cos ζ. The inset sketch in Fig. 4–12 shows the s-plane loci of poles having certain constant parameters, e.g.:

1. Poles having the same value of ω_n lie on a circle of radius ω_n with center at the origin.
2. Poles having the same value of ζ lie on a straight line making an angle $\pm \theta$ with the real axis.
3. Poles having the same value of damped frequency $\omega_n \sqrt{1 - \zeta^2}$ lie on lines parallel to the real axis.
4. Poles having the same values of $\zeta\omega_n$ lie on a vertical line parallel to the imaginary axis.

The effect of the component properties on the location of poles in the complex plane can be shown in a similar manner. For example, consider the spring-mass-damper component with transfer function given by

$$\frac{X(s)}{F(s)} = \frac{1}{Ms^2 + Ds + K_x} = \frac{1}{D(s)} \qquad (4\text{–}18b)$$

where $D(s)$ represents the denominator of the transfer function. To show the locus of the poles (or the root locus of the denominator, as it will be called later—see Fig. 7–1), when the ratio D/M is held constant and K_x varied, it is convenient to factor the denominator as follows:

$$p_1, \; p_2 = \sigma \pm j\omega = -\frac{D}{2M} \pm j\frac{1}{2M} \sqrt{4K_x M - D^2} \qquad (4\text{–}22)$$

from which it can be seen that the root locus in the complex plane has a constant real component, $D/2M$, that is independent of the value of K_x. Therefore, as shown in Fig. 4–14, this branch of the locus is a straight line parallel to the imaginary axis with a real part equal to $D/2M$, and labeled branch 1.

When K_x/M is held constant and D is allowed to vary, the denominator factors are the same as before, having real part σ and imaginary part ω as

$$p_1,\ p_2 = \sigma \pm j\omega = \frac{-D}{2M} \pm j\frac{1}{2M}\sqrt{4K_xM - D^2} \qquad (4\text{--}23)$$

Observe that

$$\sigma^2 + \omega^2 = \frac{D^2}{4M^2} + \frac{K_x}{M} - \frac{D^2}{4M^2} = \frac{K_x}{M} = r_1^2 \qquad \text{(constant)}$$

which is the equation of a circle on the s-plane with radius $\sqrt{K_x/M}$ and center at the origin. This locus branch is labeled 2 in Fig. 4–14 and

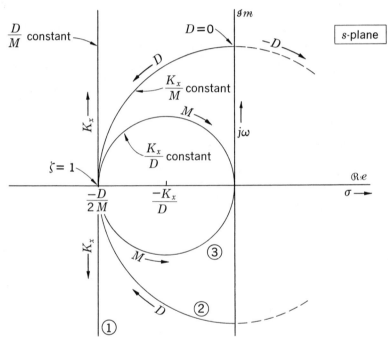

Fig. 4–14. Root-locus plot for oscillatory mechanical damper, showing the effect of varying the properties K, D, and M.

extends into the right half-plane (region of poles with positive real parts) only for negative damping.

When D/K_x is held constant and M is allowed to vary, the denominator factors are the same as before and may be arranged as

$$\left(\sigma + \frac{K_x}{D}\right)^2 + \omega^2 = \left(-\frac{D}{2M} + \frac{K_x}{D}\right)^2 + \frac{K_x}{M} - \frac{D^2}{4M^2}$$

$$= \left(\frac{K_x}{D}\right)^2 = r_2^2 \text{ (constant)}$$

which is the equation of a circle on the s-plane with radius K_x/D, and center at $(-K_x/D, 0)$. This defines branch *3* in Fig. 4-14, and it is drawn so that $K_x/D = D/4M$ for critical damping.

The root loci sketched in Fig. 4-14 show the effect of varying one component property while holding the ratio of the other properties constant, thus:

1. When D/M is constant and K_x increases, the poles move along a line parallel to the imaginary axis.
2. When K_x/M is constant and D increases, the poles move along a circle with center at the origin and the poles have constant ω_n.
3. When K_x/D is constant and M increases, the poles move along a circle with center at $-K_x/D$ and radius of K_x/D.

In summary, one can say that the pole location in the s-plane affects the time response in the following ways. Real poles of stable components give rise to decaying exponentials, e^{pt}, so that the farther the pole is to the left (the more negative p becomes) the faster the exponential dies away. Complex poles give rise to oscillatory response of the form

$$e^{-\zeta \omega_n t} \sin (\omega_n \sqrt{1 - \zeta^2}\, t - \phi)$$

so that the smaller $\zeta \omega_n$ becomes, the closer the pole is to the imaginary axis and the longer it takes the damped sinusoidal component to decay. The larger $\omega_n \sqrt{1 - \zeta^2}$ becomes, the farther the complex poles are from the real axis and the higher is the oscillation frequency of this component. If a pole is far removed from the other poles and zeros of a component, that pole will have little effect on the total response. Also, as will be seen in a later chapter, if a zero is near a pole, the coefficient of the transient response term due to this pole will be small and the pole will have little effect on the response.

Transportation Lag Component, $e^{-\tau s}$. In many physical systems, the transfer of matter, position, or energy occurs so rapidly that it may be assumed to occur instantaneously. However, in process engineering there are many situations where the process signal moves through some part of the system with a finite velocity giving rise to a time delay known as a distance/velocity lag or *dead time*. Electric signals move through processes with a speed approaching the velocity of light, so that lags due to transmission of electric signals are negligible. This is not the case with signals such as temperature and concentration changes, which are carried through the system by a low-velocity fluid. The situation is shown in Fig. 4-15 where a temperature or concentration change $f(t)$ may occur instantaneously in the vessel, owing to addition of heat or material to the vessel. (Vessel contents are uniformly mixed at all times.) However, the signal change is not felt in the fluid downstream

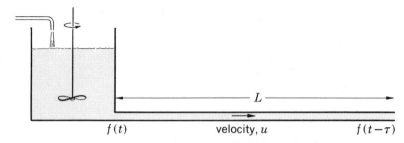

$f(t)$ velocity, u $f(t-\tau)$

Fig. 4–15. Transportation lag due to signal being carried by a low-velocity fluid. The signal at a point L feet from the vessel is delayed a time $\tau = L/u$ sec after the appearance of the signal at the pipe inlet.

at distance L until the downstream fluid has been displaced by fresh fluid of property $f(t)$ moving a distance L which requires time $\tau = L/u$; hence the classification of this behavior as distance/velocity lag, dead time, or transportation lag.   The response of a pipeline of length L under plug flow conditions to an input signal $f(t)$ is $f(t - \tau)$, which is identical in all respects to the input except that it is delayed τ time units; in other words the response is delayed τ sec in time with respect to the input. The response function is written as

$$f(t - \tau) = 0 \qquad \text{for } t < \tau$$
$$= f(t) \qquad \text{for } t > \tau$$

and the transfer function for the transportation delay or dead time is

$$G(s) = \frac{\mathcal{L}[f(t - \tau)]}{F(s)} = e^{-\tau s} \qquad (4\text{--}24)$$

an exponential function having no poles or zeros in the finite s-plane.

The exact simulation of the dead-time transfer function by the analog computer is a difficult task, but frequently an approximate simulation is adequate for many problems.   In principle, an exact simulation could be obtained by recording $f(t)$ and reading it back into the computer delayed by time τ.   Equipment to do this satisfactorily is not generally available. A practical simulation may be based on an approximation of the exponential function by a ratio of polynomials.   The Padé approximation of $e^{-\tau s}$ is frequently used, and a few of these are given in Table 4–5.

TABLE 4–5
Padé Approximations of $e^{-\tau s}$

First order: $(2 - \tau s)/(2 + \tau s)$
Second order: $(12 - 6\tau s + \tau^2 s^2)/(12 + 6\tau s + \tau^2 s^2)$
Third order: $(120 - 60\tau s + 12\tau^2 s^2 - \tau^3 s^3)/(120 + 60\tau s + 12\tau^2 s^2 + \tau^3 s^3)$

The programming of these transfer functions for the analog computer is illustrated by use of the second-order approximation. Let

$$\frac{\mathcal{L}[f(t-\tau)]}{\mathcal{L}[f(t)]} = \frac{12 - 6\tau s + \tau^2 s^2}{12 + 6\tau s + \tau^2 s^2} = \frac{\dfrac{12}{s^2} - \dfrac{6\tau}{s} + \tau^2}{\dfrac{12}{s^2} + \dfrac{6\tau}{s} + \tau^2} \qquad (4\text{-}25)$$

This relationship may be programmed by writing the differential equation for the transfer function, solving for the highest derivative, and forming the computer program in the conventional manner. It is observed that $f(t)$ will need to be differentiated twice, and when the program is run on the machine trouble will develop from noise amplification. A better approach in this case is to divide the numerator and denominator of the transfer function by s^2 as indicated; then, on solving for the highest derivative in the differential equation, the equation to be programmed becomes

$$f(t-\tau) = f(t) - \frac{6}{\tau}\int [f(t) + f(t-\tau)]\,dt + \frac{12}{\tau^2}\iint [f(t) - f(t-\tau)]\,dt\,dt$$

The analog computer program for this equation is given in Fig. 4–16 along with the unit step response for the program with $\tau = 2$ sec. This second-order Padé approximation gives good results for frequencies less than about 3 rad/sec.

Sometimes, in the empirical analysis of process components, the transportation lag component is combined with a first- or second-order lag component to give an empirical representation of the dynamic characteristics of a plant device. For example, consider the behavior of the second purged tank in Example 4–2 in response to a unit step input change in $C_{Ai}(s)$. The transfer function for this tank in terms of the ratio of the tank output to system input is found to be

$$\frac{C_{A2}(s)}{C_{Ai}(s)} = \frac{1}{(\tau_1 s + 1)(\tau_2 s + 1)} \cong \frac{e^{-\tau s}}{\tau_2 s + 1} \qquad \text{(approx)}$$

which can be approximated by a transportation lag τ and a first-order lag $1/(\tau_2 s + 1)$ as indicated. From inspection of the straight-line approximation of $c_{A2}(t)/0.25$ in Fig. E4–2, it is seen that a dead time of $\tau = 23$ min and $\tau_2 = 40$ min should give approximate agreement with the actual response for large time.

RESPONSE. In open-loop signal paths the effect of the dead-time factor is to delay the signal passage through the device, e.g., the response of a series arrangement of a dead-time factor and a first-order time lag to a

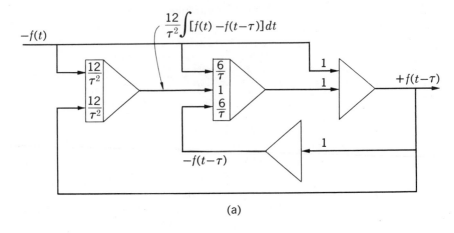

(a)

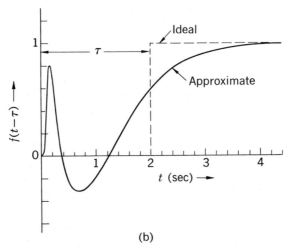

(b)

Fig. 4-16. (a) Analog computer program for transportation lag using a second-order Padé approximation. (b) The step response of a 2-second delay.

unit step input is given as

$$c(t) = \mathcal{L}^{-1}\left[\frac{e^{-\tau s}}{s(\tau_1 s + 1)}\right] = (1 - e^{-(t-\tau)/\tau_1})u(t - \tau)$$

where $u(t - \tau)$, the delayed unit step, is properly included to ensure that the response is zero for $t < \tau$.

In general, the dead-time factor may appear in both the numerator and denominator of the transfer function and in such cases the analytical problem of inverting the transform to obtain the time response presents a formidable mathematical problem.

Distributed-Parameter Component, $e^{-\sqrt{\tau s}}$. So far, in the analysis of systems, it has been assumed that the system properties consist of ideal elements located at specific points leading to the lumped-parameter simplification. It is recognized that this is an idealization of the actual process and may not be justified in many cases. If a more accurate analysis of the system is necessary, then the parameters become functions of distance (distributed parameter), such as capacity per foot, resistance per foot, and inertance per foot.

The conduction of heat through a thick body, such as a furnace wall, or the diffusion of a chemical substance through a stagnant film or a porous body are examples of systems having distributed parameters of resistance and capacity. Fourier's equation for one-dimensional heat conduction in a uniform body is

$$\frac{\partial T}{\partial t} = \alpha \frac{\partial^2 T}{\partial x^2} \tag{4–26a}$$

where α is the thermal diffusivity of the material, given as $k/C_p\rho$. (k is the thermal conductivity and $C_p\rho$ is the heat capacity per unit volume.) Partial derivatives are needed because the temperature T at a point in the material depends upon two independent variables, x and t. This equation gives the response T at a point and a time but it does not show the input signal which enters the problem as a boundary condition.

Consider the application of Fourier's equation to a bar of unit cross-sectional area and length L which is initially at a uniform temperature of 0°C. Assume the bar surfaces are impenetrable to heat except at the ends in order to satisfy one-dimensional heat-conduction requirements. Then at $t = 0$, let a heat source $T(L,t)$ be applied to the bar at the end, $x = L$, keeping the other end of the bar, $x = 0$, at 0°C; thus the boundary conditions are:

$$T(x,0) = 0 \qquad\qquad\qquad\qquad\qquad 0 \leqq x \leqq L$$
$$T(0,t) = 0 \qquad T(L,t) = T_1(t) = \text{input} \qquad t \geqq 0$$

Fourier's equation may be Laplace-transformed with respect to time with the following transforms:

$$\mathcal{L}_t[T(x,t)] = T(x,s)$$
$$\mathcal{L}_t\left[\frac{\partial T(x,t)}{\partial t}\right] = sT(x,s) - T(x,0)$$
$$\mathcal{L}_t\left[\frac{\partial^2 T(x,t)}{\partial x^2}\right] = \frac{\partial^2 T(x,s)}{\partial x^2} = \frac{d^2 T(x,s)}{dx^2}$$

The last transform is obtained by noting that the transformation is with respect to time, and that s is therefore a parameter and the partial derivative may be regarded as a total derivative in respect to x. Since $T(x,0) = 0$, the transformed Fourier equation becomes

$$\frac{d^2 T(x,s)}{dx^2} - \frac{s}{\alpha} T(x,s) = 0 \qquad (4\text{--}26b)$$

This is an ordinary linear differential equation, with boundary conditions

$$T(0,s) = 0$$
$$T(L,s) = T_1(s)$$

which can be solved in turn by Laplace transformation. Transforming in terms of p in respect to x, we have

$$\mathcal{L}_x[T(x,s)] = T(p,s)$$
$$\mathcal{L}_x\left[\frac{d^2 T(x,s)}{dx^2}\right] = p^2 T(p,s) - p T(0,s) - \dot{T}(0,s)$$

and the transformed equation becomes

$$T(p,s) = \frac{p T(0,s)}{p^2 - \tau s} + \frac{\dot{T}(0,s)}{p^2 - \tau s}$$

when $\tau = 1/\alpha$. Applying the boundary condition above and inverting this transform in respect to p gives

$$T(x,s) = \dot{T}(0,s) \frac{1}{\sqrt{\tau s}} \sinh \sqrt{\tau s}\, x \qquad (4\text{--}26c)$$

The constant, $\dot{T}(0,s)$, may now be evaluated by applying the remaining boundary condition:

$$T_1(s) = \dot{T}(0,s) \frac{1}{\sqrt{\tau s}} \sinh \sqrt{\tau s}\, L$$
$$\dot{T}(0,s) = T_1(s) \frac{\sqrt{\tau s}}{\sinh \sqrt{\tau s}\, L}$$

Substitution of this in Eq. 4–26c gives the final form of the Laplace transform of the response in terms of the transform of the input as

$$\frac{T(x,s)}{T_1(s)} = \frac{\sinh \sqrt{\tau s}\, x}{\sinh \sqrt{\tau s}\, L} \qquad (4\text{--}26d)$$

The hyperbolic functions such as $\sinh \sqrt{\tau s}$ and $\cosh \sqrt{\tau s}$ are typical of components having distributed physical properties. These functions may be written in terms of $e^{\pm\sqrt{\tau s}}$; hence this listing for the transfer function of such a component.

RESPONSE. Finding the response of a distributed component involves the mathematical problem of inverting the transform after the input is specified. Let the stimulus to the end of the bar considered above be a step function; then

$$T_1(t) = T_1 u(t) \qquad T_1(s) = \frac{T_1}{s}$$

The temperature response of the bar at any position x is given by the inversion of

$$T(x,s) = \frac{T_1}{s} \frac{\sinh x \sqrt{\tau s}}{\sinh L \sqrt{\tau s}} \tag{4-27a}$$

In the literature, this inversion has been carried out by various methods, each of which produces a series solution. The choice of the solution to use depends on the range of time being considered, since one series converges rapidly at small values of time while another converges more rapidly at large values of time. Carslaw and Jaeger* have carried out the inversion of Eq. 4–27a by means of contour integration to give the following Fourier sine series:

$$T(x,t) = \frac{T_1 x}{L} + \frac{2T_1}{\pi} \sum_{n=1}^{\infty} \frac{(-1)^n}{n} e^{-n^2 \pi^2 t / L^2 \tau} \sin \frac{n\pi x}{L} \tag{4-27b}$$

This example shows that the distributed-parameter components have transfer functions involving hyperbolic functions and give time responses involving infinite series of decaying exponentials.

Example 4–5. Both transportation lag and distributed-parameter components frequently occur in chemical process systems. Knowledge concerning the shape of their transient responses is useful in identifying these components from experimental data. Evaluate and compare the impulse and step responses of the dead time, the distributed lag, and the first-order linear lag components.

Solution. In Chapter 2 and in this chapter, it is noted that the Laplace transform for the change of variable from t to $t - \tau$ is the time-delay operator $e^{-\tau s}$; therefore, the transportation-lag responses can be written as

Impulse response: $w(t) = \mathcal{L}^{-1}[1 e^{-\tau s}] = \delta(t - \tau) u(t - \tau)$

Step response: $c(t) = \mathcal{L}^{-1}\left[\frac{1}{s} e^{-\tau s}\right] = u(t - \tau)$

The transients are plotted in Fig. E4–5 for $\tau = 1$.

* H. S. Carslaw and J. C. Jaeger, *Conduction of Heat in Solids*, Oxford University Press, New York, 1959, p. 313.

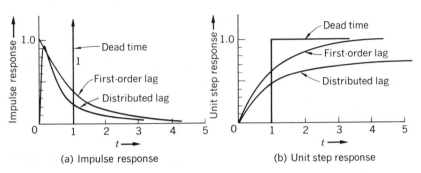

(a) Impulse response   (b) Unit step response

Fig. E4–5. Time responses of the transportation lag, distributed lag, and first-order linear lag components.

The response of the distributed-lag component is found by use of a table of Laplace-transform pairs, thus

Impulse response: $w(t) = \mathcal{L}^{-1}[1e^{-\sqrt{\tau s}}] = \sqrt{\dfrac{\tau}{4\pi}}\, t^{-3/2}e^{-\tau/4t}$

Step response: $c(t) = \mathcal{L}^{-1}\left[\dfrac{1}{s}\, e^{-\sqrt{\tau s}}\right] = erfc\left(\sqrt{\dfrac{\tau}{4t}}\right)$

The response of the first-order linear-lag component to unit impulse and unit step inputs is given by Eqs. 4–16b and c. These responses are plotted in Fig. E4–5 for $\tau = 1$. The peak of the impulse response occurs when $t = \tau/6$, and, since the step response is the integral of the impulse response, the step response has an inflection point at $t = \tau/6$. On comparing the step response of the distributed component with that of a first-order linear lag, which it resembles, it is seen that, when $t = \tau$, the step response of the distributed component is 47.9% complete, compared to 62.8% complete for the first-order lag, and the response is 99% complete at about 31 time constants, compared to 4.6 time constants for the first-order lag.

Exothermic Reaction Component, $(\tau s - 1)^{-1}$. Components showing this characteristic lag are present in a system whose response to an increase in a system variable is a further increase in that variable. The exothermic chemical reaction shows this behavior, since a temperature increase in the reacting system causes the reaction rate to increase and this in turn liberates more heat in the system, further increasing the system temperature and resulting in faster reaction rate and more heat liberation; and so on. Naturally, this characteristic leads to instability in the open-loop plant. An analysis of a simple case is given here.

Consider the chemical reaction occurring in the flow reactor shown in Fig. 4–17, in which an isomerization reaction occurs with a heat of reaction ΔH, and rate of reaction given as

$$A \xrightarrow{k} P \qquad \Delta H, \text{Btu/lb mole A}$$

$$\text{Rate} = kVc_A = A V c_A e^{-E/RT} \qquad \text{lb mole A/min}$$

where V is the reactor volume in ft³, c_A is the concentration of A in lb mole/ft³, and A and E are the reaction Arrhenius factor and activation energy, respectively (R is the gas constant). The material balance for the reactor is the nonlinear relationship

$$ic_f = ic_A + A V c_A e^{-E/RT} + V \frac{dc_A}{dt} \tag{4–28a}$$

where c_f and c_A are the concentrations of A in the feed and product, respectively, in lb mole/ft³. It is assumed that the feed rate, i ft³/min,

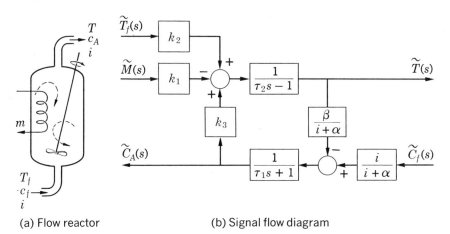

(a) Flow reactor   (b) Signal flow diagram

Fig. 4–17.   Flow reactor processing an exothermic chemical reaction.

equals the product rate and that the reactor volume is perfectly mixed. The energy balance for the adiabatic reactor requires that the following relationship hold at any time:

$$\begin{pmatrix} \text{Exothermic} \\ \text{heat of} \\ \text{reaction} \end{pmatrix} = \begin{pmatrix} \text{sensible} \\ \text{heat in} \\ \text{product} \end{pmatrix} - \begin{pmatrix} \text{sensible} \\ \text{heat in} \\ \text{feed} \end{pmatrix}$$

$$+ \begin{pmatrix} \text{heat removed} \\ \text{in cooling} \\ \text{coil} \end{pmatrix} + \begin{pmatrix} \text{energy} \\ \text{accumulation} \\ \text{in reactor} \end{pmatrix}$$

with the result that

$$(-\Delta H)A V c_A e^{-E/RT} = i\rho C_p (T - T_f) + m(T) + V\rho C_p \frac{dT}{dt} \tag{4–28b}$$

where ρ is the density of the reacting fluid, C_p is the heat capacity of the reacting fluid, $m(T)$ is the rate of heat removal by the cooling coil, and T_f and T are the temperatures of feed and reactor product, respectively. The assumptions of (1) constant heat of reaction, ΔH, (2) constant heat capacity and density of reacting mixture, and (3) perfect mixing are made to simplify the analysis. Generally, $m(T)$ depends upon the coolant and reactor temperatures but in the present analysis it is assumed to be independent of T. Using a computer, Eqs. 4–28a and b could be solved simultaneously to obtain the nonlinear behavior of the chemical reactor; however, for the present purpose, the relationships are linearized in the usual manner about an average operating point to give the transformed equations:

Material balance: $(\tau_1 s + 1)\tilde{C}_A(s) = \dfrac{i}{i + \alpha} \tilde{C}_f(s) - \dfrac{\beta}{i + \alpha} \tilde{T}$ (4–28c)

Energy balance: $(\tau_2 s - 1)\tilde{T}(s) = k_2\tilde{T}_f(s) - k_1\tilde{M}(s) + k_3\tilde{C}_A(s)$
$$(4\text{–}28\text{d})$$

where $\tau_1 = V/(i + \alpha)$
$\tau_2 = V\rho C_p k_1$
$\alpha = AVe^{-E/RT_0}$
$\beta = \alpha E c_{A0}/RT_0^2$
$k_1 = [\beta(-\Delta H) - i\rho C_p]^{-1}$
$k_2 = i\rho C_p k_1$
$k_3 = \alpha(-\Delta H)k_1$

The signal flow diagram is sketched in Fig. 4–17 according to Eqs. 4–28c and d, from which it is seen that the unstable component $(\tau s - 1)^{-1}$ occurs in the temperature branch of the diagram. This type of unstable component is not present in networks made up of passive elements but can occur in networks containing active elements such as energy sources.

RESPONSE.   Eqs. 4–28c and d represent an unstable system because the system response to a change in $\tilde{C}_f(s)$ or $\tilde{M}(s)$ will contain a term having the exponential factor $e^{+t/\tau}$, which rapidly increases in magnitude with time. The response is unbounded for any bounded input, hence the system is unstable.

Inverse Response Components. Inverse response components show a transient response which initially is opposite in direction to the final overall change. Components showing this behavior generally consist of two or more parallel components whose outputs are subtracted. For example, detailed analysis shows that a filled thermometer has an inverse response. When the thermometer is heated, the thermometer bulb responds by expansion before the filling fluid is heated, with a resultant initial decrease in indicated temperature. Fig. 4–18 shows how the difference between the step response of an integrator and a first-order lag can give an inverse response.

Many combinations of components can give rise to inverse response devices. Control of processes having this characteristic is difficult because the controller correction is initially in the wrong direction. Special compensating feedback elements are used to improve the system response (see Chapter 9).

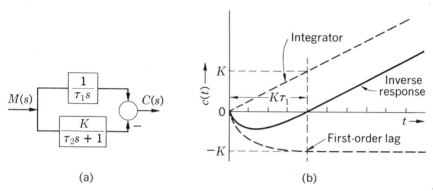

(a)   (b)

Fig. 4–18. Inverse response as the difference between the unit step response of an integrator and a first-order lag. The component exhibits inverse response when $K\tau_1 > \tau_2$. (a) Inverse response component. (b) Step input response.

4-3. INTERACTING PROCESS COMPONENTS

The basic process components have been described and illustrated by idealizations of simple devices. Complex systems, when analyzed, are found to be made up of combinations of these units. Series connections occur in all process plants and in every feedback control system. The characteristics of any combination depend upon how the units are interconnected.

Consider the potential-flow relationships in the two liquid-level systems shown in Fig. 4–19. In the non-interacting case, each vessel in the unit behaves as if the other were not present. In the interacting case, the liquid level in the downstream vessel affects the discharge rate of the upstream vessel and the two stages are interdependent.

Analysis of the non-interacting case leads to the following process equations (assuming linear resistances):

For vessel 1: $i_i - i_l - i_1 = C_1\dot{p}_1$ $i_1 = p_1/R_1$

Elimination of i_1 and transforming with zero initial conditions gives

$$\frac{P_1(s)}{R_1 I_i(s)} = \frac{1}{R_1 C_1 s + 1}\left[1 - \frac{I_l(s)}{I_i(s)}\right] \qquad (4\text{--}29a)$$

For vessel 2: $\qquad i_1 - i_2 = C_2 \dot{p}_2 \qquad i_2 = p_2/R_2$

Elimination of i_2 and transforming with zero initial conditions gives

$$\frac{P_2(s)}{R_2 I_1(s)} = \frac{1}{R_2 C_2 s + 1}$$

with the result that the overall behavior is the product of the two individual equations, thus:

$$\frac{P_2(s)}{I_i(s)} = \frac{P_2(s)}{R_2 I_1(s)} \frac{P_1(s)}{R_1 I_i(s)} \frac{R_1 I_1(s)}{P_1(s)} R_2$$

$$= \frac{R_2}{(\tau_2 s + 1)(\tau_1 s + 1)}\left[1 - \frac{I_l(s)}{I_i(s)}\right] \qquad (4\text{--}29b)$$

where $\tau_1 = R_1 C_1$ and $\tau_2 = R_2 C_2$. The signal flow diagram in Fig. 4–19a plainly indicates that the process is two non-interacting first-order lags in series.

Analysis of the interacting case in Fig. 4–19b gives the following process equations:

For vessel 1: $\quad i_i - i_l - i_1 = C_1 \dot{p}_1 \qquad i_1 = (p_1 - p_2)/R_1$

Notice that the flow from this vessel depends upon the downstream pressure p_2. Elimination of i_1 from the equations given

$$R_1(i_i - i_l) + p_2 = R_1 C_1 \dot{p}_1 + p_1$$

For vessel 2: $\qquad i_1 - i_2 = C_2 \dot{p}_2 \qquad i_2 = p_2/R_2$

Elimination of i_2 and p_1 from these equations and transforming the result with zero initial conditions gives the overall behavior of this system as

$$\frac{P_2(s)}{I_i(s)} = \frac{R_2}{(\tau_2 s + 1)(\tau_1 s + 1) + R_2 C_1 s}\left[1 - \frac{I_l(s)}{I_i(s)}\right] \qquad (4\text{--}30)$$

The signal flow diagram shows that flow i_1 depends upon p_1 and p_2 (downstream) and that the process must be analyzed as a single unit. A comparison of the two overall equations shows an additional term $R_2 C_1 s$ in the denominator which is due to the interaction effect. However, the denominator may be factored to form two equivalent non-interacting components when desired.

Most process systems exhibit interaction between the components, and the process engineer must be alert to analyze all such components as a single group. Likewise, in simulating interacting components on an

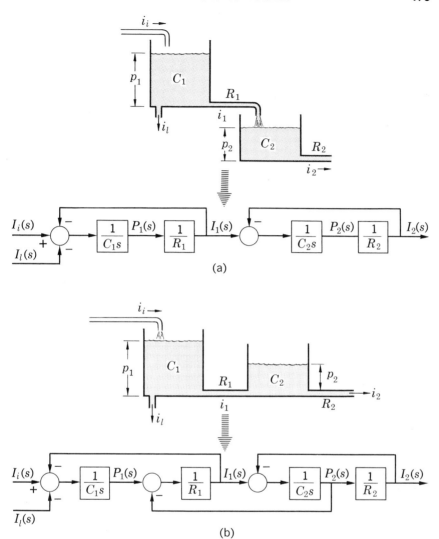

Fig. 4–19. The two first-order processes in series showing (a) non-interacting and (b) interacting behavior.

analog computer the engineer must work from the process equations to be sure that no loading effects are neglected.

PROBLEMS

4–1. Find the Laplace-transformed equations which describe the dynamic behavior of the devices shown in Fig. P4–1. Assume linear relationships, lumped

physical properties, and zero initial conditions.   Also, draw signal flow diagrams
for each device.

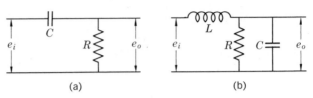

(a)   (b)

Fig. P4–1

4–2. Repeat Problem 4–1 for these pneumatic devices (Fig. P4–2).

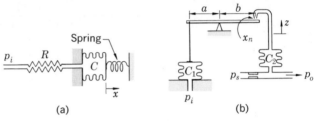

(a)   (b)

Fig. P4–2

4–3. Repeat Problem 4–1 for these mechanical devices (Fig. P4–3).

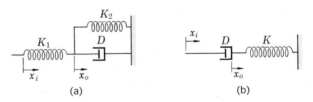

(a)   (b)

Fig. P4–3

4–4. Repeat Problem 4–1 for these thermal devices (Fig. P4–4).   Assume that
the fluid volumes are well mixed and that the flow rates are constant.

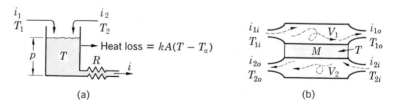

(a)   (b)

Fig. P4–4

4–5. Repeat Problem 4–1 for these liquid-level processes (Fig. P4–5).

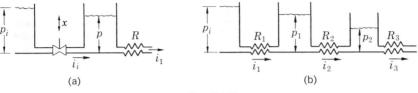

(a)   (b)

Fig. P4–5

4–6. Repeat Problem 4–1 for the assigned devices listed (Fig. P4–6).

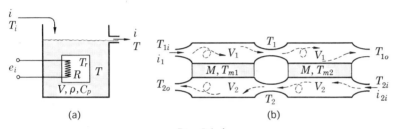

(a)   (b)

Fig. P4–6

4–7. A pressure surge tank containing n lb moles of air is placed in a water flow line to damp out pressure fluctuations in the line (Fig. P4–7). Let the cross-sectional area of the tank be A, the density of the water be ρ lb$_m$/ft^3, and the height of liquid in the tank be h. Neglect inertia of the fluid. Consider the two cases of no resistance and resistance in the connecting line as shown and derive a process equation for the fluid pressure p in terms of the difference between the fluid flow into and out of the device. Neglect the liquid head h in comparison to fluid pressure p.

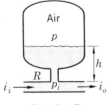

Fig. P4–7

4–8. A proposed differential pressure measuring device is shown in Fig. P4–8. The input pressures are applied to two large diaphragms of equal area A_1 separated by a liquid contained in two chambers. A diaphragm bellows of area A_2 separates the two liquid-containing chambers. The position x of the diaphragm

A_2 is detected by a linear differential transformer. Let the diaphragm bellows and transformer armature have mass M and a spring constant K. Derive an operational equation giving x in terms of the input pressure and the system parameters.

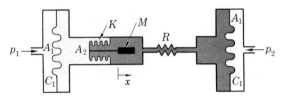

Fig. P4-8

4-9. A first-order lag component of unknown time constant is tested by subjecting it to a ramp input $m(t) = kt$ and recording the output. Compare the input and output signals, and show how the first-order time constant could be found. Write expressions for the dynamic error and time lag between the input and output signals. Note that the transient term decays quickly but that the dynamic steady-state terms increase without limit.

4-10. Show by analytical reasoning that the equivalent time constants of an overdamped second-order component can be obtained from step-increase response data using the graphical technique applied in Example 4-2, provided the time constants are unequal.

4-11. A first-order lag component with a gain of 2 psig/ft³ gives the following response to a step input increase of 3 ft³:

Time, hr	$c(t)$, psig
0	18.3
0.4	20.0
0.8	21.2
1.2	22.2
2.0	23.2
3.0	23.8
∞	24.3

Find the time constant of the device and the frequency for which the output would lag 30° behind the input in a frequency response test of this device. What is the magnitude ratio for that frequency?

4-12. Prepare an analog computer program for Eq. 4-13c with $n = 3$ and $\tau = 10$ min.

4-13. Draw analog computer circuits for these equations. Assume all initial conditions are zero.

(a) $\ddot{x} + 6\dot{x} = 5$
(b) $\ddot{x} + 10\dot{x} + 3x = 4t$
(c) $\dddot{x} + 5\ddot{x} + 25\dot{x} + 125x = 0$
(d) $\ddot{x} - 1.4\dot{x} - 0.9x = \sin 3t$

4–14. Second-order lag components having $\zeta > 1$ can be represented by two first-order lag components in series. Find the time constants of the first-order lag devices equivalent to the following second-order components:

(a) Component has $\zeta = 2$ and $\omega_n = 5$.
(b) Component has $\zeta = 2$ and $\omega_n = 10$.

4–15. A process thermometer in a thermometer well gave the following response to a 20°C step increase in process fluid temperature:

Time, min	T, °C	Time, min	T, °C
0	60.5	7	70.1
1	60.9	8	71.5
2	61.3	10	73.9
3	62.9	12	75.7
4	64.5	15	77.7
5	66.5	20	79.3
6	68.5	25	80.1

Assume that the thermometer is a second-order instrument, and find the ζ and ω_n to fit these data and also the time constants of the two equivalent first-order lag components.

4–16. The impulse response of a relaxed second-order oscillatory component reached a maximum value at 1.76 min and had the first zero value 5 min after the impulse was applied to the component. Find the value of ζ and ω_n for the component.

4–17. The overshoot of the unit step response of a second-order device depends only on its damping ratio. From the data in Fig. 4–12, make a plot of percentage overshoot against the damping ratio and find the value of ζ for which the overshoot is 15%.

4–18. The following specifications are given for a pair of complex conjugate poles. Sketch the region in the s-plane where these poles could be located.

(a) $\omega_n > 1$ rad/min and $\zeta > 0.707$
(b) $\omega_n < 1$ rad/min and $\zeta < 0.707$
(c) $5 < \omega_n < 10$ rad/min and $0.3 < \zeta < 0.5$

4–19. A second-order device has poles located at $p_1, p_2 = -2 \pm j4$.

(a) From Fig. 4–11, estimate the maximum value of the impulse response of this device and the time when it is reached.
(b) From Fig. 4–12, estimate the overshoot in the unit step response of this device and the first-time to zero error in the response.

4–20. Steady-state frequency response data may be found from the transfer function by making the substitution $s = j\omega$. Compare the frequency response of transportation lag and distributed-parameter components by plotting the magnitude and phase angles of the components on Bode plots in terms of $\omega\tau$.

4–21. Interaction between components cannot be determined by inspecting transient data. Find the unit step response of two non-interacting first-order lags in series. Let $R_1 = R_2 = 1$ megohm and $C_1 = C_2 = 1$ μf. Next allow them to interact, and find the unit step response. What are the time constants of an equivalent non-interacting system? Plot the unit step responses of both systems on the same coordinates. Which system is faster in responding to 62.8% complete response?

4-22. A device has the following transfer function:

$$G(s) = \frac{K_1}{\tau_1 s + 1} - \frac{K_2}{\tau_2 s + 1}$$

(a) Find the conditions for which the device shows inverse response.
(b) Compute and sketch the unit step response of this device for $K_1 = 2K_2$, $\tau_1 = 3$, and $\tau_2 = 1$ min.

5

Process Controllers

The industrial process controller is a special computing device that links the controlled process variable to the control valve in a feedback system. Usually, as shown in Fig. 1–7b, the industrial controller contains the set-point information, the error-sensing device, and a network that responds in various preselected modes to the error information, producing a signal which manipulates the control valve. The controller response is therefore a computed result. Typical error detectors, the ideal controller equations, and some typical controlling devices will be discussed in this chapter.

Industrial process controllers operate on pneumatic, hydraulic, or electric signals. The controller consists of (1) a differencing mechanism which forms the actuating error signal by subtracting the primary feedback signal from the reference input signal and (2) a computing mechanism which forms the controller output signal from the actuating error signal according to the control action selected. The computing mechanism has adjustable parameters by which the process engineer is able to adjust or tune the controller to fit the process plant characteristics. A brief discussion of a few typical controller components follow.

5–1. ERROR-DETECTING COMPONENT, $e = r - c$

This algebraic component is needed to compare the reference set-point value with the primary feedback signal, which can be either c or b (see Table 1–1). Table 5–1 shows a few possible error-detecting components, selected from electric, mechanical, and fluid applications.

Electric Resistance Bridge. This component is made up of a power source in parallel with two potentiometers whose wiper arms are positioned in proportion to a reference position or angle and to a controlled position or angle. The error voltage e results from the imbalance in potentiometer arms and is proportional to the difference ·in position or

TABLE 5–1
Analogous Error-Detecting Components

1. Signal flow.

Signal flow symbol for signal difference. Equation:

$$e = r - c$$

2. Electric resistance bridge.

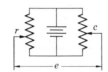

The potentiometer wipers may be positioned by linear or rotary motion. Position control application.

3. Mechanical lever.

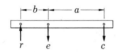

Widely used in pneumatic and hydraulic components.

4. Pressure balance.

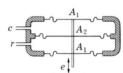

Useful in pneumatic control. The displacement has limited travel in force balance systems.

5. Analog computer.

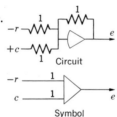

Useful for analog simulation.

---

angle between the reference and the controlled variable, provided both potentiometer windings are linear and no current is drawn from the wiper contacts.

Mechanical Lever. The lever is frequently used as a displacement error detector in hydraulic and pneumatic controllers in the form shown in Table 5–1 (item 3). For small displacements, the lever system relationship is

$$e = \frac{1}{a + b}(ar - bc) \tag{5–1}$$

Pneumatic Force Balance. The force-balance pneumatic device shown in Table 5-1 (item 4) compares the set-point and controlled-variable signals by applying the pressures r and c to a stacked diaphragm assembly and thereby produces an output force on the diaphragm assembly that is proportional to $(r - c)$. Let the positive values of force be in the upward direction; then the force on the diaphragm assembly due to pressure c, diaphragms A_1 and A_2, and atmospheric pressure p_a is

$$f_c = -(A_2 - A_1)c - A_1 p_a$$

The force on the diaphragm assembly due to pressure r is

$$f_r = (A_2 - A_1)r + A_1 p_a$$

Therefore, the resultant force from the device becomes the error force e_f due to the difference $(r - c)$:

$$e_f = f_c + f_r = (A_2 - A_1)(r - c) \tag{5-2}$$

5-2. IDEAL CONTROLLER COMPONENTS

Most process system parameters are fixed when the plant is built, and therefore they are not easily adjustable to improve the system performance. Of course, good plant design practice will consider the need for automatic control at every step in the design procedure and adequate attention to process control capability will be built into the plant; but still, there will be a need for process controllers (also called stabilization and compensation devices) to enable the closed-loop system to achieve its purpose of counteracting the effects of load changes and disturbances in the system. The present-day process controllers consist of either pneumatic, electric, or hydraulic components and combinations of these components. The discussion here is limited to a few idealized examples of several controller components.

The on-off or two-position controller is the most common controller in use today. It is found in many domestic applications, such as refrigerators, heaters, ventilation systems, water pumps, and in industrial machines. It is a discontinuous controller (as described in Chapter 1) that alternates two predetermined output signals at the control point (set point) depending upon the error polarity. This action gives rise to continuous cycling in the system, which may be undesirable, especially if the cycle amplitudes become great or the frequency high.

The cyclic response characteristic of systems using a two-position controller can be avoided by using a continuous controller. The basic continuous linear control actions are proportional, integral, and derivative.

These actions may be combined to obtain the advantages of two or more actions in a single controller. The commonly used ideal controller actions are discussed below and their responses to four frequently used test inputs are shown in Table 5–2. Their frequency response characteristics are sketched in Table 5–3.

TABLE 5–2
Responses of Ideal Controllers to Standard Inputs

	Impulse	Step	Ramp	Sinusoidal (Steady-State)
Standard inputs				
1. Proportional. $\tilde{m} = K_c \tilde{e}$ $\tilde{M}(s) = K_c \tilde{E}(s)$				
2. Integral or reset. $\tilde{m} = \dfrac{1}{\tau_1} \displaystyle\int_0^t \tilde{e}\, dt$ $\tilde{M}(s) = \dfrac{1}{\tau_i s} \tilde{E}(s)$				
3. Derivative or rate. $\tilde{m} = \tau_d \dfrac{d\tilde{e}}{dt}$ $\tilde{M}(s) = \tau_d s \tilde{E}(s)$				
4. Proportional + reset. $\tilde{m} = K_c \left(\tilde{e} + \dfrac{1}{\tau_i} \displaystyle\int_0^t \tilde{e}\, dt \right)$ $\tilde{M}(s) = K_c \left(1 + \dfrac{1}{\tau_i s} \right) \tilde{E}(s)$				
5. Proportional + rate. $\tilde{m} = K_c \left(\tilde{e} + \tau_d \dfrac{d\tilde{e}}{dt} \right)$ $\tilde{M}(s) = K_c(1 + \tau_d s) \tilde{E}(s)$				
6. Proportional + reset + rate. $\tilde{m} = K_c \left(\tilde{e} + \dfrac{1}{\tau_i} \displaystyle\int_0^t \tilde{e}\, dt + \tau_d \dfrac{d\tilde{e}}{dt} \right)$ $\tilde{M}(s) = K_c \left(1 + \dfrac{1}{\tau_i s} + \tau_d s \right) \tilde{E}(s)$				

Proportional Action (P). The ideal proportional controller produces an output that is proportional to the actuating error input:

$$m - m_o = \tilde{m} = K\tilde{e}, \qquad \text{or} \qquad \frac{\tilde{M}(s)}{\tilde{E}(s)} = K_c \qquad (5\text{-}3a)$$

where K_c is the controller proportionality or gain, m_o is a constant equal to the value of the controller output when the error e is zero (i.e., when the controlled process is at steady-state conditions), and $\tilde{m}$ is the value of the controller output referred to the previous steady-state value. The gain K_c is a ratio, units of output per unit error. The controller output is proportional to the actuating error, and therefore the rate of controller output change is proportional to the rate of change of actuating error. Suppose that, in a pneumatic temperature controller, a 5°F error gave a 1.2-psi change in controller output pressure; then the gain of the controller would be 1.2/5 or 0.24 psi/°F.

Another method of stating the gain is in terms of the proportional band of the controller, which is the percentage range of the controlled variable for which the controller will produce full range (100%) of its output. The normal range of a pneumatic controller is 3 to 15 psig (12-psi change) so that for the above controller an actuating error of $12/0.24 = 50$°F would be necessary to cause the controller output to change 12 psi. Now, if the range of the temperature measurement of the controller is 100°F to 250°F, the proportional band of the controller is set at $50/(250 - 100) = 33.3\%$. The general relationship between gain K_c and proportional band PB is

$$K_c = \frac{100}{\text{PB}} \frac{\text{(full range of output)}}{\text{(full range of input)}} \qquad (5\text{-}3b)$$

where K_c is expressed in units of $\tilde{m}$ per unit of $\tilde{e}$ and PB is a percentage.

Proportional control gives a continuous control action that is proportional to the actuating error $(r - c)$ or deviation in the process. Since a linear final control element (the control valve) moves the same amount for each unit of input change, the proportional controller can force the final control element to a definite position for each value of the controlled variable which gives a modulating or throttling control effect without cycling. At very high values of gain, the action of the proportional controller approximates on-off action, which leads to cycling in the process. There is an upper limit to the corrective action that a proportional controller can produce in a stable system since, for processes having dead time or two or more time lags, too high a value of controller gain will make the system (controller plus process) unstable. Table 5-2 shows the response of this controller to four different input signals.

Integral or Reset Action (I).   The integral controller produces an output that is proportional to the integral of the actuating error:

$$m - m_o = \tilde{m} = \int_0^t \frac{\tilde{e}}{\tau_i} dt \qquad \text{or} \qquad \frac{\tilde{M}(s)}{\tilde{E}(s)} = \frac{1}{\tau_i s} \tag{5-4}$$

where τ_i is the integral action constant having the units of error time per output ($1/\tau_i$ is the floating, or reset, rate), m_o is a constant, and $\tilde{m}$ is the output change from a previous steady-state value.   The unique characteristic of this control action is that, so long as actuating error exists, the controller output continues to increase and therefore its output is proportional to the magnitude and time duration of the error.   When this action is used alone it is called *proportional speed floating*, because the rate of change of output is proportional to the actuating error signal.

This control action is frequently used on flow control and ratio control applications.   It is applicable to fast processes having small time constants but it is necessary that the floating rate of this controller be slower than the process response; otherwise, instability will result.   Table 5–2 shows the response of this controller to four different input signals.   Single-speed floating control is integral action which responds to time duration of error and not to error magnitude.   It is little used because it leads to continuous cycling.   In practice, single-speed floating control is used with a neutral zone so that, when the process is on set point, the control valve is motionless and process cycling is prevented.

Derivative or Rate Action (D).   The derivative controller produces an output proportional to the derivative of the actuating error:

$$m - m_o = \tilde{m} = \tau_d \frac{d\tilde{e}}{dt} \qquad \text{or} \qquad \frac{\tilde{M}(s)}{\tilde{E}(s)} = \tau_d s \tag{5-5}$$

where τ_d is the derivative constant, m_o is the output when e is constant, and $\tilde{m}$ is the output change from a previous steady-state value m_o.   For this control action the rate of change of the output is proportional to the second derivative of the actuating error.   This action is never used alone in a controller since it responds only to rate of change of error.   It is combined with proportional or with proportional-and-integral control actions.   The derivative action responses to the unit impulse and unit step inputs called doublet and impulse when discussed in Chapter 2, become infinite as shown in Table 5–2 (item 3).   Actually, no physical device can produce this control action exactly.

Proportional-plus-Integral Action (PI).   This controller combines the actions of proportional and integral modes to give the sum as

$$m - m_o = \tilde{m} = K_c\left(\tilde{e} + \int_0^t \frac{\tilde{e}}{\tau_i} dt\right) \qquad \text{or} \qquad \frac{\tilde{M}(s)}{\tilde{E}(s)} = K_c\left(1 + \frac{1}{\tau_i s}\right) \tag{5-6}$$

where K_c is the proportional gain and τ_i is the integral time constant of the controller, in units of time. The responses of this controller to several inputs are shown in Table 5–2 (item 4). For the response to a step input, shown in Fig. 5–1a, observe that the proportional response $K_c\tilde{e}$ is

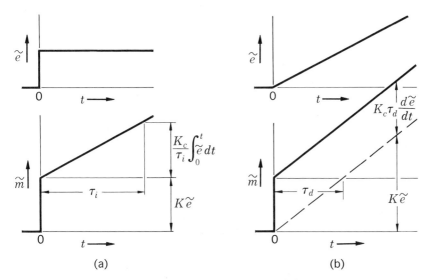

Fig. 5–1. Response of two controller actions. (a) Response of a proportional-plus-integral (PI) controller to a step increase in actuating error. The time required for the integral action to duplicate the proportional action is the integral time constant. (b) Response of a proportional-plus-derivative (PD) controller to a ramp actuating error. The time required for the proportional action to duplicate the derivative action is the derivative time constant.

immediate and that the integral response $K_c\tilde{e}t/\tau_i$ increases with time. The integral time constant τ_i may be found from the step response as the time when the integral response equals the proportional response, for then $K_c\tilde{e}t/\tau_i = K_c\tilde{e}$ and necessarily, $\tau_i = t$ at that instant. Some commercial controllers have reset mechanisms calibrated in repeats per unit of time, which is the reciprocal of the τ_i units in time. Small values of τ_i mean large integral action and large values of τ_i correspond to small integral action effects. A most desirable characteristic of this control action is that the controller response continues to grow as long as an input error continues. In a closed-loop system, this means that the integral action works to eliminate any error in the system and that, in time, it will force the system input and output into exact agreement. An undesirable characteristic of integral action is that it does not contribute to the stability of the system and can lead to large overshoot of controlled variable on start-up of processes.

Proportional-plus-Derivative Action (PD). This controller combines the actions of proportional and derivative modes to give the sum as

$$m - m_o = \tilde{m} = K_c\left(\tilde{e} + \tau_d \frac{d\tilde{e}}{dt}\right) \qquad \text{or} \qquad \frac{\tilde{M}(s)}{\tilde{E}(s)} = K_c(1 + \tau_d s) \quad (5\text{-}7)$$

where K_c is the proportional gain and τ_d is the derivative time constant of the controller.   The responses of this controller to several inputs are shown in Table 5–2 (item 5).   The behavior of this controller is best demonstrated by use of a ramp actuating error, as shown in Fig. 5–1b.   The proportional response to a ramp input is a ramp output equal to $K_c\tilde{e}$. The derivative response to the ramp input is instantaneous and equal to a constant $K_c\tau_d\, d\tilde{e}/dt$ since $d\tilde{e}/dt$ is a constant for a ramp error.   The combined controller response is a displaced ramp as shown.   Observe that the combined response is ahead of the proportional response in time by the time constant τ_d.   Also, when $t = \tau_d$, the proportional response and the derivative response to the ramp input are equal, i.e., $K_c\tilde{e} = K_c\tau_d\, d\tilde{e}/dt$. Then the derivative time τ_d is the time required for the proportional response to become equal to the derivative response when the input to the controller is a ramp actuating error.   For this reason it is sometimes said that the derivative action is an anticipatory action since in effect it advances the proportional action.   The magnitude of the derivative response to a changing input is proportional to the rate of change of the input.

Rate action produces a stabilizing effect in closed-loop systems since its action opposes all change in the system; however, it cannot eliminate steady-state errors.

Proportional-plus-Integral-plus-Derivative (PID).   The three-action controller combines the proportional, integral, and derivative modes in an additive way to give

$$m - m_o = \tilde{m} = K_c\left(\tilde{e} + \frac{1}{\tau_i}\int_0^t \tilde{e}\, dt + \tau_d \frac{d\tilde{e}}{dt}\right)$$

$$\text{or} \qquad \frac{\tilde{M}(s)}{\tilde{E}(s)} = K_c\left(1 + \frac{1}{\tau_i s} + \tau_d s\right) \quad (5\text{-}8)$$

where the constants have their usual significance.   Three adjustments are usually provided in the controller to allow tuning of the controller to match the process characteristics.   The responses of this controller to four inputs are shown in Table 5–2.   This is a commonly used controller since it can be modified quickly (by selecting values of K_c ,τ_i, and τ_d) into a device giving many different types of response suitable for process compensation. The response to a sinusoidal input is calculated in Example 5–1 below.

Example 5–1. Find the separate and the combined responses of a proportional-plus-integral-plus-derivative controller to a sinusoidal actuating error input of unit amplitude $\tilde{e} = \sin \omega t$.

Solution. The separate responses of the controller actions are found to be

(a) For proportional action $\quad \tilde{m}_P = K_c \sin \omega t$

(b) For integral action $\qquad \tilde{m}_I = -\dfrac{K_c}{\omega \tau_i} \cos \omega t$

(c) For derivative action $\qquad \tilde{m}_D = K_c \tau_d \omega \cos \omega t$

The combined response is the sum of the separate responses, or

$$\tilde{m} = K_c \left[\sin \omega t + \left(\omega \tau_d - \frac{1}{\omega \tau_i} \right) \cos \omega t \right]$$

from which it is seen that the response depends on the controller adjustments K_c, τ_i, and τ_d and the frequency ω of the input. This sum may be represented graphically and vectorially at a fixed frequency as shown in Fig. E5–1. From

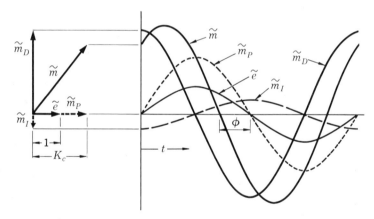

Fig. E5–1. Response of the three-action controller to a sinusoidal input.

physics, it is known that a sinusoidal function can be represented by a rotating vector having constant angular velocity ω rad/min. Then, as shown in the figure, the unit vector representing the actuating error and the vector representing the proportional response K_c are in phase. The vector representing the integral response of magnitude $K_c/\omega \tau_i$ lags the error by 90° ($-\cos \omega t = \sin (\omega t - \pi/2)$) and the derivative response of magnitude $K_c \tau_d \omega$ leads the error by 90° ($\cos \omega t = \sin (\omega t + \pi/2)$). The combined controller response can lead or lag the error signal, depending on the magnitude of $(\omega \tau_d - 1/\omega \tau_i)$. The phase angle between the response output and error input is zero when $\omega = 1/\sqrt{\tau_i \tau_d}$, and at other conditions the magnitude and angle of the output are read from the vector diagram as

Output magnitude: $\tilde{m} = K_c \sqrt{1 + (\omega \tau_d - 1/\omega \tau_i)^2}$

Output angle: $\underline{/\phi} = \tan^{-1}(\omega \tau_d - 1/\omega \tau_i)$

Response of Ideal Controller Actions. The time responses of the ideal controller actions to unit impulse, unit step, unit ramp, and steady-state sinusoidal inputs are sketched in Table 5–2. In studying this table, it must be remembered from Chapter 2 that the integral of a unit impulse is the unit step and the derivative of a unit impulse is the unit doublet. From the table, it is clear that the ideal controller actions do not interact in any manner.

Under steady-state conditions, the sinusoidal forcing of a linear component results in a sinusoidal response of the same frequency which differs from the forcing function in amplitude and phase. These two characteristics, called the *frequency response*, are usually reported in the form

$$G(j\omega) = \text{AR}(\omega) \; \underline{/\phi(\omega)} \qquad (5\text{–}9)$$

where $\text{AR}(\omega)$ is the magnitude ratio of output to input amplitudes at real frequency ω, and $\phi(\omega)$ is the phase angle between output and input at real frequency ω (see Chapter 2 for details on the Nyquist, Bode, and Nichols plots).

As discussed in Chapter 2, the frequency response is readily obtained from the transfer function by making the substitution of $j\omega$ for s. The purpose of this section is to develop the frequency response functions for the ideal controller actions discussed above.

PROPORTIONAL ACTION (P). The proportional control has no dynamic characteristics; therefore its frequency response is written as

$$\frac{\tilde{M}(j\omega)}{\tilde{E}(j\omega)} = G(j\omega) = K_c$$

from which the magnitude ratio and phase angle are

$$\left. \begin{array}{l} \text{AR} = K_c \\ \underline{/\phi} = 0° \end{array} \right\} \qquad (5\text{–}10\text{a})$$

In Table 5–3 the response is sketched on the Nyquist plot and the Bode plot.

INTEGRAL ACTION (I). An ideal integral controller is a pure integrator, and its frequency response is written as

$$\frac{\tilde{M}(j\omega)}{\tilde{E}(j\omega)} = G(j\omega) = \frac{1}{j\omega\tau_i} = \frac{-j}{\omega\tau_i}$$

TABLE 5-3

Frequency Response of Ideal Controller Modes

Control Mode, $G(j\omega)$	Nyquist Polar Plot	Bode Plot
1. Proportional ——— K 2. Integral - - - - - - $\dfrac{1}{j\omega\tau_i}$ 3. Derivative —·——·— $j\omega\tau_d$		
4. Proportional + integral ——— $K\left(1 + \dfrac{1}{j\omega\tau_i}\right)$ 5. Proportional + derivative - - - - - - $K(1 + j\omega\tau_d)$		
6. Proportional + integral + derivative $K\left(1 + \dfrac{1}{j\omega\tau_i} + j\omega\tau_d\right)$ Drawn for $\tau_d = \tau_i/6$ and corner frequencies of $\omega\tau_i = 1.27$ and 4.23		

from which the magnitude ratio and phase angle are

$$\left.\begin{array}{l} \mathrm{AR} = 1/\omega\tau_i \\ \underline{/\phi} = \tan^{-1} - \infty = -90° \end{array}\right\} \tag{5-10b}$$

On the plots in Table 5-3, notice that the magnitude is the reciprocal of $\omega\tau_i$ and the phase angle is constant at $-90°$ (lag). The frequency $\omega\tau_i$ is a parameter on the Nyquist plot.

DERIVATIVE ACTION (D). The ideal derivative action is a pure differentiator, and its frequency response is written as

$$\frac{\tilde{M}(j\omega)}{\tilde{E}(j\omega)} = G(j\omega) = j\omega\tau_d$$

from which the magnitude ratio and phase angle are

$$\left. \begin{array}{l} \text{AR} = \omega\tau_d \\ \underline{/\phi} = \tan^{-1} \infty = +90° \end{array} \right\} \tag{5-10c}$$

The magnitude is proportional to the frequency and the phase angle is constant at $+90°$ (lead). The frequency $\omega\tau_d$ is a parameter on the Nyquist plot.

PROPORTIONAL-PLUS-INTEGRAL ACTION (PI). The frequency response of the ideal PI controller is written as

$$\frac{\tilde{M}(j\omega)}{\tilde{E}(j\omega)} = G(j\omega) = K_c \left(1 + \frac{1}{j\omega\tau_i} \right) = K_c \left(1 - \frac{j}{\omega\tau_i} \right)$$

from which the magnitude ratio and phase angle are

$$\left. \begin{array}{l} \text{AR} = \dfrac{K_c}{\omega\tau_i} \sqrt{\omega^2\tau_i^2 + 1} \\[2mm] \underline{/\phi} = \tan^{-1} \dfrac{-1}{\omega\tau_i} \end{array} \right\} \tag{5-10d}$$

A change of gain K_c does not affect the phase angle but it does multiply the magnitude ratio directly. At zero frequency the magnitude ratio is infinite (due to the integral action) and the phase angle is $-90°$, and at high frequency the magnitude ratio approaches K_c and the phase angle approaches zero. The low-frequency and high-frequency asymptotes are easily used to represent the frequency response on the Bode plot. The asymptotes are: At low frequency, for $\omega\tau_i \ll 1$,

$$\text{AR} \cong \frac{K_c}{\omega\tau_i} \qquad \ln \text{AR} \cong \ln K_c - \ln \omega\tau_i$$

At high frequency, for $\omega\tau_i \gg 1$,

$$\text{AR} \cong K_c \qquad \ln \text{AR} \cong \ln K_c$$

These equations represent the straight-line approximations sketched on the Bode plot in Table 5–3, when the abscissa is in units of $\omega\tau_i$. They intersect at $\omega\tau_i = 1$ so that $\omega = 1/\tau_i$ is called the *corner frequency* for the approximation. The greatest error in this approximation occurs when $\omega\tau_i = 1$, for then the magnitude ratio is

$$\text{AR} = K_c \sqrt{1 + 1} = 1.414K_c$$

and the approximation value of the magnitude ratio is $\text{AR} \cong K_c$. There is no simple, adequate approximation for the phase angle. Plastic templates which give the correct values of magnitude ratio and phase angle are used for graphical manipulations of transfer functions on the Bode plot.

PROPORTIONAL-PLUS-DERIVATIVE ACTION (PD). The frequency response of the ideal PD controller is written as

$$\frac{\tilde{M}(j\omega)}{\tilde{E}(j\omega)} = G(j\omega) = K_c(1 + j\omega\tau_d)$$

from which the magnitude ratio and phase angle are

$$\left.\begin{array}{l} \text{AR} = K_c\sqrt{1 + \omega^2\tau_d^2} \\ \underline{/\phi} = \tan^{-1}\omega\tau_d \end{array}\right\} \qquad (5\text{--}10e)$$

The straight-line approximations for use on the Bode plot are, at low frequency, for $\omega\tau_d \ll 1$,

$$\text{AR} = K_c \qquad \ln\text{AR} = \ln K_c$$

and at high frequency, for $\omega\tau_d \gg 1$,

$$\text{AR} = K_c\omega\tau_d \qquad \ln\text{AR} = \ln K_c + \ln\omega\tau_d$$

The corner frequency for the approximation is $\omega = 1/\tau_d$, as shown in Table 5–3. The error in the approximation is the same as that for the PI controller. Notice that the phase angle is independent of the gain K_c and that the magnitude ratio increases with the frequency. The abscissa on the Bode plot has units of $\omega\tau_d$.

PROPORTIONAL-PLUS-INTEGRAL-PLUS-DERIVATIVE ACTION (PID). The frequency response of the ideal PID controller is written as

$$\frac{\tilde{M}(j\omega)}{\tilde{E}(j\omega)} = G(j\omega) = K_c\left(1 + \frac{1}{j\omega\tau_i} + j\omega\tau_d\right) = K_c\left[1 + j\left(\omega\tau_d - \frac{1}{\omega\tau_i}\right)\right]$$

from which the magnitude ratio and phase angle are

$$\left.\begin{array}{l} \text{AR} = K_c\sqrt{1 + (\omega\tau_d - 1/\omega\tau_i)^2} \\ \underline{/\phi} = \tan^{-1}(\omega\tau_d - 1/\omega\tau_i) \end{array}\right\} \qquad (5\text{--}10f)$$

The response is sketched in Table 5–3 for $\tau_d = \tau_i/6$. For ease in sketching the straight-line asymptotes, the controller equation can be factored as

$$G(j\omega) = K_c\left(1 + \frac{1}{j\omega\tau_i} + \frac{j\omega\tau_i}{6}\right) = \frac{K_c}{j\omega\tau_i}\left(\frac{j\omega\tau_i}{4.73} + 1\right)\left(\frac{j\omega\tau_i}{1.27} + 1\right)$$

and the corner frequencies are seen to be at $\omega\tau_i = 1.27$ and 4.73. The controller phase angle is independent of gain K_c and the magnitude ratio approaches infinity at low frequencies due to integral action and at high frequencies due to derivative action.

5-3. ACTUAL CONTROLLER COMPONENTS

The many industrial controller designs using pneumatic, electronic, and hydraulic signals are too numerous and too complex to discuss in detail. In practice it is not possible to design controllers giving exactly the ideal actions discussed above but many controllers approach this ideal in their normal operating range. Moreover, any industrial controller design must consider the economic factors of cost and competition as well as the technical factors of performance and maintenance and service requirements in the operating plant.

The basic principles of proportional elements and lag networks are used to produce the desired control action in pneumatic, hydraulic, or electric process controllers. Similar equipment using each of these systems is available to the process engineer. The choice of system is determined on a basis of plant experience, safety, equipment performance and reliability, and cost. The pneumatic system requires a source of clean, dry compressed air; the hydraulic system requires a supply of clean hydraulic fluid under pressure with provision for fluid return; and the electric system requires continuous electric power service. The electric and pneumatic systems are competitive in many industrial process applications. It is stated that the electric controls are inherently more sensitive than pneumatic or hydraulic controls and that the electric controls are generally more compatible with data logging, data processing, and computing control devices than are pneumatic mechanisms. The purpose of this section is to discuss the operation of typical industrial controllers and give a simple analysis of their behavior.

Pneumatic Controllers. Many of the pneumatic controllers which operate on the motion-balance principle fit into the general schematic block diagram shown in Fig. 5–2. Compare this diagram with that given

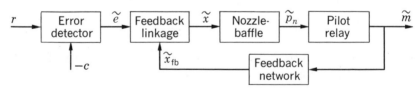

Fig. 5–2. General schematic block diagram of a typical pneumatic controller operating on the motion-balance principle.

in Figs. 4–3c, d for the pneumatic proportional component and note that the two diagrams are identical, beginning with the error signal. The diagram in Fig. 5–2 indicates that an error detector forms the actuating

error e (normally a position or a force in pneumatic systems) by some
suitable device as one of those in Table 5–1, (items 3 or 4). Then, by
means of a floating linkage, the error and feedback position are combined
to give a nozzle-baffle clearance $\tilde{x}$ which determines the nozzle pressure $\tilde{p}_n$.
Finally, amplification of $\tilde{p}_n$ gives the controller output pressure $\tilde{m}$. A
typical motion-balance pneumatic proportional controller is shown in the
diagram in Fig. 5–3. The relationship for the feedback linkage there is
given as

$$(a + b)\tilde{x} = b\tilde{e} - a\tilde{x}_{\text{fb}} \qquad (5\text{--}10)$$

where $(a + b)$ is the lever length, a is the distance of the nozzle from the
error end of the lever, and b is the distance of the nozzle from the feedback
end of the lever. The nozzle pressure $\tilde{p}_n$ is amplified by the pilot relay to
give the controller output signal $\tilde{m}$. In Chapter 4 the nozzle-baffle and
pilot relay combination was discussed and a linearized functional relationship was given as

$$\tilde{m} = k\tilde{x} \qquad (5\text{--}11)$$

where $\tilde{m}$ and $\tilde{x}$ represent the signals measured from a reference value or a
previous steady-state value and k is the pilot relay and nozzle-baffle gain
constant. Pneumatic networks that generate specific controller actions
are placed in the feedback loop around the nozzle. In general the feedback network has an equation written as

$$\tilde{x}_{\text{fb}} = \tilde{m}g(t) \qquad (5\text{--}12)$$

Then, combining Eqs. 5–10, 5–11, and 5–12 to eliminate $\tilde{x}$ and $\tilde{x}_{\text{fb}}$ and
transforming, the equation for a specific controller action becomes

$$\frac{\tilde{M}(s)}{\tilde{E}(s)} = \frac{(1 - k_e)k}{1 + kk_eG(s)} \qquad (5\text{--}13)$$

where $k_e = a/(a + b)$ and $1 - k_e = b/(a + b)$. This method is used in
the following discussion of pneumatic controllers.

PROPORTIONAL CONTROLLER (P). A proportional action controller is
given in Fig. 5–3 showing the actuating error detector, the proportional
linkage, the nozzle-baffle, the pilot relay, and the feedback network. The
controlled process variable c is measured by bellows B_1, whose movement
is transmitted to the error linkage L_1. The reference input r, which is the
desired value of the process variable (process set point), is connected to
the opposite end of the lever. The error lever computes the error signal
and transmits a position e to the proportional linkage L_2. If the error
lever has equal arms as shown, then $e = \frac{1}{2}(r - c)$. The nozzle divides
the proportional linkage L_2 into arms a and b whose ends are acted on by
the error signal and the feedback signal, respectively. The position of

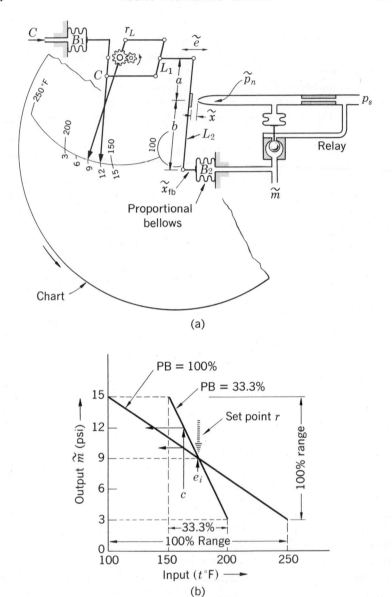

Fig. 5-3. (a) Schematic diagram of a pneumatic proportional controller showing the error detector, the proportional bellows, and feedback linkage. The controller gain is 0.24 psi/°F or a 33.3% proportional band. The proportional band is outlined on the instrument chart. (b) The graph of the output versus input for the controller shows that the position of the controlled variable within the proportional band determines the controller output.

the nozzle along the linkage determines the gain of the controller. The feedback network here is bellows B_2 with spring constant k_{fb}, therefore substitution of $G(s) = 1/k_{fb}$ in Eq. 5-13 gives the proportional controller equation which was previously derived as Eq. 4-8b,

$$\frac{\tilde{M}(s)}{\tilde{E}(s)} = \frac{(1 - k_e)k}{1 + \dfrac{kk_e}{k_{fb}}} \cong \frac{b}{a}k_{fb} = K_c \qquad (5\text{-}14)$$

where K_c is the controller gain. The approximation depends upon kk_e/k_{fb} being large in comparison to unity. Notice that feedback has made the performance of the device independent of the nozzle-baffle characteristics. The controller design provides for moving the nozzle position along the linkage L_2 or in some other way varying the ratio b/a so as to vary the controller gain. Large values of b/a give high controller gain values.

The operation of the controller may be studied by following the effect of an input signal change as it moves through the controller. Suppose r and c are equal, so that there is no error signal to the controller, and that the controller output is at midvalue, 9 psig (midvalue between 3 and 15 psig). Now let the process variable c decrease so that $r - c$ is positive. (The same effect can be obtained by moving r upscale.) Positive values of $\tilde{e}$ correspond to moving arm a on the linkage L_2 to the right, thereby decreasing x, the nozzle-baffle clearance, and consequently increasing the nozzle back pressure and the output pressure. At the same time the proportional bellows B_2, because of increased output pressure, moves the lower arm of linkage L_2 to the left, tending to increase the nozzle-baffle clearance and thus to decrease the output pressure. Immediately there is established a new position of the nozzle-baffle clearance and a resultant increased output pressure signal $\tilde{m}$ which now corresponds to an increase in corrective action to the process which will increase the controlled variable c until a new steady-state condition obtains.

The proportional controller gain K_c is the ratio of output to input and may be expressed as the ratio $\tilde{m}/\tilde{e}$ or as a percentage of the proportional band, where the proportional band is the percentage of range of input signal necessary to cause 100% range of output signal, i.e., percentage of input range necessary to move the final control element (control valve) over its complete range. In Fig. 5-3 the proportional band is indicated on the instrument chart and on the graph as centered on the controller set point. This controller has an input temperature range of 100 to 250°F and a gain of 0.24 psi/°F, or a proportional band of $12/(0.24)(250 - 100) = 33.3\%$. Therefore an actuating error of $0.33(150) = 50°F$ is necessary to change the controller output by 100%.

The controller output pressure depends upon the position of the controlled variable within the proportional band (PB), and for the controller in Fig. 5–3 this range is from 3 to 15 psig. When the actuating error is zero ($r = c$), the output is 9 psig; when $r > c$, the output is greater than 9 psig; and when $r < c$, the output is less than 9 psig, as indicated on the chart. These same relationships are displayed on the graph in Fig. 5–3b, which shows an output of 12 psig for an $r - c = 12.5°F$ and $PB = 33.3\%$, i.e., the controlled variable is 12.5°F below the set-point value of 175°F. For a $PB = 100\%$ and an error of 12.5°F, the output $\tilde{m}$ shown on Fig. 5–3b is 10 psig. Observe that the product of gain and proportional band is a constant for a given controller and that as the gain increases to infinity or as the proportional band goes to zero, the proportional controller becomes a two-position or on-off controller.

PROPORTIONAL-PLUS-INTEGRAL-PLUS-DERIVATIVE (PID). A typical three-action pneumatic controller mechanism (motion-balance principle) which has the integral and derivative feedback resistances in parallel is shown in Fig. 5–4. To illustrate the movement of signals through this device, assume that the error linkage $\bar{e}$ moves to the right. This motion decreases the nozzle-baffle clearance, which increases back pressure $\bar{p}_n$ and the relay output pressure $\tilde{m}$. The increased output pressure acts on the derivative and integral feedback bellows through time lags τ_d and τ_i, respectively, to give the feedback response $\bar{x}_{fb}$, which acts on the proportional linkage L_2. The method of controller analysis previously developed for motion-balance pneumatic controllers applies to this controller; the problem is to determine the feedback network characteristic $G(s) = \tilde{X}_{fb}(s)/\tilde{M}(s)$. Assume that the mechanism is at steady-state conditions with output pressure m_o at time zero. Then let the error input increase to the right, giving an output pressure change $\tilde{m} = m - m_o$. This pressure change acts on the derivative and integral feedback bellows through first-order lags to give the individual bellows pressure changes as follows:

$$\tilde{M}_I(s) = \frac{\tilde{M}(s)}{\tau_i s + 1} \qquad \tilde{M}_D(s) = \frac{\tilde{M}(s)}{\tau_d s + 1} \qquad (5\text{--}15)$$

where τ_i and τ_d are the R_iC_i and R_dC_d time constants of the first-order lags and $\tilde{M}_I(s)$ and $\tilde{M}_D(s)$ are the Laplace-transformed pressure changes in each bellows. The position $\tilde{X}_{fb}(s)$ of the proportional linkage is proportional to the difference between $\tilde{M}_D(s)$ and $\tilde{M}_I(s)$ thus:

$$\tilde{X}_{fb}(s) = k_{fb}^{-1}[\tilde{M}_D(s) - \tilde{M}_I(s)] \qquad (5\text{--}16)$$

where k_{fb} is the spring constant for the combined bellows (both bellows have the same area). Elimination of $\tilde{M}_D(s)$ and $\tilde{M}_I(s)$ between Eqs. 5–15 and 5–16 gives the feedback network characteristic $G(s)$ as

$$G(s) = \frac{\tilde{X}_{fb}(s)}{\tilde{M}(s)} = k_{fb}^{-1}\left(\frac{1}{\tau_d s + 1} - \frac{1}{\tau_i s + 1}\right) \qquad (5\text{--}17)$$

Substitution of this value for $G(s)$ in the general controller equation (Eq. 5–13) results in the controller equation for this mechanism as

$$\frac{\tilde{M}(s)}{\tilde{E}(s)} = \frac{k'(\tau_d s + 1)(\tau_i s + 1)}{(\tau_d s + 1)(\tau_i s + 1) + k''s} \tag{5–18}$$

where $k' = (1 - k_e)k$ and $k'' = k_e k k_{fb}^{-1}(\tau_d - \tau_i)$. This equation can be rearranged into the ideal form of the three-action controller as

$$\frac{\tilde{M}(s)}{\tilde{E}(s)} = \frac{k'(\tau_d + \tau_i)(T_d s + 1 + 1/T_i s)}{(\tau_d + \tau_i + k'')\left[\dfrac{\tau_d \tau_i s}{\tau_d + \tau_i + k''} + 1 + \dfrac{1}{(\tau_i + \tau_d + k'')s}\right]} \tag{5–19}$$

where $T_d = \tau_d \tau_i/(\tau_d + \tau_i)$ and $T_i = \tau_d + \tau_i$. Now if the controller design is such that k'' is large enough to make the first and last terms in the denominator small in comparison to unity, the controller will approximate the ideal three-action controller equation.

The typical three-action controller in Fig. 5–4 becomes a two-action PI controller when R_d becomes zero. Then the derivative action feedback

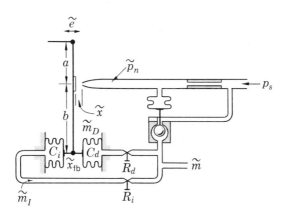

Fig. 5–4. Schematic diagram of a pneumatic proportional-plus-integral-plus-derivative (PID) controller.

bellows becomes a proportional bellows and the position $\tilde{X}_{fb}(s)$ of the proportional linkage becomes

$$\tilde{X}_{fb}(s) = k_{fb}^{-1}[\tilde{M}(s) - \tilde{M}_I(s)]$$

where $\tilde{M}(s)$ is the output pressure change and $\tilde{M}_I(s)$ is the corresponding pressure change in the integral bellows. The feedback network characteristic equation for this case becomes

$$G(s) = \frac{\tilde{X}_{\mathrm{fb}}(s)}{\tilde{M}(s)} = k_{\mathrm{fb}}^{-1}\left(1 - \frac{1}{\tau_i s + 1}\right) = k_{\mathrm{fb}}^{-1}\left(\frac{\tau_i s}{\tau_i s + 1}\right)$$

Substitution of this relationship in Eq. 5–13 gives the controller equation for the mechanism in Fig. 5–4 with $R_d = 0$ as

$$\frac{\tilde{M}(s)}{\tilde{E}(s)} = \frac{k'(1 + 1/\tau_i s)}{(1 + 1/k'' s)} \qquad (5\text{–}20)$$

where $k' = (1 - k_e)k/(k_e k_n k_{\mathrm{fb}}^{-1} + 1)$ and $k'' = \tau_i(k_e k k_{\mathrm{fb}}^{-1} + 1)$. Again, if the controller design is made so that k'' is a large number, then the controller mechanism will approach the ideal equation in its performance.

In a like manner it can be shown that the three-action PID controller becomes a two-action PD controller when $R_i = 0$. Of course the two two-action controller equations can be obtained from Eq. 5–19 by first letting $\tau_d = 0$ for the PI controller equation and then, for the PD controller equation, letting $\tau_i = 0$. From these simple analyses it is seen that an actual controller cannot give the performance required by the ideal controller equation but that it can give performance approaching the ideal equations.

FORCE-BALANCE CONTROLLERS. Another type of pneumatic controller, based on the force-balance principle, is shown in Fig. 5–5. The chief difference between this design and the motion-balance controllers already discussed is that in the force-balance controller both the set-point and controlled process variables are converted into proportional pressures r and c acting on a diaphragm instead of on a proportioning linkage. This controller is made in a compact stacked unit for installation on the plant process equipment to minimize time lags in penumatic signal transmission. It is connected to the process control room so that the set-point signal can be adjusted by the operator and the process variable signal observed and recorded there.

In the operation of the controller shown in Fig. 5–5, the set-point and controlled process variable pneumatic signals act on opposite sides of the diaphragm A_2, applying on the diaphragm stem a downward force equal to

$$e_f = (r - c)(A_2 - A_1) \qquad (5\text{–}21\mathrm{a})$$

the error force in the controller. The nozzle-baffle clearance x determines the output signal, which may be amplified, if necessary, to give higher output pressures or larger volumetric flows. The output pressure acts on the lower diaphragm of area A_3 directly, resulting in a proportional negative feedback force on the diaphragm assembly. Through the RC

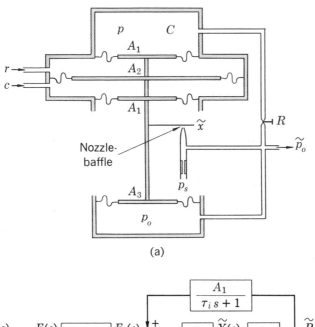

(a)

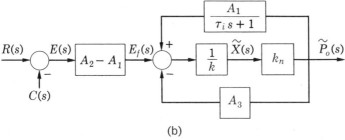

(b)

Fig. 5-5. (a) Force-balance pneumatic controller generating PI control action. (b) Signal flow diagram.

network the output pressure produces the lagging pressure p, which acts on the upper diaphragm of area A_1 as a positive feedback force on the diaphragm assembly.

A simplified analysis of the controller shows that the algebraic sum of the forces acting on the diaphragm stem must be zero. Let the positive direction of force be downward. Assume an initial equilibrium condition when $e_f = 0$, and let r increase so that the error force is $\tilde{e}_f$. A force balance on the diaphragm stem, using transformed variables, gives

$$\tilde{E}_f(s) + A_1\tilde{P}(s) - A_3\tilde{P}_0(s) - k\tilde{X}(s) = 0 \qquad (5\text{-}21\text{b})$$

where the tilde variables are deviations from the initial equilibrium condition and $k\tilde{X}(s)$ is the stem displacement force. Other relationships in the controller are:

Feedback pressure $\tilde{P}(s)$: $\tilde{P}(s) \ (\tau_i s + 1) = \tilde{P}_o(s)$ (5-21c)

Nozzle-relay output pressure $\tilde{P}_o(s)$: $\tilde{P}_o(s) = k_n \tilde{X}(s)$ (5-21d)

where $\tau_i = RC$. These equations are used to construct the controller signal flow diagram in Fig. 5-5b from which it is seen that the controller action originates from the dynamics in the positive feedback loop. The PI controller equation results from the elimination of $\tilde{X}(s)$ and $\tilde{P}(s)$ from the equations, thus:

$$\frac{\tilde{P}_o(s)}{\tilde{E}_f(s)} = \frac{K_c(\tau_i s + 1)}{\alpha \tau_i s + 1}$$ (5-21e)

where $K_c = k_n/[k + k_n(A_3 - A_1)]$ and $\alpha = (k + k_n A_3)/[k + k_n(A_3 - A_1)]$. This is a typical equation for a commercial PI controller. A constant α value is built into the device and only K_c and τ_i are controller parameters.

This article has discussed a few pneumatic circuits for generating control actions and has given basic analyses of the circuits neglecting minor effects in the devices. It is not practical to build controllers having the ideal responses and the commercial controllers have limiting values of gain for the integral and derivative actions at low and high frequencies instead of the infinite values of the ideal actions. Transfer functions of particular commercial controllers are available from the manufacturer. Some typical forms of transfer functions of commercial controllers are listed below:

1. Proportional-plus-integral: $K_c \left(\dfrac{\tau_i s + 1}{\alpha \tau_i s + 1} \right)$ $\begin{array}{l} 5 < \alpha < 100 \\ 0.5 < K_c < 100 \end{array}$

2. Proportional-plus-derivative: $K_c \left(\dfrac{\tau_d s + 1}{\beta \tau_d s + 1} \right)$ $0.02 < \beta < 1$

3. Proportional-plus-integral-plus-derivative: $K_c \left(\dfrac{\tau_i s + 1}{\alpha \tau_i s + 1} \right) \left(\dfrac{\tau_d s + 1}{\beta \tau_d s + 1} \right)$;

also, $K_c \left[\dfrac{1}{\tau_i s} + \left(1 + \dfrac{\tau_d}{\tau_i} \right) + \tau_d s \right]$

Electronic Controllers. There are various types of electric and electronic process controllers available. The electronic type discussed here is distinguished by the use of amplifiers with appropriate feedback network to produce the desired control action. At present there is no standardization of different signal types and levels used in the control system (measuring and transmitting circuits) but there is apparent agreement on controller output as a direct-current signal with a 5-to-1 ratio of maximum to minimum signal. The controllers described here are built around an operational amplifier and, in fact, the analog computer can simulate the controller by using the same feedback networks.

The analysis of any process controller depends upon recognition of the three essential parts of a controller: error detector, amplifier, and a suitable feedback network to give the desired control action. For the controllers shown in Fig. 5–6 it is assumed that the measured variable signal is avail-

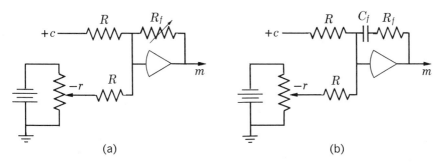

Fig. 5–6. Electronic controllers based on the operational amplifier. (a) Proportional. (b) Proportional-plus-integral.

able as a d-c signal with positive polarity. The negative set-point signal is obtained from a potentiometer and voltage source. Then the equation for the proportional controller in Fig. 5–6a is obtained from Eq. 4–5 as

$$m = -\frac{R_f}{R}(c - r) \qquad \text{or} \qquad \frac{M(s)}{E(s)} = K_c \qquad (5\text{–}22)$$

where R_f/R is the gain, K_c, of the controller. The tilde notation for deviation variable is not used here. The controller in Fig. 5–6b has a control action found in the same way as

$$m = \frac{Z_f}{Z_i}(c - r)$$

For the feedback network of R_f and C_f in series, Z_f is given as

$$Z_f = R_f + \frac{1}{C_f s} = \frac{R_f C_f s + 1}{C_f s}$$

and

$$Z_i = R$$

so that the control action equation becomes

$$\frac{M(s)}{E(s)} = \frac{R_f C_f s + 1}{R C_f s} = \frac{R_f}{R}\left(1 + \frac{1}{\tau_f s}\right) = K_c\left(1 + \frac{1}{\tau_f s}\right) \qquad (5\text{–}23\text{a})$$

where $K_c = R_f/R$ is the controller gain and $\tau_f = R_f C_f$ is the controller integral constant. These simple examples are typical of the basic control actions used in industrial controllers; however, the practical controller must have provision for overload, manual operation, remote recording, safety devices in case of malfunction, etc., built into the equipment, so that the practical controller is more complex than these diagrams indicate.

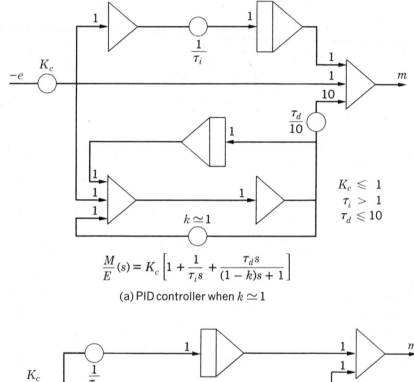

$$\frac{M}{E}(s) = K_c \left[1 + \frac{1}{\tau_i s} + \frac{\tau_d s}{(1 - k)s + 1} \right]$$

(a) PID controller when $k \simeq 1$

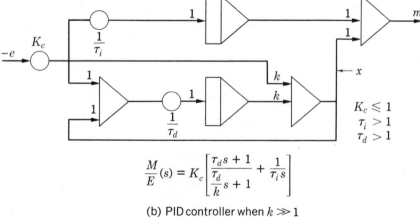

$$\frac{M}{E}(s) = K_c \left[\frac{\tau_d s + 1}{\frac{\tau_d}{k} s + 1} + \frac{1}{\tau_i s} \right]$$

(b) PID controller when $k \gg 1$

Fig. 5-7. Analog computer simulation of ideal PID controller.

Computer Simulation. The computer simulation of process control systems requires simulation of process controllers. Fig. 5–7 shows two programs for simulation of a PID controller. Also, P, I, PD, and PI signals can be obtained from these programs. The task in controller simulation is to obtain a good derivative signal in the presence of noise in the error signal. In Fig. 5–7a differentiation is performed by the practical differentiator in Fig. 4–5d and the potentiometer k should be close to unity. Values of $k < 1$ add a first-order filtering effect which removes high-frequency noise from the derivative signal, as indicated in Eq. 4–10c.

The signal x in Fig. 5–7b is given as

$$\frac{X(s)}{E(s)} = -K_c \frac{\tau_d s + 1}{1 + \tau_d s/k} \qquad (5-23b)$$

When $k \gg 1$, the x signal approaches a PD signal from which high frequencies due to noise in the input have been filtered by the first-order lag with a time constant of τ_d/k. The PID signal is obtained by summing x and the integral signal. Step changes in e will saturate these controllers (depending upon the value of k) and care should be exercised in using them with inputs having large derivatives. The controller parameter ranges are shown on the diagrams. Other values can be obtained by changing the gain on the proper amplifiers.

Hydraulic Controllers. The analysis of pneumatic and hydraulic control systems is based on the fluid flow laws. The fluid source is a high pressure pump which draws fluid from a return sump and discharges it into a high-pressure accumulator. A cooler may be needed in the fluid circuit to control the temperature since the work of compression appears in the fluid as heat. When compared to other control devices, the corresponding hydraulic device is more rugged, can provide larger output power to size ratios, gives high speed of response, and provides high gain per stage.

The most important component in a hydraulic control system is the pilot valve which controls the direction and amount of fluid flow to a receiving unit. Several types of pilot valves are used, such as the jet, the four-way valve, etc., but only the four-way valve will be discussed here. Fig. 5–8a shows a typical four-way hydraulic pilot valve and double-acting power cylinder. The pilot valve consists of a shell having a supply port and four discharge ports and a movable spool that controls the flow through the ports. When the valve spool is moved to the right as shown, port A, being partially uncovered, becomes an orifice supplying high-pressure fluid to the right side of the power cylinder and forcing the cylinder to move toward the left. At the same time port B is partially opened to drain and the released fluid is returned to the pump sump.   The valve input is the error signal e that positions the pilot valve spool and the output is the power cylinder position m that is used to position a final control element.

A simple analysis of the pilot valve–cylinder component assumes that the areas of the valve port orifices are proportional to the spool displacement and that fluid leakage and compressibility are negligible.   The volume flow rate through each port is identical and given by the orifice equation

$$i_i = ke \sqrt{p_s - p_1} = ke \sqrt{p_2} \qquad (5\text{-}24\text{a})$$

where $p_s - p_1 = p_2$ is the pressure drop across each orifice, e is the spool displacement, and k is a constant.   The supply pressure p_s is constant but

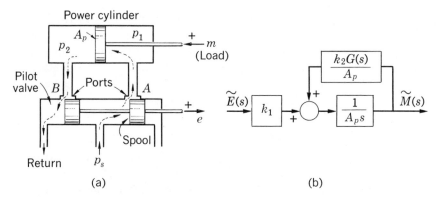

(a)   (b)

Fig. 5-8. (a) Hydraulic pilot valve–cylinder component and (b) its signal flow diagram.   The feedback is negative since k_2 is negative.

p_1 and p_2 depend on the cylinder load so that a force balance on the cylinder piston gives

$$\text{Cylinder load} = A_p(p_1 - p_2) = A_p p_l$$

where $p_l = p_1 - p_2$, the pressure drop across the piston, and A_p is the piston area.   Because p_s is constant, the flow rate i_i into the cylinder is a function only of displacement e and load pressure drop p_l and the linearized relationship is

$$\tilde{i}_i = k_1 \tilde{e} + k_2 \tilde{p}_l \qquad (5\text{-}24\text{b})$$

where k_1 and k_2 are partial derivatives which are assumed to be constant in the normal operating range of the device and are evaluated at $\tilde{e} = 0$ and at $\tilde{p}_l = 0$, thus:

$$k_1 = \left.\frac{\partial i_i}{\partial e}\right|_{\tilde{p}_l = 0} \qquad\qquad k_2 = \left.\frac{\partial i_i}{\partial p_l}\right|_{\tilde{e} = 0}$$

The flow rate into the power cylinder determines its rate of movement by a flow rate balance,

$$\tilde{\imath}_i = A_p \frac{d\tilde{m}}{dt} \tag{5–24c}$$

which neglects cylinder leakage and fluid compressibility. The relationship between the position of the power cylinder m and the load pressure drop $\tilde{p}_l$ depends upon the load dynamics and may be written generally in terms of deviation variables as

$$A_p \tilde{p}_l = \text{change in load force} = g(\tilde{m},t) \tag{5–24d}$$

$\tilde{p}_l$ and $\tilde{\imath}_i$ may be eliminated among Eqs. 5–24b, c, and d to give the relationship

$$k_1 \tilde{e} + \frac{k_2}{A_p} g(\tilde{m},t) = A_p \frac{d\tilde{m}}{dt} \tag{5–24e}$$

which can be Laplace-transformed with zero initial conditions to give the pilot valve–cylinder transfer function

$$\frac{\tilde{M}(s)}{\tilde{E}(s)} = \frac{k_1 A_p}{A_p{}^2 s - k_2 G(s)} \tag{5–24f}$$

The signal flow diagram is shown in Fig. 5–8b, where the feedback around the integrator appears to be positive; however, the feedback is actually negative since k_2 is always negative. If i_i is independent of p_l, i.e., $k_2 = 0$, the analysis reduces to the simple equation of a reset controller with integral time A_p/k_1:

$$\frac{\tilde{M}(s)}{\tilde{E}(s)} = \frac{k_1}{s A_p} \tag{5–24g}$$

which states that for a given input $\tilde{e}$ there corresponds a proportional output velocity $d\tilde{m}/dt$.

Example 5–2. Analyze the pilot valve–cylinder component in Fig. E5–2 to find a transfer function for the device, and draw the signal flow diagram. Assume k_2 in Eq. 5–24b is zero for this device.

Solution. The floating lever in this component is a motion-balance device, and the position $\tilde{m}$ is given by

$$\tilde{m} = \frac{\partial m}{\partial e} \tilde{e} + \frac{\partial m}{\partial m_1} \tilde{m}_1$$

where the coefficients may be found from similar triangles. To find the coefficient $\partial m/\partial e$, keep m_1 fixed and allow e to change, then

$$\frac{\partial m}{\partial e} = \lim_{\Delta e \to 0} \frac{\Delta m}{\Delta e} = \frac{a}{b}$$

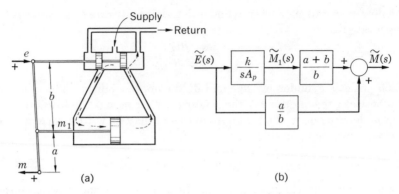

Fig. E5–2. (a) Hydraulic pilot-valve cylinder. (b) Signal flow diagram.

Similarly, when e is fixed and m_1 changes, the coefficient

$$\frac{\partial m}{\partial m_1} = \lim_{\Delta m_1 \to 0} \frac{\Delta m}{\Delta m_1} = -\frac{a+b}{b}$$

The minus sign is needed so that the motion will agree with the sign convention on the lever. The equation for the lever is

$$\tilde{m} = \frac{a}{b}\tilde{e} - \frac{a+b}{b}\tilde{m}_1 \tag{a}$$

The simple equation for the pilot valve–cylinder applies (Eq. 5–24g)

$$\tilde{M}_1(s) = -\frac{k_1}{sA_p}\tilde{E}(s) \tag{b}$$

Laplace transformation of Eq. a and elimination of $\tilde{M}_1(s)$ between Eqs. a and b give the transfer function for the component as

$$\frac{\tilde{M}(s)}{\tilde{E}(s)} = K_c\left(1 + \frac{1}{\tau_i s}\right)$$

where $K_c = a/b$ and $\tau_i = A_p a/(a+b)k_1$. This is the equation of the proportional-plus-integral controller. The signal flow diagram constructed from Eqs. a and b is shown in Fig. E5–2b, which shows the feedforward nature of the device.

5–4. PNEUMATIC DIAPHRAGM—SPRING ACTUATOR

The final control element in a system is usually a valve which responds to the controller signal by manipulating the flow of the control agent. An automatic control valve consists of a valve body carrying the control agent and a valve actuator that determines the plug-seat relationship in the valve body. Several types of valve bodies are discussed in Chapter 3.

A pneumatic diaphragm spring-type actuator (air to close) is sketched in Fig. 5–9a with input pressure signal p_a and output position x. The diaphragm is a flexible premolded sheet that forms an airtight chamber

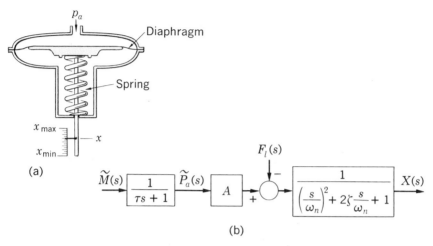

Fig. 5–9. (a) Pneumatic diaphragm spring actuator. (b) Signal flow diagram.

with the upper diaphragm case and is supported by the diaphragm plate. As the air pressure p_a builds up in the chamber, the downward force of this pressure on the diaphragm and supporting plate begins to stroke the stem. The spring assures linearity between the pressure and the stem position. This actuator has a normal input range of 3–15 psig for full stroke, which may be from $\frac{1}{4}$ inch to 2 or 3 inches.

The operating characteristics of a pneumatic actuator depend upon its size and distance from the controller, the inertia, friction, and spring forces in the actuator, and external load conditions. Assuming lumped physical properties of the transmission line (see Chapter 9), the pressure at the actuator p_a will lag the controller output signal by at least one time lag, thus:

$$\tilde{P}_a(s) = \left(\frac{1}{\tau s + 1}\right) \tilde{M}(s)$$

where τ is the time constant for the transmission line. The inertia, friction, and spring forces in the actuator correspond to a second-order oscillatory component; therefore the actuator force is

$$A\tilde{P}_a(s) = \left[\left(\frac{s}{\omega_n}\right)^2 + 2\zeta\frac{s}{\omega_n} + 1\right] K\tilde{X}(s) + \tilde{F}_l(s)$$

where A is the effective diaphragm area, $\omega_n = \sqrt{K/M}$ and $\zeta = D/(2\sqrt{MK})$ are the parameters of the actuator, and $F_l(s)$ is the external load conditions on the valve, such as thrust forces from the fluid flowing through the body and friction forces due to valve stem packing. Then the signal flow diagram can be constructed as shown in Fig. 5–9b and the transfer function from controller output to actuator output is found as

$$\tilde{X}(s) = \frac{1/K}{\dfrac{s^2}{\omega_n^2} + 2\zeta \dfrac{s}{\omega_n} + 1} \left[\frac{A\tilde{M}(s)}{\tau s + 1} - \tilde{F}_l(s) \right]$$

Nonlinear stem friction and external load forces can seriously impair operation of the actuator. Also, large transmission time constants corresponding to large actuator chambers or great transmission distances are undesirable. These difficulties can be overcome to some extent by use of a positioner on the actuator. The positioner is a feedback device which can greatly improve the dynamic performance of a sluggish pneumatic actuator. (See Problem 5–12 for a valve positioner diagram.)

PROBLEMS

5–1. Derive equations which describe the behavior of these devices (Fig. P5–1). See Problem 5–4 for a description of the pneumatic device.

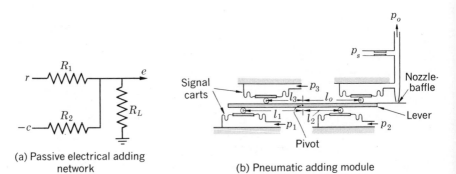

(a) Passive electrical adding network

(b) Pneumatic adding module

Fig. P5–1

5–2. Write equations for the response of the four ideal controller actions (P, PI, PD, PID) to the following inputs. Let $K_c = 4$ units output/unit error, $\tau_i = 5$ min, and $\tau_d = 2$ min, and take initial conditions to be zero.

(a) $e = 0.5e^{2t}$
(b) $e = 2 \cos (5t)$
(c) $e = 4t^{1/2} - t^2$
(d) $e = 2te^t$

5–3. Sketch the response of the four controller actions (P, PI, PD, PID) to the graphical inputs (Fig. P5–3). Let the initial conditions be zero, and take values of the constants as follows: $K_c = 2$, $\tau_i = 1$ min, and $\tau_d = 1$ min.

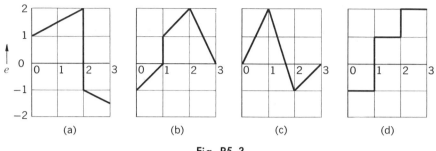

Fig. P5-3

5-4. Various pneumatic analog computing and controlling components are commercially available. The basic mechanism of one design (Fig. P5-4) is a lever pivoted at the center and maintained in equilibrium by a feedback element activated by a nozzle-baffle attached to the lever. Torques are applied to the lever by air pressures acting on the diaphragms in signal carts. All the signal carts have the same area, have negligible capacitance, and are movable along tracks to give variable gains (*ISA Journal*, Vol. 8, No. 9, pp. 38–43, and No. 10, pp. 53–55, 1961). Derive transfer functions for the following devices, assuming $l_2 = l_3$ and $i = 0$ in the p_o signal.

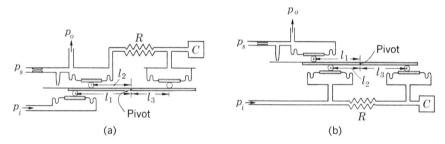

Fig. P5-4

5-5. Derive e_o/e_i relationships for the following stabilizing networks (Fig. P5-5) useful in electric control systems. Designate the type of control action present in each case, and sketch the frequency response on a Bode plot. Review Chapter 4 if necessary.

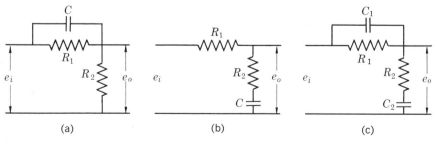

Fig. P5-5

5–6. Derive x_o/x_i relationships for the following mechanical compensators (Fig. P5–6) useful in mechanical systems. Designate the type of control action present in each case. (Review Chapter 4 if necessary.)

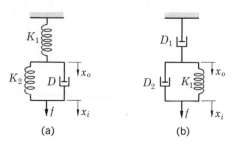

(a)   (b)

Fig. P5–6

5–7. A commercial control component having "inverse derivative" action generates this transfer function:

$$G(s) = K_c \frac{\sigma \tau_d s + 1}{\tau_d s + 1}$$

(a) Using the value $\sigma = 0.1$, sketch the frequency response of this component on a Bode plot by means of the straight-line approximations.

(b) This control action is commonly used in series with a PI controller. Sketch the frequency response of the series combination on a Bode plot. Let $\tau_i = \tau_d$ and $\alpha = 50$ and $\sigma = 0.1$.

5–8. Write equations describing the simplified electronic controllers shown in Fig. P5–8:

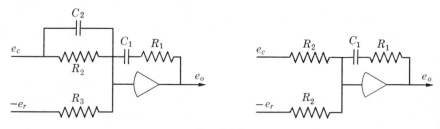

Fig. P5–8

5–9. Devise an analog computer program to simulate the controller in the block diagram of Fig. P5–9. What are the controller parameters?

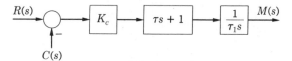

Fig. P5–9

5–10. Repeat Problem 5–6 for the hydraulic components given in Fig. P5–10. Neglect the cylinder piston load.

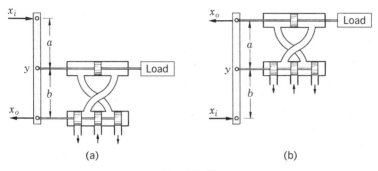

(a)   (b)

Fig. P5–10

5–11. Sketch the frequency response on the Bode plot of a commercial PI controller with $K_c = 5$, $\tau_i = 1$, and $\alpha = 30$ in series with a control actuator having the following parameters:

(a) Transmission lag time constant $\tau = 0.5$ min, and unity gain.

(b) Transmission lag of unity gain and $\zeta = 0.2$, and $\omega_n = 2$ rad/min.

5–12. A pneumatic actuator positioner based on the motion-balance principle is given in Fig. P5–12. Analyze the device to find its transfer function, and draw a signal flow diagram for the positioner. Note any simplifying assumptions made in your analysis.

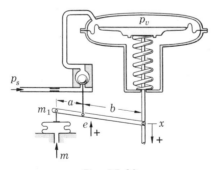

Fig. P5–12

6

System Response and
Performance Specifications

The theme of this text is the elucidation of the cause-and-effect relationships in physical systems and how these relationships may be used to control industrial processes. It is abundantly clear from the examples discussed that the system differential equation gives the response of a device in terms of the input commands. Previous chapters discussed the dynamic characteristics of typical devices in electric, mechanical, pneumatic, fluid, and thermal systems. A controlled plant is a plant to which are added other selected devices (controllers, actuators, control valves, measurement transducers, etc.), generally in feedback and feedforward networks, for the purpose of improving the plant operation. The fascinating ways in which these control devices influence the performance of the process plant is the subject of this chapter.

6-1. FEEDBACK SYSTEM EQUATIONS

The discussion of control terminology and signal flow diagrams in Chapter 1 emphasized the general advantages of control based on the use of feedforward and feedback signals. The block diagram in Fig. 6-1 is a simplification of the generalized block diagram in Fig. 1-10 for a control system using feedback. It represents the essential characteristics of a great many process control situations. The Laplace-transformed symbols have the same significance as those defined for Fig. 1-10. The system inputs are $R(s)$, the set-point variable, and $U(s)$, the load or disturbance variable. The system output is $C(s)$, the controlled variable, and the various $G_i(s)$'s represent system-component transfer functions. The transfer functions are functions of the complex variable s, but the functional notation will be omitted for simplicity here. By use of the signal flow diagram reduction rules in Chapter 1, the overall response of the

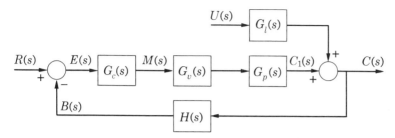

Fig. 6–1.   Block diagram of simple feedback control system.

control system is given by

$$C(s) = \frac{G_c G_v G_p}{1 + G_c G_v G_p H} R(s) + \frac{G_l}{1 + G_c G_v G_p H} U(s) \tag{6-1}$$

where the $+$ sign in the denominator denotes negative feedback. Of course, the response equation can be obtained by eliminating $E(s)$, $C_1(s)$ and $B(s)$ from the following equations:

Error detector: $\qquad E(s) = R(s) - B(s)$

Measurement: $\qquad B(s) = HC(s)$

Forward path: $\qquad C_1(s) = G_c G_v G_p E(s)$

Load summer: $\qquad C(s) = C_1(s) + G_l U(s)$

Under follower-type operation of the system, corresponding to a programmed input $R(s)$, if $U(s)$ is constant at a steady-state value, the output/set-point system equation is

$$\frac{C(s)}{R(s)} = \frac{G_c G_v G_p}{1 + G_c G_v G_p H} = \frac{\text{forward transfer function from } E(s)}{1 + \text{loop transfer function}} \tag{6-2}$$

and the error/set-point system equation is

$$\frac{E(s)}{R(s)} = \frac{R(s) - B(s)}{R(s)} = 1 - \frac{G_c G_v G_p H}{1 + G_c G_v G_p H} = \frac{1}{1 + G_c G_v G_p H} \tag{6-3}$$

Notice that $E(s) = R(s) - B(s)$ is a "computed error" and not the true error which is $R(s) - C(s)$. Usually $B(s)$ is the recorded variable and the true value of $C(s)$, the controlled variable, is not known.

Under regulator operation of the system, corresponding to steady-state control, if $R(s)$ is constant at a steady-state value, the output/load system equation is

$$\frac{C(s)}{U(s)} = \frac{G_l}{1 + G_c G_v G_p H} = \frac{\text{forward transfer function from } U(s)}{1 + \text{loop transfer function}} \tag{6-4}$$

and the error/load system equation is

$$\frac{E(s)}{U(s)} = \frac{-G_l H}{1 + G_c G_v G_p H} \tag{6-5}$$

Two algebraic terms, the loop ratio $G_c G_v G_p H$ and the characteristic equation $1 + G_c G_v G_p H$ have special significance since they occur repeatedly in the above equations. The first term is the gain experienced by the signal in traversing the loop from any point in the loop and the second term is the operational form of the system homogeneous equation called the characteristic equation of the system.

Sensitivity. Some of the characteristics of negative feedback in a control system are seen by allowing $R(s)$, $U(s)$, G_p, and H in Eq. 6-1 to vary and examining the differential coefficients when the value of $G_c G_v G_p H$ is much larger than unity.

1. The effect of changes in $R(s)$ on the controlled variable $C(s)$ is

$$\frac{\partial C(s)}{\partial R(s)} = \frac{G_c G_v G_p}{1 + G_v G_c G_p H} \sim \frac{1}{H} \qquad \text{if } G_c G_v G_p \gg 1 \tag{6-6a}$$

The $C(s)/R(s)$ relationship now depends on the low-power element H instead of the high-power units G_v and G_p. This effect was observed in the analysis of the pneumatic nozzle-baffle and other feedback devices studied. When $H = 1$ and $G_c G_v G_p \gg 1$, the system output reproduces the input. Therefore, the feedback element H must be selected for fast response, accuracy, and long-time reliability.

2. The effect of changes in load variable $U(s)$ on the controlled variable is

$$\frac{\partial C(s)}{\partial U(s)} = \frac{G_l}{1 + G_c G_v G_p H} \sim \frac{G_l}{G_c G_v G_p H} \tag{6-6b}$$

This effect is minimized when the loop ratio is large.

3. The effect of changes in plant characteristics G_p on the controlled variable is

$$\frac{\partial C(s)}{\partial G_p} = \frac{G_c G_v R(s)}{(1 + G_c G_v G_p H)^2} \sim \frac{R(s)}{G_c G_v G_p{}^2 H^2} \qquad \frac{\partial C(s)}{\partial G_p} \sim \frac{-G_l U(s)}{G_c G_v G_p{}^2 H} \tag{6-6c}$$

When the loop ratio is high, the plant response is not sensitive to changes in G_p, provided G_p is not small.

4. The effect of changes in the measurement transducer H on the controlled variable is

$$\frac{\partial C(s)}{\partial H} = \frac{-G_c{}^2 G_v{}^2 G_p{}^2 R(s)}{(1 + G_c G_v G_p H)^2} = \frac{-G_c G_v G_p C(s)}{1 + G_c G_v G_p H} \sim \frac{\bar{C}(s)}{H} \tag{6-6d}$$

showing that a given fractional change in H gives the same fractional change in $C(s)$. Therefore, highest-quality components should be selected for process measurement.

Stability. An unsophisticated, brute-force approach to the selection and adjustment of the controller components in a control system might be to select the poles and zeros of G_c to cancel the zeros and poles of G_vG_pH and to have infinite gain; for then, it would appear that $C(s) = R(s)$ at all times. Also, the system compensation would be perfect, since transients would decay in zero time and there could be no error. This approach is not practical for, in general, the plant zeros and poles shift with the wear and tear of plant operation and most systems become unstable as the controller gain is increased. Thus, the design of a practical control system becomes an entertaining problem in engineering compromise between system stability and accuracy on the one hand and system economic objective on the other.

A stable system has a bounded output for a bounded input; i.e., it will come to rest sometime after termination of any input signal. The response of a feedback system described by Eq. 6–1 depends upon the poles p_1, p_2, etc., of the transfer function of the system, for then

$$C(s) = \frac{G_cG_vG_pR(s)}{1 + G_cG_vG_pH} = \frac{k_1}{s + p_1} + \frac{k_2}{s + p_2} + \cdots \qquad (6\text{–}7a)$$

The corresponding time response is

$$c(t) = k_1e^{-p_1t} + k_2e^{-p_2t} + \cdots \qquad (6\text{–}7b)$$

If any pole is positive or has a positive real part, the corresponding transient term will contain a growing exponential term e^{+pt}, giving an unbounded response. The test for system stability is to determine if any system pole has a positive real part. A special case occurs when a pair of pure imaginary poles are present. This corresponds to an undamped sinusoidal response (system oscillation), and the system can be of no value as a production unit for constant quality product.

The above stability test requires that roots of the system characteristic equation be known. Since these are normally not available, the Routh-Hurwitz criterion (Chapter 2) will be used in this chapter to determine if any zero of the characteristic equation has a positive real part, causing the system to be unstable. The student should verify that no second-order system can be unstable when all the terms in the system equation are present and have like signs.

Zero Steady-State Error. After a process set-point or load change occurs it must not be assumed that a system will reach an error-free steady-state condition. It will be seen that a steady-state error called *offset* is a characteristic of proportional control. The control mode needed to ensure freedom from steady-state error depends upon the form of the set-point or load change and upon the transfer function of the process system.

The Laplace-transform final-value theorem provides an easy method for finding steady-state values of process responses. When it is applied to Eq. 6-3 with a unit step change in set point, $R(s) = 1/s$, the steady-state error is found as

$$\lim_{t \to \infty} e(t) = \lim_{s \to 0} s \left(\frac{1}{1 + G_c G_v G_p H} \right) \frac{1}{s} = \lim_{s \to 0} \frac{1}{1 + G_c G_v G_p H} \qquad (6\text{-}8)$$

The error will be zero only if the $G_c G_v G_p H$ term contains an integrator element ($1/s$ term). In a similar manner, if the set-point change $R(s) = 1/s^n$, then it is necessary, for zero steady-state error, that $G_c G_v G_p H$ contain an element having the transform $1/s^n$ but it is not necessary that this element be in the controller.

6-2. FEEDFORWARD SYSTEM EQUATIONS

The effects of process disturbances or load changes on a control system can be minimized by use of feedforward techniques whenever the disturbance is measurable. As discussed in Chapter 1 this technique supplements the more general feedback control methods. The use of feedforward control is shown in Fig. 6-2 where it is used to compensate for process

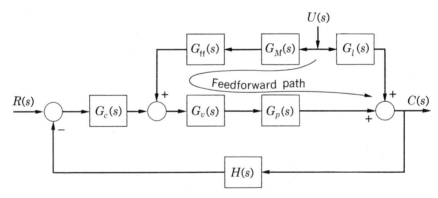

Fig. 6-2. Feedforward control used to compensate for load changes. The feedforward loop supplements the negative feedback control loop.

load change $U(s)$. G_m and G_{ff} are the load measurement and feedforward controller transfer functions respectively. Feedforward control as used here is a form of disturbance control using calibrated open-loop devices. It is very effective when used with closed-loop control. The disturbance control system equation is obtained by inspection as

$$\frac{C(s)}{U(s)} = \frac{G_l + G_m G_{ff} G_v G_p}{1 + G_c G_v G_p H} \qquad (6\text{-}9a)$$

Now it is clear that perfect compensation for changes in $U(s)$ may be obtained if the numerator is set equal to zero, so that the exact feed-forward transfer function is

$$G_{ff} = \frac{-G_l}{G_m G_v G_p} \qquad (6\text{-}9b)$$

Normally, it is expected that G_{ff} would be complex and difficult to maintain, owing to normal wear and flucutations in plant operating level, but in practice exact compensation is not necessary when a feedback loop is present, since relatively simple compensation devices are beneficial. A frequent practical difficulty in applying this control principle is the problem of measuring the disturbance signals in the system.

6-3. RESPONSE OF SIMPLE SYSTEMS

The control engineer is interested in both time response and frequency response of a controlled plant. These two responses are interrelated, and system specifications may be based on either or both responses. This article is concerned with the calculation of time response of simple systems for the purposes of showing the effect of controller action on system performance and illustrating the meaning of certain performance terms. The simple problems considered here have little practical significance and it is soon realized that the hand computation method must be abandoned in favor of machine computation, root-locus, or frequency response techniques when practical plant control problems are considered.

Proportional Control (P). Proportional controllers are widely used in process plants. Consider the control of liquid level in an open, cylindrical tank subject to controlled liquid inflow i_i and uncontrolled liquid inflow u, as shown in Fig. 6–3a. Assuming that the flow resistance and the control valve are linear, the transformed system equations are written as:

Controller equation:
$$M(s) = K_c E(s) \quad \text{or} \quad G_c = K_c \qquad \text{(I)}$$
Control valve: $\qquad I_i(s) = kM(s) \quad \text{or} \quad G_v = k \qquad \text{(II)}$
Volumetric rate balance:
$$AsC(s) = I_i(s) - I_o(s) + U(s) \qquad \text{(III)}$$
Outflow rate: $\qquad I_o(s) = C(s)/R \qquad \text{(IV)}$
Measurement: $\qquad B(s) = C(s) \quad \text{or} \quad H = 1 \qquad \text{(V)}$

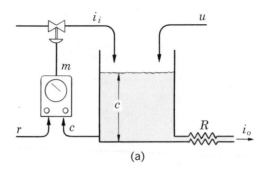

(a)

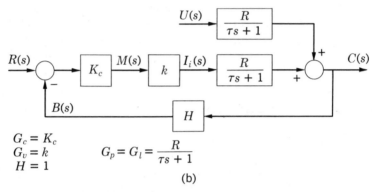

$$G_c = K_c$$
$$G_v = k \qquad G_p = G_l = \frac{R}{\tau s + 1}$$
$$H = 1$$

(b)

Fig. 6–3. (a) Proportional control system of a first-order liquid-level process. (b) Signal flow diagram.

The process equation becomes

$$C(s) = \frac{R}{\tau s + 1} [kM(s) + U(s)] \qquad G_p = G_l = \frac{R}{\tau s + 1} \qquad \text{(VI)}$$

where $\tau = RA$, the tank time constant. Values of the variables may be expressed in absolute magnitude or as deviations from steady-state values.

For negative feedback operation, the system equations of interest are Eqs. 6–2, 6–3, 6–4, and 6–5, which for this liquid-level process become

Output/set point: $\qquad \dfrac{C(s)}{R(s)} = \dfrac{K_c k R}{K_c k R + 1} \dfrac{1}{Ts + 1}$ $\qquad$ (6–10a)

Error/set point: $\qquad \dfrac{E(s)}{R(s)} = \dfrac{1}{K_c k R + 1} \dfrac{\tau s + 1}{Ts + 1}$ $\qquad$ (6–10b)

Output/load: $\qquad \dfrac{C(s)}{U(s)} = \dfrac{R}{K_c k R + 1} \dfrac{1}{Ts + 1}$ $\qquad$ (6–10c)

Error/load: $\qquad \dfrac{E(s)}{U(s)} = \dfrac{-R}{K_c k R + 1} \dfrac{1}{Ts + 1}$ $\qquad$ (6–10d)

where $T = \tau/(K_c kR + 1)$ and $\tau = RA$. It can be immediately seen that the response of the feedback system will be faster than the uncontrolled system because $T < \tau$. Thus proportional action provides increased speed of response in the system.

Consider the unit step responses of the above equations. When inputs $R(s) = 1/s$ and $U(s) = 1/s$ are substituted in the appropriate equations and the resulting equations inverted, the system step responses are:

Output/set point:

$$c_r(t) = \frac{K_c kR}{K_c kR + 1} (1 - e^{-t/T}) \qquad (6\text{-}11\text{a})$$

Error/set point:

$$e_r(t) = \frac{1}{K_c kR + 1} (1 + K_c kRe^{-t/T}) = 1 - c_r(t) \qquad (6\text{-}11\text{b})$$

Output/load:

$$c_u(t) = \frac{R}{K_c kR + 1} (1 - e^{-t/T}) \qquad (6\text{-}11\text{c})$$

Error/load:

$$e_u(t) = -c_u(t) \qquad \text{because } r(t) = 0 \qquad (6\text{-}11\text{d})$$

These four responses are plotted in Fig. 6-4 for several values of $K_c kR$ to show the effect of K_c on system response. A value of $K_c kR = 0$ corresponds to the uncontrolled system. The plots show that as $K_c kR$ increases the response is faster (system reaches a new final value sooner) and the system error is smaller, i.e., the control is "tighter."

The principle of proportional control requires a proportional relationship between valve position and controlled variable for a given controller gain. The result is that a proportional controller can produce an exact correction for only one load condition or one set-point value. When load conditions or set-point changes occur that require a new valve position, proportional action requires a change in the deviation (controlled variable if $r(t)$ is constant) giving a steady-state process error called offset. The offset is clearly shown, in the $c_u(t)$ plot in Fig. 6-4c, to depend inversely on the gain $K_c kR$. The offset, being the steady-state load error, can be found by use of the Laplace-transform final-value theorem as

$$\text{Offset} = \lim_{t \to \infty} e_u(t) = \lim_{s \to 0} sE_u(s)$$

In the present case shown in Fig. 6-4, for unit step change in load $U(s) = 1/s$, and the load offset is

$$\text{Offset} = \lim_{s \to 0} s \left[\frac{-R}{K_c kR + 1} \frac{1}{Ts + 1} \frac{1}{s} \right] = \frac{-R}{K_c kR + 1}$$

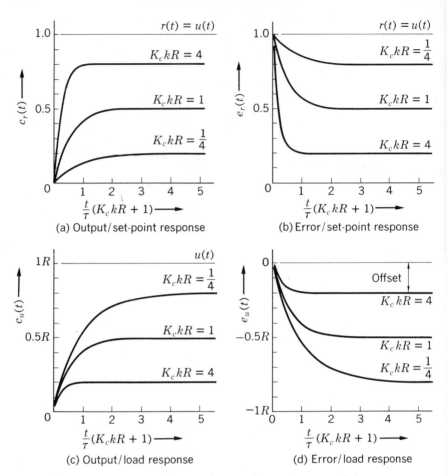

Fig. 6–4. Unit step responses of proportional control of first-order lag process.

in agreement with the response in Fig. 6–4d.   Control action is extremely helpful in counteracting process load changes.   In this case, in the absence of control (corresponding to $K_c = 0$), the load offset would be $-R$.

Offset is an inescapable result of process load changes in a system under proportional control.   It can be eliminated by manually changing the controller set-point to bring the controlled variable back to the desired value or, as will be seen later, by adding integral action to the controller.

Example 6–1.   The steady-state behavior of a proportional control system may be shown by graphically solving the operating process equations under steady-state conditions.

(a) Take the liquid-level system described above, and graphically obtain steady-state operating conditions for set-point values of $r = 4$ and 6 ft of fluid. The process equations for steady-state conditions are

Error detector: $e = r - c$
Controller: $m = e + 9$
Control valve: $i = m - 3$
Process: $c = 2i/3$

where e, r, and c are measured in ft of fluid, m in psig, and i in ft^3/min.

(b) Also show the effect of controller gain increase from 1 psig/ft to 2 psig/ft on the steady-state error.

(c) If the span of the liquid-level measurement is 6 ft of fluid, find the percentage proportional band of the controller when its gain is 1 psig/ft and when it is 2 psig/ft. Full stroke of the control valve requires a 12-psig pressure change.

Solution. (a) Graphs of the operating equations are located in Fig. E6–1 so that, by following the process signals in a clockwise manner from error → con-

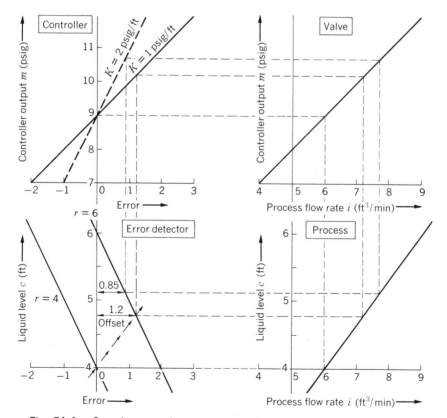

Fig. E6–1. Steady-state characteristics of controlled liquid-level plant.

troller → control valve → process → error, etc., the signal path will converge to a set of steady-state values which satisfy the equations. In one case in Fig. E6–1, the controller is adjusted to give $r = c = 4$ ft of fluid and $e = 0$ when $m = 9$ psig and $i = 6$ ft³/min as shown by the lines connecting these points on the plot. Now, suppose the controller set point is changed to $r = 6$ ft of fluid, giving an error of $e = 2$ ft of fluid to the controller. The controller output increases; the control valve begins to open; the fluid flow rate into the process increases, which raises the liquid level in the tank and decreases the error. The control valve continues to open until a new steady-state condition is reached when $e = 1.2$ ft, $m = 10.2$ psig, $i = 7.2$ ft³/min, and $c = 4.8$ ft of fluid (instead of the desired $c = 6$ ft). This is not tight control, as is shown by the low gain of the loop ratio, which is

$$\frac{\tilde{c}}{\tilde{e}} = G_c G_v G_p = \frac{\tilde{m}}{\tilde{e}} \frac{\tilde{i}}{\tilde{m}} \frac{\tilde{c}}{\tilde{i}} = 1 \times 1 \times \frac{2}{3} = \frac{2}{3}$$

where the tildes represent deviation from the initial steady-state value when $r = c = 4$ ft. The closed-loop gain is

$$\frac{\tilde{c}}{\tilde{r}} = \frac{G}{1+G} = \frac{2}{3} \times \frac{3}{5} = 0.4$$

so that a value of $\tilde{r} = 2$ ft gives $\tilde{c} = 0.8$ ft and a steady-state value of $c = 4.0 + 0.8 = 4.8$ ft of fluid, which agrees with the graphical result. One concludes that increased error leads to increased flow rate through the control value.

(b) The system error can be decreased by increasing the controller gain. When the controller gain is increased from 1 to 2 psig/ft of fluid as shown on Fig. E6–1, the system error for a value of $r = 6.0$ ft of fluid is reduced from the previous 1.2 ft to 0.85 ft of fluid.

(c) The percentage of proportional band is the percentage of controller span required to completely stroke the control valve. When the controller gain is 1 psig/ft and the valve stroke requires a 12-psig change, the proportional band is

$$\%\text{PB} = \frac{12 \text{ psig}}{\text{stroke}} \frac{1 \text{ ft}}{\text{psig}} \frac{\text{span}}{6 \text{ ft}} 100\% = 200\% \frac{\text{span}}{\text{stroke}}$$

and, when the controller gain is 2 psig/ft, the percentage proportional band is

$$\%\text{PB} = 12 \times \frac{1}{2} \times \frac{1}{6} 100\% = 100\% \frac{\text{span}}{\text{stroke}}$$

Feedback Dynamics. The measuring transducer is a source of time lags in a control loop. This discussion contrasts the effect of an additional first-order lag in the feedback branch (measurement) with its effect in the forward branch of the control loop. The two cases are shown in Fig. 6–5, where a first-order lag $(1/(\tau_1 s + 1))$ has been added in different branches of the loop. Examples of physical plants represented by these two cases could be: case 1—liquid level control of a two-capacity plant with a perfect measuring transducer, $H = 1$; and case 2—liquid-level control of a one-capacity plant with an actual measuring transducer having a time lag $H = 1/(\tau_1 s + 1)$. In case 1, $C_1(s)$ is the controlled variable and also the feedback variable, so that the true error and the system error $E(s)$ are equal and given by $R(s) - C_1(s)$. In case 2, $C_2(s)$ is the controlled variable and $C_1(s)$ is the feedback variable, so that the true error is $R(s) - C_2(s)$ and the system error $E(s) = R(s) - C_1(s)$ are not the same. The controller acts upon the system error to manipulate the process and an attached recorder would record the feedback variable, with the result that the control action is not directly proportional to the true error and the actual magnitude of the controlled variable is not recorded. Large differences may exist between the controlled and feedback variables in such systems.

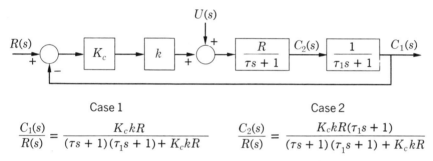

Case 1

$$\frac{C_1(s)}{R(s)} = \frac{K_c k R}{(\tau s + 1)(\tau_1 s + 1) + K_c k R}$$

Case 2

$$\frac{C_2(s)}{R(s)} = \frac{K_c k R(\tau_1 s + 1)}{(\tau s + 1)(\tau_1 s + 1) + K_c k R}$$

Fig. 6-5. Proportional control of second-order system. Case 1 has both lags in the forward branch while case 2 has one lag in the forward branch and one lag in the feedback branch of the system.

The output/set-point equations for the two cases shown in Fig. 6-5 are:

Case 1: $$\frac{C_1(s)}{R(s)} = \frac{K_c k R}{(\tau s + 1)(\tau_1 s + 1) + K_c k R} = \frac{K_c k R}{1 + K_c k R} \frac{1}{\dfrac{s^2}{\omega_n^2} + 2\zeta \dfrac{s}{\omega_n} + 1}$$
(6-12a)

Case 2: $$\frac{C_2(s)}{R(s)} = \frac{K_c k R(\tau_1 s + 1)}{(\tau s + 1)(\tau_1 s + 1) + K_c k R} = \frac{K_c k R}{1 + K_c k R} \frac{\tau_1 s + 1}{\dfrac{s^2}{\omega_n^2} + 2\zeta \dfrac{s}{\omega_n} + 1}$$
(6-12b)

where

$$\omega_n = \sqrt{\frac{K_c k R + 1}{\tau \tau_1}} \quad \text{and} \quad \zeta = \frac{\tau + \tau_1}{2\sqrt{\tau \tau_1 (K_c k R + 1)}}$$

in the control system characteristic equation. The system is always stable for $\zeta > 0$ but it will be oscillatory when $0 < \zeta < 1$. Two characteristics of closed-loop proportional control are evident from the equations. The response can be faster than the open-loop response because the damping ratio can be less than unity, and the unit step response will show a steady-state error, thus:

$$\lim_{t \to \infty} e(t) = \frac{1}{K_c k R + 1}$$

The unit step response for these two cases is found by putting $R(s) = 1/s$ and inverting the equations to give

Case 1: $c_1(t) = \dfrac{K_c k R}{1 + K_c k R}\left[1 + \dfrac{1}{\sqrt{1 - \zeta^2}} e^{-\zeta \omega_n t} \sin\left(\omega_n \sqrt{1 - \zeta^2}\, t - \phi\right)\right]$

$$(6\text{--}12c)$$

where $\phi = \tan^{-1} \sqrt{1 - \zeta^2}/(-\zeta)$, and

Case 2: $c_2(t) = \dfrac{K_c k R}{1 + K_c k R}\left\{1 + \dfrac{1}{\sqrt{1 - \zeta^2}}\right.$

$$\left. [1 - 2\zeta\omega_n\tau_1 + \tau_1^2\omega_n^2]^{1/2} e^{-\zeta\omega_n t} \sin\left(\omega_n \sqrt{1 - \zeta^2}\, t - \phi\right)\right\} \quad (6\text{--}12d)$$

where $\phi = \tan^{-1} \sqrt{1 - \zeta^2}/(-\zeta) - \tan^{-1} \omega_n\tau_1 \sqrt{1 - \zeta^2}/(1 - \zeta\omega_n\tau_1)$.

Analog computer simulation of these two cases is obtained by the program in Fig. 6–6a. For simulation purposes the system parameters are selected as: $0 < K_c < 20$, $\tau = \tau_1 = 1$ sec, $R = k = 1$. The unit step responses to change in $r(t)$ are shown in Fig. 6–6b, c for two controller gain values. The gain values of $K_c = 10$ and $K_c = 20$ correspond to damping ratios of 0.301 and 0.218, respectively; and to damped frequencies of oscillation of 3.16 and 4.47 rad/sec, respectively ($\omega_d = \sqrt{K_c}$). These values are in good agreement with the computer results. Besides showing the relationship between K_c, ω_d, and ζ, the computer results indicate that (1) the set-point error due to proportional control decreases as the gain increases, (2) the overshoot increases with gain increase, and (3) when process measurement is not perfect, the recorded feedback variable $c_1(t)$ does not directly indicate the magnitude of changes in $c_2(t)$, the controlled variable.

Integral Control (I). It is seen that proportional control of time-lag systems always results in static errors due to load or set-point changes. Introduction of integral action into the forward path of the loop, either in the controller or in the process, will give corrective action proportional to the time integral of the error and thereby eliminate the static error.

Integral control used alone is generally referred to as proportional-speed floating control. Its action is illustrated by applying it to the liquid-level process in Fig. 6–3. In this case, $G_c = 1/\tau_i s$, $H = 1$, and the output/set-

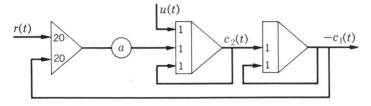

(a) Analog simulation

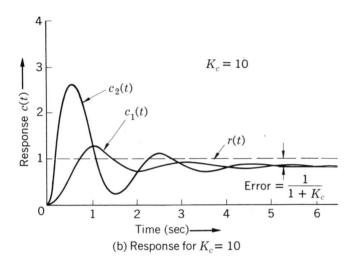

(b) Response for $K_c = 10$

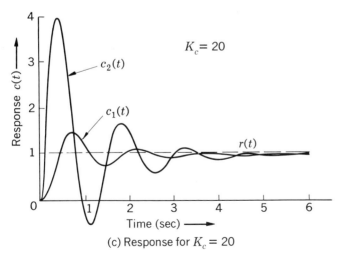

(c) Response for $K_c = 20$

Fig. 6–6. Unit step response of second-order system shown in Fig. 6–5. Values of R, k, τ, and τ_1 are unity.

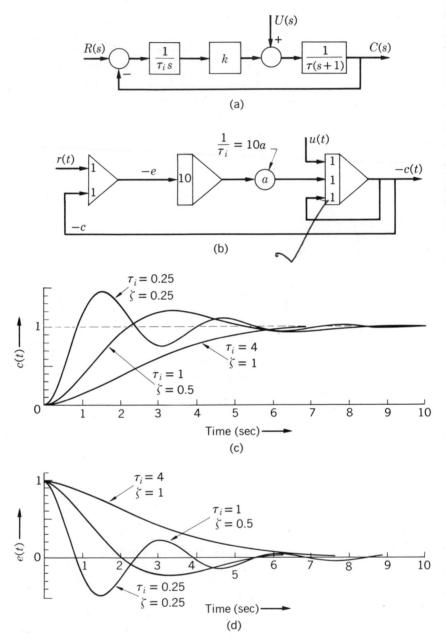

Fig. 6–7. Unit step response of single-capacity process under integral control. Integral action eliminates static error in the system. (a) Signal flow diagram. (b) Analog simulation. (c) Response of controlled variable. (d) Response of system error.

point system equation becomes

$$\frac{C(s)}{R(s)} = \frac{kR}{\tau_i \tau s^2 + \tau_i s + kR} = \frac{1}{\dfrac{s^2}{\omega_n{}^2} + 2\zeta \dfrac{s}{\omega_n} + 1} \tag{6-13a}$$

where $\omega_n = \sqrt{kR/\tau_i \tau}$ and $\zeta = \frac{1}{2}\sqrt{\tau_i/\tau kR}$. The system has the response of a second-order system and the damping ratio can be less than or greater than unity, depending upon the value of τ_i. The response of the system to a unit step change in set point is

$$c(t) = 1 + \frac{1}{\sqrt{1 - \zeta^2}} e^{-\zeta \omega_n t} \sin (\omega_n \sqrt{1 - \zeta^2}\, t - \phi)$$

$$\phi = \tan^{-1} \sqrt{1 - \zeta^2}/(-\zeta) \tag{6-13b}$$

from which it is seen that the system has no static error. Thus, integral action provides accuracy of response in the system.

An analog simulation of this system with unit values for τ, k, and R is shown in Fig. 6–7 with controlled variable and system error response curves for a unit step change in the set-point variable. Notice that integral control has eliminated static error in the system, that a value of $\tau_i = 4$ makes the system critically damped, and that as τ_i approaches zero, the damping ratio ζ approaches zero and the system approaches a sustained oscillation condition.

Proportional-plus-Integral Control (PI). Proportional and integral control modes are combined to give the stabilizing effect of proportional action and the static accuracy provided by integral action. Consider the application of this type of ideal controller to a process having two time lags τ, τ_1, and a gain R. The signal flow diagram and system equations are shown in Fig. 6–8 for two possible physical interpretations of such a

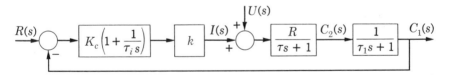

Case 1. $\dfrac{C_1(s)}{R(s)} = \dfrac{K_c kR(\tau_i s + 1)}{\tau_i s(\tau s + 1)(\tau_1 s + 1) + K_c kR(\tau_i s + 1)}$ (unity feedback)

Case 2. $\dfrac{C_2(s)}{R(s)} = \dfrac{K_c kR(\tau_i s + 1)(\tau_1 s + 1)}{\tau_i s(\tau s + 1)(\tau_1 s + 1) + K_c kR(\tau_i s + 1)}$ (lag in feedback)

Fig. 6–8. Proportional-integral control of second-order system. Case 1 exhibits unity feedback with $C_1(s)$ as the controlled variable. Case 2 considers $C_2(s)$ as the controlled variable with a first-order lag in the measuring device.

system. In case 1, the plant process is a second-order lag device and $H = 1$ for the feedback path. In case 2, the plant process is a first-order lag with $c_2(t)$ being the controlled variable and the feedback path is a first-order lag measuring device.

The output/set-point system equations for both cases have the same cubic characteristic equation, which can be symbolically factored as

$$1 + G_cG_vG_pH = \tau_i\tau\tau_1 s^3 + \tau_i(\tau + \tau_1)s^2 + \tau_i(1 + K_ckR)s + K_ckR$$

$$= K_ckR(\tau_e s + 1)\left(\frac{s^2}{\omega_n^2} + \frac{2\zeta}{\omega_n}s + 1\right) \qquad (6\text{–}14a)$$

where the relationships required by the factors are:

$$\frac{\tau_e}{\omega_n^2} = \frac{\tau_i\tau\tau_1}{K_ckR} \qquad \frac{1}{\omega_n^2} + \frac{2\zeta\tau_e}{\omega_n} = \frac{\tau_i(\tau + \tau_1)}{K_ckR} \qquad \tau_e + \frac{2\zeta}{\omega_n} = \frac{\tau_i(1 + K_ckR)}{K_ckR}$$

Then the output/set-point response of the system for the two cases is given as

Case 1:
$$\frac{C_1(s)}{R(s)} = \frac{\tau_i s + 1}{(\tau_e s + 1)\left(\dfrac{s^2}{\omega_n^2} + 2\zeta \dfrac{s}{\omega_n} + 1\right)} \qquad (6\text{–}14b)$$

Case 2:
$$\frac{C_2(s)}{R(s)} = \frac{(\tau_i s + 1)(\tau_1 s + 1)}{(\tau_e s + 1)\left(\dfrac{s^2}{\omega_n^2} + 2\zeta \dfrac{s}{\omega_n} + 1\right)} \qquad (6\text{–}14c)$$

In general, this approach is not effective for design because of the algebraic work of finding values of τ_e, ω_n, and ζ and also because the relationship between the factors and the constants of the equation is difficult to visualize; hence there is little indication which way to change a system constant to improve the system response. Other analysis techniques such as root locus, frequency response and computer simulation are available for handling practical problems.

Under certain conditions this third-order system can become unstable. Instability will be found in the factoring approach by the presence of poles with positive real parts. However, the Routh-Hurwitz theorem (Chapter 2) can detect instability without factoring the characteristic system equation. The method is illustrated by application to the cubic system represented by Eq. 6–14a. The array of equation coefficients is formed and completed as described in Chapter 2 to give

$$
\begin{array}{llll}
s^3: & \tau_i\tau\tau_1 & \tau_i(1 + K_ckR) & 0 \\
s^2: & \tau_i(\tau + \tau_1) & K_ckR & 0 \\
s: & \tau_i(1 + K_ckR) - \dfrac{\tau\tau_1 K_ckR}{\tau + \tau_1} & 0 & \\
s^0: & K_ckR & 0 &
\end{array}
$$

The Routh-Hurwitz theorem requires that all the coefficients in the first column of the array be positive for a stable system. Therefore, the conclusion is that stability in this system depends upon

$$\tau_i > \frac{\tau\tau_1}{\tau + \tau_1} \frac{K_c kR}{1 + K_c kR} \simeq \frac{\tau\tau_1}{\tau + \tau_1} \qquad \text{if } K_c kR \gg 1 \qquad (6\text{-}14\text{d})$$

It was seen in the previous article that this system was always stable with proportional control, but now it is clear that the addition of too much integral action can force the system unstable. Useful values of τ_i must be greater than the value for the unstable system and yet small enough to eliminate process offset in a reasonable time; in other words, selection of a τ_i value is an engineering compromise.

An analog simulation of this system with unit values for τ, R, k, and τ_1 is shown in Fig. 6-9. The simulation program as developed from the

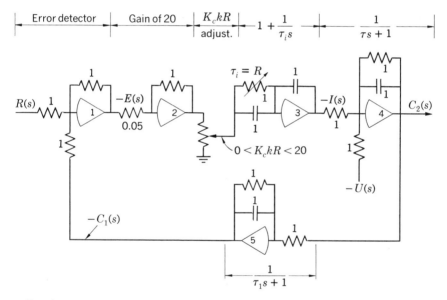

Fig. 6-9. Analog computer program for PI control of a two-capacity process. The values of resistors are in megohms and the values of capacitors are in microfarads.

transfer functions can be followed by comparing the amplifiers in Fig. 6-9 with the blocks in the signal flow diagram of Fig. 6-8. The computer program is scaled to simulate the system in real time, i.e., one second of computer time equals one second of real system time. The computer will display the transient response of this system to any input or load disturbance. For a stable system, the integral time constant must be

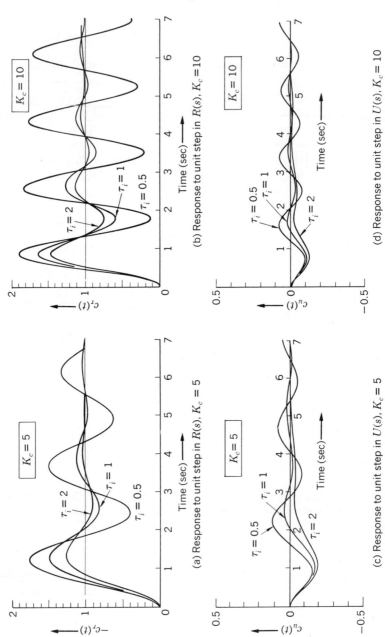

Fig. 6-10. Response of two-capacity system with PI control to unit step changes in set-point and load variables.

greater than $K_c/2(1 + K_c)$.   Responses for unit step changes in set-point and load variables are given in Fig. 6–10 for controller gains of 5 and 10 and for various integral times.   In the set-point responses in Fig. 6–10a, the controller gain is 5 and the responses are shown for $\tau_i = 2, 1, 0.5$.   The system will be unstable if $\tau_i < 0.416$.   The system is oscillatory for all cases shown, and a decrease in τ_i decreases the damping in the system, increases the extent of overshoot, and increases the damped frequency of oscillation.   The same comments apply to the curves in Fig. 6–10b for $K_c = 10$.   In Figs. 6–10c and d unit load responses are shown for the controller settings discussed above.   Notice that integral action has eliminated the offset and that higher controller gains K_c permit smaller excursions due to load changes.   The system exhibits the same damped frequency of oscillation for load and/or set-point changes.

Proportional-plus-Derivative Control (PD).   The derivative-action controller produces a correction that is proportional to the rate of change of the system error; thus, it opposes error change.   A characteristic of this action as shown in Fig. E5-1 is that the derivative output is ahead of the proportional output in time, making this control action very helpful in stabilizing systems.   When the system error is constant the derivative action exerts no control action; therefore this control action is never used alone, but always with proportional or proportional-plus-integral action.

The signal flow diagram for PD control of a second-order plant is given in Fig. 6–11.   As previously discussed, two cases are of interest: case 1 has $C_1(s)$ as the controlled variable and unity feedback, while case 2 has $C_2(s)$ as the controlled variable and a first-order lag in the (measuring device) feedback.   The output/set-point relationships are:

Case 1:

$$\frac{C_1(s)}{R(s)} = \frac{K_c kR(1 + \tau_d s)}{(\tau s + 1)(\tau_1 s + 1) + K_c kR(1 + \tau_d s)}$$

$$= \frac{K_c kR}{1 + K_c kR} \cdot \frac{1 + \tau_d s}{\dfrac{s^2}{\omega_n{}^2} + 2\zeta \dfrac{s}{\omega_n} + 1} \tag{6–15a}$$

Case 2:

$$\frac{C_2(s)}{R(s)} = \frac{K_c kR(1 + \tau_d s)(\tau_1 s + 1)}{(\tau s + 1)(\tau_1 s + 1) + K_c kR(1 + \tau_d s)}$$

$$= \frac{K_c kR}{1 + K_c kR} \cdot \frac{(1 + \tau_d s)(\tau_1 s + 1)}{\dfrac{s^2}{\omega_n{}^2} + 2\zeta \dfrac{s}{\omega_n} + 1} \tag{6–15b}$$

where

$$\omega_n = \sqrt{\frac{1 + K_c kR}{\tau \tau_1}} \qquad \zeta = \frac{\tau + \tau_1 + \tau_d K_c kR}{2\sqrt{\tau \tau_1(1 + K_c kR)}}$$

A little study of these equations suggests that a direct solution to the controller problem is to make $\tau_d = \tau_1$, so that the zero in the controller transfer

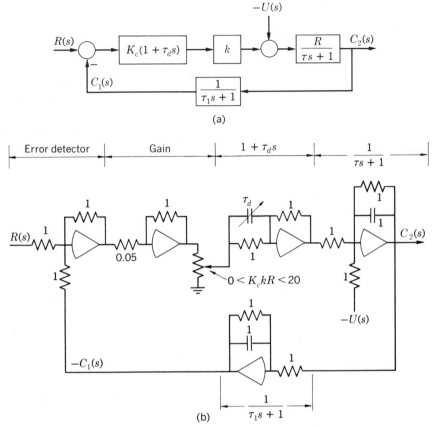

Fig. 6–11. (a) Signal flow diagram and (b) computer program for PD control of a two-capacity process.

function cancels a pole in the plant transfer function. Theoretically, this is a perfect way to adjust a derivative controller, but there are practical limits on its usefulness since the pole in the plant transfer function may not be precisely known or the plant operating conditions may cause it to shift with time. Then cancellation may be only approximate, resulting in a zero-pole dipole instead of the original pole.

Selection of zero-pole cancellation reduces the problem to the proportional control of a one-capacity system, since Eq. 6–15a for $\tau_d = \tau_1$ reduces to

$$\frac{C_1(s)}{R(s)} = \frac{K_c kR}{\tau s + 1 + K_c kR} = \frac{K_c kR}{1 + K_c kR} \cdot \frac{1}{Ts + 1} \tag{6–15c}$$

where $T = \tau/(1 + K_c kR)$; this is identical to Eq. 6–10a.

An analog simulation of this system with unit values for τ, R, k, and τ_1 is shown in Fig. 6–11. The simulation program is developed from the transfer functions in the block diagram and is scaled to display the system response in real time. The system is stable for all positive values of the damping ratio. Responses for unit step change in the set-point variable are given in Fig. 6–12 for controller gains of 10 and 20 and for various

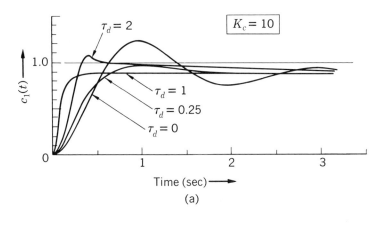

(a)

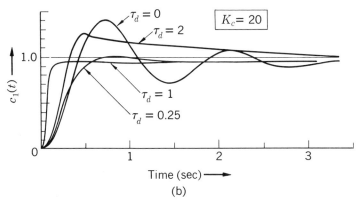

(b)

Fig. 6–12.   Response of a two-capacity system with PD control to a unit step change in set point.

derivative times. Without derivative action ($\tau_d = 0$), the system is a two-capacity plant under proportional control and shows the response given in Fig. 6–6 and in Fig. 6–12 for $\tau_d = 0$. Notice, at low gain ($K_c = 10$) as compared to high gain ($K_c = 20$), that the static error is greater, the overshoot is less, and the frequency of oscillation is lower. With a small derivative time constant in the system, $\tau_d = 0.25$, the response at both gains is improved in that the overshoot is much less and the response tends to be faster. Thus derivative action adds stability to the system. When τ_d is increased to unity, thereby cancelling a pole in the plant transfer function, the response is that of a first-order system as predicted by Eq. 6–15c. Further increase of the derivative time constant produces overshoot and a slow return to static conditions after the disturbance. Obviously, exact zero-pole cancellation produces superior performance but requires careful adjustment of the controller to fit the plant parameters and is not likely to be obtained in practice. However, the response curves show that any amount of derivative action improves the system performance.

6–4. CONTROL SYSTEM PERFORMANCE CRITERIA

The purpose of adding controls to a process is to enable the complete system to overcome or minimize the effects of process loads or upsets on output product quality or to cause the output product quality to follow a desired pattern of input signal. The quality of a process control system can be judged by how well the system accomplishes these aims. Stability is a necessary restraint on the system to ensure freedom from such extreme situations as saturation of a component. Static and dynamic system errors are common physical measures of performance. Consideration of non-physical measures of performance such as reliability, size, cost, and dollar profit on the operation, while of vast economic importance to management, is not discussed in this book.

The study of component responses in Chapter 4 showed that the way to reduce dynamic error for a first-order device was to reduce its time constant τ. If the static error is intolerable because of low gain, a proportional controller in the closed loop can decrease the system time constant and speed up the response. For second-order devices there is no obvious path to minimum error. Decrease of ζ, the damping ratio, leads to fast response, as shown in Figs. 4–12 and 4–13, but too small a ζ allows too many oscillations before the system settles down to the final value and also too much overshoot in the step response. Frequency response performance is equally as important as step response because frequency response is the basis of a much-used technique in control systems design.

Step Response Performance Criteria. Several figures of merit for specifying the performance of control systems are based on the step response. They have exact meaning for the second-order system and less precise meaning for higher-order systems. A typical step response for a high-order system is sketched in Fig. 6–13 to show the meaning of various performance terms.

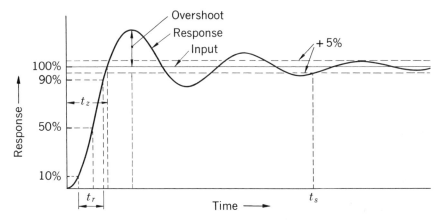

Fig. 6–13.   Sketch showing the meaning of several figures-of-merit terms as applied to the step response of a high-order system.

STABILITY.   All transients decay to zero at steady state in a stable system; however, control systems vary in their rate of approach to steady state after an upset.   This degree of stability or damping is described by several factors, as discussed here.

Overshoot.   Overshoot is the ratio of the maximum overshoot to the final value of the response.   It is the maximum error between input and output signals and indicates the relative stability of the system.

Decay Rate.   Another figure of merit sometimes used for specifying stability is the decay rate, $\zeta \omega_n$.   For a second-order system, it is the real portion of the transfer function pole and appears in the factor $e^{-\zeta \omega_n t}$ in the step response, thereby determining the rate of decay of transients.

Damping Ratio.   As shown in Chapter 4, the damping ratio ζ is a measure of energy dissipation in a second-order device and indicates the response decay per cycle of oscillation.   As the damping ratio decreases the device becomes more oscillatory and, in the limit as ζ goes to zero, the device goes into sustained oscillation—an unstable condition.   In a second-order system a value of $\zeta = 0.215$ produces one-quarter peak attenuation.

SPEED OF RESPONSE.   Several time quantities related to step response as shown in Fig. 6–13 are frequently referred to in discussing control system response.

Rise Time, t_r.   The rise time is the time between 10 and 90% of the final value of response.   Sometimes it is taken as the reciprocal of the slope of the response curve at 50% of the final value.

Settling Time, t_s.   The settling time is the time for the response to reach and remain within a specified percentage (generally 2 or 5%) of the final value of the response; it is inversely proportional to the natural frequency of the system.

First Zero Error Time, t_z.   The first zero error time is the time when the response first equals the final value of the response.

ACCURACY.   Accuracy implies smallness of error and is usually stated in terms of the error.

Steady-State Error.   The steady-state error is the error when the system is at rest.   It can be found from the system error equation by use of the Laplace-transform final value theorem.

Dynamic Error.   The dynamic error is a function of time, given either as $r - c$ or $r - b$.   Several integrated forms of the system error have been used, such as (1) time integral of the error, (2) time integral of the square of the error, (3) time integral of the absolute value of the error (IAE), and (d) time integral of the product of time and the absolute value of the error (ITAE).

Example 6–2.   Analytical methods are available for selecting the best values of control system parameters based upon a dynamic error performance index. One method is illustrated by finding the value of τ_i in Eq. 6–13a which minimizes the time integral of the error square (IES).*

Solution.   The error/set-point relationship for the system described by Eq. 6–13a is

$$\frac{E(s)}{R(s)} = 1 - \frac{C(s)}{R(s)} = \frac{\tau_i s(\tau s + 1)}{\tau_i \tau s^2 + \tau_i s + kR}$$

The transform of the dynamic error in the unit step response of the system is

$$E(s) = \frac{\tau_i(\tau s + 1)}{\tau_i \tau s^2 + \tau_i s + kR}$$

The problem is to select a value of τ_i that minimizes the integral of the error square.   This can be done in the usual manner by inverting $E(s)$ and integrating $e^2(t)$ to give IES, which is a function of parameter τ_i.   Then standard minimization procedures can be used to find the value of τ_i which minimizes IES.   Fortunately, much of the mathematical drudgery involved here may be avoided by use of a special case of Parseval's theorem, which states that the integral of the error square may be expressed in terms of its transform as

$$\text{IES} = \int_{-\infty}^{\infty} e^2(t)\, dt = \frac{1}{2\pi j} \int_{-j\infty}^{j\infty} E(s)E(-s)\, ds$$

The cited reference gives tabulated values of this integral.   For the present problem, the value of the integral becomes

$$\text{IES} = \frac{\tau}{2} + \frac{\tau_i}{2kR}$$

---

* See G. C. Newton, Jr., L. A. Gould, and J. F. Kaiser, *Analytical Design of Linear Feedback Controls*.   John Wiley & Sons, Inc., New York, 1957.

Now, τ_i must be positive for system stability and, by inspection for this problem, the value of τ_i which minimizes the integral of the error square is zero, an impractical value. In practical process systems an increasingly large gain will lead to system instability and infinitely large integral of the error square.

Frequency Response Criteria. Frequency response techniques are widely used in analysis and design of control systems so performance criteria are needed for this method. The frequency response of a first-order lag is developed in Chapter 4. The frequency response of the second-order lag will be developed here and then the common performance criteria will be discussed.

The frequency response of a component may be obtained analytically either by integration of the impulse response multiplied by $e^{-j\omega t}$ or by substitution of $s = j\omega$ in the transfer function (see Chapter 8). Using the latter method, the frequency response of a second-order system having no zeros is given by

$$G(j\omega) = G(s)\bigg|_{s=j\omega} = \frac{1}{\left(\dfrac{j\omega}{\omega_n}\right)^2 + j2\zeta\,\dfrac{\omega}{\omega_n} + 1} = \text{AR}\underline{/\phi} \qquad (6\text{–}16a)$$

where ω is the frequency of the forcing sinusoid and AR and ϕ are the frequency response magnitude ratio and phase angle, which are given as

$$\left.\begin{array}{l} \text{AR}(j\omega) = [(1 - \beta^2)^2 + (2\zeta\beta)^2]^{-1/2} \\ \underline{/\phi}(j\omega) = -\tan^{-1} 2\zeta\beta/(1 - \beta^2) \end{array}\right\} \qquad (6\text{–}16b)$$

where $\beta = \omega/\omega_n$, the ratio of the forcing frequency to the natural frequency of the system. The behavior of $\text{AR}(j\omega)$ and $\phi(j\omega)$ as the frequency varies from zero to infinity is the frequency response. The data, when plotted on particular coordinates as discussed in Chapter 2, give characteristic curves. Fig. 6–14 show the data for several values of ζ on the Nyquist polar plot, the Nichols chart, and the Bode plot.

The frequency response of a second-order system differs from that of a first-order system in several respects. First, the magnitude ratio has maxima or resonance peaks for small zeta ($\zeta < 0.707$) and second, the maximum phase lag is 180°. The maxima of the magnitude ratio are found by differentiating Eq. 6–16a and setting the result to zero to give

$$\frac{d\,\text{AR}(\beta)}{d\beta} = \frac{2(1 - \beta^2)\beta - 4\zeta^2\beta}{[(1 - \beta^2)^2 + (2\zeta\beta)^2]^{3/2}} = 0$$

so that maxima occur in the magnitude ratio when $\beta^2 = 1 - 2\zeta^2$. The value of the maximum magnitude ratio and the frequency at resonance are given by

$$\text{AR}(\beta)_{\max} = (\text{AR})_p = \frac{1}{2\zeta\sqrt{1 - \zeta^2}} \qquad 0 < \zeta < 0.707 \quad (6\text{–}16c)$$

$$\omega_r = \omega_n \sqrt{1 - 2\zeta^2} \qquad (6\text{–}16d)$$

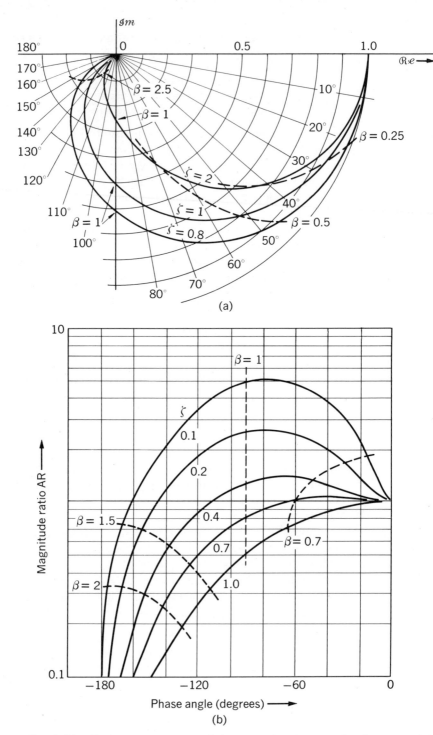

Fig. 6–14. Frequency response of the second-order transfer function. (a) Nyquist polar plot. (b) Nichols plot (gain vs. phase angle). (c) Bode plot.

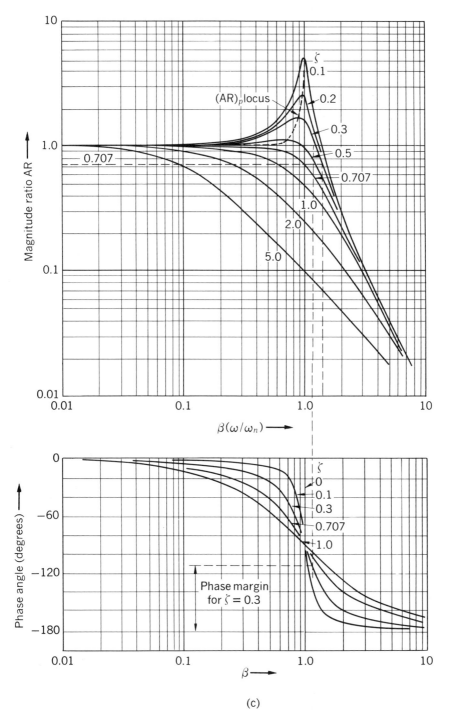

The plots give the magnitude-frequency ratio and phase angle–frequency ratio data. The phase margin for a $\zeta = 0.3$ system is shown. The gain margin for this system is infinite.

These relationships are shown by the $(AR)_p$ locus on Fig. 6–14c. Since the value of $(AR)_p$ for $\zeta = 1/\sqrt{2}$ is unity, the magnitude ratio does not exhibit maxima for ζ greater than that value. The magnitude ratio when $\beta = 1$ is equal to $1/2\zeta$. Also, when $\beta = 1$, the phase angle is $-90°$ for any value of ζ. It can be shown that the value of $d\phi/d\beta$ at $\beta = 1$ (the slope of the ϕ-vs-β curve at $\beta = 1$) is equal to $1/\zeta$.

FREQUENCY DOMAIN STABILITY. Several figures of merit for specifying control system performance are based on the frequency response technique and are simply related to the system parameters of a second-order system. Some of these specifications are discussed here.

Magnitude Ratio. The maximum value of the magnitude ratio indicates the relative stability of a system. Any value of $(AR)_p$ greater than unity indicates a tendency for resonance at frequency ω_r to occur in the system. A large resonance peak $(AR)_p$ corresponds to little damping and a large overshoot in the step response. This is shown in Fig. 6–14c for $(AR)_p$ and in Fig. 4–12 for percentage overshoot.

Gain Margin. The gain margin is the reciprocal of the system magnitude ratio (or gain) at $-180°$ phase angle:

Gain margin: $GM = [AR \text{ at } -180°]^{-1}$

It alone does not indicate the relative stability of a system. For the second-order system, the gain margin is infinite since the magnitude ratio is zero at $-180°$ phase angle. In complex systems, the gain margin is the allowable increase in the system gain before instability is reached. It may be computed directly from the system equation by Routh's criterion or easily calculated from the Nyquist polar plot, the Bode plot, or the Nichols plot.

Phase Margin. The phase margin is a direct measure of the additional amount of phase lag required to make a system unstable when the gain is unchanged. It is the angle between the -1 vector and the magnitude ratio vector when the latter has a value of unity, thus

Phase margin: $PM = 180° + \phi$ (when $AR = 1$)

From Eq. 6–16b, the phase angle when the magnitude ratio is unity for a second-order system is given as

Phase margin:

$$PM = 180° + \phi = 180° - \arctan \frac{2\zeta \sqrt{2 - 4\zeta^2}}{4\zeta^2 - 1}$$

The arc tan is in degrees. The phase margin for a second-order system with $\zeta = 0.4$ is $69°$ as found from the above equation and given by the

Nichols plot for $\zeta = 0.4$ in Fig. 6–14b. Phase margin specifications are generally in the range of 30 to 45°. Phase margin is a simple specification and, of course, it alone does not completely describe the response of a complex system. For example, it is possible for a complex system with "adequate phase margin" to overshoot badly.

FREQUENCY DOMAIN SPEED OF RESPONSE AND ACCURACY. Bandwidth is directly related to system speed of response and accuracy for changing inputs. It is usually defined as the frequency at which the magnitude ratio is equal to $1/\sqrt{2}$ of its low-frequency value. From Eq. 6–16b, the frequency ratio when $AR = 1/\sqrt{2}$ is found to be

$$\beta = [(1 - 2\zeta^2) + (4\zeta^4 - 4\zeta^2 + 2)^{1/2}]^{1/2}$$

and the bandwidth ω is given as

$$\omega = \beta\omega_n$$

The bandwidth for $\zeta = 0.3$ is shown on Fig. 6–14c as $\beta = 1.45$. Since bandwidth is related to speed of response, the rise time from frequency response data is sometimes defined as reciprocal of bandwidth. Another definition gives rise time as the reciprocal of ω_r. This rise-time figure of merit is easily found from either Nyquist or Bode plots.

6–5. SELECTION OF PROCESS CONTROLLERS

Process plants efficiently manufacture a specific product only when the operating variables are held within proper limits. Since the controller can drastically alter the behavior of the plant, it is necessary, when selecting the controller, to view process and controller as an integrated whole. The next two chapters develop the rationale for selecting and adjusting controllers on an analytical basis. The purpose of the present discussion is to present the problem and give some general observations which may be used as guides in the preliminary stages of a process control system design.

Process plant components have lumped and distributed parameters whose values depend upon the plant flow rates and operating levels. Information signals concerning process streams moving within the plant will be delayed by dead times and slowed by process lags. Set-point changes, load disturbances, and normal fluctuations in plant services are always possible system inputs which the plant must resist in order to accomplish its control function.

Most of the performance criteria are applied in the tuning or adjustment step of the control system design and so do not help in the selection of control actions.   However, several guiding principles for selection may be listed:

1. Use the simplest controller that meets system performance specifications and when possible use controllers having only one adjustable parameter.   Plant personnel normally are not trained to adjust complex controllers.   In practice, use proportional- or integral-type controllers whenever possible.

2. In the design stage the specification of the control mode is much more important than estimating its setting.

3. An integration element in the controller or in the process will eliminate steady-state errors resulting from step changes.   Ramp inputs require double integration components to eliminate steady-state error.

4. The nature of disturbances and their location in the control loop should be determined as correctly as possible.

5. Most process components in operation and measurement add time lags to transmitted signals; therefore, it is expected that derivative action will be helpful in controlling multicapacity processes.

From computer studies of simulated processes and the experience of control engineers come the following general recommendations concerning control actions.   They must not be considered a substitute for detailed analysis of a particular problem in selecting a controller.

1. On-off control is used with processes whose dynamics are dominated by a large single capacitance or time constant.   The system response is always cyclic.

2. Single-speed floating control (integral) is used with processes having small capacitance for storage of material or energy.   The response tends to be cyclic unless the proper floating rate and a neutral zone are used in the controller.

3. Proportional control is used with multiple-capacity processes having little dead time and subject to moderate load changes.   It is a general-purpose control action which increases the speed of system response but it shows offset error due to set-point or load changes.

4. Integral control is added to proportional control to eliminate offset, or to increase accuracy of the system.   It does not contribute to stability of the system and may result in large overshoot of the controlled variable on start-up of processes.

5. Derivative control is added to proportional control to speed up the system response and contribute to the system stability.   It does not eliminate offset but it can handle the effect of rapid load and set-point changes.

The preceding generalizations are tabulated in Table 6–1 for easy reference and comparison of the various control actions.

TABLE 6–1
Process Controller Types and Their Applications

Controller		Process Parameters		Size and Speed of Load Changes	Process Characteristics
Type	Responsive to Error	Capacity Stages	Reaction Rate		
On-off	Direction	Single	Slow	Any	Single, large capacity
Integral	Direction and duration	Small	Fast	Any	Small capacity, little self-regulation and/or dead time
P	Direction	Multiple	Any	Moderate	Infrequent load changes and moderate time lags
PI	Direction and duration	Multiple	Any	Moderate	Tight control requirements allowing no offset
PD	Direction and rate	Multiple	Moderate	Any	Frequent upsets
PID	Direction, rate, and duration	Multiple	Any	Any	Frequent upsets and tight control requirements

6–6. CONTROLLER ADJUSTMENT

A control system design can be checked by comparing the response of the actual plant with that predicted by the design calculations. If the control system has been assembled and the plant parameters are not known or have changed due to "wear and tear" or to modification of the plant, a logical tuning method is needed for adjusting the controller to fit the plant parameters so as to obtain the desired system performance. The instrument manufacturers have developed several procedures which find widespread use in process plants. The methods do not give the "best" settings for all systems because they were derived for one type of system and performance specification, but they are useful because they give first-trial controller settings from which small changes can be made to find the best settings for the actual plant.

Open-Loop Method. The Ziegler-Nichols method is based on the open-loop step response (process reaction curve) of the process. The method assumes that a complex system can be approximated by time-constant components and a dead-time component in series. The apparent time constants and dead-time values are obtained from the step response and used to estimate controller settings. The open-loop test is made by opening the control loop at the output of the controller (thus eliminating the controller from the loop) and recording the process reaction to a step change in control valve position as $b(t)$ on the recorder chart.   In a test, the open-loop system is brought to a steady-state condition under manual control at an average operating point.   Then the control valve position is increased or decreased by a step change in the absence of load disturbances and the system response is recorded.   A typical process response is shown in Fig. 6–15, from which the two factors R and L are obtained. R is the

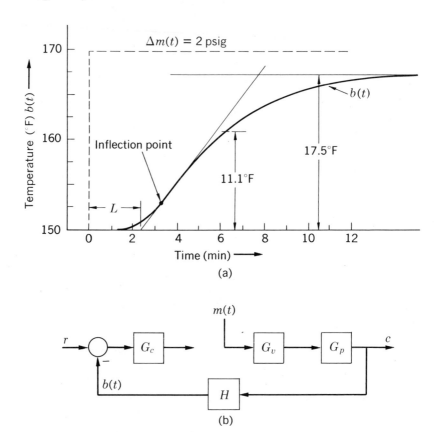

Fig. 6–15. (a) Typical process-reaction curve for the Ziegler-Nichols method. L is the apparent dead-time in minutes, and R is reaction rate, % scale/min for a Δm % change in valve position.   (b) Method for taking the process-reaction curve.

slope of the tangent to the reaction curve at the inflection point (steepest slope) found as

$$R = \frac{\% \text{ scale change in } b(t)}{\text{time change in minutes}}$$

and L is the apparent time lag in minutes between initiation of the step change and the intersection of the tangent with the zero axis. Δm is the percentage change in manipulated variable causing the change in $b(t)$. Then the Ziegler-Nichols formulas for controller adjustments are:

For proportional controllers: $\% \, \mathrm{PB} = \dfrac{100RL}{\Delta m}$

For PI controllers: $\% \, \mathrm{PB} = \dfrac{110RL}{\Delta m}$

$$\tau_i = L/0.3 \quad \text{min}$$

For PID controllers: $\% \, \mathrm{PB} = \dfrac{83RL}{\Delta m}$

$$\tau_d = 0.5L \quad \text{min}$$

$$\tau_i = \frac{L}{0.5} \quad \text{min}$$

Values of R and L should be found for both step increase and step decrease at an average set-point value. Serious disagreement between the two sets of values indicates nonlinearities in the process.

Example 6-3. Use the process reaction curve in Fig. 6-15 and compute the Ziegler-Nichols controller settings for a PID controller used with that process. Assume that the pneumatic valve has a range of 12 psig and that the controller has a range of 100°F (100-200°F).

Solution. From the process-reaction curve in Fig. 6-15, the apparent time lag is 2.4 min, $\Delta m = \frac{2}{12} = 16.7\%$, and $R = (17.5/100)/(7.8 - 2.4) = 3.24\%/\text{min}$. These values give the following setting for a PID controller.

$$\% \, \mathrm{PB} = 83(3.24)(2.4)/16.7 = 38.6\%$$
$$\tau_d = 0.5(2.4) = 1.2 \text{ min}$$
$$\tau_i = 2.4/0.5 = 4.8 \text{ min}$$

The time constant of the first-order lag can be estimated as the time required for the output to reach 63.2% of the total change. In this problem the time constant is the time when $\Delta b(t) = .632(17.5) = 11.1°F$ minus the dead time, or about 3.9 minutes.

The process reaction curve of Fig. 6-15 is typical of the step response of overdamped multiple capacity and/or distributed-parameter systems such as heat exchangers, distillation columns, and extraction equipment. When step inputs are practical for system testing, a procedure is needed to interpret empirically the response in terms of an equivalent system comprising a dead time and one or more first-order time constants. If the system is equivalent to a dead time and one time constant in series, a very crude approximation would be to let $L = \tau_d$ and the time constant would be the added time for the output to reach 63.2% of the total change.

The transfer function would be

$$G(s) = \frac{Ke^{-\tau_d s}}{\tau s + 1} \qquad \text{(approx.)}$$

where K is the gain ratio of $\Delta b / \Delta m$ at steady state.

Smith* gives an improved method of interpretation which assumes that the system can be approximated by a dead time and two time constants in series, thus:

$$G(s) = \frac{Ke^{-\tau_d s}}{(\tau_1 s + 1)(\tau_2 s + 1)} \qquad \tau_2 > \tau_1$$

The method begins with the process reaction curve in Fig. 6–16a, which is Fig. 6–15 redrawn. The steps in the graphical analysis are:

1. As before, establish the initial and final values of the transient and draw the tangent to the curve at the inflection point where the slope is steepest.
2. Read t_a, the time between the intersection of the tangent with the initial and final values of the transient, and t_c, the time between the inflection point and the intersection of the tangent with the final value of the transient.
3. Let a be the value of the transient at the time represented by the intersection of the tangent with the initial value and for the same time locate point b at $2.718a$. Then the line through b parallel to the tangent locates τ_d, the process dead time, as shown.
4. Let $x = \tau_2/\tau_1$ where $\tau_2 > \tau_1$; then it can be shown that $t_c = \tau_1 + \tau_2 = (1 + x)\tau_1$ and $t_c/t_a = (1 + x)x^{\frac{x}{1-x}}$

The value of x is obtained by finding t_c/t_a from Fig. 6–16a and solving the equation for x or reading it directly from Fig. 6–16b. Then both τ_1 and τ_2 can be calculated. The gain K is the steady-state ratio of $\Delta b/\Delta m$. This method has been applied to Fig. 6–16a with the results shown thereon. From the chart the dead time, $\tau_d = 1.5$ min, and the ratio of t_c/t_a is 0.815, which gives $x = 6$. The time constants are $\tau_1 = t_c/(1 + x) = 4.4/7 = 0.63$ min and $\tau_2 = 3.78$ min. The gain $K = 17.5/2 = 8.75°\text{F/psi}$. The parameter values are very sensitive to errors in the graphical analysis.

Closed-Loop Method. This method, also due to Ziegler and Nichols, depends upon finding the proportional controller gain that makes the closed-loop gain unity. The test is made by eliminating reset and rate controller actions (or setting them to their lowest value) and making small changes in the controller set point and noting how the controlled variable lines out. The proportional band is decreased (controller gain

---

* O. J. M. Smith, "A Controller to Overcome Dead Time," *ISA Journal*, **6**(2), 28–33 (1959).

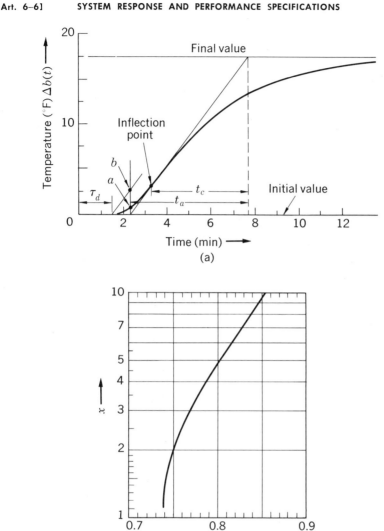

Fig. 6–16. Procedure for interpreting the process-reaction curve. (a) Test transient showing values of t_a, t_c, and τ_d. (b) Plot for obtaining x from the t_c/t_a ratio.

increased) while the process is disturbed by set-point changes until the control loop begins to cycle continuously at a constant amplitude. The proportional band that produces cycling and the period of the cycling, called the ultimate proportional band $(PB)_u$ and ultimate period P_u respectively, are characteristic of the process and these values are used to estimate the best controller settings. The Ziegler-Nichols formulas for this method are:

For proportional controllers: $\% \text{ PB} = 2(\text{PB})_u$

For PI controllers: $\% \text{ PB} = 2.2(\text{PB})_u$
$$\tau_i = P_u/1.2 \qquad \text{min}$$

For PID controllers: $\% \text{ PB} = 1.7(\text{PB})_u$
$$\tau_i = 0.5P_u \qquad \text{min}$$
$$\tau_d = P_u/8 \qquad \text{min}$$

The Ziegler-Nichols methods are based on a single-loop process model consisting of a first-order lag and a dead time. This model is satisfactory for many process units but it is not satisfactory for units having an integration element in the loop. The controller adjustments are estimated to give an oscillatory system having a quarter-decay ratio (peak attenuation). It must also be recognized that process controllers from the different manufacturers vary in design, expecially in the PID controllers, and that in general these empirical controller adjustment formulas give first-trial values only.

Both of these methods produce process upsets which some processes may not tolerate, and the process engineer must investigate this possibility before applying these methods on an operating plant.

Example 6–4. Using the time constant and dead time from the previous example, find the ultimate proportional band and ultimate period for that process and estimate PID controller settings from the Ziegler-Nichols closed loop formulas.

Solution. The ultimate period of a closed-loop system is the reciprocal of the frequency at which the open-loop phase lag is 180°. This is equivalent to forcing the characteristic equation of the closed loop to have a pole on the imaginary axis. The gain and frequency at which this occurs is found by substituting $s = j\omega$ in the characteristic equation, setting it equal to zero, and solving for $\omega = 2\pi/P_u$, thus:

$$K_c G(j\omega) + 1 = 0$$

For the process in Example 6–3 the closed-loop system equation becomes

$$K_c G(j\omega) = \frac{K_c e^{-j\omega\tau_1}}{j\omega\tau_2 + 1} = -1$$

and by separating the real and imaginary parts of the equation the equivalent equations for finding the ultimate characteristics of the system are

$$\cos \omega\tau_1 = -1/K_c \qquad \sin \omega\tau_1 = \omega\tau_2/K_c$$

To give simpler working equations, these equations can be rearranged as

$$K_c{}^2 = 1 + \omega^2\tau_2{}^2 \qquad \text{and} \qquad \tan \omega\tau_1 = -\omega\tau_2$$

By trial-and-error calculation, when $\tau_1 = 2.4$ min and $\tau_2 = 3.9$ min, the values of K_c and ω are 3.22 and 0.785, respectively. Then $P_u = 2\pi/0.785 = 8.0$ min and $(PB)_u = 100/3.22 = 31.0\%$.

The estimated PID controller settings are PB = 1.7(31.0) = 52.6%; $\tau_i = 0.5(8.0) = 4.0$; $\tau_d = 8.0/8 = 1.0$. These values agree with those found in Example 6–3 in order of magnitude and show that, although these methods may be used as guides in tuning systems, each case should be checked by a plant trial.

On the other hand, the ultimate period and the ultimate proportional band for a process can be used to find the dynamic characteristics of the process. When, from experiment, ω and K_c are known for ultimate conditions, the process equations can be rearranged to give the process dynamic parameters as

$$\tau_2 = \frac{1}{\omega} \sqrt{K_c{}^2 - 1} \qquad \tau_1 = \frac{1}{\omega} \tan^{-1}(-\omega\tau_2)$$

A plant test procedure based on these equations could give empirical plant dynamic parameters in terms of a dead time and a first-order lag.

Optimum controller settings are specific for each plant since their values depend upon the process components and arrangement and the disturbance location in the plant. The standard formulas above were developed for a specific plant and their predictions will be approximate optimum controller settings for other plants. The next step is to determine the type of plant response desired and to select a performance specification. Finally, fine tuning adjustments are made on the controller settings so that the performance specifications are met.

Fine tuning in the plant is accomplished by making step changes in the controller set point and observing the plant response on the recorder chart. This is repeated, using improved settings, until the desired response is obtained. Thus, by trial and error, the controller is tuned to the plant characteristics. Evaluation of the plant response is frequently based on the control engineers' judgment. Other criteria may be used as discussed under dynamic error specifications but the quarter-decay (peak attenuation of $\frac{1}{4}$) for underdamped systems is the easiest to use in the plant since it can be measured directly from the recorder chart. Then a set of charts showing the effects of each controller adjustment on the plant response would be helpful to the inexperienced operator. Such guides for controller tuning have been developed for a simulated second-order process with a dead time* responding to step set-point and load changes. The chart in Fig. 6–17 shows values of K_c, τ_i, and τ_d which give a quarter-decay response to setpoint changes in the simulated system. Although the chart was derived for a specific process and controller, it indicates the

* D. M. Wills, "Tuning Maps for Three-Mode Controllers," *Control Engineering*, **9**(4), 104–108, (1962); "A Guide to Controller Tuning," *Control Engineering*, **9**(8), 93–95 (1962).

direction of adjustment to obtain a desired response, and the general trends are useful for many underdamped process systems. On the chart, values τ_d/P_u are plotted on the horizontal axis and values of P_u/τ_i are shown on the vertical axis, where P_u is the ultimate period of the process. The chart shows that an increase in τ_d permits K_c to be greatly increased,

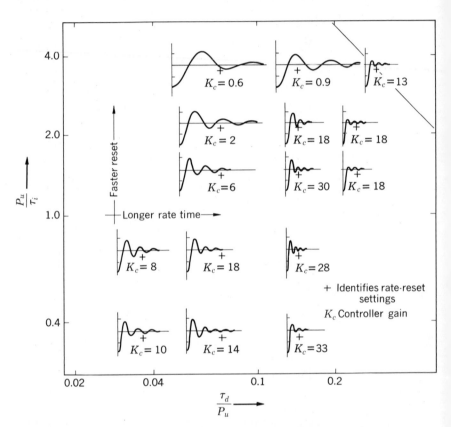

Fig. 6–17. Controller settings that give quarter-decay transient response to a step input. Controller derivative time increases to the right on the horizontal axis, and integral time decreases upward on the vertical axis. (From *Control Engineering*, 9(4), 105, 1962; by permission.)

whereas an increase in $1/\tau_i$ requires that K_c be decreased. Also note that an increase of τ_d speeds up the system response (ω_n increased) and an increase in τ_i slows the system response. The diagonal line represents settings where $\tau_d = \tau_i$, which some manufacturers recommend. Other charts are available for critically damped responses and for step load disturbances.

PROBLEMS

6-1. Use the final-value theorem, and consider the general requirement for zero steady-state error to unit step and unit ramp inputs to the system in Fig. 6–1. Suppose $G_l = G_p$ and $G_cG_v = K$, and show the effects of putting s or $1/s$ terms in the feedback path (H) on the steady-state error response to a step load change. Is there a restriction on the location of the s and $1/s$ terms in eliminating steady-state errors?

6-2. Two alternate schemes for using feedforward disturbance controllers are shown in Fig. P6–2. Find the ideal transfer function for G_{ff} for both schemes when $G_c = K_c(1 + 1/\tau_i s), G_v = 1, G_p = G_l = M/(\tau_1 s + 1)$, and $H = \tau_2 s/(\tau_2 s + 1)$.

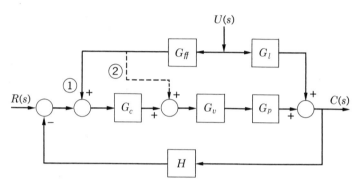

Fig. P6–2

6-3. Originally, feedforward control was proposed to improve the output/set-point performance of systems. Equate the $C(s)/R(s)$ equation for the system shown (Fig. P6–3) to unity—for $c(t)$ to track $r(t)$ exactly—and find G_{ff} for this condition. Then let $G_vG_p = R/(\tau s + 1)^2$ and $H = M/(\tau_m s + 1)$, and find values of G_{ff} for PI and PD controllers.

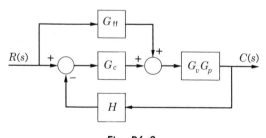

Fig. P6–3

6-4. In the single-capacity liquid-level process in Fig. 6–3, let $G_c = K_c(1 + 1/\tau_i s)$, and find relationships for the system damping ratio and natural frequency.

(a) Find the value of K_c, psi/psi, that gives $\zeta = 0.3$ when $\tau_i = 1$ min, $\tau = 25$ min, $k = 10$ gpm/psi, $H = 2$ psi/ft fluid, and $R = 0.1$ ft fluid/gpm. What is the natural frequency of the system?
(b) Find the response of the system to a step change in load variable, $u(t) = 5$ gpm, using $K_c = 3.42$ psi/psi.

6–5. In Fig. 6–8, for case 1, let $H = (1 + \tau_d s)$, and write the output/load system equations.

(a) Using the values of $\tau_d = \tau = 1, \tau_1 = 10$ min, and $R = k = 1$, find values of K_c and τ_i that just make the system unstable.
(b) Determine a value of K_c that gives a damping ratio of 0.265 when $\tau_i = 0.59$ min.

6–6. In Fig. 6–1, let $G_c G_v = K_c, G_p = 5/(3s + 1)(5s + 1)$, and $H = 1/(2s + 1)$, and write the output/set-point system equation. The time constants are in minutes.

(a) Find the value of K_c that makes the system unstable.
(b) Find the response of the system to a set-point change of 4 units from a static condition when $K_c = 1.2$.

6–7. Repeat Problem 6–6 above with $G_c G_v = K_c(1 + \tau_d s)$ with $\tau_d = 2$ and $K_c = 1.2$.

6–8. Write an analog computer program for the system in Problem 6–4.

6–9. Write an analog computer program for the system in Problem 6–6. Scale the problem to speed up the analog simulation, if necessary. See Appendix C for information on time scaling of analog computers.

6–10. In the single-capacity process in Fig. 6–3, let $G_c = K_c(1 + 1/\tau_i s + \tau_d s)$, and find relationships for the system damping ratio and natural frequency. Let $\tau_i = 4\tau_d$.

6–11. In Fig. 6–1, let $G_c G_v = 1/\tau_i s, G_p = 2/(5s + 1)$, and $H = 1$.

(a) Write the error/set-point system equation.
(b) Find a value of τ_i that would give a 10% overshoot in the unit step response of the system.
(c) Determine the system error transient response when $R(s) = 1/s$.

6–12. In Fig. 6–1, let $G_c G_v = 1/\tau_i s, G_p = 2/(5s + 1)$, and $H = 1/(s + 1)$.

(a) Find the value of τ_i that makes the system unstable.
(b) Select a value of τ_i that gives the system a pair of oscillatory roots with $\zeta = 0.4$.
(c) Find the system transient response for $R(s) = 1/s$.

6–13. Consider the control of liquid level in a holding tank of diameter 10 ft which supplies a positive-displacement pump (i.e., the tank outflow is independent of the tank liquid level) as shown in Fig. P6–13. Let $G_c = G_c; G_v = 10/(0.5s + 1)$ ft³/min-psi; and G_p is determined from the problem statement.

(a) Find the expression for $C(s)$ as determined by $R(s)$ and $I_o(s)$.

(b) Let $G_c = 5$ psi/ft, and find $C(s)$ for a change in setpoint of $R(s) = 5/s$ and $I_o(s) = 50/s$ ft³/min from equilibrium.

(c) Find the steady-state value of c in part b.

(d) If $G_c = 1/\tau_i s$, is there a value of τ_i that can stabilize the system?

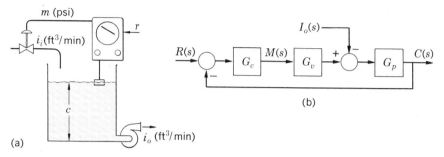

Fig. P6–13

6–14. It is informative to compare the various dynamic performance criteria when they are applied to a single system. Consider the proportional control of a plant having $G_p = (s + 1)^{-3}$ and unity feedback. Let $G_c G_v = K_c$.

(a) Use Routh's criterion to find the value of K_c which will make the closed-loop system unstable. Find the resulting sustained frequency of oscillation which is also the ultimate period P_u of the closed-loop system.

(b) Let $K_c = 1$, and determine the system damping ratio and decay rate, and compute the unit step response of the system.

(c) Sketch the frequency response of the open-loop system $G(j\omega)$ on Bode coordinates, and find the system gain margin and phase margin when $K_c = 1$.

7

The Root-Locus Method

The time response of second- or third-order control systems is obtainable by simple analytical methods, as shown in Chapter 6. Higher-order systems always occur in practice, and it becomes necessary to abandon the simple analytical approach to time response in favor either of computer simulation or a graphical procedure called the *root-locus method*. As pointed out in Chapter 6, the coefficients in the system-characteristic equation are functions of the system parameters; therefore, the roots of the characteristic equation, since they depend upon the coefficients, are functions of the system parameters. Evans* devised the graphical root-locus method to show the relationship between any system parameter and the roots of the characteristic equation. Using the root-locus method, the process engineer can determine the effects of variation in system parameters on the root location. Armed with this knowledge, he can adjust the plant and controller parameters so that the control system meets the performance specifications. This is the only method of analysis and design which enables one to maintain control of both transient and frequency responses of the system.

7-1. ROOT-LOCUS METHOD

The response of a single-loop system having a forward transfer function $G(s)$ and a feedback transfer function $H(s)$ is obtained by inverting the closed-loop relationship

$$C(s) = \frac{G(s)}{1 + G(s)H(s)} R(s) + \frac{G_l(s)}{1 + G(s)H(s)} U(s) \qquad (6\text{-}1)$$

under the desired conditions of $R(s)$ and $U(s)$. Observe again that the denominator $1 + G(s)H(s)$ is the operational form of the system homogeneous equation (characteristic equation) and that the roots of this equa-

---

* W. R. Evans, *Control System Dynamics*, McGraw-Hill Book Co., Inc., New York, 1954.

tion fix the general form of the response expressions.   For simplicity in writing equations, only the $C(s)/R(s)$ term in Eq. 6–1 will be used and the "function of s" notation is understood.   For lumped-parameter systems (excluding dead-time and distributed-parameter components) the open-loop ratio GH can be written as a ratio of factored polynomials in s having a magnitude and phase angle, as

$$GH = \frac{K \prod_{1}^{i} \tau_i(s + 1/\tau_i)}{\prod_{1}^{k} \tau_k(s + 1/\tau_k)} = A e^{j\theta} \qquad (7\text{–}1)$$

where K is the open-loop gain.   Each factor in the GH function is written in the root-locus form $(s + 1/\tau)$ and is a complex quantity having magnitude and phase (Chapter 2).

   The roots of the characteristic equation are values of s which force the equation to vanish, as

$$1 + GH = 0 \qquad \text{or} \qquad GH = -1 \qquad (7\text{–}2a)$$

Since GH is a complex function, the requirement that $1 + GH$ vanish furnishes two expressions which are the basis of the root-locus method:

Angle: $\qquad \angle GH \equiv \theta = \pm 180°, \ \pm 540°, \ \pm 900°, \text{ etc.} \qquad (7\text{–}2b)$
Magnitude: $\quad |GH| \equiv A = 1 \qquad\qquad\qquad\qquad\qquad\qquad (7\text{–}2c)$

The requirements for any s_1 to be a root of $1 + GH$ are that it make the magnitude of GH unity and the angle of GH an odd multiple of $\pm 180°$.

   Second-Order System.   In Fig. 4–14, the root loci for a mass–spring-damper device are shown as functions of the parameters K_x, D, and M. The development is repeated here, using a standard form of second-order transfer function to show the generalized parameters ζ and ω_n on the complex plane.   With K_x/M held constant, Eq. 4–18b for the mechanical damper becomes

$$\frac{X(s)}{F(s)} = \frac{K_1}{s^2 + 2\zeta\omega_n s + \omega_n^2} \qquad (4\text{–}18b)$$

where $\omega_n^2 = K_x/M$, $K_1 = 1/M$, and $2\zeta\omega_n = D/M$.   The root locus for this component is the set of values of s which make the denominator zero. They are found by setting $s^2 + 2\zeta\omega_n s + \omega_n^2$ equal to zero or, in root-locus form,

$$1 + \frac{\zeta(2\omega_n s)}{s^2 + \omega_n^2} = 0 \qquad (7\text{–}3)$$

and using the quadratic formula to give

$$s_1, s_2 = \sigma \pm j\omega = -\zeta\omega_n \pm \omega_n \sqrt{\zeta^2 - 1} \qquad (7\text{-}4a)$$

This set divides naturally into two groups, depending upon the value of ζ. For $\zeta < 1$:

$$\sigma_1, \sigma_2 = -\zeta\omega_n \qquad \omega_1, \omega_2 = \pm\omega_n \sqrt{1 - \zeta^2} \qquad \sigma_1^2 + \omega_1^2 = \omega_n^2 \qquad (7\text{-}4b)$$

For $\zeta > 1$:

$$\sigma_1, \sigma_2 = -\zeta\omega_n \pm \omega_n \sqrt{\zeta^2 - 1} \qquad \omega_1, \omega_2 = 0 \qquad \sigma_1 \cdot \sigma_2 = \omega_n^2 \qquad (7\text{-}4c)$$

For the critically damped case of $\zeta = 1$, $\sigma_1 = \sigma_2 = -\omega_n$. These values are plotted on the complex plane in Fig. 7–1a to give the root locus under conditions of variable ζ and $\omega_n = 3$ rad/time. When $\zeta = 0$, the real part of the root σ is zero, the imaginary part of the root is ± 3, and the root locus originates on the imaginary axis at $\omega = \pm 3$ (poles of root-locus form of Eq. 7–3). As ζ increases, σ becomes more negative $(-\zeta\omega_n)$, ω decreases, and the root locus forms a semicircle of radius ω_n as required by Eq. 7–4b. When $\zeta = 1$, the locus cuts the real axis $(\omega = 0)$ and then remains on the real axis for all $\zeta > 1$, with one branch moving to the left and the other branch moving to the right in Fig. 7–1a. As $\zeta \to \infty$, the left branch terminates at infinity and the right branch at zero (the zero of Eq. 7–3). Values of ζ between 0 and 1.2 are marked on the $\omega_n = 3$ locus and values of ω_n between 0 and 4 are marked on the $\zeta = 0.5$ locus in Fig. 7–1a.

Eqs. 7–4b for the roots of an oscillatory second-order system may be generalized on Fig. 7–1a as follows:

1. Roots of constant ω_n lie on circles about the origin with radius of ω_n since the equations require $\sigma^2 + \omega^2 = \omega_n^2$.
2. Roots of constant ζ lie on a straight line through the origin with slope of $\sqrt{1 - \zeta^2}/ - \zeta$ since $\sigma = -\zeta\omega_n$ and $\omega = \omega_n \sqrt{1 - \zeta^2}$.
3. Roots of constant decay rate $\zeta\omega_n$ lie on lines parallel to the imaginary axis since $\sigma = -\zeta\omega_n$.
4. Roots of constant damped frequency $\omega_n \sqrt{1 - \zeta^2}$ lie on horizontal lines since $\omega = \omega_n \sqrt{1 - \zeta^2}$.

The location of the roots in the complex plane determines the nature of the step response of a system. Complex roots give rise to damped oscillations of the form

$$e^{-\zeta\omega_n t}[\sin (\omega_n \sqrt{1 - \zeta^2}\, t - \psi)]$$

where $\zeta\omega_n$ is the decay rate, $\omega_n \sqrt{1 - \zeta^2}$ is the frequency of the damped oscillations, and ψ is a phase angle. The effect of root location on the step response is shown in Fig. 7–1b, where typical response curves are sketched for $\zeta = 0$, 0.5, 0.707, 0.9, and 1.0. For $\zeta > 1$ the roots lie

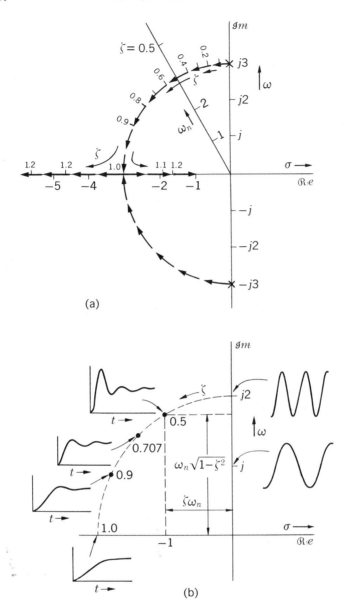

Fig. 7–1. (a) Root-locus plot of second-order system with $\omega_n = 3$ and variable damping ratio ζ. A line of $\zeta = 0.5$ with variable ω_n is shown. (b) Root location affects both the frequency and the decay rate $\zeta\omega_n$ in the step response.

along the real axis and the response is overdamped.   From the sketches
it is noted that, as the imaginary part of the root increases, the frequency
of the damped oscillation increases, and that, as the real part of the root
($\zeta\omega_n$) increases, the oscillation decays away faster.   Therefore, it follows
that the roots closest to the origin dominate the system response and that
in many cases the roots far removed from the origin may be neglected
in computing the system response.

Root-Locus Construction.   The open-loop transfer function GH is
always written in the root-locus form as

$$GH = \frac{K(s - z_1)(\cdot \ \cdot \ \cdot)}{(s - p_1)(s - p_2)(\cdot \ \cdot \ \cdot)} \qquad (7\text{--}5)$$

where the z's are the zeros of GH and the p's are the poles of GH.   As a
review, note the usage of terms related to GH and $1 + GH$:

1. A zero is a value of s which makes the numerator of GH zero.
2. A pole is a value of s which makes the denominator of GH zero.
3. A root is a value of s which makes $1 + GH = 0$.

Notice that a pole of GH is also a pole of $1 + GH$ and a root of $1 + GH$ is
a closed-loop pole of $C(s)/R(s)$.

Each of the complex factors in Eq. 7–5 has a magnitude and angle which
can be represented as

$$s - p = Pe^{j\theta_p} \qquad s - z = Ze^{j\theta_z}$$

where P and Z are the magnitudes and θ_p and θ_z are the angles of a pole
and a zero, respectively.   Therefore, the magnitude and phase angle of
GH can be written as

$$GH = \frac{K(Z_1e^{j\theta_{z1}})(\cdot \ \cdot \ \cdot)}{(P_1e^{j\theta_{p1}})(P_2e^{j\theta_{p2}})(\cdot \ \cdot \ \cdot)} = \frac{KZ_1 \cdot \cdot \cdot}{P_1P_2 \cdot \cdot \cdot} e^{j(\theta_{z1}+\cdots-\theta_{p1}-\theta_{p2}-\cdots)} \quad (7\text{--}6a)$$

For a point s to be on the root locus it must give GH a value of unity and
an angle of odd multiple of $\pm180°$, so that for Eq. 7–6a the requirements
are:

Angle: $\theta_{z1} + \cdot \ \cdot \ \cdot - \theta_{p1} - \theta_{p2} - \cdot \ \cdot \ \cdot = \pm180°, \pm540°,$ etc.   (7–6b)

Magnitude: $\dfrac{KZ_1 \cdot \cdot \cdot}{P_1P_2 \cdot \cdot \cdot} = 1$ or $K = \dfrac{P_1P_2 \cdot \cdot \cdot}{Z_1 \cdot \cdot \cdot}$ (7–6c)

The root locus is plotted in the complex plane by finding all values of s
which satisfy the angle requirement, Eq. 7–6b.   Then the locus is scaled
by applying Eq. 7–6c to locate values of K along the locus.

Consider construction of the root locus for the integral-controlled liquid-
level process in Fig. 6–7a.   The open-loop transfer function for the system

with $Rk = 1$ and $\tau = 1$ is

$$GH = \frac{1}{\tau_i s(s+1)} = \frac{K}{s(s+1)} \qquad (7\text{-}7)$$

where $K = 1/\tau_i$, the open-loop gain. In this example GH has poles at $s = 0, -1$; they are designated by crosses on the plot in Fig. 7-2. (Poles

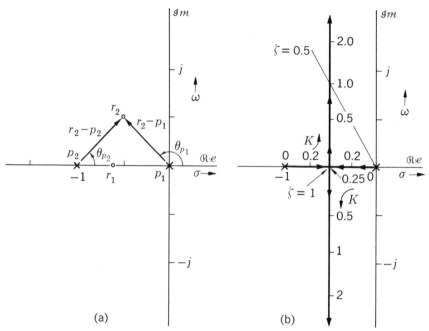

Fig. 7-2. Root-locus plot of $GH = 1/[\tau_i s(s+1)]$. (a) Angles and magnitudes for one point on root locus. (b) Complete root locus with gain scale, $K = 1/\tau_i$.

are designated by crosses and zeros by circles on the root-locus plot.) The root locus originates at the poles. Any point r_1 on the real axis between the two poles is on the root locus: the angle requirement is satisfied since the angle of $r_1 - p_1 = 180°$ and the angle of $r_1 - p_2 = 0$.* It is more difficult to locate points on the locus in the complex plane. Assume that $r_2 = -0.5 + j0.5$ is a root of $1 + GH$. The point r_2 is plotted on Fig. 7-2a and the vectors $r_2 - p_1$ and $r_2 - p_2$ are drawn. If r_2 is on the root locus of GH the angle requirement of Eq. 7-6b must

---

* Generally, the p's are symbolically used to represent values of s which make GH infinite. Therefore, the pole factor is written symbolically as $r_1 - p_2$ but it has the value $r_1 + 1$ when the value of $p_2 = -1$ is substituted.

be met, i.e.,

$$-(\theta_{p1} + \theta_{p2}) = \pm 180°$$

It is found by measurement that $\theta_{p1} = 135°$ and $\theta_{p2} = 45°$, so that

$$-(\theta_{p1} + \theta_{p2}) = -(135 + 45) = -180°$$

Thus the angle requirement is satisfied and r_2 is a point on the root locus. It is clear that the complex conjugate of r_2, $(-0.5 - j0.5)$, also satisfies the angle requirement and is on the root locus. The magnitude of K for r_2 is given by Eq. 7–6c as

$$K = \frac{P_1 P_2}{1} = (0.71)(0.71) = 0.5 \qquad \text{or} \qquad \tau_i = 1/K = 2$$

(Note that Z_1 is replaced by unity since GH has no zeros in this case.)

Repeated estimation and checking of points in the complex plane completes the root locus for this system as shown in Fig. 7–2b. Values of K are plotted along the root locus and values for $\zeta = 0.5$, and 1.0 are shown. Step responses of this closed-loop system for the same values of damping ratio are given in Fig. 6–7c. The root locus gives the poles of the closed-loop system for any K, so that the transient response for any input can be computed by obtaining the closed-loop poles from Fig. 7–2b and using Eq. 6–1 for the response. As an example, if $\zeta = 0.5$ is specified, Fig. 7–2b shows that the necessary K is 1.0 and the closed-loop poles are

$$1 + GH = (s + 0.5 + j0.866)(s + 0.5 - j0.866) = 0$$

Construction Rules. The root-locus construction based on Eqs. 7–6b and c, as illustrated above, is a slow trial-and-error procedure. Fortunately a set of rules can be derived from the equations which enable the process engineer to quickly sketch the root locus. The utility of the method lies in the use of these rules.

Rule 1: *Number of branches.* A branch is a part of the locus having all values of K on it and determining one root of $1 + GH$. Since an equation of order n has n roots and one branch determines only one root (for any K), the number of branches of the root locus must equal the order of $1 + GH$. The root locus in Fig. 7–2 has two branches, corresponding to the second-order system equation.

Rule 2: *Origin and termination of root locus.* For zero system gain $(K = 0)$, the open-loop poles are the roots of $1 + GH$; therefore, the branches originate from the open-loop poles. Let

$$GH = \frac{KN(s)}{D(s)}$$

the characteristic equation then becomes

$$1 + GH = 1 + \frac{KN(s)}{D(s)} = 0 \quad \text{or} \quad D(s) + KN(s) = 0 \quad (7\text{–}8)$$

When $K = 0$, the equation becomes $D(s) = 0$, whose roots are the poles of GH. When $K \to \infty$, Eq. 7–8 becomes

$$\lim_{K \to \infty} \left[\frac{D(s)}{K} + N(s) \right] = 0 \qquad N(s) = 0$$

whose roots are the finite zeros of GH. Thus, as gain K approaches infinity, the locus approaches the open-loop zeros. Whenever the number of zeros n_z is less than the number of poles n_p of GH, a number of branches $n_p - n_z$ must terminate at infinity.

Rule 3: *Segments in the complex plane.* The characteristic equation $1 + GH = 0$ for linear systems is a polynomial having real coefficients; therefore, its complex roots occur in conjugate pairs and the root locus must be symmetrical around the real axis.

Rule 4: *Segments on real axis.* Since complex conjugate pairs of poles contribute a net angle of zero to the angle of GH for values of s along the real axis, the poles and zeros on the real axis alone determine the angle of GH there. Poles and zeros to the left of a trial point on the real axis contribute zero angle; whereas poles and zeros to the right of a trial point contribute $-180°$ and $+180°$, respectively, to the angle of GH. Therefore, segments of the locus lie along the real axis to the left of an odd number of poles and zeros, as shown in Fig. 7–3a.

Rule 5: *Asymptotes for large s.* Usually $n_p > n_z$ for GH and $n_p - n_z$ branches of the locus terminate at infinity along asymptotes. Fig. 7–3b

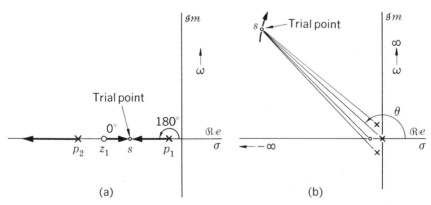

(a)   (b)

Fig. 7–3. Illustrations of rules 4 and 5. The trial point s is on the locus. (a) The locus exists on the real axis to the left of an odd number of poles plus zeros. (b) For large s, the loci approach asymptotes.

shows a trial point of the locus in a remote region from the poles and zeros of GH. The vectors drawn from the poles and zeros to the trial point have approximately the same angle θ, as seen in Fig. 7–3b. The trial point will satisfy the root-locus angle condition, if θ has the value

$$\theta(n_p - n_z) = \pm 180°, \pm 540°, \ldots$$

Then the angle of the asymptote with the real axis must be

$$\theta = \frac{\pm 180°}{n_p - n_z}, \frac{\pm 540°}{n_p - n_z}, \text{ etc.} \qquad (7\text{–}9a)$$

From the theory of polynomial equations, it can be shown that the asymptote lines radiate from a point on the real axis given as

$$C = \frac{\Sigma \text{ (value of poles)} - \Sigma \text{ (value of zeros)}}{n_p - n_z} \qquad (7\text{–}9b)$$

The asymptotes are useful as guides in sketching the root locus near the origin.

Rule 6: *Breakaway and breakin points on real axis.* The locus must depart from or return to a segment occurring on the real axis between two poles or two zeros, respectively. The location of a breakaway point is found by taking a trial point $(\sigma, \Delta\omega)$ off the axis in the neighborhood of the breakaway point, applying the angle condition, and solving the

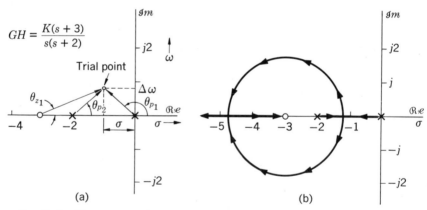

Fig. 7–4. Illustration of breakaway and breakin points on a root locus. (a) Breakaway point. (b) Completed root locus.

resultant equation for σ by trial and error. An example is shown in Fig. 7–4 for the function

$$GH = \frac{K(s + 3)}{s(s + 2)} \qquad (7\text{–}10a)$$

The poles and zeros are plotted as shown and a trial point $(\sigma, \Delta\omega)$ is assumed. The root-locus angle requirement for the trial point gives

$$\theta_{z1} - (\theta_{p1} + \theta_{p2}) = \pm 180° \tag{7–10b}$$

for the particular GH. The angles may be written in terms of the geometry to give

$$\tan^{-1} \frac{\Delta\omega}{3 - \sigma} - \left(180° - \tan^{-1} \frac{\Delta\omega}{\sigma}\right) - \tan^{-1} \frac{\Delta\omega}{2 - \sigma} = \pm 180° \tag{7–10c}$$

For small values of $\Delta\omega$ the angles may be replaced by the first term of the series expansion of the arc tangent function, giving

$$\frac{\Delta\omega}{3 - \sigma} + \frac{\Delta\omega}{\sigma} - \frac{\Delta\omega}{2 - \sigma} = 0$$

$$\frac{1}{3 - \sigma} - \frac{1}{2 - \sigma} = -\frac{1}{\sigma} \tag{7–10d}$$

This equation is best solved by trial-and-error procedure since one purpose of the root-locus technique is to avoid the use of analytical methods for finding the roots of polynomials. A few trials give the breakaway point as $\sigma = 1.27$. A similar equation can be written for the breakin point between -3 and infinity. Eq. 7–10d differs with each GH function; but it can be generalized by noting that it equates the sum of the reciprocals of the distances from the poles and zeros to the trial breakaway point σ, on the left, to the sum of the reciprocals of the distances on the right of σ, with the pole and zero distances having opposite signs. The loci always make angles of $\pm 90°$ with the real axis.

Eq. 7–10d contains information on both the breakaway and the breakin points. Rearrangement of the equation gives the quadratic equation

$$\sigma^2 - 6\sigma + 6 = (\sigma - 1.27)(\sigma - 4.73) = 0$$

whose roots place the breakaway point at -1.27 and the breakin point at -4.73. The completed root locus is sketched in Fig. 7–4b.

Another analytical method for finding these points is based on the change of K with s in the complex plane. In Fig. 7–4a the gain K at the two poles is zero, and as the roots move along the locus toward the breakaway point the value of K increases so that at the breakaway point K has a maximum value. This value may be found by setting $dK/ds = 0$. In a similar manner, the gain at the two zeros $(-3, \infty)$ is infinity and as the roots move along the locus toward the breakin point the value of K decreases so that at the breakin point K has a minimum value which can be found by differentiation as before. In the present example,

$$GH = \frac{K(s + 3)}{s(s + 2)} = -1 \qquad K = -\frac{s(s + 2)}{s + 3}$$

so that

$$\frac{dK}{ds} = -\frac{(s+3)(2s+2) - (s^2 + 2s)}{(s+3)^2} = 0$$

which requires

$$s^2 + 6s + 6 = 0 = (s + 1.27)(s + 4.73)$$

The breakaway and breakin points are found at -1.27 and -4.73, respectively. This example has no complex poles or zeros to affect the breakaway point.

When complex poles and zeros of GH are located relatively far from the real-axis breakaway point, they can be neglected in the computation. However, when they are located near the real axis their presence must be taken into account. The angular contribution to Eq. 7–10d due to a pair of complex poles or zeros near the breakaway point is given by

$$\frac{2(\sigma - \sigma_1)}{\omega_1{}^2 + (\sigma - \sigma_1)^2} \qquad (7\text{–}10e)$$

where $\sigma_1 \pm j\omega_1$ are the coordinates of the complex pole or zero. The angular contribution of poles and zeros have opposite signs as described for Eq. 7–10d.

Rule 7: *Angle of departure from complex poles and arrival at complex zeros.* The angle of departure of root loci from complex poles is very useful in sketching the diagrams. As shown in Fig. 7–5a, it is found by assuming a trial point on the locus near the complex pole and applying the angle requirement. For the pole map in Fig. 7–5a, the trial point

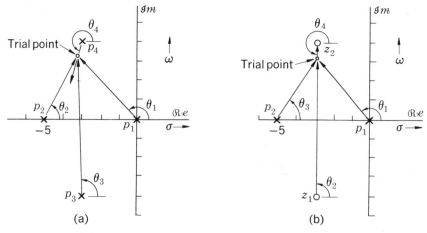

(a)   (b)

Fig. 7–5. (a) Angle of departure at complex pole. (b) Angle of arrival at complex zero.

is on the locus near p_4 and the angle of departure θ_4 is found from the root locus angle requirement as

$$-(\theta_1 + \theta_2 + \theta_3 + \theta_4) = -180°$$
$$\theta_4 = +180° - (\theta_1 + \theta_2 + \theta_3)$$

The angles are measured with a protractor to give an angle of departure in this case as

$$\theta_4 = +180° - (126° + 92° + 64°) = -102°$$

The angle of arrival at a complex zero is found in the same manner. For the pole-zero map in Fig. 7–5b the angle of arrival θ_4 is found from the root locus angle requirement as

$$\theta_4 + \theta_2 - (\theta_1 + \theta_3) = -180°$$

After measuring the angles, the angle of arrival is

$$\theta_4 = -180° + \theta_1 + \theta_3 - \theta_2$$
$$= -180° + 126° + 64° - 90° = -80°$$

The angles computed here determine the tangents to the root locus as it leaves a complex pole or as it enters a complex zero.

Rule 8: *Intersection with the imaginary axis.* Passage of the root locus from the left half into the right half of the s-plane represents a stable system becoming unstable as the locus crosses the imaginary axis. The point of intersection which represents the onset of instability can be found from the Routh, Nyquist, or other stability criteria.

Rule 9: *Gain calibration.* After the root locus has been sketched and located, it is calibrated for gain values by the root-locus magnitude relationship

$$K = \left| \frac{P_1 P_2 \cdots}{Z_1 \cdots} \right| \tag{7-6c}$$

In other words, K is the open-loop gain associated with a specific root on the root locus. It may be computed graphically by measurement of vector lengths or it may be found analytically.

The above rules are indispensable for sketching the root locus. In fact, without them the graphical method is not practical because of the large amount of analytical work needed to locate the root locus. After the locus is sketched by use of the rules, its location is checked and improved by using a protractor or other device* to check the angle of GH. If a point on the sketched locus does not give the required angle, the trial point is relocated until it satisfies the angle requirement. In this manner

---

* The Spirule, developed by the originator of the root-locus method, is extremely useful in constructing root loci.

the locus can be improved to any degree compatible with patience and the equipment used. Finally, the root locus is calibrated for gain by use of Eq. 7–6c. The method is illustrated in the following example.

Example 7–1. Sketch the root-locus plot for the PI control of the second-order system in Fig. 6–8. Let $kR = 1, \tau = 1$, and $\tau_1 = 2$; then the open-loop transfer function becomes

$$GH = \frac{K_c(1 + 1/\tau_i s)}{(s + 1)(2s + 1)}$$

(a) Let $\tau_i = 0.33$, and sketch the root locus for variable gain K_c. Find the value of K_c which makes the system unstable, and compare it with the value given by Eq. 6–14d. Also find the roots of $1 + GH$ for $\zeta = 0.5$ and the corresponding controller gain K_c.

(b) Let $K_c = 0.12$, and sketch the root locus for variable integral time constant τ_i. Find the value of τ_i which makes $\zeta = 0.5$ for the system.

Solution. (a) The root-locus form of the transfer function is

$$GH = \frac{0.5K_c(s + 3)}{s(s + 1)(s + 0.5)}$$

The root-locus plot is made by application of the construction rules.

1. Locate the poles and zeros on the s-plane.
2. By rule 1, the locus has three branches.
3. By rule 4, the locus exists on the real axis for $-0.5 < s < 0$ and $-3 < s < -1$.
4. By rule 5, the locus asymptotes make an angle of $\pm 90°$ with the real axis and intersect it at

$$C = \frac{-1 - 0.5 - (-3)}{(3 - 1)} = 0.75$$

5. By rule 6, the breakaway point σ satisfies the relationship

$$\frac{-1}{\sigma} = -\frac{1}{0.5 - \sigma} - \frac{1}{1 - \sigma} + \frac{1}{3 - \sigma} \qquad \sigma \cong 0.22$$

6. By rule 8, the Routh criterion (Eq. 6–14d for this system) states that the system is unstable for $K_c > 1$. By trial-and-error summation of angles, the intersection on the imaginary axis is found as $s = \pm j$ and the corresponding value of gain K_c is found by vector measurement as

$$K_c = \frac{|s|\,|s + 1|\,|s + 0.5|}{0.5|s + 3|}\bigg|_{s = +j} = \frac{1(1.10)(1.45)}{0.5(3.15)} = 1.01$$

in good agreement with the Routh value of $K_c \leqq 1$ for stability.

The complete root locus is shown in Fig. E7–1a, with gain values marked at $K_c = 0.12$ and 1.0. The line of constant $\zeta = 0.5$ is drawn, and the pair of complex roots of $1 + GH$ are read at the intersection with the plot as $(-0.2 + j0.33)$ and $(-0.2 - j0.33)$. The gain at that point is found graphically as $K_c = 0.12$.

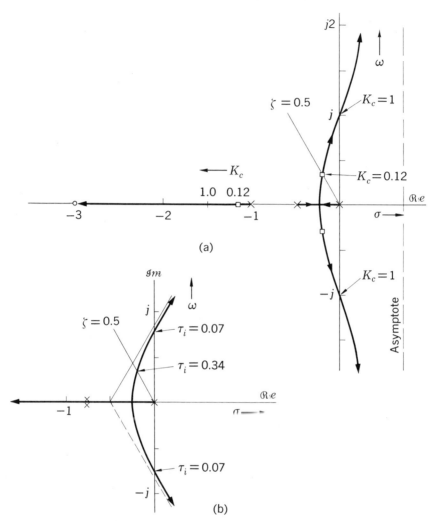

Fig. E7–1. Root locus plot for PI control of second order system. (a) Plot for $\tau_i = 0.33$ and variable K_c. System becomes unstable when $K_c = 1$. (b) Plot for $K_c = 0.12$ and variable τ_i. System becomes unstable when $\tau_i = 0.07$.

The real root of $1 + GH$ for this gain is found graphically by trial and error to be -1.15. It is also found from Eq. 2–10b, which requires that the sum of the roots of an nth polynomial must equal $-a_{n-1}$, thus:

$$r_1 + r_2 + r_3 = -a_{n-1}, \text{ and } r_1 + (-0.2 + j0.33) + (-0.2 - j0.33)$$
$$= -1.5, \text{ or } r_1 = -1.1$$

(b) To show the effect of τ_i on the root locus, the transfer function must be put in the form of $1 + GH$, with the constant in the numerator of GH. In this case, the characteristic equation

$$1 + GH = 1 + \frac{0.5K_c(s + 1/\tau_i)}{s(s + 1)(s + 0.5)}$$

can be rearranged with $K_c = 0.12$ into the form

$$1 + \frac{0.06\tau_i^{-1}}{s(s + 0.75)^2}$$

The poles are plotted on Fig. E7–1b, and the construction rules give the following information about the locus:

1. By rule 1, the locus has three branches.
2. By rule 4, the locus exists on the real axis for $-\infty < s < 0$.
3. By rule 5, the locus asymptotes make an angle of $\pm 60°$ with the real axis and intersect it at

$$C = \frac{-0.75 - 0.75}{3} = -0.50$$

4. By rule 6, the breakaway point σ satisfies the equation

$$\frac{1}{\sigma} = \frac{2}{0.75 - \sigma} \quad \text{or} \quad \sigma = -0.25$$

5. The locus crosses the imaginary axis at $s = j0.77$, and the value of τ_i is found by vector measurement as

$$\frac{1}{\tau_i} = \frac{1}{0.06}(0.77)(1.05)^2 = 1.42 \quad \text{or} \quad \tau_i = 0.07$$

This agrees with the value of $\tau_i = 0.072$ given by Eq. 6–14d.

The $\zeta = 0.5$ damping-ratio line is drawn on the plot and intersects the locus at $s = -0.20 \pm j0.35$ (the closed-loop complex poles). The gain $1/\tau_i$ at the intersection is found by vector measurement as

$$\frac{1}{\tau_i} = \frac{1}{.06}(0.66)^2(0.40) = 2.91 \quad \text{or} \quad \tau_i = 0.34$$

which agrees with part a. The two parts of this problem, of course, have the same answer. The root-locus plot in Fig. E7–1a shows the variation of closed-loop poles with change of K_c when $\tau_i = 0.33$. The plot in Fig. E7–1b gives the closed-loop poles with change of τ_i when $K_c = 0.12$.

The root-locus method shows graphically how the roots of $1 + GH$ change as one of the system parameters changes. Root loci for some simple transfer functions are sketched in Fig. 7–6 to show in general how the pole-zero map affects the plot.

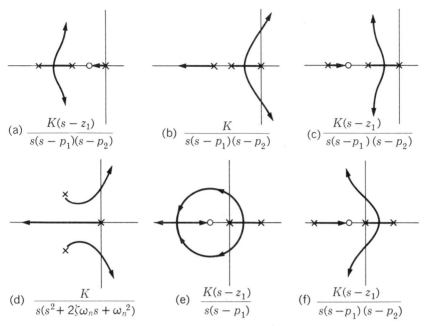

(a) $\dfrac{K(s - z_1)}{s(s - p_1)(s - p_2)}$

(b) $\dfrac{K}{s(s - p_1)(s - p_2)}$

(c) $\dfrac{K(s - z_1)}{s(s - p_1)(s - p_2)}$

(d) $\dfrac{K}{s(s^2 + 2\zeta\omega_n s + \omega_n^2)}$

(e) $\dfrac{K(s - z_1)}{s(s - p_1)}$

(f) $\dfrac{K(s - z_1)}{s(s - p_1)(s - p_2)}$

Fig. 7-6. Root-locus plots for some simple functions.

Pole-Zero Maps for Process Controllers. From the root-locus view-point, the process engineer selects a controller for the effect that its poles and zeros contribute to the overall shape and location of the root-locus plot. The ideal controller actions are discussed in Chapter 5 with the comment that they are idealizations of the actual industrial controllers. Pole-zero maps for the ideal controller actions are shown in Fig. 7-7 along with maps for two industrial controllers.

The ideal PID controller equation can be factored as

$$G_c(s) = K_c\left(1 + \tau_d s + \frac{1}{\tau_i s}\right)$$

$$= \frac{K_c \tau_d}{s}\left(s + \frac{1 + \sqrt{1 - 4a}}{2\tau_d}\right)\left(s + \frac{1 - \sqrt{1 - 4a}}{2\tau_d}\right)$$

where $a = \tau_d/\tau_i$, the ratio of derivative and integral controller time con-stants. As shown on the s-plane in Fig. 7-7c, when $a < 0.25$ the con-troller zeros are real and unequal. For $a > 0.25$ and τ_i held constant, the zeros become complex and lie on a circle passing through the origin with center at $s = -1/\tau_i$. When τ_d is held constant, the complex zeros lie on a line passing through $s = -2/\tau_i$ parallel to the imaginary axis. When $a = 0.25$, the controller has a second-order zero at $s = -2/\tau_i$. Certain

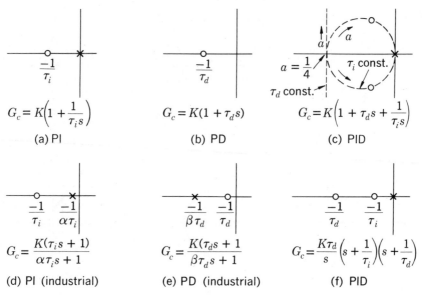

$$G_c = K\left(1 + \frac{1}{\tau_i s}\right)$$

(a) PI

$$G_c = K(1 + \tau_d s)$$

(b) PD

$$G_c = K\left(1 + \tau_d s + \frac{1}{\tau_i s}\right)$$

(c) PID

$$G_c = \frac{K(\tau_i s + 1)}{\alpha \tau_i s + 1}$$

(d) PI (industrial)

$$G_c = \frac{K(\tau_d s + 1)}{\beta \tau_d s + 1}$$

(e) PD (industrial)

$$G_c = \frac{K\tau_d}{s}\left(s + \frac{1}{\tau_i}\right)\left(s + \frac{1}{\tau_d}\right)$$

(f) PID

Fig. 7–7.   Pole-zero maps for process controllers.

industrial controllers furnishing only real zeros have transfer functions which can be factored as

$$G_c(s) = K\left(\frac{1}{\tau_i s} + (1 + a) + \tau_d s\right) = \frac{K\tau_d}{s}\left(s + \frac{1}{\tau_i}\right)\left(s + \frac{1}{\tau_d}\right)$$

The pole-zero map is given in Fig. 7–7f.

7-2. TRANSIENT RESPONSE FROM POLE-ZERO MAP

The location of the poles and zeros of the system transfer function determines the behavior of the system for any input. In this section, the transient response $x(t)$ is the response of the relaxed system to a step input applied at zero time. If the input is a unit step and if $G(s)$ is restricted to transfer functions of lumped-parameter systems having no repeated poles and zeros and no pure integrators, the transform of the transient response is

$$X(s) = \frac{1}{s}\,G(s) = \frac{K_0}{s} + \frac{K_1}{s - p_1} + \cdots + \frac{K_i}{s - p_i} \qquad (7\text{–}11a)$$

where the K's are the residues of $X(s)$ in the various poles. The unit step response becomes

$$x(t) = K_0 + K_1 e^{p_1 t} + \cdots + K_i e^{p_i t} \qquad (7\text{–}11b)$$

where the residues K_i are the amplitudes of the various response terms and are found as

$$K_i = \text{Res}\,[G(s)\,;p_i] = \lim_{s \to p_i} (s - p_i)G(s)$$

This expression for K_i may be interpreted graphically so that the residues may be found from the pole-zero map. The result is stated as

$$K_i = K_G \left[\frac{\text{Product of vectors drawn from zeros to } s = p_i}{\text{Product of vectors drawn from poles to } s = p_i} \right]$$

$$= K_G \left[\frac{\prod Z_i}{\prod P_i} \right]_{s = p_i} \tag{7-11c}$$

where K_G is the gain of the transfer function $G(s)$ in root-locus form. When a given function $G(s)$ has no finite zeros, the term Z is replaced by unity. The Spirule may be used to compute the residues graphically since it is designed to measure and multiply or divide vector lengths.

First-Order System. As an illustration of the graphical method of finding response, the effect of the presence of a zero on the unit step response of a relaxed first-order system will be found. The transfer function of a first-order lag in series with a first-order lead (a lag-lead network) is

$$G(s) = \frac{1 + as}{1 + \tau s} = \frac{a}{\tau} \frac{s + 1/a}{s + 1/\tau} \tag{7-12a}$$

where $-1/a$ is the zero and $-1/\tau$ is the pole of $G(s)$. The transform of the unit step response is

$$X(s) = \frac{a}{\tau} \frac{s + 1/a}{s(s + 1/\tau)} = \frac{K_0}{s} + \frac{K_1}{s + 1/\tau} \tag{7-12b}$$

and the response is

$$x(t) = K_0 + K_1 e^{-t/\tau} \tag{7-12c}$$

where the amplitudes K_0, K_1 are the residues and are evaluated by Eq. 7-11c as follows:

$$K_0 = \frac{a}{\tau} \left[\frac{s + 1/a}{s + 1/\tau} \right]_{s=0} = 1$$

$$K_1 = \frac{a}{\tau} \left[\frac{s + 1/a}{s} \right]_{s=-\frac{1}{\tau}} = \frac{a}{\tau} \left[\frac{-1/\tau + 1/a}{-1/\tau} \right] = \frac{a - \tau}{\tau}$$

The response is found to be

$$x(t) = 1 + \frac{a - \tau}{\tau} e^{-t/\tau} \tag{7-12d}$$

The algebraic sign of each term in the transient is determined by the sign of the residue. In general, the residue at a pole is positive if the pole lies to the left of an even number of poles and zeros on the complex plane and negative if it lies to the left of an odd number of poles and zeros.   The pole-zero map and the transient response of this lag-lead network is shown in Fig. 7–8 for values of a/τ of 0, 0.5, 1 and 1.5.   Notice that, when

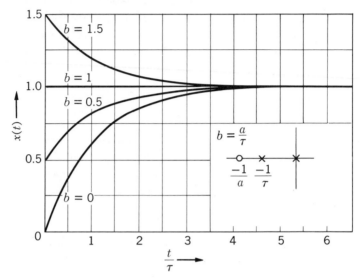

Fig. 7–8.   Effect of zero location on the step response of a first-order system.

$a < \tau$ as shown, the residue in τ is negative, giving a transient undershoot at zero time.   When $a > \tau$, the residue in τ is positive and the transient overshoots at zero time.   When $a = \tau$, the pole and zero cancel.

Another way of looking at the effect of the zero is to expand the transform

$$X(s) = \frac{1 + as}{s(1 + \tau s)} = \frac{1}{s(1 + \tau s)} + \frac{a}{1 + \tau s} \qquad (7\text{–}13a)$$

and, therefore,

$$x(t) = g(t) + a\dot{g}(t)$$

where $g(t)$ and $\dot{g}(t)$ represent the unit step response and unit impulse response of the first-order lag element, respectively.   In this example $g(t)$ has a positive slope, and the effect of the zero is to add a quantity $a\dot{g}(t)$ to the response, thus:

$$g(t) = 1 - e^{-t/\tau} \qquad \dot{g}(t) = (1/\tau)e^{-t/\tau}$$

so that the unit step response of the lag-lead network is

$$x(t) = 1 - e^{-t/\tau} + \frac{a}{\tau} e^{-t/\tau} = 1 + \frac{a - \tau}{\tau} e^{-t/\tau} \qquad (7\text{–}13b)$$

From this viewpoint, the basic response $g(t)$ is independent of the zero value and the zero adds a derivative term to the basic response.

Second-Order System. The effect on the unit step response of adding a finite zero (derivative action) to a second-order system can be seen by relating it to the response of the pure second-order system, as

$$X(s) = \frac{\omega_n^2(1 + \tau_d s)}{s(s^2 + 2\zeta\omega_n s + \omega_n^2)} = \frac{\omega_n^2}{s(s^2 + 2\zeta\omega_n s + \omega_n^2)} + \frac{\omega_n^2 \tau_d}{s^2 + 2\zeta\omega_n s + \omega_n^2}$$

$$(7\text{-}14a)$$

The first term in the inversion contains the step response of the pure second-order system and the second term is the derivative of that response, so that

$$x(t) = g(t) + \tau_d \dot{g}(t) \qquad (7\text{-}14b)$$

where

$$g(t) = 1 + \frac{1}{\sqrt{1 - \zeta^2}} e^{-\zeta\omega_n t} \sin\left(\omega_n \sqrt{1 - \zeta^2}\, t - \psi\right)$$

$$\psi = \tan^{-1} \sqrt{1 - \zeta^2} / -\zeta$$

and

$$\dot{g}(t) = \frac{\omega_n}{\sqrt{1 - \zeta^2}} e^{-\zeta\omega_n t} \sin\left(\omega_n \sqrt{1 - \zeta^2}\, t\right)$$

The pole-zero map is sketched in Fig. 7-9a and the unit step response for $\tau_d = 1$ is plotted in Fig. 7-9b. The derivative relationship between $g(t)$

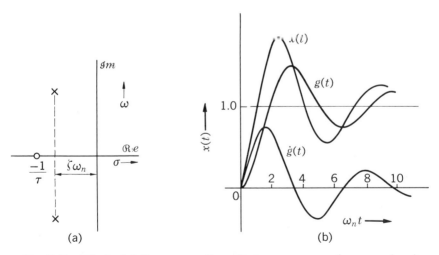

Fig. 7-9. Effect of finite zero on the unit step response of a second-order system. (a) Pole-zero map. (b) Unit step response. $x(t)$ is sketched for $\tau = 1$.

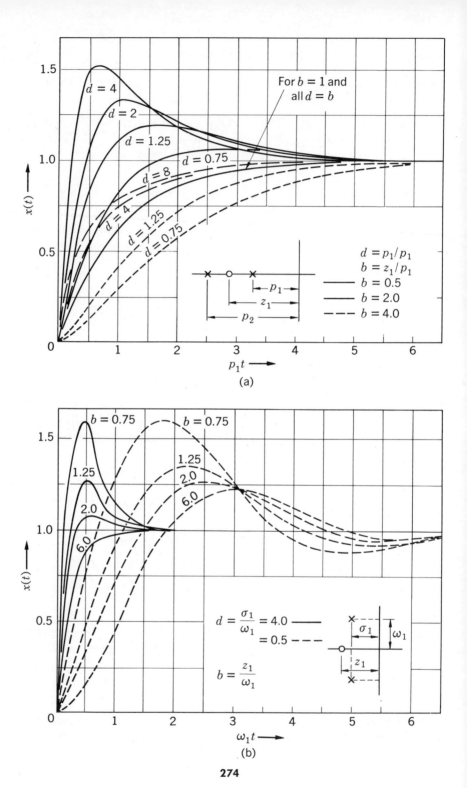

(a)

(b)

274

and $\dot{g}(t)$ requires that the maxima and minima in $g(t)$ correspond to zero values of $\dot{g}(t)$; therefore, the total response $x(t)$ passes through $g(t)$ at these points. The response $x(t)$ has a positive slope at $t = 0$, whereas the slope of $g(t)$ at $t = 0$ is zero; hence the finite zero (derivative action) speeds up the response and decreases the time to first zero error. The effect of the zero on the time to first peak, t_p, is shown by the equations

Pure second-order system: $\quad t_p = \pi/\omega_d$ $\qquad\qquad\qquad$ (4–21d)

System with zero: $\qquad\quad t_p = \dfrac{1}{\omega_d} \tan^{-1}\left[-\tau_d\omega_d/(1 - \tau_d\zeta\omega_n) \right]$

where $\omega_d = \omega_n \sqrt{1 - \zeta^2}$. Notice also that the finite zero causes increased overshoot in the response.

The derivative time constant τ_d multiplies the derivative effect. For small values of τ_d (zero located on the far left in the pole-zero map), the effect of the zero is very small and $x(t) \cong g(t)$. For large values of τ_d the effect of the zero is large, and the derivative term may dominate the total response as $x(t) \cong \tau_d\dot{g}(t)$ until the transient decays.

Elgerd and Stephens* correlated the unit step response with the pole-zero map and present charts of transient response for many pole-zero configurations. The curves in Figs. 7–10a and b show transient responses for the second-order system with one finite zero. The pole-zero maps are shown on the s-plane inset on each figure. In Fig. 7–10a for the response of a system with real poles, the time p_1t is normalized for the smaller pole and the plots are made for several pole-zero arrangements. First, observe the response traced with solid lines. These are made for $z_1 = bp_1 = 0.5p_1$ and values of $d = p_2/p_1$ between 0.5 and 4. This system has a zero to the right of both poles, i e , the zero is between the origin and the smallest pole. The effect of the zero is to cause serious overshoot in the response when the second pole is far removed from the zero. This is the only overshoot case in Fig. 7–10a and therefore it is concluded that, if derivative controller action (the source of the system zero) is to speed up this system response to the extent of making it overshoot, the zero must be to the right of both poles. The responses represented by the broken-line curves are for the zero to the left of pole $p_1(z_1 = 2p_1)$ and to the right of pole $p_2(d = p_2/p_1 = 4, 8)$, i.e., the zero is between the poles. The dotted

* O. I. Elgerd and W. C. Stephens, Effect of Closed-Loop Transfer Function Pole and Zero Locations on the Transient Response of Linear Control Systems," *Trans. AIEE*, **77**, 121–127 (1959).

Fig. 7–10. Effect of the zero location on the step response of (a) a system having one pair of real poles, and (b) a system having one pair of complex poles. (From Elgerd and Stephens, *Trans. AIEE*, **77**(42), pp. 121–127, 1959; by permission.)

response curves are for the zero to the left of both poles. The general conclusion is that the system becomes increasingly overdamped as the zero moves to the left and as the poles move to the right in the s-plane.

The step response curves in Fig. 7–10b show the effect of zero location on the response of a second-order system having a pair of complex poles. The solid-line response curves show the effect of the zero location when the complex poles have a real part equal to four times the complex part ($\sigma_1 = 4\omega_1$ or $\zeta = 0.97$). Again observe that as the zero moves toward the origin ($b \to 0$) the overshoot increases and as the zero moves away from the origin the derivative effect decreases. The broken-line curves show the effect of the zero location when the complex poles are closer the imaginary axis ($\sigma_1 = 0.5\omega_1$ or $\zeta = 0.45$). In this case the fact that the poles have a smaller damping ratio has little effect on the response when the zero is near the origin since the overshoots for $d = 4$ and $d = 0.5$ are about the same. However, the decrease of overshoot with increase of b is less sensitive to changes in b in this case because the complex poles are relatively near the imaginary axis and this factor overshadows the effect of the zero. In every case the curves show that as the zero approaches the origin the overshoot increases and the time to first peak decreases (faster response). Notice that the zero location affects neither the natural frequency nor the damping ratio of the system complex roots.

Example 7–2.

(a) Find the unit step response of the system

$$G(s) = \frac{(0.5s + 1)}{0.8s^2 + 0.8s + 1} = \frac{0.625(s + 2)}{s^2 + s + 1.25}$$

using the graphical method for evaluating residues.

(b) Compare the result in part a with the analytical result obtained by viewing the zero as a differentiator.

Solution. (a) The unit step response is obtained by finding the residues in the poles as

$$X(s) = \frac{1}{s} G(s) = \frac{0.625(s + 2)}{s(s^2 + s + 1.25)} = \frac{K_0}{s} + \frac{K_1}{s + 0.5 + j} + \frac{K_2}{s + 0.5 - j} \quad \text{(a)}$$

The pole-zero map is sketched in Fig. E7–2, from which the residues are graphically evaluated by Eq. 7–11c. The residues are

$$K_0 = \frac{0.625(2)}{(1.12\underline{/117°})(1.12\underline{/-117°})} \simeq 1.0$$

$$K_1 = \frac{0.625(1.8\underline{/-34°})}{(1.12\underline{/-117°})(2\underline{/-90°})} = 0.50\underline{/173°} = -0.50 + j0.06$$

$$K_2 = \bar{K}_1 = -0.50 - j0.06$$

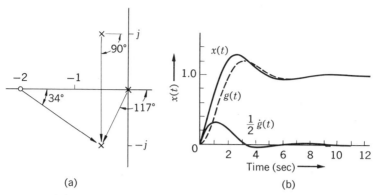

(a)   (b)

Fig. E7–2. (a) Graphical evaluation of residue K_1 from pole-zero map. (b) Unit step response found as $g(t) + \frac{1}{2}\dot{g}(t)$.

The complex terms are inverted by the Laplace-transform pair

$$\mathcal{L}^{-1}\left[\frac{a + jb}{s + \sigma + j\omega} + \frac{a - jb}{s + \sigma - j\omega}\right] = 2\sqrt{a^2 + b^2}\, e^{-\sigma t} \sin(\omega t + \psi);$$

$$\psi = -\tan^{-1} a/b \quad \text{(b)}$$

and the transient response is

$$x(t) = 1 + e^{-0.5t} \sin(t - 83°) \quad \text{(c)}$$

(b) By considering the zero as a differentiator, the response can be written

$$X(s) = \frac{1.25}{s(s^2 + s + 1.25)} + \frac{0.625}{s^2 + s + 1.25} \quad \text{(d)}$$

and

$$x(t) = g(t) + \frac{1}{2}\dot{g}(t) \quad \text{(e)}$$

where $g(t) = 1 + 1.12e^{-0.5t} \sin(t - 117°)$
$\dot{g}(t) = 1.25e^{-0.5t} \sin t$

or

$$x(t) = 1 + e^{-0.5t} \sin(t - 83°) \quad \text{(f)}$$

The graphical result agrees with this analytical result.

The transient response is plotted in Fig. E7–2b as the sum of $g(t) + \frac{1}{2}\dot{g}(t)$, from which it is seen that the effect of the zero ($\frac{1}{2}\dot{g}(t)$) is to speed up the response and increase the overshoot. $g(t)$ is the unit step response of a relaxed second-order system and can be obtained from Fig. 4–12 for $\zeta = 0.446$. The $\dot{g}(t)$ is the impulse response of a relaxed second-order system and can be obtained from Fig. 4–11 for $\zeta = 0.446$. Also, the total response $x(t)$ can be read from the chart in Fig. 7–10b for the case of $d = 0.5$ and $b = 2.0$.

Higher-Order Systems. The dynamic behavior of a system depends upon the location of the system poles and zeros in the complex plane.

The pole locations determine the general form of the response expression (the exponential functions in each term), and the zero locations, through their effect on the residues at the poles, determine the magnitude of the coefficients of each term and thereby modify the shape of the response curve.

The transfer function of a process system and its forcing function may be represented generally by the form

$$X(s) = \frac{K(s - z_1)(s - z_2) \cdots (s - z_z)}{(s - p_1)(s - p_2)(s - p_3) \cdots (s - p_p)} \quad (7\text{--}15a)$$

where the number of poles p exceeds the number of zeros z. A few generalizations concerning this expression and its response $x(t)$ are given below.

1. Initial-value theorem. The initial value of $x(t)$ is given as

$$\lim_{t \to 0} x(t) = \lim_{s \to \infty} sX(s) \quad (7\text{--}15b)$$

If the initial value of $x(t)$ is to be finite, $X(s)$ must have more finite poles than zeros. Furthermore, if $x(0)$ is zero, the number of finite poles must exceed the finite zeros by two or more.

2. Final-value theorem. When all the poles of $sX(s)$ have negative real parts the final value of $x(t)$ is given as

$$\lim_{t \to \infty} x(t) = \lim_{s \to 0} sX(s) \quad (7\text{--}15c)$$

The final value of $x(t)$ will be zero unless one pole and no zero of $X(s)$ lies at the origin. If $p_1 = 0$ (one pole of $X(s)$ lies at the origin), the final value of $x(t)$ becomes

$$\lim_{t \to \infty} x(t) = \frac{Kz_1z_2 \cdots z_z}{p_2p_3 \cdots p_p}$$

3. Time-scale change. If the pole-zero map is shrunk in the ratio of a to 1, then the corresponding time responses will be stretched in the ratio of 1 to a, or

$$aF(as) = \mathcal{L}[f(t/a)] \quad (7\text{--}15d)$$

For example, if the pole-zero map is stretched by 10, an expression such as

$$F(s) = \frac{1}{s + 1}$$

becomes

$$\frac{10}{10s + 1} = 10F(10s) = \frac{1}{s + 0.1}$$

and the corresponding time functions are

$$f(t) = e^{-t}$$

becomes

$$f(t/10) = \mathcal{L}^{-1}\left[\frac{1}{s + 0.1}\right] = e^{-0.1t}$$

Thus, in a stable system, movement of poles toward the origin in the s-plane corresponds to slowing the dynamic response of the system.

4. Approximate system responses. In high-order systems it is sometimes possible to ignore some of the finite poles and zeros without significantly changing the system response. Consider the example

$$X(s) = \frac{40(s + 0.95)}{s(s + 1)(s + 2)(s + 20)} = \frac{0.95}{s} + \frac{0.105}{s + 1} - \frac{1.17}{s + 2} + \frac{0.111}{s + 20}$$
(7–16a)

which has the response

$$x(t) = 0.95 + 0.105e^{-t} - 1.17e^{-2t} + 0.111e^{-20t} \qquad (7\text{–}16b)$$

Inspection of the equation shows that the response due to the remote pole at $s = -20$ is small at $t = 0$ and decays very quickly; hence it could, for practical purposes, be neglected, giving an approximate response function for the system as

$$X(s) = \frac{2(s + 0.95)}{s(s + 1)(s + 2)} = \frac{0.95}{s} + \frac{0.10}{s + 1} - \frac{1.05}{s + 2} \qquad (7\text{–}16c)$$

The zero at -0.95 is very close to the pole at -1.0, making the residue at $s = -1$ much smaller than the residue at the pole $s = -2$. If it is assumed that this pole-zero pair cancel each other, the response function becomes

$$X(s) = \frac{2}{s(s + 2)} = \frac{1}{s} - \frac{1}{s + 2}$$

and the dynamic response is

$$x(t) = 1 - e^{-2t} \qquad (7\text{–}16d)$$

For many engineering purposes such approximations as these can quickly give satisfactory estimates of system response.

This type of approximation is very convenient for "rough and ready" inversions, but unfortunately there are no simple rules by which the accuracy of the approximation can be judged. As usual in practical work, good engineering judgment can get a useful solution with a minimum of effort.

Another transient response chart from Elgerd and Stephens is shown in Fig. 7–11 for the effect of a zero on a third-order system having a pair of complex poles and one real pole. The damping ratio for the complex roots is constant, with $\zeta = 0.71$. The solid lines with $c = 0.5$ overshoot badly because the zero is near the origin and the real pole is relatively remote from the origin ($p_1 = 2z_1$ and $4z_1$). For $c = 2.0$ and $b < 2$ the zero is left of the real pole and the response is overdamped, as shown by the dash-dot lines, because the real pole, being near the origin, dominates the system response.

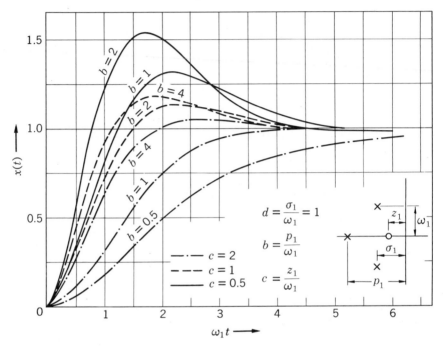

Fig. 7–11. Effect of the zero location on the step response of a system having one real and a pair of complex poles ($\zeta = 0.71$). (From Elgerd and Stephens, *Trans. AIEE,* 77(42), pp. 121–127, 1959; by permission.)

7–3. CONTROLLERS FOR PLANT COMPENSATION

The selection of process controllers and their adjustment to obtain best plant operation (called *system compensation*) usually involves a compromise between the degree of system stability, speed of response, maximum overshoot, and the allowable error. Generally, system compensation consists of selecting a controller action and setting its pole and zero locations and the gain required to force the root locus into the desired region of the complex plane. Chapter 6 discusses the general principles, based upon theory and experience, which are the basis of selecting and adjusting process controllers. This article will confirm those principles, using the root-locus method to analyze a typical control system.

Process Control Example. The compensation that various process controllers provide in a plant is illustrated by the control of temperature in a gas-fired heater. The block diagram of a simple process heater is shown in Fig. 7–12, with the transfer function of each block. Notice that

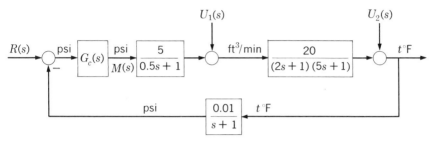

Fig. 7–12. Control of a simple process heater.

the set point is pressure, the controlled variable is temperature, and the static relationship is $t°F = 100\ m$. Lags in transmission of the pneumatic signals are neglected. The principal process disturbances (loads) are: $U_1(s)$ includes all disturbances, such as gas pressure and composition, which affect the volumetric heating value of the fuel. $U_2(s)$ includes all disturbances, such as heater load and ambient temperature, which affect the heater temperature. Root loci will be sketched for the system, making use of P, PI, PD, and PID idealized controllers. The plant operation problem is to adjust the controller to compensate the plant for best dynamic performance.

PROPORTIONAL ACTION. Under proportional control the open-loop transfer function for the control system in Fig. 7–12 is

$$GH = \frac{K_c(5)(20)(0.01)}{(0.5s + 1)(2s + 1)(5s + 1)(s + 1)}$$

$$= \frac{0.2K_c}{(s + 2)(s + 0.5)(s + 0.2)(s + 1)} \qquad (7\text{–}17a)$$

The pole-zero map and the corresponding root-locus plot are shown in Fig. 7–13. The plot shows that the system becomes unstable when $K_c = 7.4$ (13.5% proportional band) and the frequency of oscillation is 0.67 rad/min (ultimate period of 9.38 min). The Ziegler-Nichols setting suggested in Chapter 6 for good control is $K_c = (\frac{1}{2})(7.4) = 3.7$ or 27% proportional band. This value of gain as shown on Fig. 7–13 gives a dominant pair of complex roots with $\zeta = 0.2$. The other roots are on branches of the locus far removed from the origin, and therefore, they have little effect on the system response. The step response of the dominant roots ($\zeta = 0.2$) would overshoot about 50% and gain should be decreased to lower the overshoot.   A damping ratio of $\zeta = 0.5$ requires a gain $K_c = 1.4$.

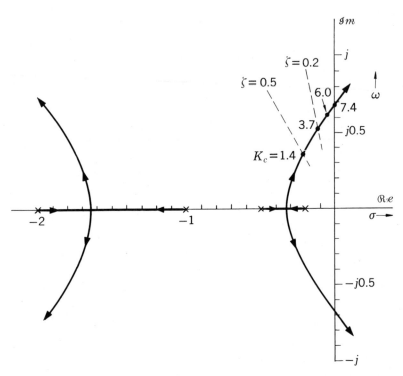

Fig. 7–13. Root-locus plot for proportional control of process heater.

The closed-loop error expression for proportional control of the system is

$$E(s) = \frac{R(s)}{1 + GH} = \frac{(0.5s + 1)(s + 1)(2s + 1)(5s + 1)}{(0.5s + 1)(s + 1)(2s + 1)(5s + 1) + K_c} \quad (7\text{-}17\text{b})$$

and the steady-state error for a unit step input as found from the final-value theorem is

$$e(t)_{ss} = \frac{1}{1 + K_c}$$

In other words, the control system will show offset due to a load change characteristic of proportional control.   Offset would be eliminated by using a PI controller.

PROPORTIONAL-PLUS-INTEGRAL ACTION.   The ideal PI controller adds a pole at the origin and a zero at $s = -1/\tau_i$ so that the open-loop transfer function for the present system becomes

$$GH = \frac{0.2K_c(s + 1/\tau_i)}{s(s + 0.2)(s + 0.5)(s + 1)(s + 2)} \qquad (7\text{--}18)$$

The ultimate period P_u of the closed-loop system under proportional control (determined by the Ziegler-Nichols method) is 9.38 min as found on Fig. 7–13 at a gain of 7.4.   The Ziegler-Nichols formulas in Chapter 6 suggest a trial value of $\tau_i = P_u/1.2$ which, in this case, is $9.38/1.2 = 7.8$ min.

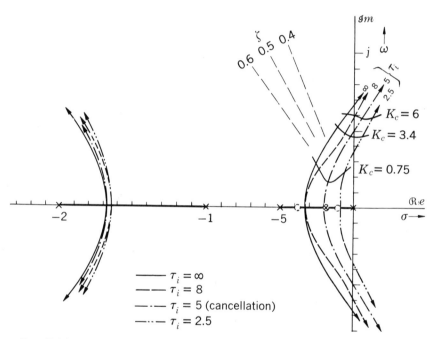

Fig. 7–14.   Proportional-integral control of process heater.   Root loci are drawn for $\tau_i = 8, 5,$ and 2.5 min.   Integral action attracts the locus toward the origin and thereby slows the process system.

The pole-zero map for Eq. 7–18 is shown in Fig. 7–14, where root loci are sketched for several values of τ_i, beginning with $\tau_i = 8$ min, the approximate Ziegler-Nichols value.   A value of $\tau_i = 5$ corresponds to pole-zero cancellation and $\tau_i = 2.5$ represents an extreme value.   Notice that the integral time constant has little effect on the left branches of the root loci. The region near the origin is of most interest, and values of $K_c = 0.75$,

3.4, and 6.0 have been plotted on the loci. Damping ratio values of $\zeta = 0.4$ and 0.6 are indicated for the pair of complex poles near the origin. Inspection of the plots shows that the integral controller has slowed the system (decreased ω_n) and made it less stable (decreased ζ at constant K_c). At the low gain of $K_c = 0.75$ a value of $\tau_i = 5$ gives the system a minimum $\zeta = 0.7$, but at this low gain the system response would be very sluggish. In some systems the integral controller can increase stability but with this process the only purpose in using it is to eliminate the steady-state error in response to a step input. In general, the integrating pole and zero $(-1/\tau_i)$ are placed closer to the origin than the process poles and zeros.

PROPORTIONAL-PLUS-DERIVATIVE ACTION. The ideal PD controller adds a zero at $s = -1/\tau_d$, giving the open-loop transfer function for the process heater system as

$$GH = \frac{0.2K_c\tau_d(s + 1/\tau_d)}{(s + 0.2)(s + 0.5)(s + 1)(s + 2)} \qquad (7\text{--}19)$$

When τ_d is small, the zero is located far to the left on the s-plane and it has little effect on the root locus. For a larger τ_d, the zero enters the region of process plant poles and zeros and affects the shape of the root locus. For very large τ_d, the zero is close to the origin resulting in undersirable noise amplification and serious overshoot in the step response.

The pole-zero maps and resulting root-loci plots are shown in Fig. 7–15 for values of $\tau_d = 1, 2, 5$ min. These values were selected to cancel the process poles at -1, -0.5, and 0.2. Inspection of the plots shows that a zero close to the origin has the effect of pushing the locus to the left into the region of higher frequency and rapid decay. For example, when $\tau_d = 5$, the unstable point is reached when $K_c = 10.8$ and the frequency of oscillation is 1.85 rad/min. These values contrast sharply with $K_c = 7.4$ and $\omega = 0.67$ rad/min for the unstable point for proportional control. Lines of constant gain are drawn on the loci so that the effect of changing τ_d at constant K_c can be observed. In general, PD control of a plant (1) increases the system damped frequency, thereby decreasing the rise time, and (2) increases the damping ratio thereby increasing the stability of the system.

PROPORTIONAL-PLUS-INTEGRAL-PLUS-DERIVATIVE ACTION. The PID controller adds two zeros (real or complex) and a pole at the origin. For the present example the open-loop expression becomes

$$GH = \frac{0.2K_c\tau_d(s + 1/\tau_d)(s + 1/\tau_i)}{s(s + 0.2)(s + 0.5)(s + 1)(s + 2)} \qquad (7\text{--}20)$$

A series-connected controller is assumed here, so that the zeros are always real. The Ziegler-Nichols formulas suggest the following values for this

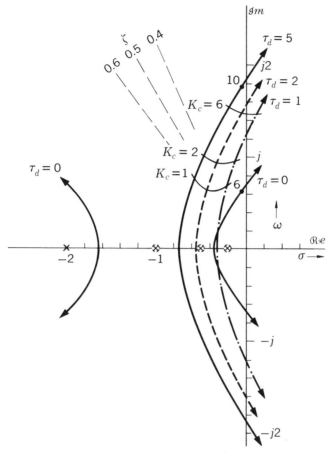

Fig. 7–15. Proportional-derivative control of process plant by pole-zero cancellation. Modification of the left root-loci branches are not shown.

system:

$$K_c = 7.4/1.7 = 4.35 \qquad \tau_i = 0.5(7.4) = 3.7 \qquad \tau_d = 7.4/8 = 0.93$$

These values approximately correspond to cancellation of the process poles at -1 and -0.2. Fig. 7–16 shows root-loci sketches for several values of τ_i and τ_d. In Fig. 7–16a the controller cancels two poles by letting $\tau_i = 5$ and $\tau_d = 1$ with the result that the system stability is increased over that of the proportional system. In Fig. 7–16b the controller cancels the poles at -0.5 and -0.2 ($\tau_i = 5$ and $\tau_d = 2$) with further improvement in system stability as shown by the higher gain at a given damping ratio. On comparison of the two cases for $\zeta = 0.5$ it is seen that case a

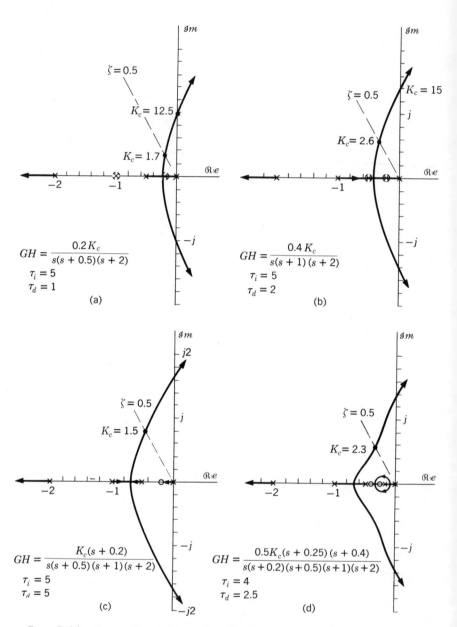

Fig. 7–16. Proportional-integral-derivative control of process heater. Effects of zero-pole cancellation are shown in (a) and (b). The non-cancellation in (c) and (d) introduces a system root near the origin.

allows $K_c = 1.7$ and gives a decay ratio $(\zeta\omega_n)$ of 0.2 while case b allows $K_c = 2.6$ and gives a decay ratio of 0.32. Both cases show zero steady-state error for a step input (poles at the origin) and show about the same overshoot; but the system in case b responds faster to upsets and transients decay away in about 50% less time than for the system in case a.

In Figs. 7–16c and d the non-cancellation of process poles by the controller introduces a root near the origin which leads to a slowly decaying exponential in the transient response. The controller settings in case d are more desirable than those for case c because the roots near the origin have a higher decay ratio.

Example 7–3.

(a) Prepare a root-locus plot for the process heater control system in Fig. 7–12, using a PID controller, with $a = 0.3$ and $\tau_d = 1.5$ min, which gives complex zeros.

(b) Find the controller gain that gives a minimum damping ratio to the dominant pair of complex roots. Find the other roots of $1 + GH$.

(c) Compute the response of the system to a unit step in input.

Solution. (a) The PID controller contributes complex zeros at $s + 0.33 \pm j0.15$ so that the open-loop expression for the system becomes

$$GH = \frac{0.3K_c(s + 0.33 + j0.15)(s + 0.33 - j0.15)}{s(s + 0.2)(s + 0.5)(s + 1)(s + 2)} \tag{a}$$

The root-locus plot for this expression is sketched in Fig. E7–3.

(b) Inspection shows that the two branches near the origin move and terminate on the controller zeros in such a way as to give a pair of roots having a minimum damping ratio. The complex pair is located at $s + 0.18 \pm j0.23$, has a damping ratio of 0.63, and results from gain $K_c = 2.0$. As seen on the sketch, another complex pair of roots is located at $s + 0.55 \pm j0.33$, has a damping ratio of 0.86, and results from the same gain. The other root is real and is located at $s + 2.23$. The system roots are listed as

$$s + 0.18 \pm j0.23 \quad s + 0.55 \pm j0.33 \quad s + 2.23$$

and designated by squares on Fig. E7–3.

(c) The system response to a unit step change in input is found as the inverse of $C(s)$, given as

$$C(s) = \frac{1}{s}\frac{G}{1 + GH} = \frac{30K_c(s + 0.33 + j0.15)(s + 0.33 - j0.15)(s + 1)}{s(s + 2.23)(s + 0.55 + j0.33)(s + 0.55 - j0.33)}$$
$$(s + 0.18 + j0.23)(s + 0.18 - j0.23)$$

$$= \frac{K_0}{s} + \frac{K_1}{s + 2.23} + \frac{K_2}{s + 0.55 + j0.33} + \frac{\overline{K_2}}{s + 0.55 - j0.33}$$
$$+ \frac{K_3}{s + 0.18 + j0.23} + \frac{\overline{K_3}}{s + 0.18 - j0.23} \tag{b}$$

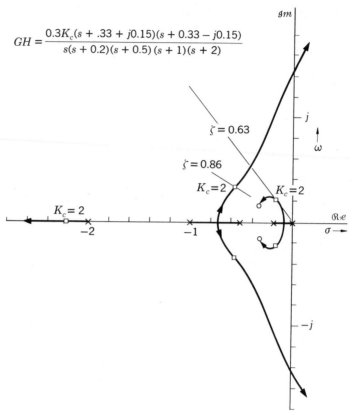

$$GH = \frac{0.3K_c(s + .33 + j0.15)(s + 0.33 - j0.15)}{s(s + 0.2)(s + 0.5)(s + 1)(s + 2)}$$

Fig. E7–3. Root locus for process heater system. Squares are roots of system for $K_c = 2$.

where $K_c = 2$ and the K's are the residues which may be evaluated either graphically or algebraically. Observe that the pole of H becomes a zero of $C(s)$. The residues are found graphically as

$$K_0 = 101 \quad K_1 = 9.5 \quad K_2 = -25.5(0.42 - j0.91) \quad K_3 = -50.6(0.87 + j0.49)$$
$$= 25.5\underline{/-245°} \qquad = 50.6\underline{/-150.5°}$$

The system response is obtained by inverting Eq. b, with the result

$$c(t) = 101 + 9.5e^{-2.23t} - 51e^{-0.55t} \sin (0.33t + 25°)$$
$$- 101.2e^{-0.18t} \sin (0.23t + 119.5°)$$

This is an approximate result because the polynomial factoring, the gain computation, and the residue values were found graphically. However, it agrees very well with the expected initial and final values of 0 and 100; i.e., a unit step change in $R(s)$ would produce a 100° F change in $c(t)$ at steady state.

7–4. ROOT LOCUS OF MULTIPLE-LOOP SYSTEMS

When a single-loop control system cannot meet performance specifications due to large time lags, uncontrolled load changes, or other disturbances, the process engineer can add another process controller in a secondary loop within the primary loop to include the input of the most serious
disturbances. In such an application the primary controller manipulates
the set point of the secondary controller which maintains tight control
in the secondary loop. In the process industries this arrangement is
called *cascade control*. The secondary loop is purposely made a fast system to provide quick correction for disturbances entering within it and in
this way a slow process block is replaced by a fast loop. The root-locus
analysis of a multiple-loop system starts with the innermost loops and
continues outward until the complete system is analyzed. In this way
each loop in turn is analyzed, has its gain set, and is replaced by the
equivalent process block as the analysis progresses to the next larger loop.
The method is illustrated here by adding a secondary loop to the process
heater example.

Inspection of the process heater block diagram in Fig. 7–12 reveals that
fuel flow rate to the heater would be seriously affected by variations in the
supply pressure. Large pressure variations lead to large fuel-flow variations and correspondingly large temperature variations which the temperature controller cannot correct soon enough. The dynamic performance of the heater is improved by adding a flow control loop which can
correct the flow variations quickly without waiting for the resulting temperature effect to be felt around the entire control loop. However, constant fuel-flow rate cannot maintain constant heater temperature when
the heater process load and the fuel calorific value change so that the
temperature controller must manipulate the flow controller set point to
balance the fuel supply to the heater demand. This cascade arrangement
is shown in Fig. 7–17, where it is seen that the secondary loop has added a
proportional flow controller of gain K and a flow transducer with gain of

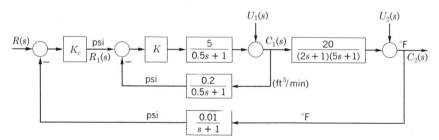

Fig. 7–17. Cascade control of a simple process heater.

0.2 psi-min/ft³ and a 0.5-min time constant. The open-loop expression for the flow control loop is

$$GH = \frac{5(0.2)K}{(0.5s + 1)^2} = \frac{4K}{(s + 2)^2} \tag{7-21a}$$

A root-locus plot for this loop is sketched in Fig. 7–18a. The loop is stable for all gain values. Arbitrarily, the controller gain is set for a

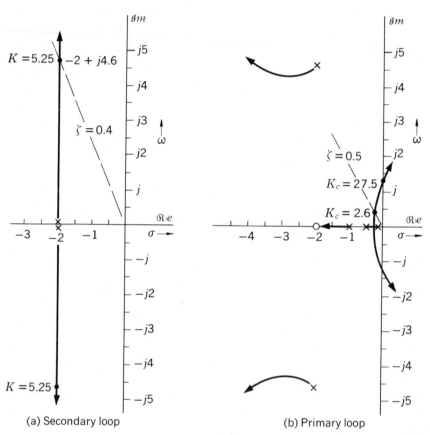

(a) Secondary loop   (b) Primary loop

Fig. 7–18. Root-loci plots for cascade control of process heater. (a) Root locus of secondary loop with roots selected for $\zeta = 0.4$. (b) Root locus of system for proportional control.

damping ratio of $\zeta = 0.4$, which requires that $K = 5.25$, making the roots of $1 + GH$ have the complex value $s + 2 \pm j4.6$. This secondary loop is now replaced in the primary loop by its equivalent block

$$\frac{C_1}{R_1}(s) = \frac{G}{1 + GH} = \frac{52.5(s + 2)}{(s + 2 + j4.6)(s + 2 - j4.6)} \tag{7-21b}$$

Observe that the pole in the feedback path contributes a zero in the closed-loop block.

The open-loop expression for the primary loop, using a proportional temperature controller, becomes

$$GH = \frac{1.05K_c(s + 2)}{(s + 0.2)(s + 0.5)(s + 1)(s + 2 + j4.6)(s + 2 - j4.6)} \quad (7\text{-}21c)$$

The root-locus plot is sketched in Fig. 7-18b. The plot shows that a gain of $K_c = 2.6$ gives the system a dominant pair of roots having a damping ratio $\zeta = 0.5$. Under proportional control of the single-loop system, a gain of $K_c = 1.4$ gives the same damping ratio. The higher gain in the cascade control system, contributed by the poles of the secondary loop, permits tighter control and decreased steady-state error. A PI controller would eliminate steady-state error and a PID controller would eliminate the error and speed up the system, as normally experienced with single control loops.

Cascade control can usually improve the performance of a single-loop system if the major disturbances enter the system near or through the control valve. Proportional control with high gain is used in the secondary loop. The primary controller uses the control action that would usually be installed in the single loop. Adjustment of the primary controller is made according to the standard formulas after the secondary controller is properly set.

Loops Containing Dead Time. Dead time in the control loop adds mathematical complexity to the root-locus sketch since the exponential form introduces multiple roots into the characteristic equation. The results of the analysis of a simple system are discussed here.

A frequently used empirical model for a process plant has a dead-time component in series with a first-order lag represented as

$$G_p(s) = \frac{ke^{-\tau s}}{a\tau s + 1} \quad (7\text{-}22a)$$

where k is the process gain, τ the process dead time, and $a\tau$ the process time constant. Under proportional control the open-loop transfer function becomes

$$G(s) = \frac{K_c ke^{-\tau s}}{a\tau s + 1} \quad (7\text{-}22b)$$

With unity feedback $(H(s) = 1)$, the roots of the system characteristic equation must satisfy

$$G(s) = -1 = \frac{K_c ke^{-\tau s}}{a\tau s + 1}$$

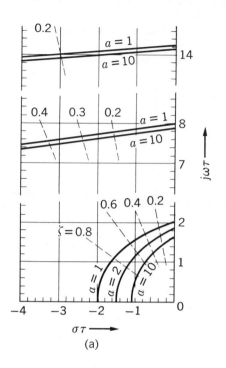

(a)

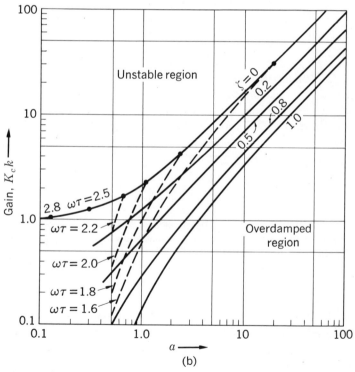

(b)

292

and the root-locus requirements for any $s = \sigma + j\omega$ are

Angle: $\angle e^{-\tau s} - \angle(a\tau s + 1) = \pm n180°$ $n = 1, 3, 5, \ldots$ (7–22c)

Magnitude: $\left| \dfrac{e^{-\tau s}}{a\tau s + 1} \right| = \dfrac{1}{K_c k}$ (7–22d)

The root locus is difficult to plot from the usual procedures because the exponential factor gives multiple roots to the characteristic equation. One approach is to use a polynomial approximation such as

$$e^{-\tau s} = \frac{1 - \tau s/2}{1 + \tau s/2}$$

and proceed with the sketch. Chu* shows a method for sketching the root locus from phase angle loci (see Appendix A) of the system components. The method is easy to apply but for brevity it is not described here. Three branches of the root-locus plot are shown on coordinates of $\sigma\tau$ and $j\omega\tau$ in Fig. 7–19a for values of $a = 1, 2, 10$. The roots at the fundamental frequency will dominate the system response since the higher-frequency roots will quickly decay. The lower half of the s-plane is not shown, as the plot is symmetrical about the real axis. Values of gain $K_c k$ are located on Fig. 7–19a by use of Eq. 7–22d.

The effect of gain $K_c k$ on the closed-loop system damping ratio is shown on the stability chart in Fig. 7–19b, which is a cross-plot of the $K_c k$, ζ, and a data for the fundamental-frequency branch of the root-locus plot. When $a = 0$, the system has only dead time and it will be stable but oscillatory for $K_c k < 1$. If high gain is needed for accuracy in a dead-time system, a first-order lag may be added for stability. As the value of a increases, the allowed system gain increases and the system may be underdamped or overdamped, depending on the value of $K_c k$.

Example 7–4. A plant is represented by a first-order time constant of 1 min and a 1-min dead time.

(a) Find the value of $K_c k$ needed to give the closed-loop system a damping ratio of 0.5.

(b) Find the unit step response of the system.

Solution. (a) The system has a value of $a = 1$. Reading from Fig. 7–19b for $\zeta = 0.5$, $a = 1$, the gain $K_c k = 0.68$, and the damped frequency of oscillation is about 1.63.

* Y. Chu, "Feedback Control Systems with Deadtime Lag or Distributed Lag by Root Locus Method," *Trans. AIEE*, **71**, 29–96 (1952).

Fig. 7–19. (a) Root locus plot and (b) stability chart for a process having dead time and first-order lag in series. The stability chart expedites selection of the gain needed to achieve a desired damping ratio in the system. (From *Control Engineering*, **11**(4), pp. 79–81, 1964; by permission.)

(b) Interpolating from Fig. 7–19a for $K_c k = 0.68$ or $\zeta = 0.5$ gives the first two pairs of closed-loop poles as

$$s_{1,2} = -0.89 \pm j1.63 \qquad s_{3,4} = -4.30 \pm j7.42$$

and the unit step response will be the inverse of

$$C(s) = \frac{1}{s} \frac{G(s)}{1 + G(s)}$$

which becomes

$$c(t) = 0.405 + 0.893e^{-0.89t} \cos(1.63t + 81.8°) + 0.228e^{-4.30t} \cos(7.42t + 54°)$$

This is an approximate result which is poor at short times and better at larger values of time, since the higher-frequency roots have been neglected.

7–5. FREQUENCY RESPONSE FROM POLE-ZERO MAP

The system frequency response can be obtained graphically from the pole-zero map by restricting values of s to the imaginary axis on the complex plane, i.e., substituting $j\omega$ for s in the transfer function. Then the magnitude and phase angle of the frequency response of any ω may be evaluated by measuring the vectors from the zeros and poles to the fre-

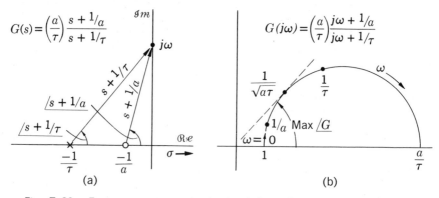

Fig. 7–20. Frequency response obtained from the pole-zero map for Eq. 7–18b with $a > \tau$, which gives a phase lead system. (a) "Elastic" vectors from pole and zero to $j\omega$. (b) Polar plot of $G(j\omega)$.

quency on the imaginary axis $(j\omega)$, as shown in Fig. 7–20a for the first-order lag-lead network discussed above.

$$G(s) = \frac{a}{\tau} \frac{(s + 1/a)}{(s + 1/\tau)} \qquad G(j\omega) = \frac{a}{\tau} \frac{(j\omega + 1/a)}{(j\omega + 1/\tau)} \qquad (7\text{-}23a)$$

At any frequency ω the magnitude and phase angle of the complex numbers $(j\omega + 1/a)$ and $(j\omega + 1/\tau)$ may be measured with rule and protractor and the frequency response found from

$$G(j\omega) = \left(\frac{a}{\tau}\right) \frac{\text{vector from zero at } -1/a \text{ to } j\omega}{\text{vector from pole at } -1/\tau \text{ to } j\omega} \qquad (7\text{--}23b)$$

When $\omega = 0$, the vector $(j\omega + 1/a)$ has a length of $1/a$ and zero angle, the vector $(j\omega + 1/\tau)$ has a length $1/\tau$ and zero angle, and the frequency response $G(j0) = 1\underline{/0°}$. Assume $a > \tau$ as shown in Fig. 7–20a and observe the lengths of the two vectors as ω increases to infinity. Since the zero $(-1/a)$ is closer to the origin than the pole $(-1/\tau)$, the magnitude of vector $(j\omega + 1/a)$ will increase faster, in terms of percentage, than will that of vector $(j\omega + 1/\tau)$, causing the ratio $|G(j\omega)|$ to increase from unity at $\omega = 0$ to a value of a/τ as $\omega \to \infty$. As ω increases from zero, the angle of $(j\omega + 1/a)$ is larger than the angle of $(j\omega + 1/\tau)$ and the phase angle of $G(j\omega)$ is always positive. As $\omega \to \infty$, both angles approach $+90°$ and the phase angle of $G(j\omega)$ decreases toward zero. The frequency response forms a semicircle on a polar plot, as shown in Fig. 7–20b, from which it is seen that the system always has a positive or leading phase angle (derivative action) and a maximum phase lead when $\omega = 1/\sqrt{a\tau}$, given as

$$\underline{/G(j\omega)}|_{\max} = \tan^{-1}\frac{a - \tau}{2\sqrt{a\tau}} \qquad (7\text{--}23c)$$

As a second example, consider the frequency response of an oscillatory second-order system. The transfer function and frequency response expression are

$$G(s) = \frac{\omega_n{}^2}{(s + \zeta\omega_n + j\omega_d)(s + \zeta\omega_n - j\omega_d)} \qquad G(j\omega) = \frac{\omega_n{}^2}{(\omega_n{}^2 - \omega^2) + j2\zeta\omega_n\omega}$$

where $\omega_d = \omega_n\sqrt{1 - \zeta^2}$ is the damped oscillation frequency in the system transient response. The pole-zero map for the system is sketched in Fig. 7–21a and "elastic" vectors are drawn from the poles to $j\omega$. When $\omega = 0$, the two vector lengths are equal to ω_n, the frequency response magnitude is unity, and the phase shift is zero. As ω increases from zero, the upper vector shortens until $\omega = \omega_d$, after which it lengthens indefinitely. The lower vector lengthens indefinitely from its initial value. The magnitude of $G(j\omega)$ is the reciprocal of the product of the two vectors and is sketched on the Bode plot in Fig. 7–21b. Since the upper vector has a minimum length, it is expected that $G(j\omega)$ will show a maximum value $(\text{AR})_p$ (depending on ζ) at a frequency called the *resonant frequency*, ω_r. As frequency $\omega \to \infty$, the magnitude ratio approaches zero along a straight line asymptote having a slope of -2 on log-log coordinates. The phase angle of $G(j\omega)$ begins at zero for $\omega = 0$, as shown on the Bode plot in Fig. 7–21b, and it is negative for all frequencies and approaches $-180°$ as the frequency approaches infinity. The phase shift is $-90°$ at $\omega = \omega_n$ for all values of damping ratio.

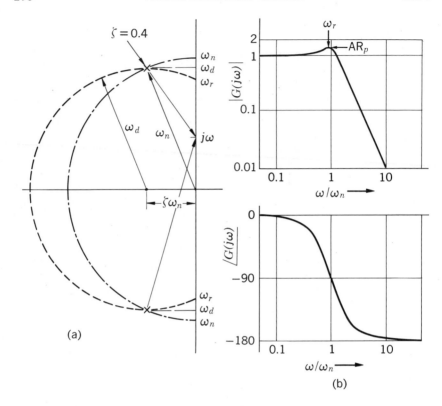

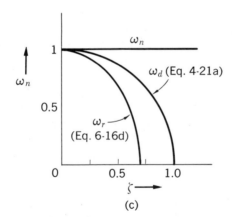

Fig. 7-21. Frequency response of second-order system showing the natural frequency, damped frequency, and resonant frequency on the pole-zero map. (a) "Elastic" vectors from pair of complex poles. (b) Bode plot of $G(j\omega)$. (c) ω_r and ω_d as functions of ζ.

In Chapter 6 the expression for resonant frequency of a second-order component was

$$\omega_r = \omega_n \sqrt{1 - 2\zeta^2} \qquad (6\text{–}16\text{d})$$

and in Chapter 4 the damped-oscillation frequency was defined as

$$\omega_d = \omega_n \sqrt{1 - \zeta^2} \qquad (4\text{–}21\text{a})$$

These two equations relate ω_d (from transient response) to ω_r (from frequency response) by

$$\omega_r^2 + \zeta^2\omega_n^2 = \omega_d^2 \qquad (7\text{–}24)$$

The graphical construction based on this relationship is shown in Fig. 7–21a where ω_r is the intersection of a circle of radius ω_d and center at $(-\zeta\omega_n, 0)$ with the imaginary axis. Inspection of the construction shows that $\omega_r < \omega_d < \omega_n$ for all values of damping ratio greater than zero. Furthermore, as shown by the plots of ω_r and ω_d versus ζ in Fig. 7–21c, for small values of ζ these three frequencies have approximately the same magnitude, but in well-damped systems ($\zeta > 0.5$) the differences in magnitude of ω_r, ω_d, and ω_n are well defined. From the plots it is also seen that ω_r is zero for $\zeta = 0.707$, and consequently for $\zeta > 0.707$ there is no resonant peak in the frequency response magnitude curve.

PROBLEMS

7–1. Sketch the root-locus diagram for integral control of the second-order system given as

$$GH = \frac{1}{\tau_i s(s + 1)(2s + 1)}$$

(a) What value of τ_i makes the closed-loop system unstable?
(b) Find a value of τ_i which gives the system a $\zeta = 0.4$.

7–2. Sketch the root-locus diagram for the following feedback control systems, and determine the value of K_c which makes the system unstable. Estimate a value of K_c which gives $\zeta = 0.5$ for the dominant pair of complex roots.

(a) $G_c = K_c$ $\qquad G_p = \dfrac{1}{(0.5s + 1)(2s + 1)^2} \qquad H = \dfrac{5}{s + 1}$

(b) $G_c = K_c$ $\qquad G_p = \dfrac{1}{(0.5s + 1)(2s + 1)^2} \qquad H = 5(s + 1)$

(c) $G_c = K_c(1 + s)$ $\qquad G_p = \dfrac{1}{(0.5s + 1)(2s + 1)^2} \qquad H = \dfrac{5}{s + 1}$

7–3. The plant and controller in a unity feedback control system has the following transfer function:

$$G = \frac{G_c}{(4s + 1)(2s + 1)(s + 1)}$$

(a) Let $G_c = K_c$, and find values of K_c which give damping ratios of 0 and 0.4 to the dominant pair of complex roots.

(b) When $\zeta = 0.4$, estimate values of ω_n, ω_d, ω_r, and M_p for the system.

7–4. Repeat Problem 7–3, letting $G_c = K_c(1 + 1/4s)$

7–5. Repeat Problem 7–3, letting $G_c = K_c(1 + 2s)$

7–6. Repeat Problem 7–3, letting $G_c = 8K_c(s + 0.25)^2/s$

7–7. Repeat Problem 7–3, letting $G_c = 2K_c(s + 0.25 + j0.43)(s + 0.25 - j0.43)/s$

7–8. The open-loop expression for a proposed chemical reactor control system is

$$GH = \frac{G_c}{(s - 1)(0.5s + 1)(4s + 1)}$$

(a) Sketch the root-locus diagram for the system when G_c is a PI controller, and determine if any value of τ_i will stabilize the system.

(b) Let $G_c = K_c(2s + 1)$, and find the gain K_c for which a pair of complex roots has the minimum damping ratio.

7–9. A suitable controller is to be selected for the system shown in Fig. P7–9.

(a) If $G_c = K_c$, is there any value of K_c which will stabilize the system?

(b) If $G_c = 4(1 + 2s)$, find values of ζ, ω_n, and ω_d.

(c) Find the unit step response of the system for part b.

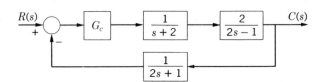

Fig. P7-9

7–10. Given: $X(s) = \dfrac{K(s + z)}{s(s + p)(s^2 + 2\zeta\omega_n s + \omega_n{}^2)}$

(a) Determine a value of K which makes $x(\infty) = 1$.

(b) What is the value of $x(0)$?

(c) For a given $\zeta\omega_n$, are there values of p and z for which $x(t)$ will not overshoot its final value?

7–11. Obtain the response of the given two systems and compare.

$$X_1(s) = \frac{2(s + 1)}{s(s + 2)(s + 3)} \qquad X_2(s) = \frac{2(s - 1)}{s(s + 2)(s + 3)} = \frac{-2(-s + 1)}{s(s + 2)(s + 3)}$$

(a) Find the steady-state values of x_1 and x_2.

(b) Estimate the overshoot, if any, in both cases.

(c) Relate the response to the pole-zero map.

7-12. The control system shown in Fig. P7-12 shows a sluggish response to load changes in the system. Process load changes occur frequently, and it is necessary to improve the system performance.

(a) Sketch a root-locus diagram for the system, and determine K_c for $\zeta = 0.55$. Is there a better value for τ_i?

(b) Replace the PI controller with the PID controller,

$$0.2K_c(s + 0.5)(s + 0.2)/s$$

Find K_c for $\zeta = 0.55$ and the corresponding oscillating frequency.

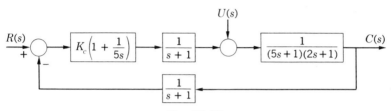

Fig. P7-12

7-13. A secondary loop inclosing the load variable is added to the control system in Problem 7-12 as shown in Fig. P7-13. Select a value of K that gives the roots of the secondary loop a $\zeta = 0.4$, and make a root-locus plot for the modified system using the PID controller in Problem 7-12b. In what manner has the system performance been improved? Find ζ for the system when $K_c = 30$ for the PID controller.

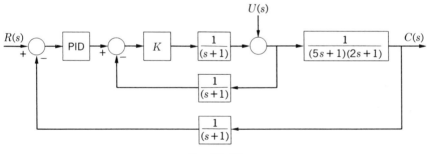

Fig. P7-13

7-14. Plot the pole-zero map of the assigned system in Problem 7-2, and sketch the open-loop frequency response for $K_c = 1$ on Bode coordinates.

7-15. Sketch the open-loop frequency response of the system in Problem 7-1, using $\tau_i = 1$.

8

The Frequency Response Method

Frequency response analysis of systems is one of the oldest techniques used by process engineers in the study and control of dynamic systems. It arose naturally in the study of electrical systems because of the prevalence of oscillating signals in electrical devices and today its application in the study of linear process systems is widespread. The frequency response method is the study of steady-state system response to sinusoidal inputs over a range of input frequencies. It has major importance in analysis and design of process control systems for several reasons.

1. Frequency response is related to all other responses. Since the system parameters determine the system response to all inputs, the frequency response and transient responses are only different ways of expressing the properties of a system. All periodic signals have a Fourier series representation in terms of sums of sine and cosine functions. In a real sense an input excites a system at those frequencies contained in the input signal. Therefore, if the system response is known for all sinusoidal excitations, the system response to all periodic signals can be evaluated by summing the response of the sinusoidal components in the signal.

2. Frequency response of a system may be obtained from the system differential equation without integrating the equation. This feature makes it especially easy to work with high-order systems, which contrasts sharply with the difficulty of obtaining transient responses of third- or higher-order systems.

3. Frequency response can be measured experimentally. Sine wave generators and ancillary recording techniques and equipment are available for measuring plant frequency response to a great many process variables such as temperature, flow, pressure, composition, etc. In fact, the experimental approach is used both to confirm mathematical models resulting from system analysis and to give actual system characteristics from which empirical analytical models can be constructed by curve fitting.

8-1. FREQUENCY TRANSFER FUNCTIONS

When a linear system is forced by a constant-frequency, constant-amplitude sinusoidal signal, its steady-state response is a sinusoid of the same frequency, differing from the forcing signal only in magnitude and phase.   The system frequency response is a set of steady-state magnitude ratios (output/input) and phase angles (referenced to the input sine wave) for all frequencies from zero to infinity.   The set of data may be given as a table, chart, or equation.

From an experimental standpoint, the frequency response is the set of magnitude-ratio and phase-angle data obtained by measurements made over a range of experimental input frequencies.   A sinusoidal input is superimposed on the static input and the magnitude ratio at any given frequency is obtained by measuring the amplitude of the steady-state output and dividing by the amplitude of the input.   The phase angle is the phase lag between the input and output signals at any given frequency and is obtained from a phasemeter, an oscillograph pattern, or other phase-measurement technique.   In Fig. 8-1, the phase angle is the dis-

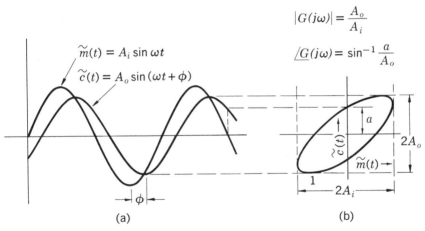

$$|G(j\omega)| = \frac{A_o}{A_i}$$

$$\underline{/G(j\omega)} = \sin^{-1}\frac{a}{A_o}$$

$$\widetilde{m}(t) = A_i \sin \omega t$$

$$\widetilde{c}(t) = A_o \sin (\omega t + \phi)$$

(a)   (b)

Fig. 8-1.   Test data for computing frequency response at a single frequency. Test on a first-order system, $\tau = 0.5$ sec, using a 0.25-cps signal giving $G(j\omega) = 0.78\underline{/-38°}$.   (a) Input and output signals.   (b) Oscilloscope pattern.

tance between the input and output peaks, divided by the distance for one cycle, and multiplied by 360°.   The two quantities are obtained for the range of frequencies which display interesting effects of the process parameters.   Fig. 8-1 shows the input and output test data for the sinusoidal forcing of a first-order system ($\tau = 0.5$ sec) at a frequency of

1.57 rad/sec (0.25 cps). In Fig. 8–1a, the data are recorded against time (usually on separate channels) and the magnitude ratio and phase angle are measured as described above. In Fig. 8–1b, the data are recorded as $\tilde{c}(t)$ versus $\tilde{m}(t)$* as an x–y oscilloscope pattern from which the magnitude ratio and phase angle are found as

$$|G(j\omega)| = \frac{A_o}{A_i} \qquad \angle G(j\omega) = \text{arc sin} \frac{a}{A_o}$$

where A_i and A_o are the maximum amplitudes of the input and output signals, respectively, and a is the value of $\tilde{c}(t)$ when $\tilde{m}(t) = 0$. Observe that A_o/A_i may not be dimensionless and that the oscillations of the input and output signals are about some average values not necessarily equal to zero. The ratio is dimensionless when $\tilde{m}(t)$ and $\tilde{c}(t)$ have identical units. The amplitude ratio can always be made dimensionless by dividing by the component gain, K. Care should be taken to express frequency in ω radians per unit time (2π radians/cycle) unless specifically required to do otherwise.

One of the attractions of the frequency response method is the simple relationship between frequency response and the transfer function. The transfer function of any linear system may be written in the form of a rational fraction in s, as

$$\frac{C(s)}{M(s)} = G(s) \tag{8–1a}$$

where $C(s)$ is the transform of the output, $M(s)$ is the transform of the input, and $G(s)$ is assumed to be a rational fraction. For a sinusoidal input, $A_i \sin \omega t$, the transform of the output becomes

$$C(s) = G(s)M(s) = G(s)\frac{A_i\omega}{s^2 + \omega^2}$$

A partial fraction expansion of $C(s)$ has the form

$$C(s) = A_i\omega G(s) \frac{1}{(s + j\omega)(s - j\omega)}$$
$$= A_i \left[\frac{K_1}{s - p_1} + \frac{K_2}{s - p_2} + \frac{K_3}{s - p_3} + \cdots + \frac{C_1}{s + j\omega} + \frac{C_2}{s - j\omega} \right] \tag{8–1b}$$

where p_1, p_2, p_3, . . . are the poles of $G(s)$. The time response of the system, obtained by inverse Laplace transformation of each term, becomes

$$c(t) = A_i \left\{ [K_1 e^{p_1 t} + K_2 e^{p_2 t} + K_3 e^{p_3 t} + \cdots] + \mathcal{L}^{-1} \left[\frac{C_1}{s + j\omega} + \frac{C_2}{s - j\omega} \right] \right\}$$
$$\tag{8–1c}$$

---

* Tilde symbols are used here to emphasize that the variables are deviations about their average operating point.

For a stable system, all the poles p_i are negative and the resulting exponential terms will decay to zero. However, the pair of imaginary poles $\pm j\omega$ contribute a sustained sinusoidal response. After the transients decay with increasing time, the sinusoidal steady-state response will be

$$c(t)_{FR} = A_i \mathcal{L}^{-1} \left[\frac{C_1}{s + j\omega} + \frac{C_2}{s - j\omega} \right] = A_i[C_1 e^{-j\omega t} + C_2 e^{j\omega t}] \qquad (8\text{--}1d)$$

The constants C_1 and C_2 are complex conjugates and are determined by the techniques given in Chapter 2 as

$$C_1 = G(s) \frac{(s + j\omega)\omega}{(s + j\omega)(s - j\omega)} \bigg|_{s = -j\omega} = \frac{G(s)\omega}{s - j\omega} \bigg|_{s = -j\omega} = \frac{G(-j\omega)}{2(-j)}$$

$$C_2 = \overline{C_1} = \frac{G(j\omega)}{2j}$$

Since $G(j\omega)$ and $G(-j\omega)$ are conjugate complex numbers they may be arranged in the form

$$G(j\omega) = a + jb; \qquad G(-j\omega) = a - jb$$
$$|G(j\omega)| = |G(-j\omega)| = \sqrt{a^2 + b^2}$$

where a and b are real numbers and functions of ω. The sinusoidal part of the response becomes

$$c(t)_{FR} = A_i \left[\frac{G(-j\omega)}{2(-j)} e^{-j\omega t} + \frac{G(j\omega)}{2j} e^{j\omega t} \right]$$
$$= A_i \left[\frac{-(a - jb)}{2j} e^{-j\omega t} + \frac{a + jb}{2j} e^{j\omega t} \right] \qquad (8\text{--}1e)$$

which can be simplified to

$$c(t)_{FR} = A_i \sqrt{a^2 + b^2} \sin(\omega t + \phi) \qquad (8\text{--}1f)$$

where $\phi = \tan^{-1} b/a$. The ratio of the magnitude of the output to the magnitude of the input is actually the absolute value of the complex number $G(j\omega)$, that is,

$$\text{AR} = \frac{A_i \sqrt{a^2 + b^2}}{A_i} = \sqrt{a^2 + b^2} = |G(j\omega)| \qquad (8\text{--}2a)$$

And the phase shift, ϕ, of the sinusoidal part of the output is

$$\phi = \tan^{-1} b/a = \angle G(j\omega) \qquad (8\text{--}2b)$$

Thus, the stated definition of frequency response leads to a complex quantity which has exactly the properties of the transfer function when $j\omega$ is substituted for s. Therefore, a system whose transfer function is $G(s)$ has a frequency response which is $G(j\omega)$. This substitution greatly simplifies the computation of the system frequency response because it bypasses the need to solve the system differential equations. It was shown in Chapter 4 that the frequency response can be obtained from the impulse response by integration. In fact, it is possible to obtain the frequency response from any transient response of the system, but the difficulties of the mathematical operations always indicate the method of choice to be the substitution of $s = j\omega$ in the transfer function.

Graphical Representation. The frequency response of any process involves the interrelation between three variables, $|G(j\omega)|$,* $\angle G(j\omega)$, and ω, where ω is usually considered to be the independent variable. The relationship may be presented graphically either as a single plot of $|G(j\omega)|$ versus $\angle G(j\omega)$ on which values of ω can be marked, if desired; or as a pair of parametric plots with $|G(j\omega)|$ and $\angle G(j\omega)$ plotted versus ω individually. Although a variety of graphical presentations have been used in the literature, all of them are variations of the two types mentioned above. The two most popular graphical representations are: (1) separate plots of log $|G(j\omega)|$ versus log ω and $\angle G(j\omega)$ versus log ω, known as Bode plots; and (2) the polar plot $|G(j\omega)|$ versus $\angle G(j\omega)$ on polar coordinates with ω indicated at various points on the curve, known as a Nyquist plot. Both of these graphical presentations of frequency response have been used for various illustrations in previous chapters in order to familiarize the reader with the plots. In general, most of the discussion of frequency response will emphasize Bode plots because of their ease of construction and their general acceptance.

BODE (LOGARITHMIC) PLOTS. Bode plots, also called Bode diagrams, consist of two charts which display the $|G(j\omega)|$, $\angle G(j\omega)$, and ω relationships. The magnitude chart is a log-log plot of $|G(j\omega)|$ versus ω and the phase angle chart is a semilog plot of $\angle G(j\omega)$ versus ω. This is the most useful graphical presentation of frequency response data for the following reasons:

1. Most frequency transfer functions have simple straight-line approximations on these coordinates.
2. The logarithmic frequency scale permits a wide frequency range to be shown, and it has the added merit of emphasizing equally all portions of the frequency behavior.
3. The frequency transfer functions of non-interacting components in series are easily combined on these coordinates since the logarithmic scale transforms magnitude multiplication into addition.

NYQUIST (POLAR) PLOTS. The Nyquist diagram is a polar plot of magnitude ratio and phase angle with frequency as a varying parameter

---

* In this text, the magnitude ratio (AR) is always given its numerical value. In control theory literature associated with electrical technology the magnitude ratio is given in decibels, defined as db $= 20$ log $|G(j\omega)|$.

along the plot. The polar diagram shows the frequency response plot for the entire frequency range in a single chart. Its disadvantages are the inconvenience of combining non-interacting components in series by complex multiplication, and the nonlinear spacing of frequency increments along the curve.

8–2. FREQUENCY RESPONSE PLOTS FOR BASIC COMPONENTS

Frequency response data for various devices have been discussed throughout this book. The basic process components are listed and discussed in Chapter 4 with some mention of the frequency response of the first-order lag. The frequency response plots for controller components are discussed in Chapter 5. Some frequency response criteria for component and/or system performance are listed in Chapter 6, and Chapter 7 shows the relationship between the pole-zero map and the frequency response of a system. In all cases the frequency transfer function has been found by replacing s with $j\omega$ in the transfer function. The frequency response of the basic process components are discussed below.

Proportional Component, K. This component shows instant response with no dynamics and the frequency response is

$$G(j\omega) = K\angle 0°$$
$$\text{AR} = K \qquad \phi = 0° \tag{8–3}$$

Integration or Differentiation Component, $s^{\pm 1}$. The frequency response of a pure integrator is

$$G(j\omega) = (j\omega)^{-1} = \frac{1}{\omega} \angle -90°$$
$$\text{AR} = \frac{1}{\omega} \qquad \phi = -90° \tag{8–4a}$$

which is a vertical line at $-90°$ on the polar plot. On the Bode plots the relationships are

$$\log \text{AR} = -\log \omega \qquad \phi = -90° \tag{8–4b}$$

which gives a straight line with a slope of -1 on the log-magnitude-ratio-vs.-log-ω plot and a horizontal line at $-90°$ on the phase-angle-vs.-log-ω plot. These plots are shown in Table 8–1.

The frequency response of a pure differentiator is

$$G(j\omega) = j\omega = \omega\angle 90°$$
$$\text{AR} = \omega \qquad \phi = 90° \tag{8–4c}$$

TABLE 8-1
Frequency Response of Basic Process Components

Process Component	Pole-Zero Map	Nyquist Plot	Bode Plot
1. Proportional gain. $$K$$	None		
2. Pure integration or differentiation. $$\frac{1}{s}$$ ——— $$s$$ - - - - -			
3. First-order lag. $$\frac{1}{\tau s + 1}$$ (See Chapter 4.)			
4. Second-order lag. $$\frac{1}{\dfrac{s^2}{\omega_n{}^2} + \dfrac{2\zeta}{\omega_n} s + 1}$$ (See Chapter 6.)			
5. Transportation lag. $$e^{-\tau s}$$			
6. Distributed parameter. $$e^{-\sqrt{\tau s}}$$			
7. Exothermic reaction. $$\frac{1}{\tau s - 1}$$			
8. Inverse response. $$\frac{1 - \tau s}{1 + \tau s}$$			
9. Process controllers.	See Table 5-3 in Chapter 5.		

which has a magnitude ratio equal to the frequency and a phase angle of 90°. The sketch in Table 8–1 shows that the frequency response of the integrator and differentiator components are reciprocally related.

First-Order Lag. The frequency response of this component is developed in Chapter 4. The equations are presented here for illustration. The frequency transfer function is

$$G(j\omega) = \frac{1}{j\omega\tau + 1} = \frac{1}{\sqrt{\omega^2\tau^2 + 1}} \angle - \tan^{-1}\omega\tau \qquad (8\text{–}5)$$

where τ is the time constant of the component. On the Nyquist diagram, the plot is a semicircle with frequency as a parameter, as shown in Table 8–1. The construction of the curve on the Bode plot is simplified because of the straight-line asymptotes. The magnitude ratio and phase-angle equations are:

$$\log \text{AR} = -\tfrac{1}{2}\log(\omega^2\tau^2 + 1) \qquad \phi = -\tan^{-1}\omega\tau$$

The magnitude ratio on the log-log coordinates has the following straight-line asymptotes:

For $\omega^2\tau^2 \ll 1$:

$$\log \text{AR} \cong -\tfrac{1}{2}\log(1) = 0 \qquad \text{AR} \cong 1 \text{ and } \phi \cong 0$$

For $\omega^2\tau^2 \gg 1$:

$$\log \text{AR} \cong -\log \omega\tau \qquad \text{AR} \cong \frac{1}{\omega\tau} \text{ and } \phi \to -90°$$

For $\omega\tau = 1$:

$$\log \text{AR} = -\tfrac{1}{2}\log 2; \qquad \text{AR} = 0.707;\ \phi = -45°$$

Thus, the Bode magnitude diagram can be approximated by the two straight-line asymptotes which intersect at $\omega\tau = 1$, where $\omega = 1/\tau$ is called the corner frequency. The maximum error in this representation occurs when $\omega\tau = 1$, where the true value of AR is 0.707 and the approximation gives 1.0. The error can be minimized by smoothing the intersection by a curve which passes through 0.707 at the corner frequency. The phase angle may be sketched from the approximation in Fig. 8–2 where a straight line with a slope of $-45°$/decade is drawn through the points $0.1/\tau$, $0°$; $1/\tau$, $-45°$; and $10/\tau$, $-90°$. The maximum error in this straight-line representation is less than 6° as shown. The error can be minimized by sketching the smooth curve through the true points $0.1/\tau$, $-5.7°$; $1/\tau$, $-45°$; and $10/\tau$, -84.2 as indicated in Fig. 8–2. Also, when desired for greater accuracy a scale of phase angle and frequency like that on the abscissa of Fig. 8–2 can be made to fit the process engineers' log frequency paper and used to simplify the phase-angle plotting. The best

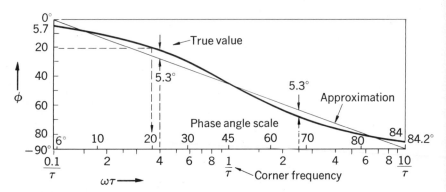

Fig. 8-2. Phase-angle approximation for first-order lag. The approximation applies to first-order lead phase angles by reversing the sign of the angle.

sketching method is to use a template cut with the correct magnitude and phase-angle contours to fit a standard graph paper.

The polar and logarithmic plots are shown in Table 8-1. The frequency responses of first-order lag and first-order lead components (e.g., a derivative controller) are reciprocally related and can be approximated by reciprocal constructions.

Second-Order Lag. The overdamped second order lag can be factored into two first order lags in series as discussed in Chapter 4. The underdamped second-order lag has more interesting characteristics and its frequency response relation is

$$G(j\omega) = \cfrac{1}{\left(\cfrac{j\omega}{\omega_n}\right)^2 + 2\zeta\left(\cfrac{j\omega}{\omega_n}\right) + 1} = \frac{1}{1 - \beta^2 + j2\zeta\beta}$$

$$\text{AR} = \frac{1}{\sqrt{(1 - \beta^2)^2 + (2\zeta\beta)^2}} \qquad \phi = -\tan^{-1} 2\zeta\beta/(1 - \beta^2) \qquad (8\text{-}6a)$$

where $\beta = \omega/\omega_n$, the normalized frequency, and ζ is the damping ratio of the component. This component has complex poles for $\zeta < 1$ which cause the magnitude ratio to have a maximum value

$$(\text{AR})_p = (2\zeta \sqrt{1 - \zeta^2})^{-1}$$

at the so-called resonant frequency, $\omega_r = \omega_n \sqrt{1 - 2\zeta^2}$ (see Chapter 6). The frequency response depends upon two parameters, ζ and ω_n, and it is not possible to show the effects of both parameters on one curve. The plots in Table 8-1 are for $\zeta = 0.4$. The plots show that the magnitude ratio increases with frequency from unity at zero frequency to a maximum $((AR)_p = 1.36 \text{ for } \zeta = 0.4)$ at the resonant frequency and then approaches zero as the frequency approaches infinity while the phase angle decreases to $-90°$ when $\omega = \omega_n$ and approaches $-180°$ as the frequency approaches infinity. The magnitude-ratio and phase-angle equations are

$$\log \text{AR} = -\frac{1}{2} \log [(1 - \beta^2)^2 + (2\zeta\beta)^2] \qquad \phi = -\tan^{-1} \frac{2\zeta\beta}{1 - \beta^2}$$

$$(8\text{-}6b)$$

For $\beta \ll 1$, the straight-line asymptotes on the Bode plots are

$$\log \text{AR} \cong -\tfrac{1}{2} \log 1 = 0 \qquad \text{AR} \cong 1 \text{ and } \phi \simeq 0°$$

for $\beta \gg 1$ and $\zeta \leq 1$,

$$\log \text{AR} \cong -2 \log \beta \qquad \text{AR} \cong \beta^{-2} \text{ and } \phi \to -180°$$

for $\beta = 1$,

$$\log \text{AR} = -\log 2\zeta\beta \qquad \text{AR} = \frac{1}{2\zeta\beta} \text{ and } \phi = -90°$$

Thus, the Bode magnitude diagram can be approximated by the two straight-line asymptotes which intersect at the corner frequency $\beta = \omega/\omega_n = 1$. This approximation is not satisfactory for small damping ratios, as can be seen from Table 8-1 for $\zeta = 0.4$. The frequency responses of second-order lag and lead components are reciprocally related.

The foregoing stable transfer functions have no poles or zeros in the right-half s-plane and because of this, for a given magnitude-ratio frequency function, they show a minimum phase change as ω goes from zero to infinity. Such transfer functions, called *minimum phase functions*, have uniquely related magnitude-ratio and phase-angle functions, i.e., one function can be computed from the other when necessary. Transfer functions having poles or zeros in the right-half s-plane, called *non-minimum phase functions*, do not have uniquely related magnitude-ratio and phase-angle functions. Processes showing these characteristics may require special attention in control system design. The following four components are non-minimum phase type.

Transportation Lag, or Dead Time. The frequency transfer function for the transportation lag is

$$G(j\omega) = e^{-j\omega\tau} = \cos \omega\tau - j \sin \omega\tau = 1\angle -\omega\tau \qquad (8\text{-}7a)$$
$$\text{AR} = 1 \qquad \phi = -\omega\tau \qquad (8\text{-}7b)$$

The magnitude ratio is unity for all frequencies; the phase angle decreases with frequency without limit and does not approach a minimum value as do the first- and second-order lag components discussed above. The plots in Table 8–1 show this on the polar and logarithmic coordinates.

Distributed-Parameter Component. The frequency transfer function for the distributed-parameter component is

$$G(j\omega) = e^{-\sqrt{j\omega\tau}} = e^{-(1+j)\sqrt{\frac{\omega\tau}{2}}} = e^{-\sqrt{\frac{\omega\tau}{2}}} \angle - \sqrt{\frac{\omega\tau}{2}} \qquad (8\text{--}7c)$$

because $\sqrt{2j} = (1 + j)$. On log-log coordinates, the magnitude ratio becomes

$$\log AR = -\sqrt{\frac{\omega\tau}{2}} \log e \qquad \phi = -\sqrt{\frac{\omega\tau}{2}} \qquad (8\text{--}7d)$$

Both the magnitude ratio and the phase angle decrease with frequency without limit. The polar and logarithmic plots are shown in Table 8–1.

Exothermic Reaction Component. This is an unstable non-minimum phase component whose frequency response cannot be directly measured experimentally; however, its frequency transfer function is readily calculated as

$$G(j\omega) = \frac{1}{j\omega\tau - 1} = \frac{1}{\sqrt{\omega^2\tau^2 + 1}} \angle - \tan^{-1} \omega\tau / -1 \qquad (8\text{--}8a)$$

On log-log coordinates, the magnitude ratio becomes

$$\log AR = -\tfrac{1}{2} \log (\omega^2\tau^2 + 1) \qquad \phi = -\tan^{-1} \omega\tau / -1 \quad (8\text{--}8b)$$

which has the same straight-line asymptotes as that of the first-order lag. Observe that the phase angle ranges from $-180°$ to $-90°$ as the frequency ranges from zero to infinity.

Inverse Response Component. The zeros of most process components, if they occur at all, are located at infinity ($e^{-\tau s}$ and $e^{-\sqrt{\tau s}}$), in the left half of the s-plane (PI controller), or on the imaginary axis. A simple component having a zero in the right-half s-plane is the all-pass network

$$G(s) = \frac{1 - \tau s}{1 + \tau s} \qquad (8\text{--}9a)$$

whose frequency transfer function is

$$G(j\omega) = \frac{1 - j\omega\tau}{1 + j\omega\tau} = 1 \angle \tan^{-1} - \omega\tau - \tan^{-1} \omega\tau \qquad (8\text{--}9b)$$

The magnitude ratio and phase angle are

$$AR = 1 \qquad \phi = -2 \tan^{-1} \omega\tau \qquad (8\text{--}9c)$$

The all-pass device transmits signals of all frequencies unchanged in magnitude but delayed in time; hence, it is a time-delay device similar to a simple polynomial approximation to a transportation delay. The polar and logarithmic plots are shown in Table 8-1.

Process Controllers. Various process controllers are described in Chapter 5 and their frequency response plots are given in Table 5-3.   In general it is observed that their frequency transfer functions consist of certain combinations of proportional, first-order lead or lag, second-order lead or lag, and pure integration components.

8-3. CONSTRUCTION OF FREQUENCY RESPONSE PLOTS

Control systems consist of many components acting in series and/or parallel and the process engineer needs a procedure for quickly plotting frequency response data for various combinations of components.   Most often the analysis begins with the forward open-loop system transfer function $GH(j\omega)$ in factored form since it generally consists of components in series, as in

$$GH(j\omega) = G_c G_v G_p H(j\omega) \qquad (8\text{--}10)$$

Several approaches are possible in evaluating $GH(j\omega)$ from the separate frequency-dependent G's:

1. The analytical approach involves the evaluation of the magnitude ratio and phase angle of each component at each frequency of interest and multiplying the magnitude ratios and summing the phase angles to obtain the frequency response.   The procedure offers accuracy of computation at the expense of time and effort.   This approach is not recommended except when high accuracy is desired or a computer is available.
2. The magnitude ratio and phase angle contributed by the poles and zeros at each frequency of interest can be graphically evaluated by working on the pole-zero map as illustrated in Chapters 2 and 7.   This method is simple to use when a Spirule is available for multiplying the vector lengths and adding the angles.
3. The quickest graphical procedure is to use straight-line approximations to sketch the Bode magnitude and phase-angle diagrams.   This procedure can be expedited and improved in accuracy for many components by using plastic templates on which the true magnitude ratio and phase angle curves are cut to fit the log-log and semilog graph paper being used.

The latter procedure is illustrated by developing the Bode diagram for a given transfer function using the following steps:

1. Convert the transfer function to the standard time-constant form (rather than the pole-and-zero form used for root-locus plotting) and sub-

stitute $s = j\omega$ to obtain the frequency transfer function, as for example

$$G(s) = \frac{2(\tau_1 s + 1)e^{-s}}{s(\tau_2 s + 1)^2}$$

becomes

$$G(j\omega) = \frac{2(j\omega\tau_1 + 1)e^{-j\omega}}{j\omega(j\omega\tau_2 + 1)^2} \qquad (8\text{--}11a)$$

2. Recognize the separate process components and sketch their frequency response approximations for magnitude ratio and phase angle on the appropriate diagram in the frequency range of importance. In this case the components are a gain, a pure integration, two phase lags, a phase lead, and a transportation lag. The separate approximations are shown on the sketch in Fig. 8–3a for values of $\tau_1 = 3$ and $\tau_2 = \frac{1}{3}$. The gain component contributes constant magnitude and zero phase angle. In fact, it could be moved to the left side of the equation, giving $G(j\omega)/2$ a dimensionless value. The magnitude-ratio and phase-angle approximations of the first-order lead and lag components are sketched from the straight-line approximations. The magnitude ratio of the repeated lag decreases with a slope of -2 from the corner frequency. The phase angles are sketched in by plotting a few points using the phase-angle approximation in Fig. 8–2. The phase angle of the repeated lag is twice the angle of a single lag component. Notice that the phase angle of the transportation lag decreases without limit as the frequency increases while its magnitude ratio remains at unity.

3. Obtain the approximate Bode plots by multiplying the component magnitude ratios and summing their phase angles. In this case, the logarithm of the frequency transfer function and its phase angle are written as

$$\log |G(j\omega)| = \log 2 + \log |(j\omega\tau_1 + 1)| + \log |e^{-j\omega}|$$
$$- \log |j\omega| - 2 \log |(j\omega\tau_2 + 1)| \qquad (8\text{--}11b)$$

$$\angle G(j\omega) = \tan^{-1} \omega\tau_1 - \omega - \frac{\pi}{2} - 2 \tan^{-1} \omega\tau_2 \qquad (8\text{--}11c)$$

Remember that the absolute value of $e^{-j\omega}$ is unity. The plots give the logarithms of the component magnitude ratio directly, so that graphical addition of the vertical distances on the plots gives the resultant magnitude ratio. Likewise, graphical additions of the vertical distances on the semilog phase-angle plots gives the total phase angle directly. The Bode diagram straight-line approximation is shown in Fig. 8-3b. The largest errors in the approximation occur at the corner frequencies and these errors can be minimized by smoothing these corners, as indicated by the dashed curves drawn in Fig. 8–3b. The Nyquist plot shown in Fig. 8–3c

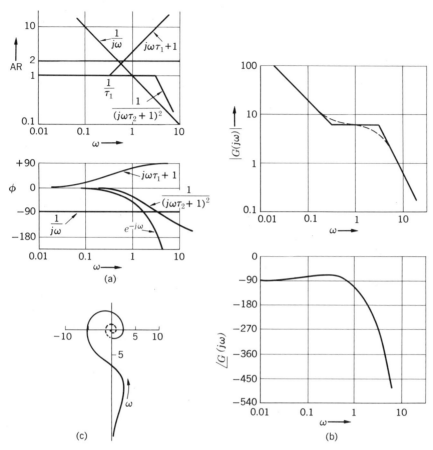

Fig. 8-3. Graphical approximation of Bode diagram and Nyquist plot for frequency transfer function $G(s) = 2(3s + 1)e^{-s}/s(\frac{1}{3}s + 1)^2$. (a) Component approximations. (b) Smoothed Bode diagram. (c) Polar plot.

is plotted from the smoothed Bode plots. Observe these trends in the Nyquist plot: (1) the plot begins at infinity and phase angle $-90°$ because of the presence of the pure integrator; (2) the first-order lead component temporarily pulls the plot over into the fourth quadrant; (3) as the phase angle lag continues to grow with frequency due to the transportation delay, the plot slowly spirals into the center.

4. *Generalization.* In this illustration, the frequency response plot starts at infinity and $-90°$ for $\omega = 0$ because of the pure integrator and it terminates at zero and infinite angle because of the transportation lag. In the absence of transportation lags and distributed-parameter com-

ponents, the general transfer function is written in polynomial form as

$$G(s) = \frac{K(b_m s^m + b_{m-1} s^{m-1} + \cdots + 1)}{s^k(a_n s^n + a_{n-1} s^{n-1} + \cdots + 1)}$$

where k, m, and n are integers and $n + k > m$. The frequency transfer function shows the following limiting values. When $k = 0$,

$$G(j\omega)_{\omega \to 0} = K\underline{/0°} \qquad \text{(steady-state gain)}$$

$$G(j\omega)_{\omega \to \infty} = 0\underline{/90\ (m - n)°} \qquad \frac{d \log |G(j\omega)|}{d \log \omega} = (m - n)$$

When $k = k$,

$$G(j\omega)_{\omega \to 0} = \infty\underline{/-90k°}$$

$$G(j\omega)_{\omega \to \infty} = 0\underline{/90(m - n - k)°} \qquad \frac{d \log |G(j\omega)|}{d \log \omega} = (m - n - k)$$

These generalizations are useful in sketching the $G(j\omega)$ plots for extreme values of ω. When $G(s)$ contains the delay factor $e^{-\tau s}$, the locus on the Nyquist plot will spiral into the origin as ω approaches infinity.

Example 8–1. Sketch the Bode diagram for the process control example in Chapter 7 when (a) $K_c = 1.4(\zeta = 0.5)$ and (b) $K_c = 7.4$ (unstable).

$$G(s) = \frac{K_c}{(0.5s + 1)(2s + 1)(5s + 1)(s + 1)}$$

Solution. When the gain K_c is to be studied, it is usual either to set $K_c = 1$ or form the dimensionless $G(s)/K_c$ from the frequency transfer function for the preliminary plotting. In this case, let $K_c = 1$, and the frequency transfer function to be studied becomes

$$G(j\omega) = \frac{1}{(j0.5\omega + 1)(j2\omega + 1)(j5\omega + 1)(j\omega + 1)}$$

which consists of four first-order lags.

The following limiting values apply to the frequency response plot:

$$G(j0) = 1\underline{/0°} \qquad G(j\infty) = 0\underline{/-360°}$$

The usual Bode approximations for the first-order lags are sketched and combined in Fig. E8–1a. The Nyquist plot in Fig. E8–1b is made from the smoothed Bode plot.

The gain values $K_c = 1.4$ and $K_c = 7.4$ are constants which move the Bode magnitude plot vertically by an amount equal to $\log K_c$. The curves with $K_c = 1.4$ and $K_c = 7.4$ are not shown in Fig. E8–1a, but the gain margin (reciprocal of system gain at $-180°$; see Chapter 6) is calculated as $1/0.15 = 6.7$ from Fig. E8–1b; i.e., a value of $K_c = 6.7$ would make the closed-loop system unstable.

In Chapter 7, the root-locus plot for this system (Fig. 7–13) indicated instability at a gain of $K_c = 7.4$.   The disagreement in gain for instability is due to the use of approximations in sketching the Bode plots.   The Nyquist plot in Fig. E8–1b indicates instability for $K_c = 7.4$, since that curve encircles the -1 point.   It will be seen that this is a general test for instability on the polar plot.

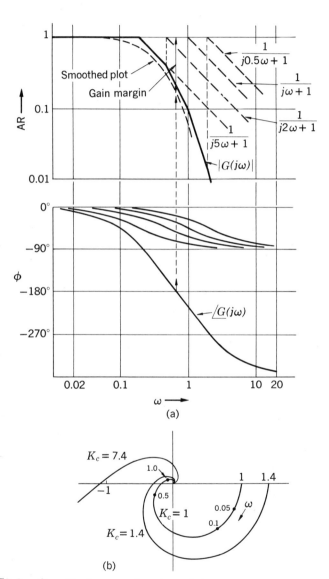

Fig. E8–1. Graphical approximation of frequency response of process.
(a) Bode plots. (b) Nyquist plot.

8–4. CLOSED-LOOP SYSTEM FREQUENCY RESPONSE

An open-loop system has the input applied directly to the system, and it responds in accordance with the system parameters. The open-loop response may be taken experimentally (by transient test or frequency response tests) to measure the system parameters or it may be calculated if the system transfer function is known. To provide better process performance a feedback loop may be placed around the open-loop system, thereby converting it to a closed-loop system. The closed-loop system has the input applied directly to an input-output comparator whose difference is used to control the system. The next development is to show how, by conformal transformations, the closed-loop response is obtained from the open-loop response. The closed-loop frequency response indicates the overall system performance equally as well as does the transient response. The frequency response analysis and design of control systems is greatly simplified by the ease with which the closed-loop response can be computed from the open-loop response.

Unity Feedback Systems, $H(s) = 1$. For systems with unity feedback, the closed-loop equations from Chapter 6 are

$$C(s) = \frac{G}{1 + G} R(s) + \frac{G_l}{1 + G} U(s) \tag{6–1}$$

$$E(s) = \frac{1}{1 + G} R(s) - \frac{G_l}{1 + G} U(s)$$

where $G = G_c G_v G_p$ means $G(s)$, the open-loop system transfer function which normally is $C(s)/E(s)$. The closed-loop output/set-point ratio for the frequency response is

$$\frac{C}{R}(j\omega) = \frac{G(j\omega)}{1 + G(j\omega)} = M\underline{/\alpha} \text{ or } Me^{j\alpha} \tag{8–12}$$

where M and α are the closed-loop frequency response magnitude ratio and phase angle, respectively. The problem is to relate $G(j\omega)$ to M and α. This is done in Appendix A by making use of a conformal mapping procedure. Review the development in Appendix A and consider this summary.

The frequency response method restricts s-plane values to the imaginary axis so that the transfer function $G(s)$ maps values of $s = j\omega$ from the s-plane into the $G(j\omega)$ plane and the open-loop frequency transfer function becomes

$$G(j\omega) = u + jv$$

where u and v, the real and imaginary parts of $G(j\omega)$, are functions of the frequency. A typical polar plot of an open-loop transfer function is shown in Fig. 8–4. At a given frequency ω, the vector from the origin to the solid curve gives $G(j\omega)$, the open-loop response $C(j\omega)/E(j\omega)$. The vector from the $-1 + j0$ to the solid curve gives $1 + G(j\omega)$. Now, the closed-loop frequency response $Me^{j\alpha}$ is obtained by complex division as $G(j\omega)/(1 + G(j\omega))$. At low frequency as $\omega \to 0$, the open-loop response $G(j\omega) \to \infty$ because of the integrator, $1/s$, and the closed-loop response $M \to 1$ as shown by the dashed line on Fig. 8–4. At high frequency as

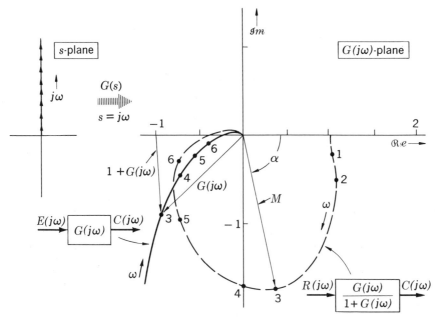

Fig. 8–4. Conformal mapping of $s = j\omega$ onto the $G(j\omega)$ plane and representation of $1 + G(j\omega)$ and the closed-loop frequency transfer function $G/(1 + G)$.

$\omega \to \infty$, $G(j\omega) \to 0$ and the closed-loop response $M \to 0$. At other frequencies, the closed-loop response could be computed as the ratio of $G(j\omega)$ to $(1 + G(j\omega))$, with the result that $G(j\omega)$ and M and α are related as shown by the solid line and the dashed line in Fig. 8–4.

Generally, the direct analytical approach as discussed in Appendix A is useful in constructing curves of constant values of M and α on the complex plane. The closed-loop frequency transfer function expressed in terms of u and v is

$$\frac{C}{R}(j\omega) = \frac{G}{1 + G} = \frac{u + jv}{(1 + u) + jv} = Me^{j\alpha}$$

where M and α are the magnitude ratio and phase angle of the closed-loop response at any frequency. As shown in Appendix A, the relationship between u, v, M, and α are circles on the complex plane, as revealed by the equations

For magnitude ratio:

$$\left[u + \frac{M^2}{M^2 - 1} \right]^2 + v^2 = \left[\frac{M}{M^2 - 1} \right]^2$$

For phase angle:

$$\left[u + \frac{1}{2} \right]^2 + \left[v - \frac{1}{2 \tan \alpha} \right]^2 = \frac{1}{4} \left[1 + \frac{1}{\tan^2 \alpha} \right]$$

When constant M and α values are plotted on the u, v coordinates, the contours are the M and α circles, which intersect at right angles, as seen on the Hall chart in Fig. 8–5d.

The circles for $M < 1$ have centers on the real axis in the right half-plane; whereas, circles for $M > 1$ have centers on the real axis in the left-hand plane. The tangents from the origin to all $M > 1$ circles are tangent at $u = -1$. All the α circles have centers along the line $u = -\frac{1}{2}$ and pass through the points $-1 + j0$ and $0 + j0$. Only the contours for $\alpha < 0°$ are shown on Fig. 8–5b; the contours for $\alpha > 0°$ would be the mirror image of those given. When constant M and α contours are plotted on the log $|G(j\omega)|$-vs.-$\angle G(j\omega)$ coordinates the result is the Nichols chart shown in Fig. 8–5b and in Appendix D, which gives the same open-loop-to-closed-loop transformation data as the Hall chart in Fig. 8–5d. The transformation on both charts is shown by the following illustration.

Consider the system discussed in Example 7–1, where the open-loop transfer function is

$$G(s) = \frac{3K_c \left(\frac{1}{3} s + 1 \right)}{s(s + 1)(2s + 1)}$$

In that example the problem was to find that value of K_c which made the system unstable and a value of K_c that gives $\zeta = 0.5$ for a pair of complex roots. The frequency response problem is to find the K_c which stabilizes the system and a value of K_c that satisfies a closed-loop frequency response specification on M_p, phase margin, or gain margin. In this case, let $K_c = 0.12$, the value found in Example 7–1 for a damping ratio of 0.5; the problem is to find the resultant value of M_p. The first step is to convert $G(s)$ to $G(j\omega)$, replace K_c by unity, and make the $G(j\omega)$ plot. The Bode and Nyquist plots for this system are shown in Figs. 8–5a and c for $K_c = 1$; from these it is seen that the open-loop magnitude ratio is unity when the phase angle is $-180°$. This is an unstable condition (as will

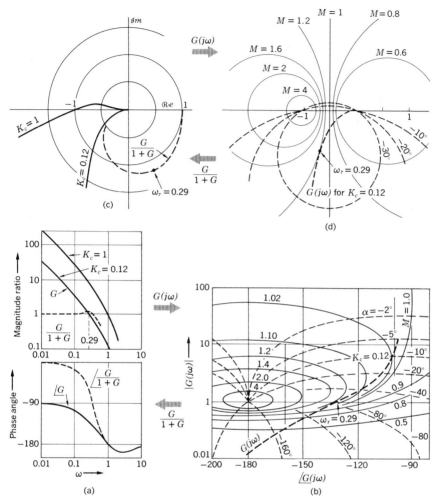

Fig. 8–5. Use of the Nichols chart and the Hall chart for converting open-loop frequency response data into closed-loop frequency response data. (a) Bode plot. (b) Nichols chart. (c) Nyquist plot. (d) Hall chart.

be shown) and therefore a gain of $K_c = 1$ makes the system unstable. The next step is to find the closed-loop response for the open-loop transfer function $0.12G(j\omega)$. Plots of $0.12G(j\omega)$ are shown on Figs. 8–5a and c. Note that changing the gain K_c does not affect the phase angle of $G(j\omega)$. The plots of $0.12G(j\omega)$ are transferred as dashed lines to the Nichols chart and Hall chart in Figs. 8–5b and d, from which the M and α values are read and plotted as dashed lines on the Bode and Nyquist charts to give the closed-loop frequency response for this system. The plot of $0.12G(j\omega)$ on the Nichols chart is tangent to the $M = 1.2$ line, which corresponds to the peak on the Bode plot at $\omega_r = 0.29$ rad/time. Likewise, the plot on the Hall chart is tangent to the $M = 1.2$ circle at $\omega_r = 0.29$ rad/time. Thus, a value of $K_c = 0.12$ gives a frequency response peak magnitude ratio of 1.2 to the closed-loop system. This illustration shows the use of both the Hall chart and the Nichols chart in obtaining closed-loop frequency response from the open-loop frequency response. Each chart provides the same transformation data but the Bode plots and Nichols chart are easier to manipulate (because of the straight-line approximations and gain adjustment) and they will be used generally in frequency response problems.

Non-Unity Feedback, $H = H(j\omega)$. For systems having feedback dynamics, the transformation from open-loop to closed-loop frequency response requires an additional step. As shown in Fig. 8–6 a non-unity feedback system has an equivalent unity feedback system which can be analyzed by the above methods. The equations for negative feedback systems which were developed in Chapter 6 may be arranged into equiva-

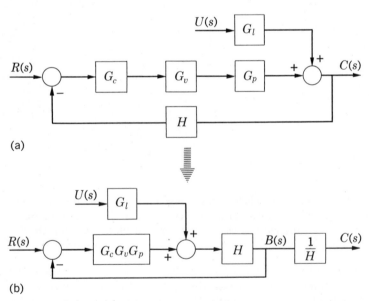

Fig. 8–6. Block diagram manipulation to obtain an equivalent unity feedback system. The open-loop transfer function $G_cG_vG_pH$ is observed by opening the loop at any point. Most often the loop is opened experimentally immediately after the controller. (a) Non-unity feedback system. (b) Equivalent unity feedback system.

lent unity feedback system equations as follows (see block diagram algebra rule 7 in Chapter 1).

$$C(s) = \frac{1}{H} \frac{GH}{1 + GH} R(s) + \frac{G_l}{GH} \frac{GH}{1 + GH} U(s)$$

$$E(s) = \frac{1}{GH} \frac{GH}{1 + GH} R(s) - \frac{G_l}{G} \frac{GH}{1 + GH} U(s)$$

(6-1)

where $G = G_c G_v G_p$ means $G(s)$. The open-loop transfer function is GH, and the Hall and Nichols charts can be used in the usual way to obtain $GH/(1 + GH)$, which can be multiplied by $1/H$ to obtain the output/set-point control ratio, $C(s)/R(s)$; or by G_l/GH to obtain the output/load control ratio, $C(s)/U(s)$. Likewise, the error/set-point ratio $E(s)/R(s)$ or the error/load ratio $E(s)/U(s)$ could be obtained from $GH/(1 + GH)$ by multiplying by the proper factor required by the equation. Note that all the response equations have the same characteristic equation, $1 + GH$, and that the responses will be similar in form, so that frequently only the $GH/(1 + GH)$ response need be used for adjusting control systems by frequency response methods.

8-5. STABILITY OF CLOSED-LOOP SYSTEMS

System stability is of utmost concern to the process engineer since a process control system must be stable before it can perform useful production. In previous chapters it was seen that a closed-loop system should have a large open-loop gain if steady-state system errors are to be minimized and that instability can result from too high a gain, so that the process engineer must watch for plant instability and learn how to avoid it.

Passive networks consisting of RLC elements are always stable, since resistance is a dissipative element. However, each component in a closed-loop system may be stable and yet the closed-loop system can be unstable. Likewise, feedback can be used to stabilize unstable components such as exothermic chemical reactors. The concept of stability is embodied in the idea that a system will attain a steady-state condition when not being pushed, i.e., a system is stable if its response is bounded for every bounded input. The causes of closed-loop system instability are loop gain of material or energy generated by the process or added by the control valve, and the time lags encountered by the signals moving around the loop. For example, in Fig. 8-1, if the open-loop signal magnitude $\tilde{m}(t)$ should equal $\tilde{c}(t)$ at a phase angle of $-180°$, the closed-loop system would be unstable because the $180°$ phase lag of the plant plus the $-180°$ phase lag of the corrective action ($r - c = m$, in this case) would make the feedback signal equal in magnitude and in phase with the forcing signal so that the system would oscillate without an input $\tilde{m}(t)$.

In other words, the unaided system would sustain oscillations—clearly an unstable condition.

The system characteristic equation is $1 + GH(s)$ and the instability problem is to determine if any of its roots lie in the positive-half s-plane. The following methods for determining stability of linear systems are considered in this book.

1. Factoring the characteristic equation for its roots is discussed in Chapter 2.
2. Using the Routh-Hurwitz criterion is explained in Chapters 2 and 6.
3. Simulating the system on an analog computer is explained in Chapter 6.
4. Plotting the root-locus diagram is demonstrated in Chapter 7.
5. Using Nyquist and Bode diagrams is discussed here.

The Nyquist Criterion for Stability. The Nyquist criterion for stability is a direct application of Cauchy's argument principle given in Appendix A for finding the excess of zeros over poles $(Z - P)$ of a complex function inside a simple closed curve C, as in

$$Z - P = \frac{1}{2\pi} \Delta_C \theta = \pm N \tag{A-13}$$

where N is the number of encirclements of the origin on the complex-function plane as s moves along the curve C on the s-plane. The sign convention is selected according to the direction of movement along the curve C in the s-plane; use $+$ for counterclockwise and $-$ for clockwise encirclements as below. In the present case, the complex function is $1 + GH(s)$ and the closed curve C is selected as the positive-half s-plane, as shown in Fig. 8–7a for the system:

$$GH(s) = \frac{2(s + 1)}{s(s - 1)} \quad \text{or} \quad GH(j\omega) = \frac{-2(j\omega + 1)}{(j\omega + \omega^2)} \tag{8-13a}$$

The pole-zero map for this system is shown on the s-plane in Fig. 8–7a with the curve C extended to infinity so that it encloses all the positive-half s-plane except an infinitesimal area in the neighborhood of the pole at the origin. Notice that the curve C encloses one pole of $GH(s)$. As the point $s = j\omega$ moves along the curve C in a clockwise manner (negative direction) from $\omega = 0^+$ to $\omega = +\infty$, the function $1 + GH(j\omega)$ moves along the curve in Fig. 8–7b from $\infty\angle-270°$ to $1\angle0°$ as shown. As ω moves from $-\infty$ to zero, the $1 + GH(j\omega)$ function path (shown dashed) is the mirror image of the path for $0 < \omega < +\infty$ and need not be computed separately. The pole at the origin is excluded from the closed curve C, and it is necessary to determine how the $1 + GH(j\omega)$ plot is closed in going from $\omega = 0^-$ to $\omega = 0^+$. Let the path excluding the origin be semicircular and defined as

$$s = \delta e^{j\theta} \tag{8-13b}$$

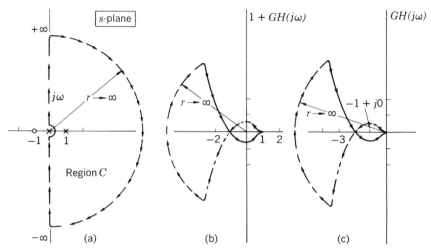

Fig. 8–7. Illustration of principle of Cauchy's argument to show the Nyquist criterion of closed-loop system stability. (a) Closed curve C enclosing all of positive half of s-plane except area in the neighborhood of the origin. (b) Plot of $1 + GH(j\omega)$ in the complex plane. (c) Plot of $GH(j\omega)$ in the complex plane.

with $\delta \to 0$ and θ changing from $-\pi/2$ to $+\pi/2$ through zero. In the neighborhood of the origin, $s \to 0$ and Eq. 8–13a reduces to

$$GH(s) = \frac{-2}{\delta e^{j\theta}} = -\frac{2}{\delta} e^{-j\theta} \qquad (8\text{–}13c)$$

whose magnitude $2/\delta \to \infty$ as $\delta \to 0$ and whose phase angle goes from $-\pi/2$ through $-\pi$ to $-3\pi/2$ as s moves around the origin in the indicated direction. This demonstrates that the $1 + GH(j\omega)$ curve is closed, as shown in Fig. 8–7b, by going from $-\pi/2$ to $-3\pi/2$ at infinity as $\omega = 0^-$ changes to $\omega = 0^+$. Following the path of the curve $1 + GH(j\omega)$ in the complex plane as s encircles region C in the s-plane, it is seen that $\Delta_C\theta$, the net change in phase angle of $1 + GH(j\omega)$, is 2π (one encirclement of the origin in the positive direction); hence Cauchy's argument principle gives

$$Z - P = -1 \qquad (8\text{–}13d)$$

The poles of $GH(s)$ are the poles of $1 + GH(s)$. In this case $GH(s)$ has one pole in region C so that $P = 1$; then $Z = 0$, showing that the characteristic equation $1 + GH(s)$ has no zeros (roots) in the positive-half s-plane, i.e., the closed-loop system is stable. In this example, the open-loop system is unstable but the closed-loop system is stable.

The map from the s-plane to the $GH(j\omega)$ plane is the Nyquist plot, and it differs from the $1 + GH(j\omega)$ plot by $+1$. Therefore, it is more convenient to use the $GH(j\omega)$ plot directly and count the net change in phase angle around the $-1 + j0$ point on the $GH(j\omega)$ plot rather than the angle change around the origin on the $1 + GH(j\omega)$ plot. The Nyquist stability criterion is stated as:

For any open-loop rational transfer function $GH(j\omega)$ which maps $s = j\omega$ on the complex plane for $-\infty < \omega < +\infty$ in a clockwise direction, find N (the number of encirclements of the $-1 + j0$ point on the $GH(j\omega)$) then Z, the number of zeros or roots of $1 + GH(j\omega)$, is given by

$$Z = P - N \qquad (8\text{--}14)$$

where P equals the number of poles of $GH(s)$ in the positive-half s-plane. If $Z > 0$, the closed-loop system is unstable.

In the application of this stability test, note that P is determined from knowledge of the pole-zero map of $GH(s)$, and that N is determined from the $GH(j\omega)$ mapping. Since most control systems have stable open-loop components (that is, $P = 0$) a simplification of the Nyquist stability criterion is generally stated thus: For a closed loop system to be stable, its open-loop contour $GH(j\omega)$ must not encircle the $-1 + j0$ point as ω follows the contour encircling the positive-half s-plane in a clockwise direction.

Although the Nyquist stability criterion is commonly used with the Nyquist plot of $GH(j\omega)$, it can be used with the Bode plot for well-behaved, minimum-phase $GH(s)$. In this case, the closed-loop system is stable if the magnitude is less than unity when the phase angle is $-180°$. In uncertain cases or involved situations one should use the general Nyquist stability criterion for determination of closed-loop system stability.

Example 8-2. Consider the PI control of a plant made up of two non-interacting first-order lags in series as shown in Fig. 6–8. Use unit values for τ, τ_1, R, and k, and let $\tau_i = 0.2$ so that the open-loop transfer function becomes

$$G(s) = \frac{5K_c(0.2s + 1)}{s(s + 1)^2}$$

(a) Find the value of K_c which makes the closed-loop system unstable.
(b) Find the value of K_c for a phase angle of $-145°$.
Solution. The frequency transfer function is

$$\frac{G(j\omega)}{K_c} = \frac{5(0.2j\omega + 1)}{j\omega(j\omega + 1)^2}$$

and the Bode plot is obtained as shown in Fig. E8–2a, using the smoothed straight-line approximations and corner frequencies for the magnitude ratio and phase

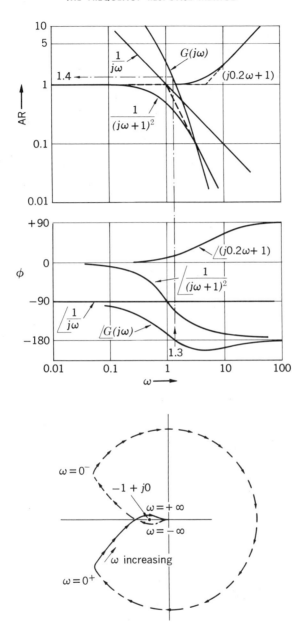

Fig. E8–2. (a) Bode plot and (b) Nyquist plot for determining the closed loop stability of the open-loop transfer function $GH(s) = 5K_c(0.2s + 1)/s(s + 1)^2$.

angle of the lead and lag components.   The curves for the gain of 5 and the pure integrator are exact.   The components are combined, and the magnitude ratio and phase angles are shown on both the Bode plot and the Nyquist plot.   Remember that instability is determined by encirclements of the $-1 + j0$ point on the Nyquist plot.   As ω encircles the positive-half s-plane in a clockwise direction (increasing from zero to $+\infty$ on to $-\infty$), the $G(j\omega)$ function moves as indicated on Fig. E8–2b.   The Nyquist plot is closed by the device used previously; i.e., near the origin, let $s = \delta e^{j\theta}$, then

$$G(s) \cong \frac{5}{\delta}\, e^{-j\theta}$$

and, as θ increases from $-\pi/2$ through zero to $+\pi/2$, the angle of $G(s)$ decreases from $\pi/2$ through zero to $-\pi/2$ as shown on the diagram.   From the plot, it is seen that the function $G(j\omega)$ encircles the $-1 + j0$ point twice in the positive direction, $Z = 2$, the system is unstable, and $1 + G(s)$ has two roots in the positive-half s-plane for $K_c = 1$.   Since $G(s)$ has no unstable poles, the simple Nyquist stability criterion is applicable.

(a) Return to the Bode plot, and notice that encirclement of the $-1 + j0$ point on the Nyquist plot corresponds to a magnitude ratio greater than unity when the phase angle is $-180°$ on the Bode plot, which is the stability test on the Bode plot.   In Fig. E8–2a, it is seen that the magnitude ratio has a phase angle of $-180°$ when $\omega = 1.3$ rad/time and $|G(j\omega)/K_c| = 1.4$.   The closed-loop system will also be unstable when the open-loop magnitude ratio is reduced to unity and the phase angle to $-180°$; therefore, the system is unstable for $1.4K_c = 1$ or $K_c = 0.7$.   This value of K_c for instability can be compared with the value given by Routh's criterion in Eq. 6–14d as

$$\tau_i = 0.2 > \frac{1}{2}\frac{K_c}{1 + K_c} \qquad \text{or} \qquad K_c > 0.67$$

which agrees very well with the graphical result found here.

(b) From Fig. E8–2a, the phase angle of $-145°$ occurs at a frequency of $\omega = 0.6$ and a value of $|G(j\omega)/K_c| = 7$ so that the necessary controller gain K_c is

$$7K_c = 1 \qquad \text{or} \qquad K_c = 0.14$$

Thus, a substantial decrease in K_c is needed to move the system from the edge of stability to a relative stability considered acceptable or safe.

Relative Stability.   The absolute stability of a closed-loop system, as discussed above, is concerned with encirclement of the $-1 + j0$ point on the Nyquist diagram.   The relative stability of a system is determined by the closeness of approach of the Nyquist curve to the $-1 + j0$ point from the stable direction.   Both the transient and frequency response system performance-criteria discussed in Chapter 6 are related through the closed-loop system pole-zero map.   If the system has a dominant complex pair of closed-loop poles, with any additional poles located far to the left in the s-plane, its response can be adequately characterized in terms of a second-order system.   If the system has multiple closed-loop poles which contribute significantly to the response, empirical criteria such as gain margin and phase margin are used to characterize the frequency response.

Gain margin (GM) is the reciprocal of the open-loop gain at $-180°$, i.e., it is the factor by which the gain could be increased before instability occurs. The phase margin (PM) is the angle between $180°$ and $\angle GH(j\omega)$ when $|GH(j\omega)| = 1$, thus it is the additional phase lag required to make a system unstable when the open-loop gain is unity. The maximum closed-loop magnitude ratio M_p is a direct measure of the relative system stability. These definitions are shown on Nyquist and Bode plots in Fig. 8–8 for the open-loop transfer function

$$GH(s) = \frac{K_c}{s(s+1)(0.5s+1)}$$

for $K_c = 2$ and $K_c = 5$. Upon inspection of the Nyquist plot in Fig. 8–8a it is apparent that the closed-loop system is stable with $K_c = 2$ since the $-1 + j0$ point is not enclosed; but with $K_c = 5$ the system is unstable since the $-1 + j0$ point would be enclosed. The $K_c = 2$ curve crosses the negative real axis (phase angle of $-180°$) when $GH(j1.4) = 0.67$ so that the gain margin GM $= 1/0.67 = 1.5$, which means that the system would be unstable if $K_c = 2(1.5) = 3$. The $K_c = 2$ curve has a magnitude ratio of unity when the phase lag is $-168°$; therefore the phase margin is $+12°$ (stable system). The $K_c = 2$ curve is tangent to the circle $M_p = 5$ at the frequency ω_r, giving the maximum in the closed-loop frequency response magnitude ratio as 5. The same information is available on the Bode plot in Fig. 8–8b. The magnitude ratio curve with $K_c = 5$ shows that the closed-loop system is unstable, for its phase margin is negative (about $-15°$) and its gain margin is less than unity ($1/1.7$). With $K_c = 2$, the open-loop magnitude ratio curve has a positive phase margin of $12°$ and a gain margin of $1/0.67 = 1.5$, showing that the closed-loop system is stable. The closed-loop magnitude ratio curve was obtained by use of the Nichols chart and shows an M_p value of 5, which is much too large (transient response is highly oscillatory) for process systems.

The damping ratio for a particular system is related to phase margin, gain margin, and M_p through a root-locus analysis. Remember that the Nyquist plot is the conformal transformation of the $+j\omega$ axis in the s-plane to the $G(s)$ plane, the root locus is the $-180°$ phase contour of $G(s)$ in the s-plane, and the negative real axis on the $G(s)$ plane is the conformal transformation of the root locus since the gain contributes zero phase angle.

The third-order system in Fig. 8–8 has the root-locus form

$$GH(s) = \frac{2K_c}{s(s+1)(s+2)}$$

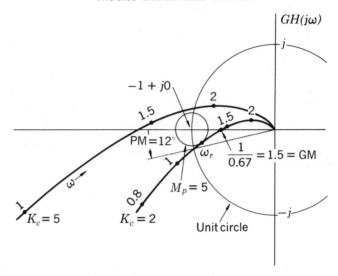

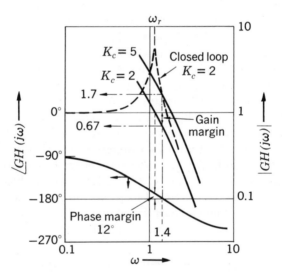

Fig. 8–8. (a) Nyquist plot and (b) Bode plot showing the definitions of phase margin, gain margin, and M_p for a third-order system $GH(s) = K_c/s(s + 1)(0.5s + 1)$ when $H(s) = 1$.

and the root-locus sketch in Fig. 8–9a gives the effect of gain K_c on the damping ratio of the complex pair of closed-loop roots as shown in Fig. 8–9b. In general, there is no "best zeta" for all systems; but it was pointed out in Chapter 4 that good control in many process systems is obtained with $0.3 < \zeta < 0.5$, which is marked on the plots in Figs. 8–9b

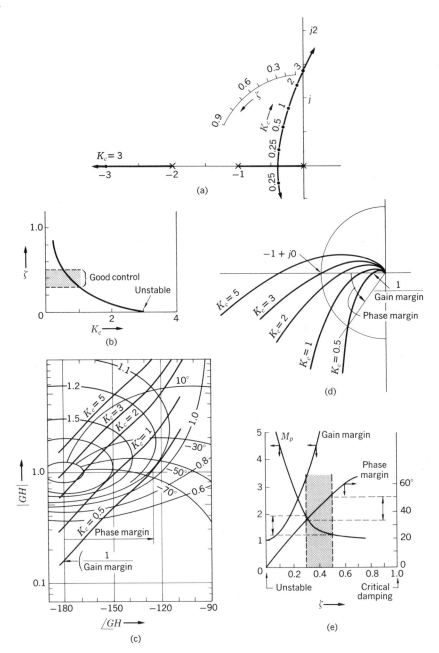

Fig. 8–9. Derivation of relationships between gain and damping ratio and between damping ratio and phase margin, gain margin, and M_p for one-control system $GH(s) = K_c/s(s + 1)(0.5s + 1)$. (a) Root locus plot. (b) K_c vs. ζ relationship. (c) Nichols plot. (d) Nyquist plot. (e) Performance criteria.

and e. The effect of gain on the Nyquist and Nichols plots for this system are given in Figs. 8–9c and d with indications of the definitions of phase margin and gain margin. The gain K_c contributes zero phase angle to the open-loop frequency transfer function, so that on the Nichols plot the effect of K_c is to raise or lower the complete magnitude ratio curve and on the Nyquist plot the effect of K_c is to increase or decrease the magnitude ratio with the resultant "fanning out or in" of the curve at a fixed phase angle. This simple effect of K_c on the Nichols plot makes it especially easy to set K_c for a desired M_p, using this plot. The phase margin and gain margin values as determined by K_c are easily read from the Nichols plot. The phase margins are read as the $GH(j\omega)$ curves cross the unity magnitude ratio value. The gain margins are the reciprocals of the $GH(j\omega)$ magnitude ratios at $-180°$ phase angle. Values of M_p are read from the closed-loop magnitude ratio contours which are just tangent to the $|GH(j\omega)|$ for each gain K_c. The three frequency response performance criteria are displayed in Fig. 8–9e as a function of damping ratio for this system with the area of "good control" marked for $0.3 < \zeta < 0.5$.

The M_p-, PM-, and GM-vs.-ζ relationships vary for different systems, but the range of values which give satisfactory performance are relatively the same for all systems, so that these values have become "rules of thumb" for use as rough-check and first-trial values in adjusting and designing control systems. The rules suggest that, for good control of process systems, it is expected that M_p will be between 1.3 and 2 and the phase margin will be between 30° and 45°. Gain margin is not often used in performance specifications.

Example 8–3. Derive a relationship between damping ratio ζ and phase margin ϕ_m for a second-order system. The open-loop frequency response expression for a closed-loop second-order oscillatory system is

$$G(j\omega) = \frac{\omega_n^2}{j\omega(j\omega + 2\zeta\omega_n)} = \frac{\omega_n^2}{-\omega^2 + j2\zeta\omega_n\omega}$$

Solution. Phase margin ϕ_m is 180° plus the phase angle of the open-loop process at unity gain as defined in Fig. 8–8. The value of ω that makes the magnitude ratio of $G(j\omega)$ equal to unity is found by solving the equation

$$|G(j\omega)| = \frac{\omega_n^2}{\sqrt{\omega^4 + 4\zeta^2\omega_n^2\omega^2}} = 1 \qquad \underline{/G(j\omega)} = -\tan^{-1}\frac{2\zeta\omega_n}{-\omega}$$

with the result that

$$\omega^2 = \omega_n^2(\sqrt{4\zeta^2 + 1} - 2\zeta^2)$$

The phase margin is

$$\phi_m = 180° - \tan^{-1}\frac{2\zeta\omega_n}{-\omega} = \tan^{-1}\frac{2\zeta\omega_n}{\omega}$$

$$= \tan^{-1}\frac{2\zeta}{\sqrt{\sqrt{4\zeta^2 + 1} - 2\zeta^2}}$$

which is plotted in Fig. E8–3. The range of "good damping ratio" between 0.3 and 0.5 corresponds in the second-order system to a phase margin of 31° to 47° and M_p between 1.74 and 1.16 as shown in Fig. E8–3. The M_p relation shown is plotted from Eq. 6–16c.

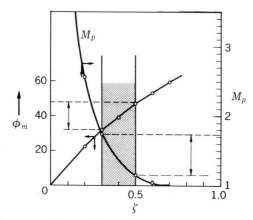

Fig. E8–3. Phase margin, ϕ_m, M_p, and damping ratio, ζ, for a second-order system.

Example 8–4. The value of M_p for a given closed-loop system can be determined by complex differentiation. Find M_p for the system whose open-loop transfer function is (assuming $H = 1$)

$$G(s) = \frac{2}{s(s + 1)(0.5s + 1)}$$

Solution. The closed-loop frequency transfer function is

$$\frac{C}{R}(s) = \frac{G}{1 + G} = \frac{4}{(s^3 + 3s^2 + 2s + 4)} = M(s)$$

Now

$$M(j\omega) = M(s)|_{s=j\omega} = M(\omega)e^{j\alpha(\omega)}$$

Differentiating and setting the derivative to zero will give the maximum M_p as shown below. The derivative of $M(j\omega)$ is

$$\frac{dM(j\omega)}{d\omega} = e^{j\alpha}\frac{dM}{d\omega} + jMe^{j\alpha}\frac{d\alpha}{d\omega}$$

which can be rearranged into real and imaginary parts as

$$\frac{1}{Me^{j\alpha}}\frac{dM(j\omega)}{d\omega} = \underset{\text{(real)}}{\frac{1}{M}\frac{dM}{d\omega}} + \underset{\text{(imaginary)}}{j\frac{d\alpha}{d\omega}} \tag{a}$$

Then the maximum M_p is found by setting $dM(j\omega)/d\omega = 0$, which corresponds to setting the real part of Eq. a to zero as

$$\mathcal{R}e\left[\frac{1}{Me^{j\alpha}}\frac{dM}{d\omega}\right] = 0$$

In terms of the closed-loop transfer function this corresponds to writing

$$\mathcal{R}e\left[j\frac{1}{M(s)}\frac{dM(s)}{ds}\right]^*_{s=j\omega} = 0 \qquad\qquad (b)$$

which gives $\omega = \omega_r$ at the maximum value. M_p is then found by substituting $\omega = \omega_r$ in the $M(j\omega)$ expression. In this case,

$$j\frac{1}{M(s)}\frac{dM(s)}{ds} = -j\frac{3s^2 + 6s + 2}{s^3 + 3s^2 + 2s + 4}$$

and ω_r is found by letting $s = j\omega$ and setting the real part to zero as given by Eq. b which requires

$$(4 - 3\omega^2)6\omega + (3\omega^2 - 2)(2\omega - \omega^3) = 0$$

and gives $\omega_r = 1.17$. Finally,

$$M_p = \frac{4}{(\omega^6 + 5\omega^4 - 20\omega^2 + 16)}\bigg|_{\omega=1.17} = 5.26$$

This computed value of M_p is exact, whereas the value $M_p = 5$, obtained graphically for this system in Fig. 8–9, has accumulation of errors due to use of graphical procedures.

8–6. PLANT COMPENSATION WITH PROCESS CONTROLLERS

In process plant design the process engineer must satisfy the static plant design capacity requirements and at the same time give full attention to those plant dynamic characteristics which improve the control problem. He then selects the proper controller functions that enable the system to meet the specified system performance. As shown in the sketches of Fig. 8–10, each controller action as described in Chapter 5 shapes the open-loop frequency transfer function in a unique manner. The open-loop Nyquist diagram in Fig. 8–10a represents a plant to which controller actions are added as shown in the other sketches.

Proportional control is usually present in all process compensation schemes. The effect of proportional control is to add constant gain at all frequencies and no phase angle to improve speed of response and diminish

* In case $M(s) = N(s)/D(s)$, the bracketed term can be simplified as

$$\frac{1}{M(s)}\frac{dM(s)}{ds} = \frac{1}{N(s)}\frac{dN(s)}{ds} - \frac{1}{D(s)}\frac{dD(s)}{ds}$$

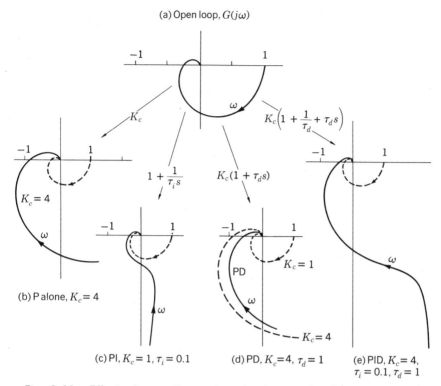

(a) Open loop, $G(j\omega)$

K_c

$K_c\left(1 + \dfrac{1}{\tau_d} + \tau_d s\right)$

$1 + \dfrac{1}{\tau_i s}$

$K_c(1 + \tau_d s)$

$K_c = 4$

PD $K_c = 1$

(b) P alone, $K_c = 4$

$K_c = 4$

(c) PI, $K_c = 1, \tau_i = 0.1$ (d) PD, $K_c = 4, \tau_d = 1$ (e) PID, $K_c = 4,$
$\tau_i = 0.1, \tau_d = 1$

Fig. 8–10. Effect of controller actions in shaping the frequency transfer function. The dashed curve is $G(j\omega)$ of the plant to which the controller $G_c(j\omega)$ is added to give the sketched results.

static error. The controller gain is set as large as possible, consistent with adequate system stability. Increase in gain reduces the system damping and static error, but in most systems too much gain will cause instability even when the static error is large, as shown in Fig. 8–10b where the system is approaching instability at a low gain of $K_c = 4$. In this case the gain must be decreased to increase the system damping, but then perhaps the offset or static error will be intolerable. The addition of other controller actions makes it possible to achieve simultaneously high gain and adequate damping for good control.

1. Integral action, $(1 + 1/\tau_i s)$. Integral action in a controller assures system accuracy. It adds gain that is inversely proportional to frequency and phase lag that decreases with frequency to give high gain at low frequency without altering the high-frequency performance, as shown in Fig. 8–10c. Notice that the phase shift due to integral action is low at high frequencies and nearly -90 at low frequencies. A pure-integration

controller called "floating control" $1/\tau_i s$ is frequently used in liquid-flow processes and processes dominated by a large dead time.

2. Derivative action, $(1 + \tau_d s)$. Generally, derivative action improves the system stability. The derivative action adds gain that is proportional to frequency and phase lead that increases to 90° at high frequencies. The effect of the phase lead is to cancel some of the phase lags in the control loop and thereby reduce the high-frequency gain at the same phase angle without altering the low-frequency performance. In Fig. 8–10d the dashed lines are drawn for $K_c = 1$ and for $K_c = 4$, the gain in Fig. 8–10b. Compare the PD curve with the $K_c = 4$ curve and note that the PD system is more stable and that the curves approach each other as frequency decreases. Thus, derivative action does not improve static error, but it may improve the system stability so much that the proportional gain may be increased and thereby decrease static error. The largest τ_d permissible in process systems is limited by the amount of extraneous high-frequency noise present in the process signals.

3. PID action, $\left(1 + \dfrac{1}{\tau_i s} + \tau_d s\right)$. This controller action gives the combined effects of the separate actions. As seen in Fig. 8–10c the integral action gives high gain at low frequencies (for accuracy) while the derivative action adds phase lead at high frequencies (for stability). The combined effect is shown in Fig. 8–10e.

Rules of Thumb. From the process design viewpoint it is vastly more important to have the correct compensation in the control loop than to have an exact prediction of a certain controller setting. From the plant operation viewpoint it is important to have as few controller adjustments as possible since an operator can adjust a single knob controller but an expert is needed to properly adjust a multiparameter controller. Controller settings for the frequency response method may be derived either from the rules of thumb concerning good values of M_p and phase margin or from the Ziegler-Nichols formulas in Chapter 6 for the closed-loop method. After the controller settings are selected, the choice should be verified by a transient trial on the plant or on a process simulator if available.

1. Gain selection for a specified M_p or phase margin. The gain selection for a specified M_p is best achieved on the Nichols chart by plotting the open-loop plant transfer function $G(j\omega)$ without compensation on the $\log |G(j\omega)|$-vs.-$\angle G(j\omega)$ coordinates and finding the gain K_c needed to move the $G(j\omega)$ curve so that it is tangent to the specified M_p curve. This is easily accomplished by using a transparent overlay to move vertically up or down until $G(j\omega)$ and the selected M_p curves are tangent. Then the needed gain K_c is the ratio of the gain scale of the overlay to the gain

scale of the $G(j\omega)$ plot. Refer to Fig. 8–9c and note that gain increases move the open-loop transfer function upward, giving larger M_p values to the closed-loop system. For process control systems, it is expected that typical M_p values will be in the range of 1.5 to 3.0.

Gain adjustment by phase margin is accomplished by taking the reciprocal of the $G(j\omega)$ curve when the phase angle is $-180°$ + phase margin specification. Typical values of phase margin in process control systems are in the range of 30 to 45°.

2. Integral action. Since integral action adds phase lag to the open-loop system, the overall phase lag will reach $-180°$ at a lower frequency and therefore integral action slows the system response. Because of this, too much integral action can of itself cause instability. The general rule limits the phase lag added by this action to 5 to 10° in the neighborhood of the closed-loop resonant frequency. Generally, the integral controller break frequency $1/\tau_i$ is about $0.1\omega_r$.

3. Derivative action. Since derivative action adds phase lead to the open-loop system, the overall phase lag will reach $-180°$ at a higher frequency; this action improves the response by increasing the bandwidth of the system. This effect is dramatic for systems having a steep log-magnitude-ratio-vs.-log-ω curve and a relatively flat phase-angle-vs.-log-ω curve near the $-180°$ phase-angle condition, for then the controller phase lead results in a large increase in resonant frequency. This is the case for normal processes having no dead time. If large dead time is present in the process, the magnitude ratio curve will be relatively flat and the phase-angle curve will be steep near the $-180°$ phase-angle condition and derivative action will contribute little improvement in the system performance.

When large dead time is not present, a rule suggests that a first-trial derivative time constant would be one that contributes 45 to 60° phase lead at the resonant frequency which corresponds approximately to $\tau_d = 2/\omega_r$. For practical reasons in the design of controllers and because process noise amplification must be avoided in controller application, the derivative action in commercial controllers may have gain and phase lead limits as shown by the commercial controller equations in Chapter 5. Generally, the derivative controller is set to give its maximum phase lead at the resonant frequency of the closed-loop system.

Ziegler-Nichols Closed-Loop Method. The process characteristics P_u and $(PB)_u$ are determined, as discussed in Chapter 6, by increasing the proportional controller gain, in the absence of integral or derivative control actions, until the control system sustains oscillations. The gain which makes the control system unstable, i.e., makes $G(j\omega) = -1$, is the process ultimate gain K_u (reciprocally related to $(PB)_u$) and the period of oscillation is the ultimate period $P_u(=2\pi/\omega_u)$, where ω_u is the ultimate frequency. The Ziegler-Nichols formulas for first trial controller settings as written in terms of K_u and ω_u are:

Controller: P $K_c = \dfrac{1}{2}K_u$

PI $K_c = \dfrac{1}{2.2}K_u$ $\tau_i = 2\pi/1.2\omega_u$

PID $K_c = \dfrac{1}{1.7}K_u$ $\tau_i = \pi/\omega_u$ $\tau_d = \pi/4\omega_u$

Process Control Example. The control of the process heater discussed in Chapter 7 will be analyzed here by the frequency response method to show the effects of P, PI, and PD idealized controllers on shaping the frequency transfer function and the closed-loop system response.

PROPORTIONAL ACTION. The open-loop frequency transfer function of the process heater in Fig. 7–12 is

$$GH(j\omega) = \frac{K_c}{(0.5j\omega + 1)(2j\omega + 1)(5j\omega + 1)(j\omega + 1)}; H(j\omega) = \frac{0.01}{j\omega + 1}, \frac{\text{psi}}{{}^{\circ}\text{F}}$$

$$(7\text{--}17a)$$

The root-locus plot for this system is sketched in Fig. 7–13 where it is found that $K_c = 7.4$ gives instability and $K_c = 3.7$ and 1.4 give a dominant pair of closed-loop complex poles having $\zeta = 0.2$ and 0.5, respectively. The frequency transfer function locus is sketched on the Nichols plot in Fig. 8–11, which shows a magnitude ratio of 0.135 for $K_c = 1$ at the ultimate frequency $\omega_u = 0.68$ rad/time, i.e., a gain of $K_c = 1/0.135 = 7.41$ would make the system unstable. This agrees with the value of $K_c = 7.4$ found by the root-locus analysis.

The open-loop gain K_c for a desired closed-loop M_p for $G/(1 + G)$ can be set by finding the multiplier K_c which would make $K_cG(j\omega)$ just tangent to the desired M_p curve on the Nichols chart. This is illustrated in Fig. 8–11a for the process heater, where it is seen that $K_c = 3.7$ gives an $M_p \cong 2$ and $K_c = 1.4$ gives M_p of 0.65. In this case, as shown by the inset diagram in Fig. 8–11b, after the system of Fig. 7–12 is changed to a unity feedback loop,

$$\frac{B}{R}(j\omega) = \frac{GH(j\omega)}{1 + GH(j\omega)} \qquad \frac{C}{R}(j\omega) = \frac{B}{R}(j\omega)\frac{1}{H(j\omega)} \qquad (8\text{--}15)$$

The gain setting of $K_c = 3.7$ produces an $M_p \cong 2$ for the $(B/R)(j\omega)$ signal with a larger M_p being obtained for $(C/R)(j\omega)$ because the $1/H(j\omega)$ factor increases the maximum value about 15%. Notice that the gain constant of 100°F/psi has been included to make the C/R ratio dimensionless. If the effect of neglecting $H(s)$ (as was done here) is unacceptable,

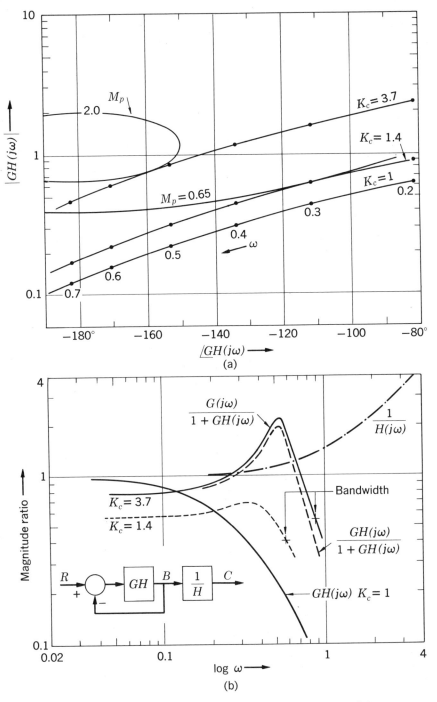

Fig. 8–11. Gain setting for control of process heater. (a) Using the Nichols chart to set the gain for a specified M_p. (b) Graphical determination of $(C/R)(j\omega)$ from $(B/R)(j\omega)$.

then a cut-and-try procedure can be used in the next trial to adjust K_c to the desired M_p for $(C/R)(j\omega)$. Thus, dynamics in $H(s)$ requires an additional step in setting the controller gain to meet an M_p specification. Notice, in Fig. 8–11b, that this system will show a static error (because $M < 1$ as $\omega \to 0$) and that increased gain K_c gives a faster-responding system having a wider bandwidth ($\omega = 0.9$ rad/time when $K_c = 3.7$) than the lower-gain system (for $K_c = 1.4$, bandwidth $\omega = 0.58$ rad/time). With $K_c = 3.7$, this system is too oscillatory ($M_p = 2.3$ or $\zeta = 0.2$) and with a lower gain the static error will increase; therefore this system needs integral action to eliminate static errors.

PROPORTIONAL-PLUS-INTEGRAL ACTION. Using an ideal PI controller with $\tau_i = 15$, Eq. 7–18 for the process heater becomes

$$GH(j\omega) = \frac{K_c(15j\omega + 1)}{15j\omega(0.5j\omega + 1)(2j\omega + 1)(5j\omega + 1)(j\omega + 1)} \quad (8\text{–}16)$$

This selection of τ_i is based upon the rule that the integral action will contribute between 5 and 10° of phase lag at the resonant frequency. The magnitude ratio and phase angle of integral action alone ($K_c = 1$) is given by Eq. 5–10d as

$$\text{AR} = \frac{1}{\omega\tau_i}\sqrt{\omega^2\tau_i^2 + 1} \qquad \angle\phi = \tan^{-1}\frac{-1}{\omega\tau_i} \quad (5\text{–}10\text{d})$$

The time constant for a 7° phase lag at the resonant frequency of 0.54 rad/time is found as

$$7° = \tan^{-1}\frac{-1}{0.54\tau_i} \qquad \text{or} \qquad \tau_i = 15 \text{ time units}$$

The plots in Fig. 8–12a show the original uncompensated open-loop frequency transfer function with $K_c = 3.7$ as the dashed line and the open-loop function compensated with integral action ($\tau_i = 15$) as the solid line. Two effects of integral action are noted: (1) the low-frequency magnitude ratio approaches infinity and (2) the low-frequency phase lag approaches $-90°$. The resulting closed-loop frequency response $(C/R)(j\omega)$ (obtained from the Nichols chart with inclusion of feedback dynamics) is shown as a solid line with an M_p value of 3 at the resonant frequency of 0.5 rad/time and a low-frequency magnitude of unity (no static error permitted). The bandwidth of the system is slightly decreased. The slight decrease in bandwidth and resonant frequency and some increase in M_p are small sacrifices in performance balanced against the elimination of static error.

PROPORTIONAL-PLUS-DERIVATIVE ACTION. Using an ideal PD controller with $\tau_d = 5$ pole-zero cancellation occurs and Eq. 7–19 for the process heater becomes

$$GH(j\omega) = \frac{K_c}{(0.5j\omega + 1)(2j\omega + 1)(j\omega + 1)} \qquad (7\text{--}19)$$

This selection of τ_d is higher than the rule-of-thumb values; this is $2/\omega_r = 2/0.54 = 3.7$, and for 60° phase lead at ω_r the value τ_d is 3.2 time units.

The plots in Fig. 8–12b show the uncompensated and compensated open-loop frequency response. Two effects of derivative action are to decrease the open-loop phase angle at a given frequency and to increase the open-loop bandwidth. The low-frequency magnitude ratio is not changed; hence the system will show a closed-loop static error. The closed-loop frequency response (obtained from the Nichols chart with inclusion of feedback dynamics) is shown with an M_p value of 2.5 at the resonant frequency of 1.2 rad/time, a low-frequency magnitude of 0.786,

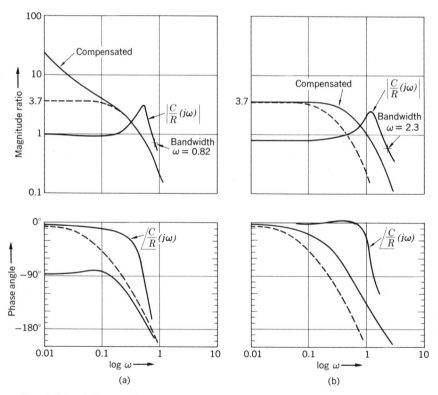

Fig. 8–12. Effects of PI and PD controllers on frequency response of process heater. (a) Bode plot of effect of PI controller. (b) Bode plot of effect of PD controller.

and a bandwidth of 2.3 rad/time.   In summation, derivative action has increased the system bandwidth, increased the system speed of response, and has not affected the static system error.

Example 8–5.   The compensation of a process plant having simple process lags whose time constants differ by factors of 5 or more has a simple interpretation. Consider the application of P, PD, and PID controllers to the control of a third-order process plant having time constants $\tau_1 \gg \tau_2 \gg \tau_3$.   Select controller gains for a 45° phase margin, and show that the controller gain is simply related to the two larger time constants and that the commercial type of controller modes provide zero-pole cancellation which either increases the largest process lag or reduces the next-to-largest process lag.

Solution.   The straight-line approximation of $G_p(j\omega)$ is shown in Fig. E8–5b for $\tau_1 = 5$, $\tau_2 = 1$, $\tau_3 = 0.2$ time units.   The phase angle for each first-order

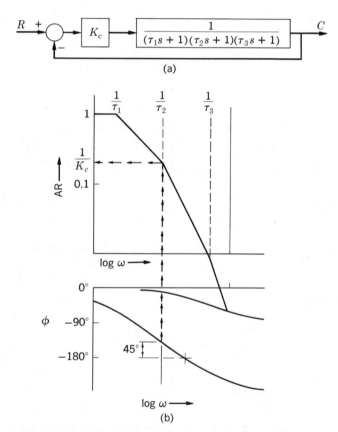

(a)

(b)

Fig. E8–5.   Frequency response analysis of process having three widely separated time constants.   (a) Control system.   (b) Bode plot of $G_p(j\omega)$.

lag is $-45°$ at its corner frequency, and, if the time constants differ by a factor equal to or greater than 5, then the phase angle contributed by τ_1 and τ_2, when $\omega = 1/\tau_2$, will be approximately $-135°$ (or $45°$ phase margin) as seen in Fig. E8–5b. Then the controller gain K_c is made equal to the reciprocal of the process gain. Refer to the Bode magnitude ratio plot in Fig. E8–5b, and note that the process gain has a slope of -1 between $\omega = 1/\tau_1$ and $\omega = 1/\tau_2$; therefore, the process gain at $\omega = 1/\tau_2$ becomes

$$\text{Slope} = -1 = \frac{\log 1 - \log \left(\dfrac{1}{K_c}\right)}{\log \left(\dfrac{1}{\tau_1}\right) - \log \left(\dfrac{1}{\tau_2}\right)} = \frac{\log K_c}{\log \dfrac{\tau_2}{\tau_1}}$$

and the controller gain for a $45°$ phase margin becomes

$$K_c = \tau_1/\tau_2$$

(a) P controller. High controller gain which is desired for accuracy and fast response may be achieved by either increasing τ_1, the largest time constant in the process, or reducing τ_2, the next-to-largest time constant in the process.

(b) PI controller. The commercial PI controller has a typical transfer function (see Chapter 5).

$$K_c \frac{(\tau_i s + 1)}{(\alpha \tau_i s + 1)}$$

where $5 < \alpha < 100$. If the controller is set to make $\tau_i = \tau_1$, the effect is to replace the largest process time constant τ_1 by the larger controller time constant $\alpha \tau_i$, and the controller gain can be increased by the factor α.

(c) PD controller. The commercial PD controller has a typical transfer function

$$K_c \frac{(\tau_d s + 1)}{(\beta \tau_d s + 1)}$$

where $0.02 < \beta < 1$.

Again, if τ_d is set to cancel τ_2, the next-to-largest time constant, the effect is to replace τ_2 by a smaller time constant $\beta \tau_d$, and the controller gain can be increased by the factor $1/\beta$.

(d) PID controller. The commercial PID controller typically cascades the PI and PD actions so that the $45°$ phase-margin settings replace the largest process time constant by the larger $\alpha \tau_i$ controller time constant and the next to largest process time constant by the smaller $\beta \tau_d$ controller time constant as discussed above. Then the allowed increase in K_c generally improves system stability and speed of response.

Effect of Dead Time in Loop. Transportation lag, or dead time, occurs when process materials move through a unit without experiencing any change in their composition or properties. The simplest example is fluids moving through pipelines that interconnect process vessels. Presence of dead time in a control loop results in slow response and a tendency for instability that is difficult to overcome.

Dead time in systems is easier to handle by frequency response methods than by root-locus methods. The system consisting of a dead-time τ and first-order time constant $a\tau$, for which the root-locus plot is given in Fig. 7–19a, will be analyzed, using frequency response. The system frequency transfer function is

$$G(j\omega) = \frac{K_c k e^{-j\omega\tau}}{ja\omega\tau + 1}$$

and its Nichols plot for various values of a are shown in Fig. 8–13. The gain $K_c k$ needed to give an M_p values of 2 and the resonant frequency $\omega_r\tau$

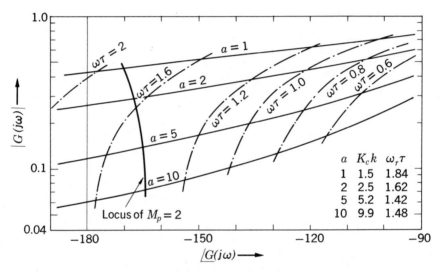

Fig. 8–13. Nichols plot for system having dead time τ and first-order lag $a\tau$ components in series. Gain table is computed for $M_p = 2$.

may be found from the plot by superimposing the closed-loop M_p grid on the Nichols plot and finding $K_c k$ which makes the $M_p = 2$ contour tangent to the proper $G(j\omega)$ line. A table of the necessary gain values and resulting $\omega_r\tau$ is shown in the right-hand corner of Fig. 8–13. On comparing these data with the charts of damping ratio for this system in Fig. 7–19, it is found that the value of $M_p = 2$ for this system corresponds to a damping ratio ζ of about 0.2. This $M_p = 2$ is probably too high for best process operation of this system. Gains for other values of M_p may be found by use of the closed-loop M_p grid.

PROBLEMS

8–1. Process frequency response tests may require excessive plant time. Estimate the time required for the magnitude ratio of the response of a first-order component to be within 5% of the steady-state value when $\omega\tau = 0.5$ and the time constant is (a) 10 min and (b) 1 hour. Assume the component is at rest when the sinusoidal signal is applied.

8–2. Write analytical expressions for the magnitude ratio and phase angle of the frequency response of the following transfer functions by substituting $s = j\omega$:

(a) $G(s) = \dfrac{Ke^{-\tau s}}{2\tau s + 1}$

(b) $G(s) = \dfrac{K(\tau s + 1)}{s(2\tau s + 1)^2}$

8–3. Prepare Bode plots for the following transfer functions, using any method of your choice. Plot $|G(j\omega)/K_c|$, and make the plots in the order a, b, c, d.

(a) $G(s) = \dfrac{5K_c}{s + 1}$

(b) $G(s) = \dfrac{5K_c}{(s + 1)(s + 2)}$

(c) $G(s) = \dfrac{5K_c}{s(s + 1)(s + 2)}$

(d) $G(s) = \dfrac{K_c 5(2s + 1)}{s(s + 1)(s + 2)}$

Determine the maximum gain K_c for closed-loop stability and the frequency at $-180°$ phase angle for the transfer function c.

8–4. Plot Bode diagrams for the following transfer function.

$$G(s) = \left(1 + \frac{1}{10s}\right)\frac{K_c e^{-s}}{(s + 1)(s^2 + 0.45s + 1)}$$

Determine the maximum gain for closed-loop stability and the frequency at $-180°$ phase angle.

8–5. (a) A thermometer shows a 20° phase lag behind a bath temperature that is varying sinusoidally at a frequency of 1 cycle per min. Assume the thermometer has the dynamic response of a first-order device, and find its time constant. Use Fig. 4–8 for graphical solution.

(b) Find the magnitude ratio and the phase lag of the response when the same thermometer is placed in a bath whose temperature varies sinusoidally at the rate of 2 cycles per min.

8–6. Frequency response measurements made on a process plant and measurement device connected in series gave the following results. Find the plant parameters. From practical considerations, it is known that the plant contains two first-order lags and a dead time. The dynamics of the measurement device are negligible in this frequency range.

ω rad/min	$|GH(j\omega)|$	$\underline{/GH(j\omega)}$	ω rad/min	$|GH(j\omega)|$	$\underline{/GH(j\omega)}$
0.02	2.0	$-6.8°$	0.5	0.67	$-110°$
0.05	1.9	$-18.4°$	1.0	0.27	$-153°$
0.1	1.8	$-35.4°$	2	0.088	$-205°$
0.2	1.4	$-61°$	5	0.016	$-310°$

8-7. Sketch Nyquist plots of these transfer functions, and determine the range of K_c for which the closed-loop systems are stable, if any.

(a) $GH(s) = \dfrac{K_c}{s}\dfrac{s+1}{(s-2)}$

(b) $GH(s) = \dfrac{K_c(s+1)}{(s-2)(s+0.5)}$

Use the Routh criterion to check your conclusions.

8-8. Determine a range of K_c for which the following open-loop transfer functions represent stable closed-loop systems. Report the ultimate frequency.

(a) $GH(s) = \dfrac{K_c e^{-2s}}{(2s+1)}$

(b) $GH(s) = \dfrac{K_c e^{-2s}(1+s)}{s(2s+1)}$

(c) $GH(s) = \dfrac{K_c e^{-2s}(1+s)}{(2s+1)}$

8-9. Sketch Bode diagrams for the following feedback control systems, and determine a value of K_c which makes the system unstable. Compare this result with the value found from the root-locus Problem 7-2, if available. Estimate a value of K_c which gives $M_p = 1.3(GH/(1+GH)$ for the closed-loop system and the corresponding phase margin.

(a) $G_c = K_c$ $G_p = \dfrac{1}{(0.5s+1)(2s+1)^2}$ $H = \dfrac{5}{s+1}$

(b) $G_c = K_c$ $G_p = \dfrac{1}{(0.5s+1)(2s+1)^2}$ $H = 5(s+1)$

(c) $G_c = K_c(1+s)$ $G_p = \dfrac{1}{(0.5s+1)(2s+1)^2}$ $H = \dfrac{5}{s+1}$

8-10. The open-loop transfer function of a unity feedback control system is

$$G(s) = \frac{K_c\left(1 + \dfrac{1}{2s} + 2s\right)}{(4s+1)(2s+1)(s+1)}$$

(a) Will any value of K_c make the closed-loop system unstable?

(b) Find the smallest value of K_c which makes $M_p = 1.3$, and estimate ω_r, and ζ for the dominant pair of complex roots.

Compare your results with the values found for Problem 7-7, if available.

8-11. Solve Problem 7-9, using analytical methods. Omit part c, and find the closed-loop frequency response for part b.

8–12. Determine the "best settings" for a three-mode controller, using the ultimate method. The process transfer functions are

Plant:
$$G_p(s) = \frac{4}{(2s + 1)^2(s + 2)}$$

Measurement:
$$H(s) = \frac{0.5}{(0.5s + 1)}$$

Prepare the Bode plot for the closed-loop system responses $(B/R)(j\omega)$ and $(C/R)(j\omega)$. List ω_r, M_p, and the bandwidth of the system.

8–13. The selection of a P or PD controller is under consideration for the system in Fig. P8–13.

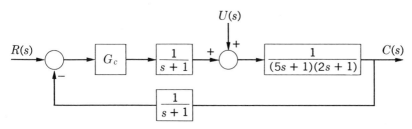

Fig. P8–13

(a) Select K_c for a proportional controller, using a 30° phase-margin criterion. Compare this value of K_c with that given by the ultimate method.

(b) Select K_c and τ_d for a PD controller, using criteria of 30° phase margin and 50° derivative phase lead at the resonant frequency.

(c) Plot $(C/R)(j\omega)$ and $(C/U)(j\omega)$ responses on the Bode plot. Note that ω_r is independent of the disturbance location but that offset and magnitude of deviations depend on disturbance location in a system.

8–14. A process plant has a gain of two, a dead time of 0.5 min, and a first-order time lag of 1 min. The measurement transducer has unity gain and a first-order time lag of 5 min.

(a) Find the maximum permissible gain K_c in the controller.

(b) Plot $(C/R)(j\omega)$ (actual response) and $(B/R)(j\omega)$ (measured response) when the controller gain is 40% of the maximum value.

(c) If the measurement time constant were reduced by 50%, how would K_c be changed? Also, compare the ultimate frequencies in both cases.

8–15. A process may be represented by a gain $k = 0.5$, a dead time $\tau = 1$ min, and a first-order lag $\tau = 2$ min. Select a proportional controller gain K_c to give a value of $M_p = 1.6$. Plot the closed-loop frequency response, and characterize it as a second-order response by finding a natural frequency and damping ratio. From those data, write a transfer function for the closed-loop system. Compare those values with similar values read from the root-locus plot in Fig. 7–19.

9

Process Models and Control Design

Previous chapters in this book are concerned with the technical problems of manipulating the time behavior of simple systems for control of a single variable. A process factory consists of multiloop systems having many interacting variables working together for the objectives of management. The managerial problem is concerned with stating the factory objectives in terms of plant operations, labor and raw materials costs, product market and pricing, and production schedules. The supervisory control problem is concerned with achieving the factory objectives in every subsystem in terms of input variables, control loops, and plant characteristics, using available feedback and feedforward control techniques.

The process factory consists of various mixing, reacting, and separating systems, which have several distinguishing characteristics.

1. Product quality and economic plant performance are the indirect result of the actions of many plant variables. For example, the product quality from a separator depends upon the operation of the separator as well as the values of variables in the reactor and feed preparation unit preceding the separator.

2. Transducers for rapid measurement of process stream composition and product quality are not common, so that it may be necessary to measure and control a subsidiary property instead of the final product quality.

3. Many chemical and physical phenomena interact in process systems, resulting in the well-known complexity of chemical processes. Control systems for these processes always contain multiple, interacting loops with the result that process supervision becomes complex. The process operator may find that a process correction to bring one product quality back on specification has made another unacceptable so that several corrections to dependent variables may be needed to bring all the process products within specification limits.

Together with the technical problems which these process characteristics present, and the ever present financial considerations, the factory management must consider many objectives such as these:

1. Maximize profit from process operation.
2. Maintain product qualities within customer specifications.
3. Maintain production schedules and satisfy customer orders.
4. Practice good factory maintenance and minimize costs by avoiding waste of materials and energy.
5. Protect plant personnel and equipment.

Simultaneous achievement of these objectives is difficult and in some cases may be contradictory, as when product yield decreases with increased production rate, thereby increasing raw material costs. Disturbances which complicate achievement of the factory objectives are ever present and include these situations:

1. Fluctuation of raw material costs and product values.
2. Variation in chemical and physical quality of raw materials.
3. Changing customer demands for product quality and quantity.
4. Variation in process performance due to wear and tear in equipment.
5. Emergency interruptions (reliability of equipment, supplies, etc.).
6. Ambient weather conditions.

When the limits of these disturbances are known, they become process constraints upon the operation, a constraint being a limit in one variable which prohibits a more favorable value of another variable. The one-variable analog controllers presented in this book are used to regulate any of a wide variety of process variables, and in a large factory many such control loops will be found. Overall factory objectives may be achieved by use of a digital computer which evaluates the factory performance and resets the analog controllers for best conditions. The purpose of this chapter is not to study computer control but to show the organization for computer control and to illustrate a few applications of systems engineering in the process industries.

9–1. ORGANIZATION FOR COMPUTER CONTROL

The conventional one-variable analog controller depends upon feedback principles to control the process variables. In digital computer control, more emphasis is placed on feedforward principles since this enables corrective action to be taken as soon as process disturbances occur. This control method relies on process measurements of raw materials characteristics, process conditions, and disturbance variables, and it employs a mathematical model of the process to predict the changes in process adjustments and/or controller reference inputs needed to compensate for the measured disturbances. Supervisory computer control occurs when the computer sets the plant controller reference inputs and direct digital control occurs when the computer positions the process control valves directly.

A possible scheme of computer control as discussed in Chapter 1 is shown in Fig. 9–1.   Process control computers are general-purpose digital

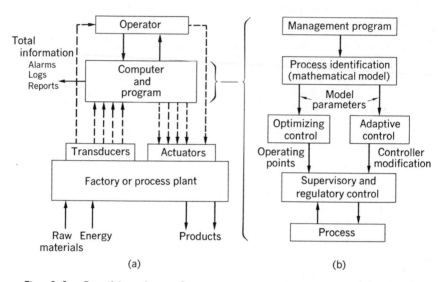

Fig. 9–1.   Possible scheme for process computer control. (a) Computer control system.   (b) Organization of computer program.

computers equipped with analog input-output systems.   Process transducers inform the computer of the factory process variables by means of analog signals.   The process operator gives the computer any additional process data, instructions, and programs necessary for directing its activities, and the operator receives processed information in the form of recordings, data logs, typed reports, limit signals, etc.   The computer, by following instructions, can deal with such matters as these:

1. Scan the process variables and report "out of limit" checks on variables.
2. Make decisions on the basis of comparison as well as computation.
3. Take control action by direct digital control or resetting a controller reference input.
4. Compute averages of process efficiencies, and complete material and energy balances.
5. Prepare detailed reports on the process and its performances.
6. Bring the factory to the best operation point, based on a model for best performance.

The general-purpose digital computer is well suited to achieve full factory performance when given complete process information and an executive strategy adequate for the tasks at hand.

Program for Computer Control. The executive strategy of the computer must be organized so that the computer can compensate for the many disturbances in the most effective manner. A possible organization of computer strategy is outlined in Fig. 9–1b. The most frequent process disturbances are upsets in the operating variables such as temperature, pressure, and concentrations which have a direct effect on production rate, and product quality. Naturally, the computer, in its first level of control, must provide fast regulatory action to keep the plant variables at their set-point values. At this level the computer controls the process variables and activates alarms when any variable exceeds a set limit or indicates overload of any plant unit.

The second level of control is concerned with less frequent disturbances caused by shifting process demands such as effects of diurnal load changes on the plant or the seasonal thermal load changes on outdoor process equipment. These disturbances may be so great that large changes in some system parameters occur and a new set of optimum process operating points and controller parameters (adaptive) are needed. Those decisions are made at the second level of computer strategy as diagrammed in Fig. 9–1b. The decisions are based on a computed figure of merit such as a minimum total cost of operation for the optimum condition or a minimum integral of error squared for adaptive control.

When normal "wear and tear" or unusual seasonal changes make modification of the process model necessary, the third level of computer strategy uses current process data to modify or update the parameters in the plant model or to adapt the controller for the new plant condition. The highest level of computer strategy supplies appropriate information to the operator or management so that proper decisions and structural changes can be made concerning the overall control strategy. In all cases, it is clear that models are *sine qua non* of the computer control strategy, since they enable the computer to make process predictions which are so essential to process control.

Direct Digital Control. Symbolic representations of direct digital control are shown in Figs. 1–12 and 9–1. This approach is termed *direct digital control* (DDC) since, under program control, the digital computer reads the process variables, computes the control valve position, and directly switches the result to the valve. This computer technique has the potential significance of greatly expanding the control application of the digital computer and giving performance that is superior to analog control because any control algorithm (not necessarily one of the three analog modes) can be programmed into the computer.

A block diagram of the possible DDC of a single loop plant is given in Fig. 9–2. The digital computer with a DDC program communicates

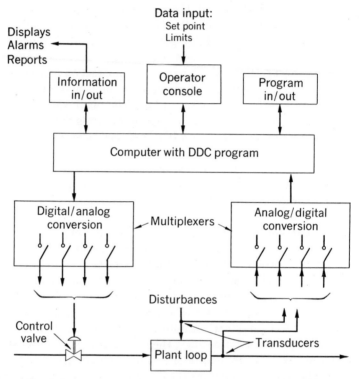

Fig. 9–2. Block diagram of direct digital control scheme.

directly with the plant to read input process variables and to issue output control valve settings and other process commands. Communication with many process loops and their separate variables is achieved by time-sharing of the capabilities of a process signal multiplexer between the computer and the analog to digital (A/D) data converters needed for each signal. The computes action is similar to that of the conventional analog controller in a loop. The operator places the loop set-point value in the computer memory and the computer, under program control, reads the process variables, including disturbance variables (for feedforward control), finds the error, computes the value of the manipulated variable from the control algorithm given in the program, and places this value in a hold amplifier which energizes the control valve actuator while the computer goes through its computations for the other loops in its program. Under time-sharing, the capability of the process computer is so great that it can handle a great number of control loops and other secondary tasks such as material and energy balance computations, efficiency calculations, alarms, and operator-demanded printout of process logs.

Direct digital control combines conventional feedback and feedforward loops with the computational ability of the digital computer to bring new flexibility and improved performance to process operations. The flexibility of DDC programming provides opportunity for the process engineer to use unique and custom-designed algorithms for each control loop with resultant increased process efficiencies. Serious control problems such as dominant transport-delay times, logical and sequence control for switching auxiliary process units, and redesign of control strategy can be handled without equipment complications. In fact, the DDC program can include adaptive or optimizing strategies without additional expenditures for plant equipment provided the computer has adequate memory.

9–2. PROCESS MODELS

Process models and their mathematical analogs are indispensable aids in simulation and control studies in that they enable the process engineer to evaluate the effect of process variables, disturbances, and process parameters on the control system performance without constructing and testing each system modification. Modeling is a mathematical or a physical representation of a process or system for procedural or computational purposes. A procedural or sequential model is a recipe or set of process conditions such as a standard operating practice. A computational model is an algorithm* for evaluating process performance, material and energy balance, supervisory control, and operation records, or for predicting dynamic or steady-state behavior following process disturbances for use in feedforward, feedback, or optimizing control.

Chapters 3, 4, and 5 present useful principles for obtaining the equations for computational models of process control systems.† In practice, the process equations are obtained by a combination of process theory and empirical experience, for they must be both realistic and useful in the intended process control problem. The theoretical analysis of processes, since it is based on process fundamentals, has the advantages of reliability, ease of modification for other operating ranges, and confidence in extrapolation. The theoretical analysis gives a set of equations which

---

* An algorithm is a step-by-step rule for constructing the solution to a problem.

† Descriptions of additional models for the process industries are given by R. G. E. Franks, *Mathematical Modeling in Chemical Engineering*, John Wiley & Sons, Inc., New York, 1967.

incorporates both steady-state and dynamic characteristics of the process as a complete process model. This is a general manner in which to approach process analysis, particularly when major process disturbances are not measurable before they enter the loop. This approach is limited when knowledge of the applicable process fundamentals is meager; for then the model must await process research or be based on an empirical process analysis. Even in theoretical analysis there are process parameters, such as the effective particle surface in a fluidized bed reactor, which are known only empirically. Empirical analysis has its place in modeling and can be dignified by statistics and economic justification when necessary.

Another approach to process model building is to develop an accurate steady-state model and add dynamic functions as needed to approximate the process dynamics. This method of modeling is most effective when the major process disturbances can be measured before they enter the loop; therefore this approach suggests effective use of feedforward control techniques in such instances. Derivation of a few computational models and their use are shown in the following applications.

Feedforward Control Modeling. Feedforward control as a compensation technique for minimizing the effect of process disturbances on plant operation is introduced in Chapter 1 and developed in Chapter 6. The load or disturbance variable is measured, and the measurement is used to compute the exact correction in the manipulated variable needed to cancel the effects of the disturbance on the process. As shown in Chapter 6, the feedforward computer uses a model of the process to find the contribution to the manipulated variable needed to prevent load disturbances from affecting the process controlled variable. The general scheme is shown in Fig. 9–3b for a single disturbance, $U(s)$. Since $U(s)$

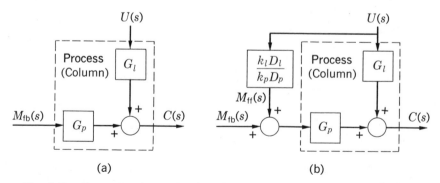

Fig. 9–3. General scheme for feedforward process control. (a) Process with feedback manipulation. (b) Process with feedforward and feedback manipulation.

and the feedforward manipulated variable $M_{ff}(s)$ enter the process at different points, each input has its own effect on the controlled variable as defined by the particular transfer function, as

$$\frac{C}{U}(s) = G_l(s) \qquad \frac{C}{M_{ff}}(s) = G_p(s) \qquad (9\text{-}1a)$$

where $G_l(s)$ and $G_p(s)$ determine the response of the process to load disturbances and manipulated variable, respectively. For the process in Fig. 9–3b, the total response $C(s)$ is a sum of the responses from $U(s)$ and $M_{ff}(s)$; assuming $M_{fb}(s) = 0$, then

$$C(s) = G_l(s)U(s) + G_p(s)M_{ff}(s) \qquad (9\text{-}1b)$$

If $C(s)$ is to remain constant $(C(s) = 0)$ while $U(s)$ changes, the change in the manipulated variable must satisfy the relationship

$$M_{ff}(s) = -\frac{G_l(s)}{G_p(s)} U(s) \qquad (9\text{-}2)$$

Note that the sign convention assumes that an increase in $U(s)$ increases $C(s)$. For an actual plant it is expected that $G_l(s)$ and $G_p(s)$ will be high-degree polynomials, but for economic reasons it is hoped that their ratio can be satisfactorily represented by a low-order lagging polynomial. In designing the computer an advantage in economics and a convenience in calibration and operation may be obtained by separating the static gain components from the dynamic functions in the computer as here:

$$\frac{G_l(s)}{G_p(s)} = \frac{k_l}{k_p}\frac{D_l}{D_p}(s)$$

where k_l/k_p is the static gain and $(D_l/D_p)(s)$ is the dynamic term in the ratio of transfer functions.

MacMullan and Shinskey* applied this technique to correct for changes in feed rate and feed composition of a superfractionator with singular success. Their development of a suitable process model for feedforward control is described here. The derivation of the model for the column in Fig. 9–4 is based on these assumptions:

1. The distillation column separates a binary feed at rate i_F and composition c_F into a distillate product at rate i_D and composition c_D, and a bottom product at rate i_B and composition c_B.
2. The column heat input is held constant at a maximum value since this gives the highest overall efficiency. However, this constraint eliminates the possibility of control of c_B.
3. Manipulation of distillate product rate i_D is used to correct for feed rate and composition changes.

* E. C. MacMullan and F. G. Shinskey, "Feedforward Analog Computer Control of a Superfractionator," *Control Engineering*, **11**(3), 69–74 (1964).

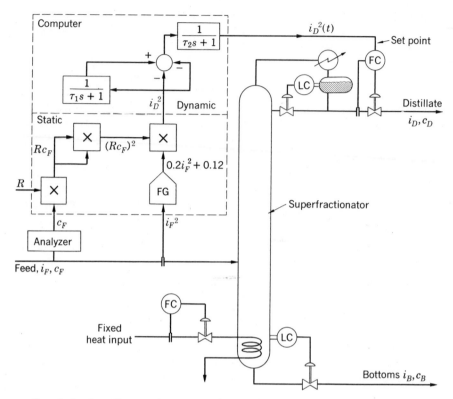

Fig. 9-4. Feedforward control of superfractionator. With a fixed heat input, the computer manipulates i_D to counteract effects of upsets in i_F and c_F on distillate quality. The computer program computes static gain and dynamic function for $c_F(t)$ and $i_F{}^2(t)$ disturbances.

STEADY-STATE MODEL. The process model is assumed to be separable into a static gain term and a dynamic function. The static gain term is derived from a steady-state material balance on the lower boiling component, thus:

$$i_F = i_D + i_B \qquad i_F c_F = i_D c_D + i_B c_B \qquad (9\text{-}3a)$$

Elimination of i_B from these equations gives the correct distillate rate for the desired distillate composition and the current feed conditions as

$$i_D = i_F \frac{c_F - c_B}{c_D - c_B} \qquad (9\text{-}3b)$$

where c_F and i_F are the load disturbances, c_D is the desired product composition, and c_B is the resultant bottom product composition. Since the heat input rate is fixed, it is expected that c_B would vary a great deal and that the theoretical relationship, while being expensive to implement (c_B must be measured), might tend to destabilize the column.   For a simpler approach, it is expected that the distillate rate i_D will be proportional to the amount of low boiling component in the feed and that this relationship will be simpler to implement.   Accordingly, an adjustable computer parameter R is defined as the average recovery of low boiling component in the feed, such that

$$i_D = R i_F c_F \qquad (9\text{-}3c)$$

Since the flow rate meters are the differential type, giving transmitted signals proportional to the flow rate squared, the computer construction can be simplified by working with the squared signals as

$$i_D{}^2 = i_F{}^2 (R c_F)^2 \qquad (9\text{-}4a)$$

A computer using this static gain term instead of the theoretical relationship in Eq. 9-3b was tried without success.   On further study of the column, the authors found that an empirical factor, less sensitive to feed rate, gave good results for the static gain term in the feedforward controller.   The steady-state computer model selected gives the correct distillate rate as

$$i_D{}^2 = (0.2 i_F{}^2 + 0.12)(R c_F)^2 \qquad (9\text{-}4b)$$

where i_F and c_F are the current properties of the feed stream and R (computed from Eq. 9-3c) is set in the computer by hand and adjusted by the operator when necessary.

DYNAMIC FUNCTION MODEL.   The dynamic function in the model comes from consideration of the linearized effect of the feed rate and distillate product rate on c_D, so that the relationship among the deviation variables is written as

$$C_D(s) = \frac{\partial c_D}{\partial i_F} I_F(s) + \frac{\partial c_D}{\partial i_D} I_D(s) \qquad (9\text{-}5a)$$

from which the following transfer functions are defined:

$$G_F(s) = \frac{\partial c_D}{\partial i_F} \qquad G_D(s) = \frac{\partial c_D}{\partial i_D} \qquad (9\text{-}5b)$$

If changes in $C_D(s)$ due to change in $I_F(s)$ are to be corrected by computed changes in $I_D(s)$, the dynamic manipulated changes in $I_D(s)$, the set-point variable, should satisfy

$$I_D(s) = -\frac{G_F(s)}{G_D(s)} I_F(s) \qquad (9\text{-}5c)$$

Both disturbances, i_F and c_F, enter the process at the same point, and it is assumed that the dynamic compensation of Eq. 9-5c applies to both.

For the column being studied, MacMullan and Shinskey used the response to step changes in feed flow rate and distillate flow rate to evaluate $G_F(s)$ and $G_D(s)$ and fitted the response to a dead-time and first-order lag model, obtaining the following transfer functions:

$$G_F(s) = \frac{e^{-30s}}{1 + 60s} \qquad G_D(s) = -\frac{e^{-20s}}{1 + 95s} \qquad (9\text{--}6a)$$

which gives the transfer function ratio as

$$\frac{G_F(s)}{G_D(s)} = -\frac{e^{-10s}(1 + 95s)}{1 + 60s} \qquad (9\text{--}6b)$$

Since analog simulation of dead time is difficult to achieve, the authors approximated the dynamic function for the feedforward computer as

$$\frac{G_F(s)}{G_D(s)} = -\frac{1 + 80s}{(1 + 40s)(1 + 10s)} = -\left(2 - \frac{1}{1 + 40s}\right)\frac{1}{1 + 10s} \qquad (9\text{--}6c)$$

and used the algebraic identity to achieve a two-constant representation for the dynamic function in the feedforward computer. The complete computer with both static and dynamic components for computing the distillate flow rate which cancels changes in feed conditions is given in Fig. 9–4. The authors reported a 4:1 improvement in quality control, increased column capacity, closer control on composition, and a very significant economic gain for the superfractionation operation. They suggest that further improvement in performance might be achieved by using a feedback signal to replace signal R and, in future designs, by implementing the rigorous material balance stated by Eq. 9–3b.

Adaptive Control Modeling. The application of conventional linear control theory requires that the dynamic characteristics of the process be known and remain reasonably constant over the expected range of process operation. These requirements may not be met in processes involving chemical reaction rates for a range of temperatures, or mass transfer rates for a range of fluid velocities. In such instances in nature, when process parameters may be unknown or may change by an order of magnitude in the expected range of operation, the plant can be controlled from a knowledge of its inputs and outputs and a performance index (figure of merit). The performance index must involve the process parameters in such a manner that the "best operating" plant conditions can be found from its use. In other words, the process engineer through his definition of the performance index enables the controlled system to find its own "best operation" condition. This more sophisticated level of control theory, called *adaptive control*, finds application in any control system which must adapt itself to compensate for large changes occurring within the system or its surroundings to maintain a high quality of control as defined by the performance index.

An adaptive control system in achieving its objective of "best point of operation" must perform the functions of identification, decision, and modification. It must identify the process by sensing variations in plant dynamics and computing a performance index that measures the quality of control response. Since the performance index may be a limiting factor of adaptive control, it should be carefully chosen to provide (1) a well defined "best point of operation," (2) an easily measured or computed value, and (3) an indication of the quality of control response over a wide range of system parameters and load disturbances. Next, an evaluator, on the basis of the identification, must decide upon the process modification (adjustments) to be made according to the established control strategy. Finally, the adaptive controller modifies the plant parameters or itself to bring the control system to the "best point of operation." This may involve adjustments in controller gain, process flow rates, process time constants, or other plant parameters and, in some cases of adaptive controls, generation of a new control signal.

Several approaches to the adaptive control problem have been investigated. One method, called the *model-reference, plant-adaptive scheme*, uses a model representing the desired plant characteristics; the adapter forces the plant to respond like the model. As shown in Fig. 9-5, the adapter may adjust either the controller or the plant as desired by the process engineer.

Crandall and Stevens* describe adaptive control of a closed-loop chemical reactor using the model reference, plant adaptive scheme shown in Fig. 9-5. The chemical reaction is an exothermic isomerization occurring

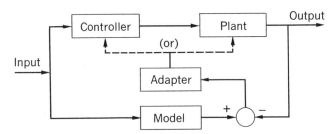

Fig. 9-5. Model reference, plant (or controller) adaptive control system.

in a continuous stirred tank reactor with internal cooling. The plant, shown in Fig. 9-6, is a single-loop process containing the reactor and a

* E. D. Crandall and W. F. Stevens. "An Application of Adaptive Control to a Continuous Stirred Tank Reactor," *A. I. Ch. E. Journal*, **11**(5), 930–936 (1965).

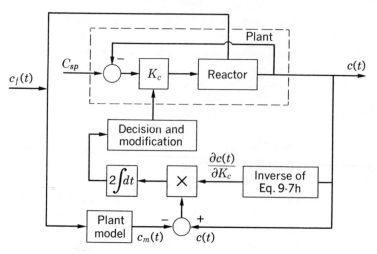

Fig. 9–6. Adaptive control scheme of Crandall and Stevens for a chemical reactor.

proportional controller. The reference model is chosen to have the best possible reactor behavior in the presence of disturbances. The input signal is reactant concentration $c_f(t)$. Adaptivity is achieved by comparing the model output $c_m(t)$ with the plant output $c(t)$, forming the error $e(t) = c(t) - c_m(t)$, which measures a deviation in plant performance from the reference-model behavior, and using the error to compute a performance index which becomes the basis of plant adjustments which force $e(t)$ to zero.

PERFORMANCE INDEX, IP. The performance index is the limiting factor in any adaptive control system since it is the quality standard for system performance. Crandall and Stevens select the integral-error-squared defined in Chapter 6 as the performance index, IP,

$$ \text{IP} = \int_0^t [c(t) - c_m(t)]^2 \, dt = \int_0^t e^2(t) \, dt \qquad (9\text{–}7a) $$

that shows a minimum for the selected adaptive parameter which, in this case, is the controller gain K_c. In general IP is an unknown function of time, but the slope of the IP curve, $\partial \text{IP}/\partial K_c$, could be used to adjust K_c and thereby keep IP at a minimum value. The slope is found as

$$ \frac{\partial \text{IP}}{\partial K_c} = \int_0^t \frac{\partial e^2(t)}{\partial K_c} \, dt = 2 \int_0^t e(t) \frac{\partial c(t)}{\partial K_c} \, dt \qquad (9\text{–}7b) $$

since $e(t) = c(t) - c_m(t)$ and $c_m(t)$ is constant. Now, $\partial c(t)/\partial K_c$ can be found from the plant relationship, so that the process identification is complete.

CHEMICAL REACTOR MODEL.   Crandall and Stevens select a simple
first-order, unidirectional, exothermic reaction for study in a continuous-
flow constant-volume stirred-tank reactor, described in Chapter 4 and
shown in Fig. 4–17.   The reactor equations are (omitting subscript A on
the concentration term c)

Material balance:

$$\frac{dc}{dt} = \frac{i}{V}(c_f - c) - Ace^{-E/RT} \tag{4–28a}$$

Reactor energy balance:

$$\frac{dT}{dt} = \frac{i}{V}(T_f - T) + \frac{(-\Delta H)Ace^{-E/RT}}{\rho C_p} - \frac{m(T)}{V\rho C_p} \tag{4–28b}$$

Coolant energy balance:

$$m(T) = [i\rho C_p]_c(T_2 - T_c) = UA'\Delta T_m \tag{9–7c}$$

where $m(T)$ is the rate of heat removal from the reactor given as the
product of the cooling fluid rate i, density ρ, heat capacity C_p (evaluated
at the average temperature of the coolant fluid), and the cooling-fluid
temperature rise $(T_2 - T_c)$.   It is assumed that the heat removal rate
also equals the product of the overall heat transfer coefficient of the coil
U, the coil area A', and the arithmetic mean temperature difference
between reactor contents and cooling coil ΔT_m.   Crandall and Stevens
linearize the reactor model Eqs. 4–28a and b and obtain equations for the
deviation variables as

$$\frac{dc}{dt} + K_4 c = K_5 c_f - K_c T \tag{9–7d}$$

$$\frac{dT}{dt} + K_1 T = K_2 c - K_3 i_c \tag{9–7e}$$

similar to the linearization in Chapter 4.   (Consult the original reference
for definition of the K's or derive them as a student exercise.)

PLANT MODEL.   The plant is the chemical reactor in a closed-loop
feedback system using a proportional controller.   Laplace-transforming
Eq. 9–7d and 9–7e with the reactor at steady state, and imposing proportional feedback control, the transfer function for concentration deviations
is

$$\frac{C(s)}{C_f(s)} = \frac{K_5(s + K_1)}{[s^2 + (K_1 + K_4)s + K_1 K_4 + K_2 K_6 + K_c K_3 K_6]} \tag{9–7f}$$

Similar relationships for $C(s)/I_c(s)$, $T(s)/C_f(s)$, and $T(s)/I_c(s)$ could be
written.

ADAPTIVE CONTROL.   Eq. 9–7f derived for the plant becomes the
model for the adaptive control scheme, i.e., $C_m(s) = C(s)$ in Eq. 9–7f,

and $e(t)$ will be zero unless the plant parameters differ from their measured steady-state values. The slope of the IP curve $\partial IP/\partial K_c$ is found by differentiating Eq. 9–7f, thus:

$$\frac{\partial C(s)}{\partial K_c} = \frac{-K_3 K_6 C(s)}{s^2 + (K_1 + K_4)s + K_1 K_4 + K_2 K_6 + K_c K_3 K_6} \quad (9\text{–}7g)$$

and

$$\frac{1}{C(s)} \frac{\partial C(s)}{\partial K_c} = \frac{-K_3 K_6}{K_5(s + K_1)} \frac{C(s)}{C_f(s)} \quad (9\text{–}7h)$$

Inversion of this equation gives $\partial c(t)/\partial K_c$ in terms of $c(t)$, and the slope of the IP curve is found from Eq. 9–7b. The block diagram for the adaptive control is given in Fig. 9–6. All the operations have been discussed except the blocks for inversion of Eq. 9–7h and the decision and controller modification, on which the reader should consult the original article for more information. The authors simulated this adaptive control system and studied its behavior for changes in c_f, T_c, and catalyst activity. The adaptive control system gave good results, and the authors recommend adaptive control whenever the improved response is needed and can be economically justified.

Optimizing Control Modeling. Economic optimization of process operations is a goal the process engineer strives to achieve. A feedback optimizer seeks to maintain the controlled variable at the "optimum value" instead of at a fixed value. A feedforward optimizer, without measuring the controlled variable, seeks to maintain it at the "optimum value" by computing the outputs that give the best plant economy.

The best plant operation is obtained by making decisions which maximize plant profit. The plant profit is given as

Profit = selling price − production costs

The production costs are the costs of raw materials, plant operation, maintenance and fixed costs. In a process plant the costs may vary with feed rate and composition, catalyst activity, and other operating conditions. The optimizing computer must compute "best values" of the manipulated variables and use them to minimize the effect of uncontrolled disturbances on plant economy.

Consider a simple gas absorber unit extracting a desired component from a gas stream (e.g., CO_2 recovery from a flue gas stream). An idealized flow sheet is given in Fig. 9–7a. In the absorber, the gas feed contacts an absorbing liquid which dissolves the desired gaseous component and carries it to the stripper. In the stripper the dissolved gas is released from the absorption liquid by heat, giving the recovered product gas and the regenerated absorbing liquid. The feed gas and off-gas flow

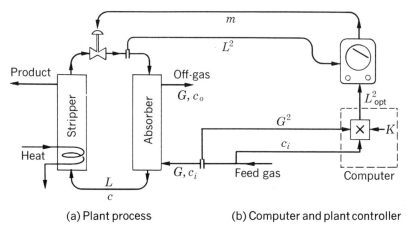

(a) Plant process   (b) Computer and plant controller

Fig. 9-7. Optimized absorption plant for recovery of product from feed gas.

rate is G (lb moles inerts/hr)* having compositions c_i and c_o (lb moles recovered component per lb mole inert), respectively. The absorbing liquid rate is L (lb moles/hr) and the composition leaving the absorber is c (lb moles recovered component per lb mole liquid). It is assumed that all of the gas is removed from the absorbing liquid in the stripper.

The plant costs are assumed to follow these simple relationships:

$$\text{Raw material} = k_1 G c_i \qquad \$/\text{hr}$$
$$\text{Process operations} = k_2 L \qquad \$/\text{hr}$$
$$\text{Off gas} = -k_3 G c_0 \qquad \$/\text{hr}$$
$$\text{Process fixed charges} = k_4 \qquad \$/\text{hr}$$

The total sales will be the production rate times the sales price, $k_5 Lc$. The constants k_i are the unit raw material and operating costs and k_5 is the product sales price. The plant profit will be given as

$$\text{Profit} = k_5 Lc - (k_1 G c_i + k_2 L - k_3 G c_0 + k_4) \qquad (9\text{-}8a)$$

The static material-balance equations for the process are:

Absorber rate: $Lc = G(c_i - c_0)$ (9-8b)
Stripper rate: $\text{Product} = Lc$

The off-gas composition varies with the feed gas composition and flow rate and with the liquid rate in a complex way. For purposes of illustration it is assumed that the off-gas composition is given by the following simplified equation:

$$c_0 = k_a G c_i / L \qquad (9\text{-}8c)$$

* Symbols G and L are used here to agree with the common usage in the industry.

where k_a is the gas absorption rate coefficient. For best plant operation L will be varied to maintain optimum plant economy for any values of G and c_i. The optimum L is found by maximizing profit as given in Eq. 9–8a, which becomes (after substituting Eqs. 9–8b and c),

$$\frac{\partial(\text{profit})}{\partial L} = \frac{\partial}{\partial L}\left[k_5(Gc_i - k_aG^2c_i/L) - k_1Gc_i - k_2L + k_3k_aG^2c_i/L + k_4\right] = 0$$

(9–8d)

and gives the optimum liquid flow rate as

$$L_{\text{opt}}^2 = KG^2c_i$$

(9–8e)

where $K = k_a(k_5 - k_3)/k_2$. A computing scheme for optimizing the plant operation is shown in Fig. 9–7b. The computer finds L_{opt}^2 by scaling the signal from a multiplication module which computes G^2c_i. The L_{opt}^2, which is computed from current values of G^2, c_i, and K, becomes the set point for a flow rate controller which manipulates L^2 to the absorber using a feedback loop. The flow rate signals are processed in the L^2 and G^2 form to simplify the computing problem since flow rates are commonly measured with differential pressure devices. Since the computer discussed here is based on the minimum economic considerations and simplified technical relationships it could not be expected to give exact plant optimum liquid rate; however, its performance will be vastly superior to that of the usual feedback control with the set point determined by the process operator. A more complex computer based on a more exact model of the plant would surely give better performance but at a higher installed cost.

The usual process plant is more complex than the example discussed above, and the search for optimum conditions may result in a multi-dimensional problem. In such a case the usual procedure is to make contour plots of constant profit for two independent variables at a time and determine a relationship for maximum profit as a function of all the independent variables. The analog computer will use this relationship to compute the optimum value of the manipulated variable from the independent variables in the process. The operating conditions in any plant are limited by the plant design and the available service facilities. In some cases the optimum conditions for plant operations may lie outside the plant potentiality and these constraints and limitations must be considered in the analysis. In other cases plant optimization may not be fruitful because the profit is not sensitive to plant operations.

9–3. PROCESS CONTROL DESIGN

This is an introductory book on process control theory, and full treatment of design procedures for control of various process reactors and operations is not intended; however, a beginning book should indicate some useful applications of the theory. A manufacturing plant is an integrated whole consisting of many diverse (sometimes conflicting), specialized units having functions satisfying several objectives. Necessity to consider both static and dynamic viewpoints has forced the process engineer to adopt the systems engineering philosophy. Systems engineering seeks to optimize the whole system by weighting the plant objectives and designing and operating the plant to achieve maximum compatibility of the units as measured by best economic return on the operating plant. Today, systems engineering selects techniques bearing on process design and operations from all engineering disciplines such as statistical studies, reliability theory, operations research, optimization, managerial planning, and market forecasting.

A manufacturing plant must make quality products that meet customer specifications and it must make them economically at an average rate equal to product sales. The plant will use tight control loops utilizing feedback and feedforward schemes to keep product quality on specification and sluggish feedback control loops to maintain material balance between plant units. Since flow of process fluids is universal in process plants, some applications dealing with quality control, material balances, surge tanks and blending are considered.

Process Product Quality. Product quality is maintained by feedback and feedforward control loops operating in a regulating capacity around reactors and separation units. This type of regulating function is displayed by most of the examples in this book.

ONE-STREAM BLENDING. Blenders find application in smoothing quality variations in a plant product stream. The blending nature of well-mixed tanks is discussed in Example 9–1.

Example 9–1. A well-stirred tank acts as a blending vessel to average the composition of the incoming streams. Assuming that a property of a stream entering the tank varies sinusoidally as $x_i \sin \omega_1 t$, then the property of the discharged stream at steady state is

$$x_o = \frac{x_i}{\sqrt{1 + \omega_1^2 \tau^2}} \sin (\omega_1 t - \phi)$$

as given by Eq. 4–16e, where $\tau = V/i$, the holding time of the blending vessel. If the blended stream is to show property variations of only 10% of that of the entering stream, find the volume of (a) one blender tank and (b) two equal-sized tanks in series. Let the inlet flow rate to the blending vessel be i ft³/min.

Solution. (a) Fig. 4–8 shows that the frequency response of the blending vessel when $\omega \tau = 10$ has an amplitude ratio of 0.1. Now, if the frequency at which the variation occurs is ω_1, the then volume ($V = i\tau$) of the single blending tank is found as

$$V = \frac{10i}{\omega_1}$$

(b) Two equal-volume blending tanks in series would show a separate amplitude ratio of $\sqrt{0.1}$ for an overall AR = 0.1 when $\omega\tau = 3$. Then the volume of each tank is

$$V = \frac{3i}{\omega_1}$$

for a total volume of $6i/\omega_1$. The two-tank blender requires less holdup than is needed in a single tank for the same blending performance.

From this example it is clear that variations in property of the blended stream can be reduced any amount by suitable choice of blending volumes. However, before extensive blending is considered, the process engineer probably should attempt to eliminate the causes of property variation instead of treating the symptom. It is also possible to use recycling, with two or more blending tanks in series.

TWO-STREAM BLENDING. Two-stream blending finds application in recovery of off-specification product by judiciously blending it with higher-quality product. One of several possible flow charts is given in Fig. 9–8, where a primary stream at flow rate i_i ft^3/min and composition c_{Ai} pounds component A per ft^3 is blended with the enriching stream of flow rate i_2 ft^3/min and constant composition c_{A2}. The flow rate i_2 is to

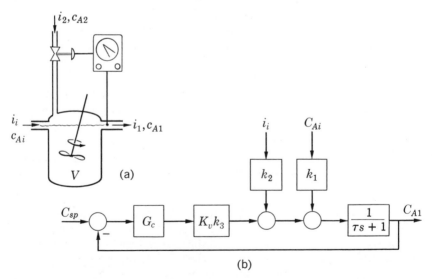

Fig. 9–8. Two-stream blending for product quality control. (a) Plant. (b) Block diagram.

be modulated so as to hold the composition c_{A1} at the set-point value c_{sp} despite changes in both c_{Ai} and i_i. It is assumed that disturbances in the primary flow rate are infrequent and relatively minor; otherwise a flow ratio control for i_i and i_2 may be desirable. The function of the mixing tank of volume V is to stabilize the system and to average any high-frequency variations in c_{A1}. The process equations are written as

Overall material balance: $\qquad i_1 = i_i + i_2 \qquad\qquad$ (9–9a)

Material balance on A: $\quad i_i c_{Ai} + i_2 c_{A2} = i_1 c_{A1} + V\dfrac{dc_{A1}}{dt} \qquad$ (9–9b)

Linearized equation:

$$k_1 \bar{c}_{Ai} + k_2 \bar{\imath}_i + k_3 \bar{\imath}_2 = \bar{c}_{A1} + \tau \frac{d\bar{c}_{A1}}{dt} \qquad (9\text{–}9c)$$

where

$$k_1 = \left[\frac{i_i}{i_i + i_2} \right]_{\text{avg}} \qquad k_2 = \left[\frac{c_{Ai} - c_{A1}}{i_i + i_2} \right]_{\text{avg}}$$

$$k_3 = \left[\frac{c_{A2} - c_{A1}}{i_i + i_2} \right]_{\text{avg}} \qquad \tau = \left[\frac{V}{i_i + i_2} \right]_{\text{avg}}$$

The control valve constant is K_v. Since the purpose of this application is to smooth the concentration variations in a process stream and to bring its quality to specification, the controller must have integral action. Using a simple floating-type controller, the closed-loop transfer function in response to inlet stream concentration becomes

$$\frac{C_{A1}}{C_{Ai}}(s) = \frac{Ks}{\dfrac{s^2}{\omega_n^{\,2}} + \dfrac{2\zeta}{\omega_n}s + 1} \qquad (9\text{–}9d)$$

where

$$\omega_n = \sqrt{\frac{K_v k_3}{\tau_i \tau}} \qquad \zeta = \frac{1}{2}\sqrt{\frac{\tau_i}{\tau K_v k_3}} \qquad K = \frac{k_1 \tau_i}{K_v k_3}$$

To achieve fast response, the controller would be set to give an underdamped response and, if additional smoothing action is desired, the effluent could be discharged through a second tank tuned to ω_d for the control system unless there is some more important pulsating disturbance. Under no circumstances would the second tank be included in the control loop. If c_{Ai} contains high-frequency components, it may be desirable to use a PI controller. Large tanks are to be avoided unless absolutely essential, for they increase both the inventory of material in process and the volume of off-quality material which would result from production change from one quality product to a different quality product.

Process Material Balance. Material balance control is of primary importance in process plant operations. It is easy to accomplish in practice since it only requires that the accumulation at all points in the plant should not change or that, on the average, the rate of process operations should equal the shipment rate from the plant. Surge vessels between process units are used to accumulate the difference between intermediate product rates and feed rates to the next process unit. However, in contrast to quality control, material balance surge control need show neither rapid response nor quick recovery from load changes, but rather, the adjustment of surge inventories should be gradual to avoid upsets in the process units. Surge vessel inventory may have any value between established minimum and maximum values.

Surge-vessel and liquid-level control systems have identical configurations as seen in Fig. 9–9a, but the function of the surge vessel is eventually

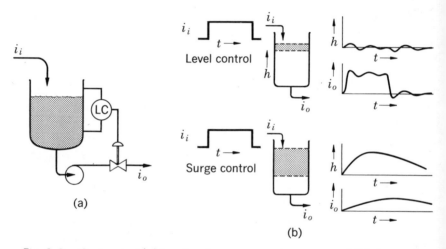

Fig. 9–9. Contrast of (a) level and surge control systems and (b) their pulse responses.

to balance inflow and outflow rates so that the accumulation does not change; whereas the function of liquid-level control is to maintain accumulation at a fixed value. The difference between these two functions is shown in Fig. 9–9b for identical pulse inflow disturbances to liquid-level and surge-vessel control systems. In level control, the outflow rate is a direct reflection of the inflow rate with the resultant constant level (or constant accumulation) in the vessel as shown in Fig. 9–9b; whereas, in surge volume control, the outflow rate is little affected by inflow rate with the result that the inflow disturbance changes the liquid level. This difference in performance is obtained by selecting a PI controller having high-gain and fast integral action for the level application and a low-gain, slow-integral-action PI controller for the surge-vessel application. In both cases the steady-state inflow and outflow rates would be equal but the surge vessel response is intentionally made slow and sluggish.

SURGE-VESSEL SIZING.* The block diagram of a simple surge-vessel control system using 3–15-psig pneumatic signals is seen in Fig. 9–10. The control system equations are listed:

Material balance on vessel:

$$i_i - i_o = A \, dh/dt \qquad A = \text{ft}^3/\text{ft}$$

Level transmitter:

$$b = K_l h \qquad K_l = \frac{12}{h_{\max}}, \; \frac{\text{psig}}{\text{ft}}$$

Control valve—Motor:

$$x = K_m m \qquad K_m = \frac{x_{\max}}{12}, \; \frac{100\% \text{ stem range}}{\text{psig}}$$

Body:

$$i_o = K_v x \qquad K_v = \frac{i_{o,\max}}{x_{\max}}, \; \frac{\text{ft}^3}{\text{min-}\% \text{ stem range}}$$

Controller: $G_c = G_c$

It is assumed that the pressure drop across the control valve is constant.

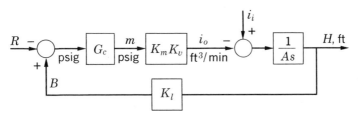

Fig. 9–10. Block diagram of surge control system.

Two system transfer functions of interest in closed-loop surge control using a PI controller are written for Fig. 9–10,

Flow ratio: $$\frac{I_o(s)}{I_i(s)} = \frac{\tau_i s + 1}{\tau \tau_i s^2 + \tau_i s + 1} \qquad (9\text{–}10\text{a})$$

Inventory / Inflow rate: $$\frac{AH(s)}{I_i(s)} = \frac{\tau \tau_i s}{\tau \tau_i s^2 + \tau_i s + 1} \qquad (9\text{–}10\text{b})$$

where $\tau = A/[K_c K_l K_m K_v]$ for the system, and the variable Ah is the surge-volume inventory at any time. In terms of the system parameters,

* This discussion follows the paper on "Surge Vessel Control Systems," by K. A. Otto, *Control Engineering*, **6**(12), 106–110 (1959).

the time constant τ has the value

$$\tau = \frac{A h_{\max}(12)}{K_c(12)i_{o,\max}} = \frac{V}{K_c i_{o,\max}} \tag{9-10c}$$

assuming a vertical cylindrical tank and a linear control value. For surge control the system would be critically damped or overdamped. For a critically damped system ($\zeta = 1$), the integral rate controller setting and the system natural frequency ω_n are found from the standard form of the second-order equation as

$$\omega_n = \frac{1}{\sqrt{\tau \tau_i}} \qquad \zeta = 1 = \frac{\tau_i}{2\sqrt{\tau \tau_i}} = \frac{1}{2}\sqrt{\frac{\tau_i}{\tau}} \tag{9-10d}$$

Then, $\omega_n = 1/2\tau$ and $\tau_i = 4\tau$.

Now the surge-vessel size is subject to the design expectations of the maximum step disturbance, $\Delta i_{i,\max}$ and the maximum allowed outflow rate $(di_o/dt)_{\max}$ from the vessel. The system equations permit a maximum outflow rate which occurs at $t = 0$ (found by differentiating the inverse of Eq. 9-10a for $I_i(s) = \Delta i_i/s$):

$$\left(\frac{di_o}{dt}\right)_{\max} = \frac{\Delta i_i}{\tau} \qquad \text{or} \qquad \tau = \Delta i_i \bigg/ \left(\frac{di_o}{dt}\right)_{\max} \tag{9-10e}$$

If the design is to allow both increase and decrease inflow rate disturbances, and if the level is at a midvalue before the disturbance occurs, then the vessel volume must be twice the maximum surge volume. The maximum volume, $(Ah)_{\max}$, found from Eq. 9-10b with $I_i(s) = \Delta i_i/s$ is

$$(Ah)_{\max} = 0.736\tau\,\Delta i_i$$

and the surge-vessel volume, which is twice the maximum surge volume, must be

$$V = 2(0.736\tau\,\Delta i_i) = 1.47\tau\,\Delta i_i \tag{9-10f}$$

which becomes

$$V = 1.47(\Delta i_i)^2 \bigg/ \left(\frac{di_o}{dt}\right)_{\max} \tag{9-10g}$$

when τ from Eq. 9-10e is substituted. This is the least surge volume that satisfies design specifications, but in practice a larger vessel would be installed to provide clearance above the liquid level. Also, limit stops may be installed to prevent flooding or emptying the surge tank. The controller settings for the system to achieve this performance are found from the above equations to be

$$\tau_i = 4\tau \qquad K_c = 1.47\Delta i_i/i_{o,\max} \tag{9-10h}$$

These relationships apply to a system having a vertical cylindrical tank and a linear control valve. Compared to level control, surge-vessel control has extremely sluggish action, with time constants of an order of magnitude greater than that of the process unit immediately downstream. The surge tank eliminates interaction between units in series and reduces the maximum design capacity needed to accomodate process upsets. Similar relationships may be derived for other surge tank-control valve systems.

Example 9-2.   For a PI-controlled surge vessel, determine the volume of surge tank needed to accommodate a maximum inflow rate of 25 ft³/min and a step change of 10% $i_{o,\max}$, when the maximum allowed increase in outflow rate is 0.1 ft³/min². Estimate the controller settings for the PI controller.

Solution.   The least volume of surge tank is given by Eq. 9-10g as

$$V = 1.47(0.1 \times 25)^2/0.1 = 92 \text{ ft}^3$$

The controller settings are found as

$$\tau_i = 4\Delta i_i \Big/ \left(\frac{di_o}{dt}\right)_{\max} = 4(0.1 \times 25)/0.1 = 100 \text{ min/repeat}$$
$$K_c = 1.47\Delta i_i/i_{o,\max} = 1.47(0.1 \times 25)/25 = 0.147 \text{ psi/psi}$$

Note the extremely large integral time and low-gain controller settings which make the system response sluggish.

It may be found from Eq. 9-10a that the outflow rate will overshoot its final value by $0.13\Delta i_i$. If overshoot is to be avoided, the controller must have only proportional action. But, then it will be found that the required volume of surge tank is much larger than for a PI-controlled system.

Process Heat Exchangers.   Heat transfer is one of the commonest operations used in process plants and much study has been devoted to the dynamics and control of heat exchange processes. Because a rigorous treatment of any heat exchanger must recognize the distributed nature of the transfer process, progress has been slow in developing theoretical dynamic response relationships for even the simplest models of heat exchange systems. Generally, heat transfer rates in a device depend upon the temperature differences within the device, the properties of the fluids, and the geometry of the transfer surfaces. Since heat quantities are conserved in the transfer process, it is clear that heat transfer from one fluid in the exchanger is accompanied by a decrease in its temperature and that, since heat transfer occurs throughout the heat exchanger length, it is necessary that the temperature of this fluid change with position in the exchanger. Therefore, under dynamic conditions the fluid temperatures in a heat exchanger depend upon the independent variables of position and time, and partial differential equations are needed to accurately describe heat exchanger response.

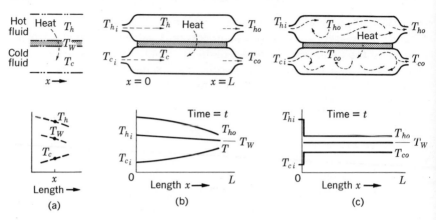

Fig. 9–11. Contrast of distributed- and lumped-parameter models for a parallel flow heat exchanger. (a) Temperatures in heat transfer. (b) Distributed-parameter model. (c) Single lumped-parameter model.

A detail of the transfer surfaces in a fluid-fluid heat exchange device is shown in Fig. 9–11a. At position x, heat moves from the hot fluid at average temperature T_h to the cold fluid at average temperature T_c by conduction through fluid films and the separating wall. As the fluids move through the exchanger (in this case by concurrent flow) their temperatures, at any time t, obey an energy-balance equation and change continuously with position in the general manner shown in Fig. 9–11b. The terminal temperature $T(L,t)$ would be the controlled variable in a process heat exchanger. The thermal capacities of the fluids and metal, $m_i C_{pi}$, are distributed with position throughout the heat exchanger, and the dynamic response shows typical distributed-parameter behavior as discussed in Chapter 4. If the thermal capacities on each side of the heat transfer surfaces can be considered as lumped and of uniform temperature throughout the volume, which would be the case if the fluid volumes were well stirred as shown in Fig. 9–11c, the dynamics of the heat exchanger can be described by ordinary differential equations and transfer functions for the device can be obtained in the usual way. Problems 4–4b and 4–6b are examples of lumping thermal capacities for simplicity in analysis. The lumped-parameter analysis of distributed systems is improved by increasing the number of lumped sections in the system. For example, the lumped-parameter model in Fig. 9–11c shows the same response for parallel and counter current flow; whereas a two-section lumped-parameter model would show different responses for the different flow conditions.

When multipass countercurrent exchangers are considered, the dynamics must be described by partial differential equations and lengthy calculations by digital computer are required to obtain the dynamic response.

Typically, the frequency response is computed rather than the time response since it is easier to obtain from the equations. In general heat exchangers are not difficult to control and simplified estimates of their behavior such as the Thal-Larsen* equations are accurate enough in practice.

SIMPLE HEAT EXCHANGER. A simple heat exchanger commonly used in process plants consists of a multiple tube pass containing liquid assumed to be in plug flow and a single shell pass containing a condensing vapor. Such an exchanger is typically a simple double-pipe heat exchanger designated here as a steam-water exchanger, although clearly many other fluids are used in such exchangers. The process dynamics of this exchanger can be obtained analytically and they have been confirmed experimentally.

The usual assumptions made in the analysis of a condensing vapor–liquid heat exchanger are plug flow of liquid in the tubes, negligible heat capacity of the steam, constant average heat capacities of the fluid and the tubes, uniform temperature of the tube walls, and constant heat transfer film coefficients. Under these conditions, the partial differential equations for such a heat exchanger may be written as

For tube fluid: $\quad M_f C_{pf} \dfrac{\partial \tilde{T}}{\partial t} + u M_f C_{pf} \dfrac{\partial \tilde{T}}{\partial x} = h_i A_i (\tilde{T}_w - \tilde{T})$ $\qquad$ (9–11a)

For tube wall: $\quad M_w C_{pw} \dfrac{\partial \tilde{T}_w}{\partial t} = h_o A_o (\tilde{T}_s - \tilde{T}_w) + h_i A_i (\tilde{T}_w - \tilde{T})$ $\quad$ (9–11b)

where M_f = mass of fluid per ft of tube, lb/ft

$\quad C_{pf}$ = heat capacity of fluid, Btu/lb-°F

$\quad \tilde{T}$ = change in fluid temperature, °F

$\quad t$ = time

$\quad u$ = linear velocity of fluid, ft/time

$\quad x$ = distance from tube entrance, ft

$\quad h_i$ = inside heat transfer film coefficient, Btu/ft²-°F-time

$\quad h_o$ = outside heat transfer film coefficient, Btu/ft²-°F-time

$\quad A_i$ = inside area of tube, ft²/ft

$\quad A_o$ = outside area of tube, ft²/ft

$\quad \tilde{T}_w$ = change in tube wall temperature, °F

$\quad M_w$ = mass of tube per ft of tube, lb/ft

$\quad C_{pw}$ = heat capacity of tube, Btu/lb-°F

$\quad \tilde{T}_s$ = change in steam temperature, °F

The equations may be put in the time-constant form as

For tube fluid: $\quad \tau_1 \dfrac{\partial \tilde{T}}{\partial t} + u \tau_1 \dfrac{\partial \tilde{T}}{\partial x} = \tilde{T}_w - \tilde{T}$ $\qquad$ (9–11c)

For tube wall: $\quad \tau_2 \dfrac{\partial \tilde{T}_w}{\partial t} = \tilde{T}_s - \tilde{T}_w + \dfrac{\tau_2}{\tau_{12}} (\tilde{T}_w - \tilde{T})$ $\qquad$ (9–11d)

* H. Thal-Larsen, *Journal of Basic Engineering*, **82**, 489 (1960).

where the time constants have the following definitions:

$$\tau_1 = \frac{M_f C_{pf}}{h_i A_i} \qquad \tau_2 = \frac{M_w C_{pw}}{h_o A_o} \qquad \tau_{12} = \frac{M_w C_{pw}}{h_i A_i}$$

In most process heat exchangers the dynamics of the terminal temperatures of the streams are of primary importance. In the case of the steam-water exchanger considered here, the effects and the relative importance of both the flowing fluid and the tube wall dynamics will be studied. Laplace-transformation of Eqs. 9–11c and d in respect to time gives

$$\tau_1 s \tilde{T}(s) + u \tau_1 \frac{d\tilde{T}(s)}{dx} = \tilde{T}_w(s) - \tilde{T}(s) \tag{9-11e}$$

$$\tau_2 s \tilde{T}_w(s) = \tilde{T}_s(s) - \tilde{T}_w(s) - \frac{\tau_2}{\tau_{12}} (\tilde{T}_w(s) - \tilde{T}(s)) \tag{9-11f}$$

and elimination of $\tilde{T}_w$ between these two equations gives the first-order linear differential equation for fluid temperature in terms of position x:

$$\frac{u}{f_1} \frac{d\tilde{T}(s)}{dx} + \tilde{T}(s) = \frac{f_1}{f_2} \tilde{T}_s(s) \tag{9-11g}$$

where f_1 and f_2 are functions of the transform variable s:

$$f_1(s) = \frac{(\tau_1 s + 1)(\tau_2 \tau_{12} s + \tau_{12} + \tau_2) - \tau_2}{\tau_1(\tau_2 \tau_{12} s + \tau_{12} + \tau_2)}$$

$$\frac{f_1(s)}{f_2(s)} = \frac{\tau_{12}}{(\tau_1 s + 1)(\tau_2 \tau_{12} s + \tau_{12} + \tau_2) - \tau_2}$$

Functional notation is not always used with the f's but it is always implied.

Various transfer functions can be obtained from this differential equation, depending upon the boundary conditions imposed. If steam pressure or temperature is the manipulated variable, a most important transfer function is the response of fluid outlet temperature to variation in steam temperature. This is obtained by solving the differential equation with the boundary condition on $\tilde{T}(x,t)$ at the entrance ($x = 0$) as $\tilde{T}(0,t) = 0$ for all time, which implies for all s, noting that $\tilde{T}$ is the deviation from steady state.

The position transfer function which is the solution to the differential equation, is

$$\frac{\tilde{T}(s,x)}{\tilde{T}_s(s)} = \frac{f_1}{f_2} (1 - e^{-f_1 x/u}) \tag{9-11h}$$

It is interesting to note that x/u is the time required for an entering particle of fluid to reach position x and the term $e^{-f_1 x/u}$ is effectively that of a dead-time element since f_1 has a net excess power of s in the numerator. Fluid inflow rate and temperature are the likeliest disturbances to be encountered in heat exchanger control. Fluctuation in inflow fluid temperature is easy to handle by applying the boundary conditions

$$\tilde{T}(0,t) = \tilde{T}_i, \; \tilde{T}_s(x,t) = 0$$

which lead to the position transfer function

$$\frac{\tilde{T}(s,x)}{\tilde{T}_i(s)} = e^{-f_1 x/u} \qquad (9\text{–}11\text{i})$$

Both equations give the transform of the response in terms of position as well as time. The two transfer functions relating the outlet temperature at $x = L$ to changes in steam temperature and fluid inlet temperature are

$$\frac{\tilde{T}_o(s)}{\tilde{T}_s(s)} = \frac{f_1}{f_2} \, (1 - e^{-af_1}) \qquad (9\text{–}11\text{j})$$

and

$$\frac{\tilde{T}_o(s)}{\tilde{T}_i(s)} = e^{-af_1} \qquad (9\text{–}11\text{k})$$

where $a = L/u$. These are the open-loop transfer functions which together with the controller and measurement transfer functions are needed to determine the closed-loop dynamics of a heat exchanger process subject to fluctuations in feed temperature.

When the resistance and capacity of the wall are negligible,

$$f_1(s) = \frac{\tau_1 s + 1}{\tau_1}$$

where τ_1 is now a function of the overall heat transfer coefficient U. The transfer functions thus become

$$\frac{\tilde{T}_o(s)}{\tilde{T}_s(s)} = \frac{1}{\tau_1 s + 1} \left(1 - e^{-a\left(\frac{\tau_1 s + 1}{\tau_1}\right)} \right) = \frac{1}{\tau_1 s + 1} (1 - e^{\frac{-a}{\tau_1}} e^{-as}) \qquad (9\text{–}11\text{l})$$

$$\frac{\tilde{T}_o(s)}{\tilde{T}_i(s)} = e^{-a\left(\frac{\tau_1 s + 1}{\tau_1}\right)} = e^{\frac{-a}{\tau_1}} e^{-as} \qquad (9\text{–}11\text{m})$$

Note that the gain term $e^{\frac{-a}{\tau_1}}$ is the steady-state solution of the equation for steam temperature changes and at steady state

$$\frac{T_s - T_o}{T_s - T_i} = e^{\frac{-a}{\tau_1}} \qquad (9\text{–}11\text{n})$$

where the T's are steady-state values, not deviations from steady state. If the tube were insulated so that $U = 0$, τ_1 would become infinite and the steam temperature transfer function would have the trivial value

$$\frac{\tilde{T}_o(s)}{\tilde{T}_s(s)} = 0$$

Of more interest is the feed temperature transfer function, which now becomes the simple dead-time element

$$\frac{\tilde{T}_o(s)}{\tilde{T}_i(s)} = e^{-as} \qquad (9\text{--}11\text{o})$$

Application of these equations is shown in the following example.

Example 9-3. Consider a steam-water heat exchanger consisting of one tube pass and one shell pass. The tubes are of Admiralty brass, $\frac{5}{8}$ in. O.D. with 18-BWG wall and 10 ft long. Water enters the tubes at 80°F and flows at the rate of 2 gpm per tube. Steam fills the shell and is normally at 240° F.

(a) Evaluate the transfer functions which give the effect of the steam and entering fluid temperature on the exit fluid temperature.

(b) Assess the importance of considering the wall thermal capacity on the system dynamics.

Solution. The physical properties of the system can be determined or estimated from handbook data:

Tube properties:

$$A_i = 0.1380 \text{ ft}^2/\text{ft}$$
$$A_o = 0.1636 \text{ ft}^2/\text{ft}$$
$$M_w = 0.33 \text{ lb/ft}$$
$$S = 0.00152 \text{ ft}^2 \text{ (cross-sectional area)}$$
$$C_{pw} = 0.09 \text{ Btu/lb-°F}$$
$$h_w = \frac{(65)(12)}{0.049} = 16{,}000 \text{ Btu/hr-ft}^2\text{-°F (wall conductance)}$$

Fluid properties:

$$\rho = 62 \text{ lb/ft}^3 \text{ (at the average water temperature)}$$
$$C_{pf} = 1.0 \text{ Btu/lb°-F}$$
$$u = \frac{2}{(60)(7.48)(0.00152)} = 3 \text{ ft/sec}$$
$$M_f = (0.00152)(62) = 0.094 \text{ lb/ft (liquid holdup)}$$
$$h_i = 500 \text{ Btu/hr-ft}^2\text{-°F (estimated effective liquid film coefficient)}$$
$$h_o = 2300 \text{ Btu/hr-ft}^2\text{-°F (estimated steam film coefficient)}$$

(a) The parameters in Eqs. 9-11j and k are evaluated from the system data above.

$$\tau_1 = \frac{M_f C_{pf}}{h_i A_i} = \frac{(0.094)(1.0)}{(500)(0.138)} (3600) = 4.9 \text{ sec}$$
$$\tau_{12} = \frac{M_w C_{pw}}{h_i A_i} = \frac{(0.33)(0.09)}{(500)(0.138)} (3600) = 1.55 \text{ sec}$$
$$\tau_2 = \frac{M_w C_{pw}}{h_o A_o} = \frac{(0.33)(0.09)}{(2300)(0.1636)} = 0.28 \text{ sec}$$

$$f_1 = \frac{(4.9s + 1)}{4.9} \frac{(0.28)(1.55)s + 1.55 + 0.28 - 0.28}{(1.28)(1.55)s + 1.55 + 0.28} = 0.192(4.9s + 1)$$

$$\frac{f_1}{f_2} = \frac{1.55}{(4.9s + 1)(0.435s + 1.83) - 0.28} = \frac{1}{(5.9s + 1)(0.22s + 1)}$$

$$a = L/u = \frac{10}{3} = 3.33 \text{ sec}$$

The required transfer functions are obtained directly by substitution into the appropriate equations

The steam temperature transfer function is

$$\frac{\tilde{T}_o(s)}{\tilde{T}_s(s)} = \frac{1}{(5.9s + 1)(0.22s + 1)} (1 - e^{-3.3(0.192)(4.9s+1)}) = \frac{1 - 0.53e^{-3.1s}}{(5.91s + 1)(0.22s + 1)}$$

The feed temperature transfer function is

$$\frac{\tilde{T}_o(s)}{\tilde{T}_i(s)} = e^{-.63}e^{-3.1s} = 0.53e^{-3.1s}$$

(b) If the wall thermal capacity is neglected, the single time constant becomes

$$\tau_1 = \frac{M_f C_{pf}}{U A_i}$$

But

$$\frac{1}{U} = \frac{1}{500} + \frac{1}{2300} + \frac{1}{16,000}$$

and

$$U = 400 \text{ Btu/hr-ft}^2\text{-}°F$$

hence

$$\tau_1 = \frac{(0.94)(1.0)}{(400)(.138)} (3600) = 6.1 \text{ sec}$$

the steam temperature transfer function becomes

$$\frac{\tilde{T}_o(s)}{\tilde{T}_s(s)} = \frac{1}{(6.1s + 1)} (1 - e^{-3.3\left(\frac{6.1s+1}{6.1}\right)}) = \frac{1}{6.1s + 1} (1 - 0.58e^{-3.3s})$$

and the feed temperature transfer function becomes

$$\frac{\tilde{T}_o(s)}{\tilde{T}_i(s)} = 0.58e^{-3.3s}$$

Thus, there is little effect in neglecting the wall capacity. The single time constant resulting is almost the same as the larger time constant for the more correct solution, and the dead-time element is almost the same in both cases.

The open-loop response of the outlet temperature to a change in fluid inflow rate is given by Harriott* in the form

$$\frac{\tilde{T}_o(s)}{\tilde{I}(s)} = -(\tilde{T}_s - \tilde{T}_i)(1 - b)e^{\frac{-a}{\tau_1}} \left(\frac{1 - e^{-as}}{\tau_1 s} \right) \qquad (9\text{--}11p)$$

* Peter Harriott, *Process Control*, McGraw-Hill Book Co., Inc., New York, 1964.

where b is the exponent in the velocity dependent relationship for the overall heat transfer coefficient

$$U = U_{ss}(1 + u)^b$$

Because of the $1 - ke^{-as}$ term which appears in the steam temperature transfer function and the $1 - e^{-as}$ term which appears in the inflow rate transfer function, the frequency response for heat exchangers involving these terms will exhibit resonance (or oscillations in the Bode plots) in the amplitude ratio. (See Problem 9–9e.) Also, values of k other than unity will cause oscillations in the phase-angle plot.

Such resonance effects have been observed experimentally by a number of investigators. Any closed-loop system involving control of the steam temperature would also be expected to exhibit such resonance effects. No effort is made in this book to consider the selection of controllers based on the transfer functions discussed above.

CONTROL OF HEAT EXCHANGER. Design for control of vapor-liquid heat exchangers can be based on the process transfer functions given above in Eqs. 9–11j, k, and n for the plant and for disturbances of inflow temperature and inflow rate, respectively. A typical application is shown in the block diagram in Fig. 9–12. The process engineer would select the

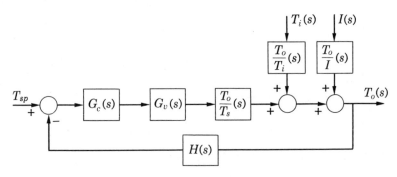

Fig. 9–12. Block diagram for control of heat exchanger by manipulation of steam temperature. Tildes are omitted from the deviation variables.

controller type on the basis of the important plant disturbances and the performance required of the control system. The temperature-measuring element $H(s)$ may be a filled bulb or a thermocouple in a protective thermowell located in the exchanger outlet. These elements introduce measuring lags which may have time constants of the order of magnitude of the main time constant of the system. High fluid velocities past the thermowell tend to minimize the measuring lag and a temperature transmitter using derivative action for lag compensation is available. In addition, the measuring element often is located somewhat down stream from the exchanger outlet and this constitutes dead time in the control system. If flow in the outlet is at a rate of 2 ft/sec, then every foot downstream that the measuring element is located adds dead time of $\frac{1}{2}$ sec in the feedback element.

Exchanger outlet temperature can be controlled by a variety of methods. Sanders* has an excellent qualitative discussion of the subject. The usual method for steam heaters is to use a temperature controller to adjust the valve in the inlet steam line, as shown in Figs. 9–13a and b. This

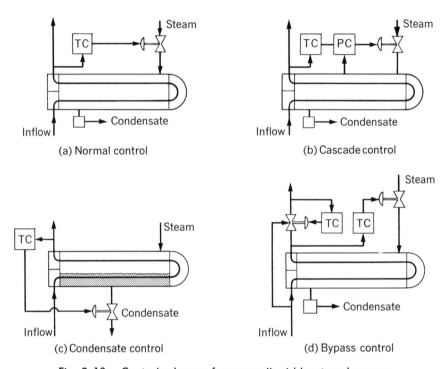

Fig. 9–13.   Control schemes for vapor-liquid heat exchangers.

effectively controls the pressure in the shell, and consequently the steam temperature, because condensation takes place essentially at equilibrium.

Although it is obviously a relatively expensive procedure, it is possible to cascade the temperature controller into a steam pressure controller which also senses and controls the pressure in the shell as indicated in Fig. 9–13b. This type of control provides rapid response to upsets in

* C. W. Sanders, "Better Control of Heat Exchangers," *Chemical Engineering*, **66**(19), 145–148 (1959).

the steam supply. The pressure controller gives faster response to steam pressure changes while the temperature controller provides fine corrections and makes any necessary adjustments of the pressure controller set point.

The effective heat transfer surface exposed to condensing steam can be varied by controlling the flow of condensate out of the exchanger as seen in Fig. 9–13c. This type of control has not been quantitatively analyzed but it is clear that, due to condensate holdup, response will be sluggish, high-frequency fluctuations will be well filtered, and there could well be a tendency toward instability. Use of this type of control scheme should probably be avoided except in situations where experience has shown it to be both satisfactory and desirable.

If an installed exchanger is somewhat oversize, a slow response may be improved by bypassing some of the inlet fluid and blending this cold fluid with the somewhat overheated fluid coming from the exchanger as shown in Fig. 9–13d. Sizing of the valve in the bypass is important and the location of sensing elements is critical. For a properly designed system the exit temperature varies only slightly with flow and exchanger lags are almost insignificant in the control loop.

9–4. COMMENTS ON PROCESS SYSTEMS

There are several outstanding differences between the dynamics of the equipment in the process industries and those of typical equipment in the electrical and mechanical industries.

Interaction Between Stages. Interaction between plant units occurs whenever the response of one unit in a plant depends upon conditions existing in neighboring plant units. Simple examples of interaction are the two-stage liquid-level tanks in Fig. 4–19 and the composition interaction between stages as in a staged separator. Of more importance is the interaction which can occur between two or more feedback control loops in a single plant or the attempt to control too many variables in a plant. An interesting instance of interaction occurs between the properties and flow rates of the feed, product, and bottoms streams, and the boilup rate in a distillation column. Analysis of such complex problems may be accomplished by use of the control principles discussed here with computer aid but such problems are beyond the purpose of this text.

Overdamped Components. Most process equipment converts input quantities of kinetic energy into heat, with the result that except for the mercury manometer and the exothermic reactor, few if any underdamped or unstable components are found in the process industries. In fact, a chief use of control is to speed up sluggish systems of heat exchange, gas absorption, liquid extraction, and like processes. Process equipment is frequently large, and the process signals encounter distributed-parameter behavior in transmission through the equipment. Example 4–5 and Fig. E4–5 show that a distributed-parameter system is slower in response than a lumped-parameter system. Plants exhibiting distributed-parameter characteristics often require special control strategies, such as feedforward and bypass compensation.

Process Nonlinearities. Nonlinearities are always present in process units and frequently are a source of the most interesting properties of chemical process systems (e.g., optimum operating points). They are difficult to handle analytically without computational aids, and for that reason they may be avoided or eliminated by the device of linearization. Chemical reactor systems show nonlinear behavior because of the temperature dependence of the rate constant and high order reaction rate mechanisms. Example 10–2 discusses the analog computer simulation of a chemical reactor system and the adaptive control system discussed above uses a computer to handle the nonlinear operations. Computers are essential for adequate solution of nonlinear control problems.

Time constants and dead times in process systems usually vary inversely with the flow rate and lead to variable loop gain characteristics, so that a control system which is properly designed for one flow rate may become unstable or very sluggish at other flow rates. In such cases, a change in the production rate "parametrically forces" the plant system by changing its properties. The most satisfactory way to compensate for this behavior is to eliminate it (if possible) or to place a function generator in the loop to maintain a constant loop gain despite flow rate changes. As shown, in Fig. 9–14 this may be achieved by inserting a compensator for process

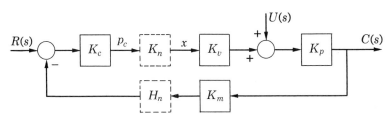

Fig. 9–14. Process control system showing possible nonlinear compensation in either the forward branch or the feedback branch.

nonlinearities either in the forward loop $K_n = \Delta x/\Delta p_c$ or in the feedback loop H_n, depending upon the nature of the plant sensitivity, dc/dm. Forward compensation, K_n, is used when dc/dm depends chiefly upon the load u and feedback compensation H_n is used when dc/dm depends chiefly upon the measured variable. The forward compensation is commonly obtained by making a proper choice of control valve characteristic, $K_v = \Delta i / \Delta x$, (see Chapter 3) or using a nonlinear valve positioner. An example of feedback compensation is the use of a square-root module to linearize the squared measurement signal from a differential-pressure flow rate meter.

Pneumatic Transmission of Signals. A control valve manipulates the input of material or energy to the process system in response to the controller signal, which may be either electronic or pneumatic. The controller may be mounted on the plant line or in a central control room. In the case of a remote pneumatic controller, the pneumatic transmission lag from controller to process should be recognized; in some cases it may be advisable to use a line-mounted controller in the plant to minimize the transmission lag.

PNEUMATIC TRANSMISSION LAG. The transmission of pneumatic signals in small tubing (typically of $\frac{1}{4}$-in. outer diameter, metal or plastic) has been studied both theoretically and experimentally. Since a pneumatic transmission system consists of the transmitter, the transmission line, and the receiver in an interacting cascade, the characteristics of the system are best found from study of the complete system. Some practical results have come from the theoretical studies of Schuder and Binder* whose model of transient flow in a long transmission line assumed fully developed laminar flow of a compressible fluid in a one-dimensional, uniformly distributed system subject to small, reversible, adiabatic pressure transients. Their experimental results were in good agreement with theoretical predictions based on this mathematical representation of the model:

Equations:
$$\frac{\partial u(x,t)}{\partial x} = -\frac{1}{\rho c^2}\frac{\partial p(x,t)}{\partial t}$$

$$\frac{\partial p(x,t)}{\partial x} = -\rho \frac{\partial u(x,t)}{\partial t} - Ru(x,t)$$

Boundary conditions: $p(x,0) = 0 \qquad p(0,t) = p_i(t)$

$$u(x,0) = 0 \qquad u(L,t) = \frac{V}{a\rho c^2}\frac{\partial p(L,t)}{\partial t}$$

where p = pressure, lb/ft²
  u = linear velocity in tubing, ft/sec
  x = distance from input, ft
  t = time, sec
  $R = 32\ \mu/d^2$, constant frictional resistance, lb-sec/ft⁴
  c = acoustic velocity in fluid, ft/sec
  ρ = density of fluid, slugs/ft³

* C. B. Schuder, and R. C. Binder, "The Response of Pneumatic Transmission Lines to Step Inputs," *Journal of Basic Engineering*, **81**, 578–584 (1959).

d = tube diameter, ft
a = tube cross sectional area, ft^2
μ = fluid viscosity, slugs/ft-sec
L = tube length, ft
V = terminal volume, ft^3

Using transform methods, Schuder and Binder found a transfer function for the transmission system as

$$\frac{P(L,s)}{P_i(s)} = \frac{1}{\cosh \nu(s) + \dfrac{V}{aL}\, \nu s \sinh \nu(s)}$$

where

$$\nu(s) = \frac{L}{c}\sqrt{s\left(s + \frac{R}{\rho}\right)}$$

After study of experimental data, Hougen* noted that a simple relation appeared to dominate the data on pressure transmission along tubing; he simplified Schuder and Binders' equation, using the approximations

$$\cosh \nu(s) \cong 1 + \tfrac{1}{2}\nu^2(s) \qquad \sinh \nu(s) \cong \nu(s)$$

to obtain

$$\frac{P(L,s)}{P_i(s)} \cong \frac{1}{\dfrac{s^2}{\omega_n{}^2} + \dfrac{2\zeta}{\omega_n}s + 1}$$

or

$$\frac{P(L,s)}{P_i(s)} \cong \frac{1}{\left(\dfrac{2\zeta}{\omega_n}\right)s + 1} \qquad \text{for } \zeta \gg 1$$

where the damping ratio ζ and the undamped natural frequency ω_n are defined as

$$\zeta = \frac{1}{2}\frac{RL}{\rho c}\left[\frac{1}{2} + \frac{V}{aL}\right]^{1/2} \qquad \omega_n = \frac{c}{L}\left[\frac{1}{2} + \frac{V}{aL}\right]^{-1/2} \qquad \frac{2\zeta}{\omega_n} = \frac{RL^2}{\rho c^2}\left[\frac{1}{2} + \frac{V}{aL}\right]$$

These parameters contain all the constants of the transmission system and are convenient for rapidly estimating dynamics of pneumatic transmission lines. Hougen presented results of pulse tests on transmission systems which showed that the second-order model was adequate for rapid analysis or design of transmission systems. When $\zeta < 1$, the model predicts ω_n with great reliability; and when $\zeta > 1$ the first-order model describes the dominant behavior of the line, especially at low pressures. At higher pressures, underdamped behavior appears and the second-order model is indicated.

---

* Joel O. Hougen, "Experiences and Experiments with Process Dynamics," Chemical Engineering Progress Monograph Series 4, Vol. 60, American Institute of Chemical Engineers, New York, 1964.

CONTROL VALVE CHARACTERISTICS. The control valve responds to the transmitted signal with a change in the valve stem position which modulates the flow of control agent to the process. Several valve characteristics are available but the linear and equal-percentage valves are most used. As shown in Chapter 3, the valve characteristics are based on a constant pressure drop across the valve; in an actual plant, the valve pressure drop will vary with valve flow rate (see Example 3–5), so that the effective valve characteristic depends upon the specific plant installation and the inherent valve characteristic. For purposes of this discussion it is assumed that the pressure drop across the control valve is constant and that the valve has been correctly sized for maximum and minimum process correction. Now the problem is to characterize the valve (flow rate versus lift) so that it can accomodate sustained changes in plant loads or production rates.

If the process plant operates at constant production rate with only minor disturbances in load, the loop gain will be constant and the control valve will remain near a normal operating position. However, as discussed above, if the plant production rate varies widely the system parameters will change with flow rates, the loop gain will change due to process nonlinearities, and the system relative stability will therefore change. The controller gain could be adjusted for each production rate to maintain constant relative stability (using an adaptive controller or an instrument technician), but a more economical solution is to select the control valve characteristic so that the loop gain remains relatively constant for any plant production rate. Refer to Fig. 9–14 and consider, for the moment, that K_n, $(= \Delta x/\Delta p_c)$, is constant and $H_n = 1$. Constant relative stability requires that the loop gain remain constant:

$$K_c K_n K_v K_p K_m = A$$

where A is the optimum loop gain for good control at average operating conditions. Remember that the various process gains K are ratios of changes in output, as in

$$K_c = \frac{\Delta p_c}{\Delta e} \quad K_n = \frac{\Delta x}{\Delta p_c} \quad K_v = \frac{\Delta i}{\Delta x} \quad K_p = \frac{\Delta c}{\Delta i} \quad K_m = \frac{\Delta b}{\Delta c}$$

If K_c is constant and if the valve motor and positioner are linear (constant K_n), the only gain that can be selected to vary with flow rate so as to compensate for the variation of A with flow rate is the valve characteristic, K_v, which must satisfy the relationship

$$K_v = \frac{\Delta i}{\Delta x} = \frac{A}{K_c K_n K_m K_p} = \frac{di}{dx}$$

Thus, for perfect compensation of nonlinearities in K_p the control valve characteristic should show a flow rate–stem position characteristic

$$K_v = \left(\frac{1}{K_c K_n K_m}\right) \frac{A}{K_p}$$

For many process applications K_c, K_n, and K_m are constant and the choice of valve characteristics may be summarized as follows:

Linear valve, K_v = constant: A/K_p should be constant
Semilog valve, $K_v \propto$ flow rate: $A/K_p \propto$ flow rate

The relationship between the process gain K_p and flow rate can be obtained either from a theoretical process analysis or from the slope of an experimental plot of c versus i in the operating range of the process. In unusual cases, an additional compensation means is available in the valve actuator by using a commercial valve positioner which generates the desired nonlinear $K_n = \Delta x/\Delta p_c$ to give the necessary compensation for loop gain changes.

The above discussion assumes that the valve is correctly sized and that the pressure drop Δp_v across the valve remains constant. A high Δp_v increases the flow rate range of a valve and favors good control but the wasted energy is an economic loss. In practice, the Δp_v will vary, due to variation in plant supply pressures and valve flow rate with the result that the effective characteristic of a linear valve approaches that of a quick opening valve and the equal-percentage valve approaches that of a linear valve as the supply line pressure drop increases (see Chapter 3). For practical reasons of substitution and maintenance, and for ease of sizing, a large majority of control valves are equal-percentage. One should remember that, with the available range of the valve and for a constant plant load, the controller will hold a constant flow rate through the valve independent of the valve pressure drop Δp_v. In any operating plant it is quite necessary that the control valve always be provided with sufficient flow rate range to hold the set point in the process without reaching its limits of a wide open or shut position.

Dead Time and Inverse Response in Control. Certain non-minimum phase processes may present severe control problems, as shown in the discussion of proportional control of a dead-time process in Chapter 7. The pure dead-time process cannot be controlled alone with a high-gain feedback loop, and the presence of a first-order lag (it may be added or it may already exist in the process) greatly improves the stability condition. Processes showing inverse response characteristics are difficult to control since, as shown in Chapter 4, the initial response is in the opposite direction to the final overall change.

The cascade compensation scheme given in Fig. 9–15 has shown merit in controlling processes having either of these types of non-minimum phase

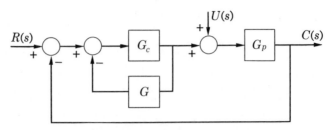

Fig. 9–15.   Cascade compensation of certain non-minimum phase processes.

behavior.   The control system response equation is

$$C(s) = \frac{G_c G_p R(s)}{1 + G_c(G + G_p)} + \frac{G_p(1 + G_c G)}{1 + G_c(G + G_p)} U(s)$$

where G_c is the usual process controller, G_p is the process transfer function, and G is a special compensating feedback component which is selected for each G_p.

DEAD-TIME PROCESS.   Dead time or transportation lag occurs in all process plants and transportation systems.   The best approach is to remove the dead time when possible.   If this is not feasible and if adequate performance is not obtainable with a P or PI controller, then, Smith* showed, a feedback loop around the controller containing an analog of dead time which passes only the higher frequencies produces good control of long dead-time processes.   For example, if the transfer function of the dead-time process is

$$G_p = G_1 e^{-\tau s}$$

(where G_1 is the minimum phase model of the process), then the feedback loop should have the transfer function

$$G = G_1(1 - e^{-\tau s})$$

and the system characteristic equation becomes

$$1 + G_c(G + G_p) = 1 + G_c G_1$$

with the result that the dead time is removed from the characteristic equation and it can no longer affect the system stability.   The term $(1 - e^{-\tau s})$ represents a pulse generator since its step response is a pulse of duration τ.   The feedback compensation can be viewed either as the minimum-phase model of the plant in series with a pulse generator which in no way alters the accuracy of the system or as the difference between the minimum-phase model and the complete non-minimum model of the plant.   Smith reports precise regulation of loops containing long dead

* O. J. M. Smith, "A Controller To Overcome Dead Time," *ISA Journal*, **6**(2), 28–33 (1959).

times using this new type of control strategy. Details on design of the pulse generator are given in the reference.

INVERSE RESPONSE PROCESS. In the PI control of inverse response processes, the initial controller correction is in the wrong direction with the result that the system may be unstable or very sluggish in response. Derivative control augments the inverse response and is not used with these processes. Again, the best approach is to eliminate the inverse response behavior, but if this is not practical, a special feedback compensator containing the plant model may be used around the controller. Iinoya and Altpeter* found that a modification of the Smith method of feedback compensation caused a marked improvement in system response. As an example, they selected the plant transfer function as

$$G_p = \frac{m_1}{\tau_1 s + 1} - \frac{m_2}{\tau_2 s + 1} = \frac{(m_1\tau_2 - m_2\tau_1)s + (m_1 - m_2)}{(\tau_1 s + 1)(\tau_2 s + 1)} \qquad \frac{\tau_1}{\tau_2} > \frac{m_1}{m_2} > 1$$

which shows inverse response under these conditions since G_p has a zero in the right-half s-plane. The Smith method removes this troublesome zero from the system-characteristic equation by selecting the feedback compensation as

$$G = k\left[\frac{1}{\tau_2 s + 1} - \frac{1}{\tau_1 s + 1}\right] \qquad k = \frac{m_2\tau_1 - m_1\tau_2}{(\tau_1 - \tau_2)}$$

and giving the system-characteristic equation as

$$1 + G_c(G_p + G) = 1 + G_c \frac{m_1 - m_2}{(\tau_1 s + 1)(\tau_2 s + 1)}$$

Iinoya and Altpeter show that the Smith method does not always give the best value for k, as shown in the example below.

Example 9–4. Iinoya and Altpeter considered the PI control of an inverse response process which was the difference between two first-order lags with $m_1 = 2, m_2 = 1, \tau_1 = 3,$ and $\tau_2 = 1$. The Smith method gives a value of $k = 0.5$ for the compensation. Let the PI controller function be $10(1 + 1/3s)$, and make a root-locus plot which shows the effect of varying k on the system damping ratio.

Solution. The system characteristic equation becomes

$$1 + G_c(G_p + G) = 1 + 10\left(\frac{3s + 1}{3s}\right)\left(\frac{1 - s}{(s + 1)(3s + 1)} + \frac{2ks}{(s + 1)(3s + 1)}\right)$$

$$= 1 + \frac{10}{3s}\left(\frac{(2k - 1)s + 1}{s + 1}\right)$$

The Smith method is to set $2k - 1$ to zero, giving $k = 0.5$, which gives a lightly damped system. It is shown below that k can be selected to control the damping

* Koichi Iinoya, and R. J. Altpeter, "Inverse Response in Process Control," *Industrial and Engineering Chemistry,* **54**(7), 39–43 (1962).

ratio for a given K_c and τ_i. The root-locus analysis for displaying the effect of k on system stability requires that the characteristic equation be put into the form $1 + kG(s)$, which, in this case, becomes

$$1 + kG(s) = s^2 + (6.66k - 2.3)s + 3.33$$

$$= 1 + \frac{6.66ks}{(s - 1.16 + j1.4)(s - 1.16 - j1.4)} = 0$$

The Routh-Hurwitz test shows that the system is stable for $k > 0.35$. The complete root-locus plot in Fig. E9-4 shows that any damping ratio can be

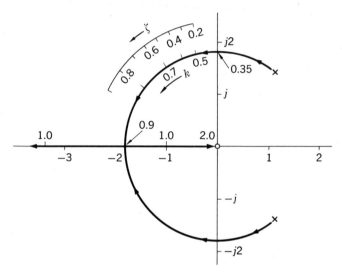

Fig. E9-4. Root locus plot showing the effect of k on the system damping ratio ζ.

obtained by varying k. The Smith method ($k = 0.5$) gives a $\zeta = 0.22$ which is probably too oscillatory for most processes. A value of $k = 0.90$ gives critical damping in the system. The system output/setpoint response is found by inverting

$$C(s) = \frac{30s(1 - s)R(s)}{3s^2 + (20k - 7)s + 10}$$

from which it is noted that inverse system response has not been eliminated and that overshoot may be a problem at low damping ratio.

PROBLEMS

9-1. Pressure transients are important in steam plants. As a simple exercise in modeling, consider the transient compression or expansion of a constant-mass two-phase mixture of water and steam within a variable-volume cylinder. A performance model of the system consists of mass, volume, and energy balances on the separate phases and on the whole mixture, based on appropriate assumptions of mechanisms concerning interphase relationships and cylinder-wall effects. Assume no heat transfer from the cylinder walls and isentropic expansion of the steam (rapid expansion). Let m_f and m_g be the mass of water and steam phases, and use the steam-table nomenclature. Write equations for the plant model, and indicate by a signal flow diagram how the cylinder pressure transient is computed as a function of the cylinder volume V when the initial conditions of m_f, m_g, V, P, and steam-table properties are given. (D. H. Brown, "Transient Thermodynamic Analysis," Report No. 62GL36, General Electric Laboratory, Schenectady, N.Y.).

9-2. Consider a model for an isothermal equilibrium stage liquid-liquid extraction process. Material A is transferred from an organic phase (raffinate) to an aqueous phase (extract) as shown in Fig. E1–2a. The phase compositions are expressed as mass ratios, and the holdup in each stage is constant at m_o and m_a pounds organic and aqueous solvents, respectively. Assume the interphase transfer rate in each stage is $k(y - y^*)$ lb A/min, where y is the composition of the organic phase and y^*, the concentration of the organic phase in equilibrium with x in the aqueous phase, is expressed by $y^* = mx + b$. Construct a model for the nth extractor stage by writing differential material-balance equations for component A in each phase in the stage. Sketch a signal flow diagram for the nth stage, and extend it to two stages, assuming the same model for the $(n + 1)$th stage. Assume the flow rates of aqueous and organic solvents are constant.

9-3. In principle, feedforward control could be used to control the liquid level in the tank in Fig. P9–3. The load disturbance is a change in the outflow rate $U(s)$ from the pump.

(a) Determine the feedforward controller function $G_f(s)$ that would provide perfect correction for any load change $U(s)$.
(b) List conditions for which this would be a satisfactory control system.
(c) Assume $H_f(s) = k_1 e^{-\tau_1 s}/(\tau_2 s + 1)$ and $G_v(s) = k_2/(\tau_3 s + 1)$, and comment on the practicality of physically achieving $G_f(s)$.
(d) Improve the system by adding a feedback control loop, and write the relationship for $C(s)$ in terms of $R(s)$ and $U(s)$.

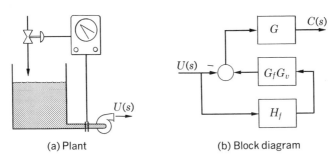

(a) Plant   (b) Block diagram

Fig. P9–3

9-4. On page 72 of their work, MacMullan and Shinskey state,that, in determining the dynamic function for the superfractionator feedforward computer, they obtained the following open-loop step response data for changes in the effects of feed rate and distillate rate on product quality c_D expressed in percentage complete response.

Time	i_F	i_D	Time	i_F	i_D
20 min	0%	0%	100 min	79.0%	57.5%
30 min	0	6.8	120 min	92.0	70.2
40 min	9.2	16.0	140 min	99.0	80.0
60 min	32.4	30.8	160 min	100.0	91.0
80 min	58.5	44.6			

Fit these response data to a plant model consisting of a dead time and a first-order lag, and compare your results with those used by MacMullan and Shinskey. Remember that the plant dynamics displayed by the early part of the response are more important in control work than those displayed near the final steady state.

9-5. A theoretical feedforward controlled process is shown in Fig. P9-5.

(a) Write the plant process equation, and show that the feedforward control strategy $M(s)$ results from substituting $C(s) = R(s)$ in the plant process equation.

(b) The transfer functions can be separated into a static term and a dynamic term as $G_l(s) = f_l g_l(s)$ and $G_p(s) = f_p g_p(s)$, where the f's are the static terms and the g's are the dynamic terms. If the system dynamic response to set-point changes is sacrificed, show that the feedforward control strategy $M(s)$ can be written as a product of a static term and a dynamic term which is the ratio $g_l(s)/g_p(s)$.

(c) Add a feedback loop to the system in part b to eliminate steady-state error, and draw the block diagram for the feedforward-feedback combination (F. G. Shinskey, "Feedforward Control Applied," *ISA Journal*, November, 1963, p. 61).

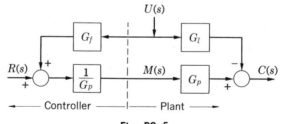

Fig. P9-5

9-6. A first-order blender is to be designed to smooth pulse-type product-quality disturbances in a product stream. Assume that the input pulse has a magnitude k and a duration τ min and that the maximum allowed change in product quality is a given fraction f of the pulse magnitude.

(a) Show that the transform of the pulse is $(k/s)(1 - e^{-\tau s})$.
(b) Find the blender volume needed to keep the exit product-quality change less than 5 % of the pulse magnitude k for a pulse of 5 min duration and a product flow rate of 50 ft³/min.

9–7. Consider the problem of surge-vessel design making use of a proportional controller. Develop the design equations corresponding to those in the text for a PI controller, and find the vessel size and K_c for the same surge conditions in Example 9–2. Assume a linear control valve and an upright cylindrical tank.

9–8. Feedforward control applied to heat exchangers may give improved performance by effectively substituting fast flow dynamics for sluggish thermal dynamics. The outlet temperature of a steam-heated oil heater is controlled by a conventional single-loop temperature controller as shown in Fig. P9–8.

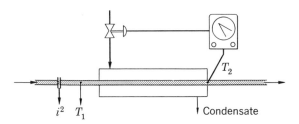

Fig. P9–8

The heater performance is not adequate for the frequent changes in hot-oil flow rate which occur. Devise a feedforward control scheme which measures the oil flow rate as a differential pressure and computes the heat duty of the exchanger. Then show how the computed signal could be used with the conventional temperature loop to improve the exchanger load performance.

9–9. Refer to the heat exchanger discussed in Example 9–3; neglect the wall thermal capacity; and compute the response of the exchanger under the following conditions.

(a) For a step change of 20°F in steam temperature, plot the response of the water outlet temperature.
(b) Repeat part a for a tube 25 ft long but with all the other parameters remaining the same.
(c) Repeat part a with the 10-ft tube but with τ_1 having twice the value used in Example 9–3.
(d) For part a, plot the temperature distribution in the tube length at steady state. At what time are steady-state conditions attained?
(e) For the same heat exchanger, plot the frequency response over a frequency range sufficient to illustrate clearly the resonant effect of the $1 - ke^{-as}$ term.

9–10. A pneumatic control valve having an actuator chamber of 150 in.^{3} is located 400 ft from a controller. Estimate the transmission lag for air signals at 9 psig and 70°F when using 0.25-in. tubing (0.17-in. I.D.) to interconnect the valve and controller. The velocity of sound in air is 1100 ft/sec.

9–11. The following dynamic compensation in the Smith manner is proposed for a process showing inverse response behavior:

$$G_p(s) = \frac{1}{s(3s + 1)} - \frac{2}{s + 1} \qquad G(s) - \frac{6s + k}{(s + 1)(3s + 1)}$$

(a) Should a P or PI controller be selected for the system?
(b) Using a proportional controller and the Routh-Hurwitz test, find the stability conditions on K_c and k.
(c) Select $K_c = 10$, and sketch a root-locus plot that shows the effect of k on the damping ratio for the system. What is the maximum possible damping ratio?

10
Analog Data Processing

Most of the system examples in this text, for simplicity, are concerned with single process variables such as pressure, temperature, and so on, but the real design and operating variables in a process plant are the mass and energy quantities and transfer rates. For example, an orifice measurement is not an accurate measure of flow rate when the fluid density fluctuates; temperature is not a true measure of heat transfer to a boiling fluid; and a single controller cannot maintain either a material balance or an energy balance on a process unit. Such process problems require data-manipulating devices in the control system. Frequently, a process engineer can use an analog computer to compute the real process variables such as true flow rate, enthalpy, and material balance and use them, when needed, to control a process operation.

Data processing is the name given to process computations which involve monitoring, computing, and evaluating information concerning the variables in a process system. The computations may range from the solution of algebraic equations to the simulation of dynamic components in the process system. In the past, these computations have been performed by hand and therefore were limited in scope and application since the hand operator could not keep pace with the plant conditions. Today the computations are made by analog or digital equipment at plant speed or faster, and the results are used in making immediate decisions concerning plant operation.

Optimization of process operation is the ultimate goal in the application of computers in control systems. The computer obtains data from process transducers and manipulates it mathematically according to the programmed relationships. In simple applications the computer may determine a "process performance index" which the operator uses in making decisions concerning plant operation. For in-process optimization the computer is placed in a control loop where it may manipulate either the controller set point or, in some cases, the control valve. When these computations and manipulations embrace a complete plant the result is computer control as discussed in Chapter 9. Data processing in the process industries is common now and will increase steadily with the widespread application of control theory in industrial plants.

10–1. OPERATIONAL AMPLIFIERS

The direct-current operational amplifier has been perfected for use in computation, measurement, control, and other signal conditioning requirements. As noted in Chapter 4, it is a high-gain d-c amplifier whose electronic properties are stabilized and compensated against offset and drift. Two types of d-c amplifiers are available, the single-ended input type which has been used throughout this book, and the differential input type. The amplifier output may also be of either the single-ended or differential type. As shown in Fig. 10–1, the single-ended amplifier has a common

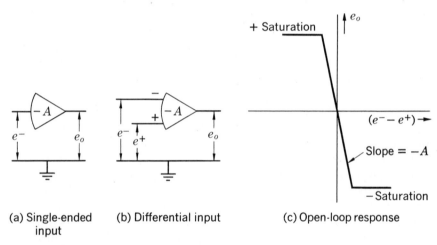

(a) Single-ended   (b) Differential input   (c) Open-loop response
     input

Fig. 10–1. Standard symbols for operational amplifiers. The open-loop gain $-A$ is the slope of the response curve.

connection between the low sides of the input and output (common ground), and its action is always inverting. The differential d-c amplifier is of a two-section design which has two sets of "floating" inputs, one of which is marked negative $(-)$ for inverting and one marked positive $(+)$ for non-inverting. Differential amplifiers amplify difference voltages (not differential voltages) and are needed to handle true signals having high common mode voltages (extraneous signals common to both leads), in amplifying voltages from grounded thermocouples, and in measuring difference voltages above ground. Grounding the positive input of a differential amplifier converts it into the usual single ended input type.

These amplifiers are available in units with open-loop voltage gains in the range of many thousand to several million at d-c frequency and with internally compensated frequency characteristics. Recall that a wide-frequency response is needed to assure precision of signal amplification because the loss of high-frequency components of non-sinusoidal signals will result in signal distortion and phase shift. However, for the amplifier to be stable under various feedback conditions, it must show a decreasing gain with increasing frequency. Other important properties of operational amplifiers are: high input impedance, low output impedance, negligible offset, and small drift with time and temperature change.

The operational amplifier is conventionally used with feedback elements, but it occasionally finds use as a decision-making switch, as in a voltage detector or comparator. In open-loop application as indicated in Fig. 10–1, the amplifier output can be switched over its full range (from − saturation to + saturation) by a small polarity change in the input. In such applications, a load-limiting resistor may be placed in the output circuit for overload protection.

Feedback Computer Elements. Feedback elements commonly used with d-c amplifiers include capacitors, resistors, and diodes. The student should refer to the analog computer discussion in Chapter 4 to review the use of capacitors and resistors in performing the linear operations of summation, integration, differentiation, etc. Diodes enable the operational amplifier to perform nonlinear operations such as saturation, limiting, and function generation.

Thermal and semiconductor diodes are nonlinear resistive elements having a low resistance to current flow in the forward bias condition (+ voltage to thermal diode plate or to p region of p-n junction) and a very high resistance to current flow in the reverse bias condition. Diode symbols and the general voltage-current characteristics of a semiconductor diode are sketched in Fig. 10–2. Notice that a small voltage in forward bias causes appreciable current flow in the diode (low resistance) whereas a large voltage (less than the Zener potential) in reverse bias causes only a small leakage current in the diode (high resistance). The diode permits current flow in the direction of the arrow in the symbol. The student is referred to a text on solid-state physics for explanation of this behavior. In computer quality diodes the "off-on" action occurs at less than a half-volt in forward bias and on reverse bias the leakage current is very small (microamperes). Heating of diodes must be avoided since the reverse current almost doubles for each 10°C increase in temperature.

At room temperature the reverse current remains very small until the reverse bias reaches the breakdown voltage and causes damaging large reverse currents to flow. If, as in Zener diodes, the current is limited by

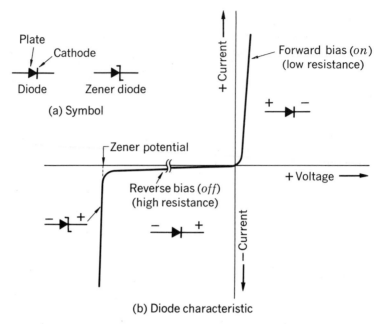

(b) Diode characteristic

Fig. 10–2. General voltage-current characteristic of a diode showing the Zener region. Forward bias on a p-n junction corresponds to positive voltage applied to the p region.

design to a safe non-destructive value, the voltage across the diode becomes almost independent of the reverse current. Zener diodes are designed to operate at reverse bias for voltage regulation purposes and are rated for Zener potential (breakdown voltage) and maximum operating current.

Analysis of Basic Circuits.[*] The internal circuitry of a good operational amplifier is of little concern to the user. However, he should study the manufacturer's literature for his equipment to be certain that he is not abusing it. Here, it is sufficient to emphasize that the amplifier input is to a high-impedance element, that direct resistance coupling is used between stages to obtain the desired gain, that high-performance amplifiers are specially stabilized, that differential inputs are "floating inputs," and that the output is a low-impedance element. The analysis of an ideal computing amplifier circuit is based on these assumptions:

1. The amplifier gain, $-A$, approaches infinity.
2. The input currents are negligible for both single-ended and differential input amplifiers.

[*] For more information, interested readers are referred to the four-volume work by Stanley Fifer, *Analogue Computation*, McGraw-Hill Book Co., Inc., New York, 1961.

3. When negative feedback is applied around an amplifier, the differential input voltage approaches zero, i.e., $e^+ - e^- = 0$.

The equivalent circuit of the ideal operational amplifier is shown in Fig. 10–3. This is also a satisfactory model for a real operational amplifier

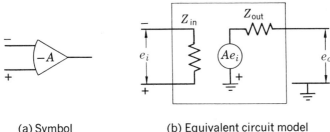

| (a) Symbol | (b) Equivalent circuit model |

Fig. 10–3. Equivalent circuit of operational amplifier. For the ideal device the parameters have these limiting values: $A = \infty$, $Z_{in} = \infty$, $Z_{out} = 0$, $e_0 = 0$ when $e_i = 0$. For a real device the parameters are less favorable.

whose circuit parameters do not reach the extreme values of the ideal device.

The analysis of analog computer circuits using a single-ended amplifier is found in Chapter 4. For circuits using a differential input amplifier, the analysis is similar, as shown below for the circuit in Fig. 10–4. Let

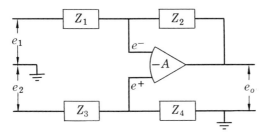

Fig. 10–4. General computing circuit for differential amplifier. The computing impedances may be real or complex.

the amplifier voltages be e^- and e^+ at the inverting and non-inverting inputs. Then the assumption that the current to each amplifier input is zero requires that for the $-$ input,

$$\frac{e_0 - e^-}{Z_2} + \frac{e_1 - e^-}{Z_1} = 0$$

or

$$e_0 = Z_2 \left[\frac{e_1}{Z_1} + e^- \left(\frac{1}{Z_1} + \frac{1}{Z_2} \right) \right] \qquad (10\text{-}1a)$$

and for the $+$ input,

$$\frac{e_2 - e^+}{Z_3} + \frac{0 - e^+}{Z_4} = 0$$

or

$$e^+ = \frac{Z_4 e_2}{Z_3 + Z_4} \qquad (10\text{-}1b)$$

This equation may be easily obtained by viewing impedances Z_3 and Z_4 as a voltage divider. Now the amplifier with negative feedback operates to force $e^- = e^+$ with the result that the computer equation for the circuit becomes

$$e_0 = -\frac{Z_2}{Z_1} e_1 + \frac{Z_4}{Z_1} \frac{(Z_1 + Z_2)}{(Z_3 + Z_4)} e_2 \qquad (10\text{-}2)$$

where the impedances, Z, may be real or complex. When the impedances are all equal, the circuit relationship simplifies to $e_0 = e_2 - e_1$. For more complex applications, the desired impedance function and circuit could be selected from Table G–1 in Appendix G.

Process engineers concerned with instrumentation and control find the operational amplifier extremely versatile in constructing special purpose computing devices. A few basic circuits are listed in Table 10–1 and discussed below.

ISOLATION. A voltage follower is used for impedance matching and to prevent interaction between two devices in series. The circuit relationship follows from the idealization that the differential input voltage to the amplifier approaches zero, i.e., $e^- = e^+$. For the voltage follower with gain, the relationships are

$$e^+ = e_1 = e^- = \frac{R}{(n+1)R} e_0$$

so that

$$e_0 = (n+1)e_1 \qquad (10\text{-}3)$$

The value of R must be selected with knowledge of e_1 and e_0 and the amplifier specifications so that the amplifier does not overload or saturate.

VOLTAGE AND CURRENT REFERENCE. The impedance-matching characteristics of operational amplifiers make them ideal for extending the use of standard voltage sources. For a voltage source without gain, the reference voltage cell is connected across the amplifier in negative feedback and $e_o = E_{\text{ref}}$. For a voltage source with gain, the reference cell is connected as shown in item 2 of Table 10–1. The amplifier drives current through resistor R to satisfy the relationship

$$e^+ = e^- = -E_{\text{ref}} + iR = 0 \qquad i = E_{\text{ref}}/R \qquad (10\text{-}4a)$$

The output voltage may be found by noting that the resistances $(R + nR)$ form a voltage divider with $E_{\text{ref}} = iR$, whence

$$e_o = i(n + 1)R = (n + 1)E_{\text{ref}} \qquad (10\text{–}4b)$$

Notice that the amplifier makes the potential across R equal to E_{ref} independent of the values of R and nR. This is a simple way to control the potential at any point in a complex network at a value E_{ref} which could be related to a temperature, concentration, position, etc. On the other hand, if R is selected as R_{std}, then the current through resistor nR is controlled as $E_{\text{ref}}/R_{\text{std}}$ independent of the value of nR.

The output of the Zener voltage source depends upon the Zener diode characteristic, E_z, and the value of n. The series resistor r limits the reverse bias current.

FEEDBACK. The inverting feedback circuit is discussed in Chapter 4. The non-inverting circuit is a generalization of the voltage follower with gain in item 1.

BRIDGES. The Wheatstone bridge is a direct way of comparing resistances. A great many process variables are measurable as changes in resistance values $(R(1 + \alpha)$ where α is the resistance change per unit change of process variable) and here the circuits in Table 10–1 are generally useful. The linear bridge can be analyzed by noting that e^+ is determined by the voltage divider across E so that $e^+ = \frac{1}{2}E$ and that e^-, likewise, is fixed by a voltage divider and given as

$$e^- = \frac{-R}{R + R(1 + \alpha)} (e_o - E)$$

The amplifier forces the relationship $e^- = e^+$ and the circuit equation becomes.

$$e_o = -\frac{E}{2} \alpha \qquad (10\text{–}5)$$

for equal bridge arm resistances. If R is linear with change in the process variable being measured, then e_o will be linear with the process variable. Analysis of the nonlinear bridge is left as a student exercise.

MISCELLANEOUS CIRCUITS. In the peak follower circuit, the input signal charges the input capacitor to the peak positive applied voltage, which is read at the output of the isolation amplifier. The capacitor value and amplifier grid impedance fix the time constant of the device. The follower is reset for the next observation by momentarily shorting the capacitor.

The absolute-value circuit is actually a full-wave rectifier having useful computer application. The output polarity can be reversed by reversing both diodes.

TABLE 10–1
Basic Computer Operations and Circuits*

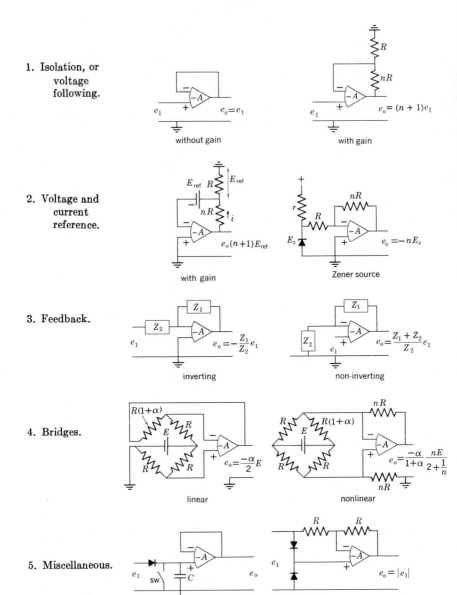

1. Isolation, or voltage following.

without gain

$e_o = e_1$

with gain

$e_o = (n+1)e_1$

2. Voltage and current reference.

with gain

$e_o (n+1)E_{ref}$

Zener source

$e_o = -nE_z$

3. Feedback.

inverting

$e_o = -\dfrac{Z_1}{Z_2} e_1$

non-inverting

$e_o = \dfrac{Z_1 + Z_2}{Z_2} e_1$

4. Bridges.

linear

$e_o = -\dfrac{\alpha}{2} E$

nonlinear

$e_o = \dfrac{-\alpha}{1+\alpha} \dfrac{nE}{2+\dfrac{1}{n}}$

5. Miscellaneous.

peak follower

absolute value

$e_o = |e_1|$

---

* Many special circuits are given in amplifier manufacturers' literature.

398

Example 10–1. Operational amplifiers find varied applications in process instrumentation. The conductance of a process stream can be measured by making a conductivity cell through which the stream flows the input impedance of an inverting amplifier. Then the amplifier output voltage will be linearly related to the conductance of the solution. Sketch a possible instrumentation circuit using a 60-cps voltage source (to avoid cell polarization) that will provide for calibration, range change, and attachment to a d-c recorder.

Solution. A possible conductance instrumentation circuit is shown in Fig. E10–1. A suitable a-c voltage is obtained from the 60-cps line using an isolating

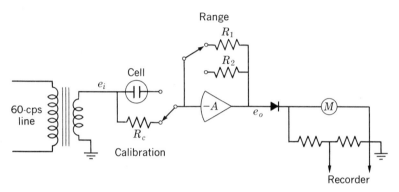

Fig. E10–1. Process conductance instrumentation.

stepdown transformer. The conductivity cell is the input resistor to the operational amplifier, while one of a series of range resistors R_f is selectable in the feedback path. Calibration of the circuit is obtained by switching R_c into the amplifier input. In this way, the output voltage depends upon the stream conductance $1/R_{cell}$ and the range resistor as

$$e_o = -R_f e_i \frac{1}{R_{cell}}$$

The diode in the output provides half-wave rectification to furnish a d-c signal to the indicating meter M and the recorder.

Some Diode Circuits. Diodes may be used in various ways as computer elements with operational amplifiers. The diode circuits in Table 10–2 are used to simulate the nonlinear characteristic shown. The circuit in item 1 produces positive saturation for $e_1 + E < 0$ because the negative input drives the output to positive saturation and the diode is reverse-biased. If $e_1 + E > 0$, the output swings negative, and the diode conducts, forcing the output to zero as shown in the graph. Usually the abrupt change in output from saturation to zero, or vice versa, is used to change the state of a switch or relay, e.g., the relay contacts could make or

TABLE 10–2
Diode Circuits for Nonlinear Phenomena

Characteristic	Circuit
1. Single-swing switch.	
2. Voltage comparator.	
3. Limiting.	
4. Dead zone.	

break a voltage contact. Signals E and e_1 may be system variables or reference voltages.

The comparator of item 2 uses two biased diodes and an operational amplifier to obtain the action sketched in the graph. Two potentiometers provide bias voltages E_{o1} and E_{o2} from the standard voltage supply.

When $e_1 < E$ the amplifier output is positive.   Under this condition diode 2 cannot conduct, and the output increases until diode 1 conducts and holds $e_o = +E_{o1}$, i.e., the anode of diode 1 becomes positive just as $e_o - E_{o1} = 0$.   Likewise, when $e_1 > E$, diode 2 conducts and holds the output voltage at $e_o = -E_{o2}$.   Voltages E and e_1 may be problem variables.   The circuit provides single-pole double-throw switching action depending on the relative magnitudes of E and e_1.

Many common nonlinear phenomena such as saturation (or limiting), backlash, and friction show magnitude dependence and are easily simulated with diodes and computer operational amplifiers.   The saturation nonlinearity exhibited by springs, flow through control valves and sonic nozzles, and other situations which show physical limitation may be simulated by the circuit in item 3.   When the input e_i increases in that circuit from zero in a positive direction, the output e_o increases from zero with a slope $R_3/(R_1 + R_2)$ (the second amplifier is a sign changer).   As e_i becomes more positive than E_{o2}, diode 2 conducts and holds e_o at the value of $E_{o2}(R_3/R_2)$ as shown on the characteristic curve.   When e_i increases in a negative direction, the output e_o decreases from zero with a slope of $R_3/(R_1 + R_2)$.   As e_i becomes more negative than E_{o1}, diode 1 conducts and holds e_o at the value of $E_{o1}(R_3/R_2)$ as shown.

The circuit in item 4 is used to simulate a dead zone characteristic in equipment.   The term refers to an operating region, usually around zero, for which there is no response to the input signal as shown in the characteristic graph.   This behavior is found in electromechanical instruments and in many gages.   The analysis of the circuit is suggested as a student exercise.

DIODE FUNCTION GENERATORS.   A function generator is a device whose output is a single-valued continuous function of its input voltage.

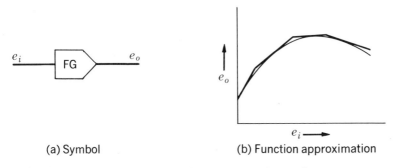

| (a) Symbol | (b) Function approximation |

Fig. 10–5.   Function generator symbol and straight line function approximation.   Diodes and operational amplifier addition circuits can generate straight line segment approximations of functions.

The function generator is used in analog process simulation and computation to insert analytical functions and graphical data (empirical relationships) into the analog program. These devices are based on such various techniques as curve followers, photoformers, tapped potentiometers, and diodes. A diode function generator generates a straight-line approximation to the desired function or graph, as shown in Fig. 10–5. The straight-line segments with adjustable slopes and breakpoints are obtained by the combined use of diodes and operational amplifier addition circuits. The operation of a logarithmic function generator is discussed below.

Logarithmic computing elements are useful in process work because they can be used for multiplication and division and many physical phenomena follow logarithmic laws, e.g., electrode potentials, equilibrium constants, activation processes, etc. One way to develop the logarithmic function using an operational amplifier is to use a logarithmic current

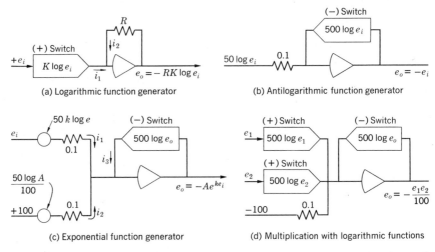

Fig. 10–6. Generation of logarithmic functions and some applications of log units.

generator to drive the amplifier output, as shown in Fig. 10–6a. A current summation at the amplifier grid requires that

$$i_1 + i_2 = i_g \cong 0$$

so that the feedback current is

$$i_2 = \frac{e_0}{R} = -i_1$$

Now, if the current function generator (diode log unit) is designed to give

$$i_1 = K \log e_i$$

the output of the operational amplifier will be

$$e_o = -RK \log e_i$$

The selection of R and K depends upon the range of e_i and the maximum amplifier output. For a computer with an output of ± 100 volts, a value of $R = 0.1$ megohm would require a driving current $i_1 = -i_2 = 100/0.1 = 10^3$ microamperes and a value of $K = 500$, and the generator equations would become

Log unit current: $i = 500 \log e_i$ microamperes   (10-6a)
Operational amplifier: $e_o = -50 \log e_i$ volts   (10-6b)

The logarithmic function generator is shown in Fig. 10-6a with a polarity switch indicated for changing polarity. Additional diodes could be used to make the polarity switching automatic.

Several applications of the logarithmic function generator are shown in Fig. 10-6. The circuit analysis is straightforward, as evidenced by the following discussion of Fig. 10-6c. The currents marked on the diagram are given in microamperes as:

$$i_1 = 50(10)ke_i \log e$$
$$i_2 = 100(10)(50 \log A)/100$$
$$i_3 = 500 \log (-e_o)$$

Since the amplifier grid current is negligible, the current summation gives

$$500ke_i \log e + 500 \log A - 500 \log (-e_o) = 0$$

or

$$e_0 = -Ae^{ke_i}$$

Thus, the device is an exponential function generator.

This method of function generation is applicable to the generation of other functions such as x^2, e^x, etc. The diode unit generates an output current proportional to the desired function $f(x)$, and the current is used as input to drive an operational amplifier. With a feedback resistor of R megohms, the output of the amplifier would be

$$e_o = -kRf(x)$$

The biased diode unit approximates the function $f(x)$ by means of straight-line segments; and hence many diodes may be needed to get a good approximation of some functions.

Functions that are the solution of differential equations can be generated by finding and solving the differential equation for the function with the appropriate initial conditions.

Multiplication and Division.   The availability of function multipliers greatly enhances the ability of analog computers to handle realistic engineering problems.   The most common analog multipliers are the servomultiplier and the quarter-square multiplier.

The servomultiplier is an electromechanical device (see Fig. 10–7) which uses a servoamplifier and motor to drive a common shaft on which is

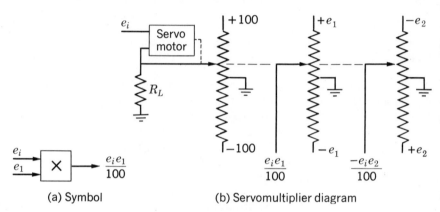

(a) Symbol   (b) Servomultiplier diagram

Fig. 10–7.   Analog multiplication symbol and the servomultiplier.

mounted a follow-up potentiometer and several computing potentiometers. The common shaft is positioned at an angle proportional to the input voltage e_i by the servosystem, using a feedback voltage from the follow-up potentiometer.   A computing potentiometer has the input voltages $+e_1$ and $-e_1$ applied across it and the voltage from the wiper is proportional to the shaft rotation and to the variable voltage.   Since the shaft rotation is made proportional to e_i, the voltage from the wiper is the product

$$z = e_i e_1 / 100 \qquad (10\text{–}6c)$$

The proportionality constant is $1/100$ since the output voltage is e_1 when e_i is 100 and the wiper is moved to the extreme end of the potentiometer. In a like manner the voltage at the wiper arm of the second computing potentiometer, having variable voltages $-e_2$ and $+e_2$ applied across it, is $w = -e_i e_2 / 100$.   The servo load resistor R_L compensates for similar load resistors to which the multiplying potentiometers are connected.   This is necessary, as pointed out in Chapter 4, to correct for potentiometer loading.   The loads must all be equal to R_L, otherwise the compensation is not exact. This circuit performs four-quadrant multiplication, since the device produces the correct sign for any polarity of e_i, e_1, and e_2. The servo multiplier is limited to operational speeds of a few cycles per second of the servo voltage e_i and to similar loading of all the potentiometers.

For high-speed multiplication, several types of electronic multipliers are used. One type is based on the logarithmic function generator and is shown in Fig. 10–6d. Another type, called the *quarter-square multiplier*, is based on the algebraic identity

$$4xy = (x + y)^2 - (x - y)^2$$

which obtains multiplication by taking a difference in squares of $(x + y)$ and $(x - y)$. Since the details of programming analog multipliers vary with the equipment used, no discussion is included here for special devices; the general symbol in Fig. 10–7a will be used to indicate analog multiplication.

The electronic analog computer has no division component. The division operation is obtained by placing a multiplier in the feedback loop

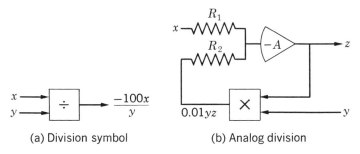

(a) Division symbol   (b) Analog division

Fig. 10-8. Analog computer division obtained by placing a multiplier in the feedback loop of a high-gain amplifier.

of a high-gain amplifier, as indicated in Fig. 10–8. The amplifier grid current is approximately zero, so that the grid current equation gives

$$\frac{x}{R_1} + \frac{yz}{100R_2} = i_g \cong 0 \qquad z = -100x/y \qquad (10\text{--}7)$$

where $R_1 = R_2$, usually taken as 1 megohm. This circuit is suitable for both negative and positive values of y, but it becomes unstable when $y = 0$, so that y must not change sign during operation. Also, the value of x must be less than y; otherwise the quotient z will exceed 100 volts, overloading the amplifier and giving unsatisfactory results.

The analog computing equipment discussed can be arranged to perform many mathematical operations. For example, the square of a function y

is obtained on an analog multiplier by multiplying the function by itself to give

$$z = 0.01y^2$$

Similarly, the square root of a function y is obtained by placing the square of the function in the feedback loop of an operational amplifier as shown

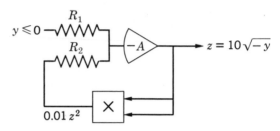

Fig. 10–9. Analog computation of square root by use of a multiplier and a high-gain amplifier.

in Fig. 10–9. Again by summing the amplifier grid current and equating it to zero, the result is

$$\frac{y}{R_1} + \frac{z^2}{100R_2} \cong 0$$

or, when $R_1 = R_2$,

$$z = 10 \sqrt{-y} \qquad (10\text{–}8)$$

For satisfactory computer operation y must be a negative voltage; then the computer gives the positive root.

Example 10–2. The effects of temperature, flow rate, and concentration on the response of a stirred-tank chemical reactor is to be studied by analog simulation. The reactor is well stirred and has a cooling jacket for temperature control as shown in Fig. E10–2. The reaction equation is

$$2A \rightarrow P + \Delta H$$
$$-\frac{dc}{dt} = kc^2 \quad k = Ae^{-a/T}$$

Make the following simplifying assumptions:

(a) There is negligible volume change due to reaction.
(b) All heat lost from reactor is transferred to coolant.
(c) The reactor and jacket equipment have negligible thermal capacity.
(d) There is perfect mixing in the reactor and in the cooling jacket.

Sketch a computer program that would simulate this system.

Solution. The jacketed reactor and its physical model are shown in Fig. E10–2a,b. First step in process simulation is to model the system by writing

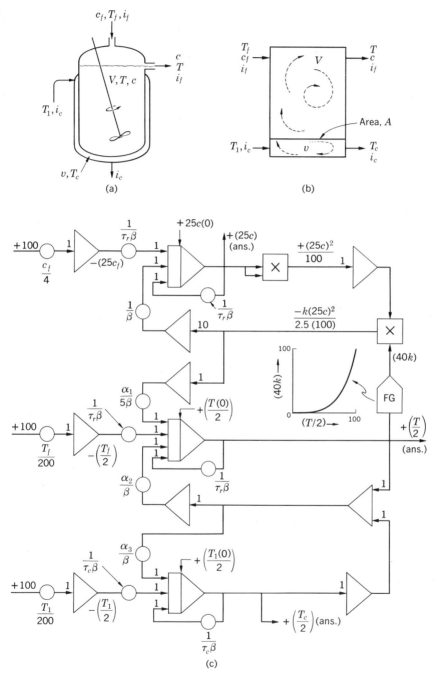

Fig. E10–2. (a) Jacketed stirred tank reactor. (b) Model for reactor.
(c) Computer program for simulation of stirred tank chemical reactor.

mathematical equations for each part of the system and listing all information about the process variables such as initial values and estimated maximum values. The following equations form the mathematical model for the reactor, subject to the listed assumptions.

Material-balance equations.

Reactor: $V \dfrac{dc}{dt} = i_f(c_f - c) - kVc^2 \qquad 0 < c < 4 \text{ lb moles/ft}^3$

Jacket: $i_c = i_c$

Energy-balance equations.

Reactor: $V\rho_r C_{pr} \dfrac{dT}{dt} = i_f \rho_r C_{pr}(T_f - T) - kV\Delta Hc^2 - UA(T - T_c)$

$$0 < T < 200° \text{ F}$$

$$k = Ae^{-a/(T + 460)}$$

Jacket: $v\rho_c C_{pc} \dfrac{dT_c}{dt} = i_c \rho_c C_{pc}(T_1 - T_c) + UA(T - T_c) \qquad 0 < T_c < 200° \text{ F}$

where c_f, c = concentrations of A in reactor feed and product, lb moles/ft³
C_{pr}, C_{pc} = heat capacities of reactor products and coolant fluid, Btu/lb-°F
i_f = input and output flow rate of reactor, ft³/hr
i_c = jacket coolant flow rate, ft³/hr
k = reaction rate constant, ft³/hr-lb mole
T_f, T = reactor feed temperature and reactor temperature, °F
T_1, T_c = input and output temperatures of jacket coolant, °F
V, v = volumes of reactor and jacket, ft³
ΔH = heat of reaction, Btu/lb mole P
U = overall heat-transfer coefficient, Btu/ft²-hr-°F
A = cooling area of jacket, ft²
ρ_r, ρ_c = densities of reactor fluid and coolant fluid, lb/ft³

The second step in process simulation is to scale the process variables so that the computer voltage range is not exceeded. Using the maximum expected values of the variables, the following scale factors are selected (for a ±100-volt computer):

$$\left(\frac{T_f}{2}\right) \quad \left(\frac{T}{2}\right) \quad \left(\frac{T_1}{2}\right) \quad \left(\frac{T_c}{2}\right) \quad (25c_f) \quad (25c) \quad (40k)$$

By grouping the parameters and substituting these scale factors in the system equations, the scaled computer equations are obtained as

$$\left(25\frac{dc}{dt}\right) = \frac{1}{\tau_r}\left[(25c_f) - (25c)\right] - \frac{k}{25}(25c)^2 \tag{a}$$

$$\left(\frac{dT}{2dt}\right) = \frac{1}{\tau_r}\left[\left(\frac{T_f}{2}\right) - \left(\frac{T}{2}\right)\right] - \frac{\alpha_1 k}{2(25)^2}(25c)^2 - \alpha_2\left[\left(\frac{T}{2}\right) - \left(\frac{T_c}{2}\right)\right] \tag{b}$$

$$\left(\frac{dT_c}{2dt}\right) = \frac{1}{\tau_c}\left[\left(\frac{T_1}{2}\right) - \left(\frac{T_c}{2}\right)\right] + \alpha_3\left[\left(\frac{T}{2}\right) - \left(\frac{T_c}{2}\right)\right] \tag{c}$$

where the symbols are defined as

$$\alpha_1 = \frac{\Delta H}{C_{\mathrm{pr}}\rho_r} \quad \alpha_2 = \frac{UA}{VC_{\mathrm{pr}}\rho_r} \quad \alpha_3 = \frac{UA}{vC_{\mathrm{pc}}\rho_c} \quad \tau_c = \frac{v}{i_c} \quad \tau_r = \frac{V}{i_f}$$

A computer program for this set of equations is presented in Fig. E10–2c.   The input values of c_f, T_f, and T_1 are obtained from reference voltage supplies through use of two potentiometers and one amplifier per variable to avoid cascading potentiometers.   The function $(40k)$, as set on the function generator, is sketched in a graph.   The program provides a choice of time scaling by selecting β. Remember that $\beta > 1$ slows the solution, while $\beta < 1$ speeds up the problem solution, and note that $1/\beta$ multiplies all the inputs to each integrator.   Using this program, the process engineer can quickly study the effects of T_f, T_1, i_f, i_c, c_f, and any reaction parameters on the behavior of the reaction system by selecting the desired potentiometer settings.

In preparation for solving this problem on a computer, the engineer would prepare a table of potentiometer settings for the particular runs to be made. A static test list of output voltages at each amplifier, multiplier, and function generator for zero time would be helpful in locating any errors in the wiring on the computer patchboard.

10-2. PLANT DATA PROCESSING APPLICATIONS

Analog computers are utilized in many ways to manipulate data in a modern process plant.   The simplest applications may involve only function generation and the solution of explicit equations.   For example, the computer can convert direct process measurements into a more meaningful variable which can be used for feedback control.   Several applications are given.

Viscosity Computer.   Viscosity control[*] in a process industry may be necessary either to meet the final product specifications or to control some primary property which is not suitable for direct measurement (e.g., molecular weight).   The viscosity property is highly temperature-dependent and sensitive to fluid rate of shear.

Poiseuille's law defines viscosity in the laminar flow region as

$$\mu_m = k_1 \frac{\Delta p}{i} \qquad (10\text{–}9a)$$

μ_m is the measured viscosity, where Δp is the differential pressure across a pipe length under steady-state conditions, i is the volumetric flow rate, and k_1 is a constant for a given pipe size and length.   The viscosity at a reference temperature μ_r depends upon Δp, i, and temperature.   If the viscosity-temperature relationship is linear, the reference temperature

---

[*] F. M. Ryan, "Putting Analog Control Computers To Work," *Control Engineering*, **11**(8), 53 (1964).

viscosity is computed from

$$\mu_r = \mu_m + \mu(T) = k_1 \frac{\Delta p}{i} + k_2(T - T_r) \tag{10–9b}$$

where T and T_r are the fluid temperature and reference temperature, respectively, and k_2 is the slope of the μ-vs.-T curve in the temperature range of interest. A better viscosity–temperature relationship is

$$\ln \mu_r = \ln \mu_m + k_3(T - T_r)$$

where k_3 is the temperature coefficient which depends upon the viscosity. Using this relationship the reference viscosity equation is given as

$$\mu_r = k_1 \frac{\Delta p}{i} \ln^{-1} k_3(T - T_r) \tag{10–9c}$$

Both equations (10–9b and 10–9c) are suitable for analog computer solution under conditions of variable temperature and flow rate. Eq. 10–9c is the basis of the computer program in Fig. 10–10. Flow rates are

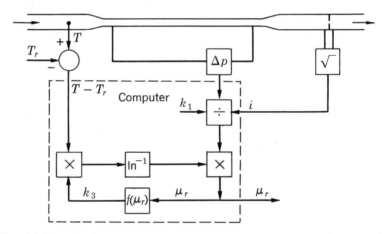

Fig. 10–10. Analog computer viscosity measurement with logarithmic temperature compensation.

generally measured with head meters, so that a square-root module is needed to give a linear flow signal. A division module divides the differential pressure signal Δp by the flow rate to give $\Delta p/i$. The fluid temperature signal is biased to produce $T - T_r$ and multiplied by the viscosity coefficient k_3, which may be set in the computer or obtained from the reference viscosity by function generation as shown in Fig. 10–10. Then the processed temperature signal passes through an antilog function generator and to a multiplier where it is multiplied by the $k_1\Delta p/i$ signal to give the reference temperature viscosity. This is a steady-state computation since the model contains no dynamic components. For application with non-Newtonian fluids, the fluid shear rate should be kept constant by controlling the flow rate.

Ratio Computer. The process engineer can use continuous process analytical instrumentation and data processing techniques to increase the efficiency of obtaining data on laboratory and plant operations. Consider the problem of studying in a pilot plant a catalytic chemical reaction such as a simple isomerization

$$A \rightleftharpoons R$$

in the gas or liquid phase. The process engineer is interested in the effects of temperature, catalyst activity, and feed flow rate on the chemical conversion. The chemical conversion is the ratio of moles R per mole (A + R) in the reactor product and is found from an analysis of the reactor product. The gas chromatograph is ideally suited to many analytic problems of this nature. It separates the components in a mixture and gives information like that in Fig. 10–11a in which output in

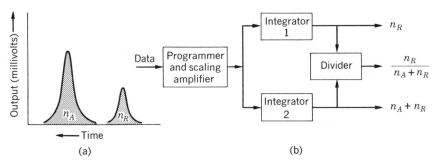

Fig. 10–11. Ratio computer scheme for data reduction in an isomerization reaction. (a) Chromatograph data. (b) Analog ratio computer.

millivolts is plotted against time. When the chromatograph is calibrated, the peaked curves correspond to the various components present and the area under the curve is proportional to the amount of that component in the mixture. Thus the data reduction problems are (1) to scale the chromatograph data, (2) to integrate the area for n_R and the total areas for $n_A + n_R$, and (3) to divide the areas to give the ratio. As indicated in Fig. 10–11b, the gas chromatograph output could be connected directly to the scaling, integrating, and division components of an analog computer to give the conversion ratio. The chromatograph is a discontinuous analytical device, since it takes samples and completes the analysis in time intervals of the order of one to ten minutes. The computer would be synchronized with the chromatograph by a programmer which would switch n_R area to integrator 1, the combined areas to integrator 2, and the completed integrator outputs to the divider for the ratio computation. The output ratio could be used as a measured variable for process control purposes.

Enthalpy Computer. The enthalpy of a homogeneous process stream is the product of the mass flow rate, the heat capacity of the fluid, and a temperature difference (actual temperature minus datum temperature). Thus, changes in the enthalpy of a flowing stream depend upon both flow rate changes and temperature variations. Using computed enthalpy as a controlled variable, the heat energy being transferred in a process plant could be controlled quantitatively. Such a control system in many applications would be superior to one using temperature or flow rate as the controlled variable.

Consider an enthalpy computer on the feed stream of a distillation column, as shown in Fig. 10–12 where the liquid feed stream is preheated

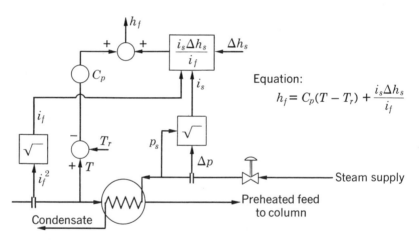

Fig. 10–12. Feed enthalpy computer. Steam enthalpy change Δh_s may be computed if the steam properties fluctuate in value.

(or partially vaporized) in a steam preheater. The enthalpy of the feed stream relative to a datum temperature T_r is the enthalpy of the stream as it enters the preheater plus the enthalpy added by the preheater, thus:

$$i_f h_f = i_f C_p(T_i - T_r) + i_s\,\Delta h_s \qquad (10\text{–}10a)$$

where i_f and i_s are the feed stream and steam flow rates, C_p and T_i are the heat capacity and temperature of the incoming feed stream, and Δh_s is the difference in enthalpy of the steam entering the preheater and the condensate leaving the preheater. Eq. 10–10a infers the enthalpy of the heated feed stream by computing the enthalpy transfer from the steam and neglecting the small thermal losses from the preheater equipment. The heat given up by each pound of steam Δh_s will be a constant for a stable steam supply. However, if the steam pressure experiences large fluctuations, it may be necessary to compute Δh_s from the steam properties and introduce it as a variable in the computer.

The enthalpy computer shown in Fig. 10–12 is based on the enthalpy equation

$$h_f = C_p(T - T_r) + i_s\,\Delta h_s/i_f \qquad \text{Btu/lb feed} \qquad (10\text{–}10\text{b})$$

The enthalpy value h_f is computed by measuring the feed temperature T and scaling the temperature signal so that it is proportional to $C_p(T - T_r)$. The feed and steam flow rates are measured, divided, and scaled to give a signal proportional to $i_s\,\Delta h_s/i_f$, which is added to the $C_p(T - T_r)$ signal to give h_f. If Δh_s is not constant, it must be computed from the steam pressure and temperature and used as a variable. The computed enthalpy h_f could be used as a measured variable in a control loop to control the enthalpy of a feed stream entering a distillation column. The computing scheme outlined above gives a static computation. It may be desirable for some plant operations to introduce dynamic lags in the computer program to match the computed result to the actual plant operation.

10–3. PROCESS CONTROL COMPUTER APPLICATIONS

In the previous article, computer components were used to compute more meaningful variables from the process measurements. The next logical step is to impose feedback control on this variable to improve process performance. The internal reflux computer shows this application. A more challenging problem for the computer is to model (simulate) the process plant for feedforward control and for process optimization, as discussed in Chapter 9. Plant modeling is difficult because the process behavior may not be well known and the model may require both static and dynamic characteristics.

Internal Reflux Control. Fractional distillation equipment operates most efficiently under steady-state conditions. In the equipment shown in Fig. 10–13 the overhead vapor is condensed and split between overhead product and external reflux which is returned to the top plate of the column. Under steady-state operation, heat and material balances exist, between the overhead vapor rate V_o, the external reflux rate R_e, the internal reflux rate R_i, and the internal vapor rate V_i entering the top plate, which can be written as:

Material balance: $R_e + V_i = R_i + V_o$ (10–11a)

Enthalpy balance: $R_e h_{el} + V_i h_{iv} = R_i h_{il} + V_o h_{ov}$ (adiabatic)

$$(10–11b)$$

where the h's represent the enthalpies of the respective streams. If the temperature of the external reflux decreases (i.e., h_{el} decreases) without a compensating decrease in flow rate, the enthalpy balance in the column is upset. The cooler external reflux will cause an increase in internal reflux flow rate R_i, resulting in a decreased overhead vapor rate V_o that will produce still cooler external reflux which acts in a regenerative manner to further upset the column. Perhaps a good temperature control on the reflux and tight control on the product composition could compensate for the change. However, a fractionator with conventional bottom temperature control will react to the cooler liquid coming down the tower by increasing the boil-up rate in the reboiler. Due to the time lags involved, the results are frequently thermal and concentration oscillations in the fractionator.

The detrimental effect of external reflux enthalpy changes on fractionator performance can be eliminated by controlling the internal reflux rate instead of the external reflux rate. In order to control the internal reflux rate, its value must be available by either measurement or computation. Since it is impractical to measure liquid flow rates inside the fractionator, a computation method has been worked out based on the energy-balance equation.* If the liquid and vapor on the top tray are at equilibrium, their temperatures must be equal, and their enthalpies are related as

$$h_{ov} = h_{il} + \lambda \qquad (10–11c)$$

where λ is the heat of vaporization. The enthalpies of the internal reflux and external reflux rates are also related, as

$$h_{il} = h_{el} + C_p(T_o - T_e) \qquad (10–11d)$$

neglecting any effect of small differences in composition. Finally, the enthalpies of vapor to the top plate and from the top plate are approximately equal (neglecting composition differences), so that

$$h_{iv} = h_{ov} \qquad (10–11e)$$

When Eqs. 10–11c, d, and e are substituted in Eq. 10–11b, the internal

* *ISA Journal*, **6**(6), 34–39 (1959).

reflux rate is found to be

$$R_i = R_e \left(1 + \frac{C_p}{\lambda} \Delta T\right) = R_e(1 + K \Delta T) \qquad (10\text{-}11f)$$

when $\Delta T = T_o - T_e$ and $K = C_p/\lambda$, a constant for a given system. Thus it is seen that the internal reflux may be computed from the external reflux rate R_e, the ΔT, and the constant K for the system, and that the internal reflux rate can be controlled for any ΔT change by manipulating R_e.

The block diagram in Fig. 10-13 indicates the computation diagram for an internal reflux analog computer. The value of $T_o - T_e = \Delta T$ is

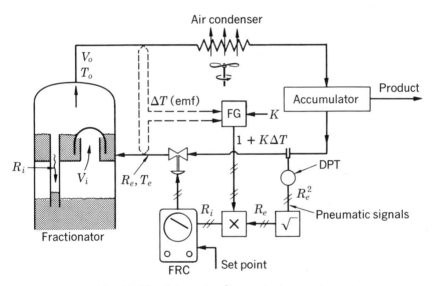

Fig. 10-13.   Internal reflux control computer.

measured by a differential thermocouple and converted into the quantity $(1 + K \Delta T)$. The differential pressure transmitter (DPT) transmits $R_e{}^2$ to a square-root device which produces R_e. Then a multiplier receives R_e and $1 + K \Delta T$, computes the product which is the internal reflux rate R_i, and transmits it as the measured variable to the flow recorder controller (FRC). The FRC acts on the information and manipulates R_e to maintain R_i constant. Thus, a difficult temperature control problem has been converted to an easy flow control problem. The internal reflux computer is accepted as a basic control device for fractionators and this example illustrates how a difficult-to-measure process variable may be computed and controlled in an actual process.

Feedforward Computer Control. One example of feedforward computer control is presented in Chapter 9. A simpler example applied to a liquid-level process from Chapter 6 is presented here for added emphasis on the technique. In feedback control, the controller drives a manipulated variable in some relation to the system error to maintain a desired value of a controlled variable. Finding the proper value of manipulated variable for a load change is a trial-and-error procedure for the feedback-controlled system and, of course, an error must exist in the system before corrective action can occur. In feedforward control, the controller drives a manipulated variable as a function of the measured load to cancel effects of load variation on the process. The feedforward controller becomes a model of the process, with the load condition for its input and a manipulated variable as its output. The exact transfer function of a feedforward controller and load measurement component is given by Eq. 6–9b as

$$G_{ff}G_m = \frac{-G_l}{G_v G_p} \qquad (6\text{–}9b)$$

Consider the application of feedforward control to the first-order liquid-level system in Fig. 6–3. In this case, $G_p = G_l$, and the exact transfer function of the feedforward control should be a proportional-plus-derivative control, since

$$G_{ff} = \frac{-1}{kG_m} = \frac{-1}{k}(\tau_m s + 1) \qquad (10\text{–}12)$$

where k is the gain of the valve, and the load-measuring device has a transfer function $G_m = 1/(\tau_m s + 1)$. The control system with a feedforward loop is shown in Fig. 10–14a. Liquid-level response curves for a unit step change in load variable $U(s)$ are given in Fig. 10–14b for no feedforward compensation and, for exact compensation, $\tau_d = \tau_m = 1$ sec. The response for no feedforward compensation is the same as that given in Fig. 6–4c. The responses were obtained by analog simulation of the system with $k = 1$, $\tau = 1$, and $K_c = 0.25$. The results are dramatic evidence of the efficacy of feedforward compensation in this simple system. The response curves for inexact compensation ($\tau_d = 0.5$ and 0.25 sec) give inexact transient results as expected; however, the static results give zero static error, which shows that feedforward compensation need not be exact to be useful in controlling process load changes.

Scaling Process Computers. Process measuring and computing instruments communicate with each other and the plant by means of standard range signals. For example, the process information from a temperature transmitter with a range of 100 to 250°F (span of 150°F)

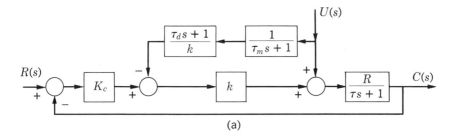

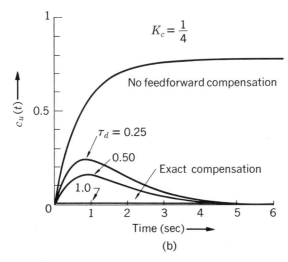

(b)

Fig. 10–14. (a) Feedforward control applied to a liquid-level process. (b) The unit step load response is given with and without feedforward compensation.

may be expressed in a pneumatic signal with a range of 3–15 psig (span of 12 psig).

The first step in deriving a set of analog computer equations from the physical process equations is to determine (1) the spans of the process variables and the corresponding computer variables and (2) the relationships between the span variables. Assume the process equation to be solved is

$$y = f(x) \tag{10–13a}$$

where x and y are the independent and dependent process variables, respectively. Let the corresponding transmitted variables be m and z. The span or range of a variable is its maximum value minus its minimum value. The value of each variable within its span is represented as a fraction of span, thus:

$$f_x = \frac{x - x_{min}}{x_{max} - x_{min}} \quad f_y = \frac{y - y_{min}}{y_{max} - y_{min}} \quad f_m = \frac{m - m_{min}}{m_{max} - m_{min}} \quad f_z = \frac{z - z_{min}}{z_{max} - z_{min}}$$
$$(10\text{–}13b)$$

The pair of variables f_x and f_y are related by the process equation, Eq. 10–13a, and the pairs of variables f_x, f_m, and f_y, f_z, are related by the process transmitter equation. For pressure transmission the output varies linearly with input ($f_m = f_x$), but for flow transmission using a head flow meter, the output varies as the square of the flow ($f_m = f_x^2$). Generally, the transmitter equations can be written in the form

$$f_x = g(f_m) \qquad f_y = h(f_z) \qquad (10\text{–}13c)$$

where f_m and f_z are the fraction of span of the transmitted signals. All the fraction of span values can be eliminated between Eqs. 10–13a, b, and c, giving as an intermediate step

$$f_x = \frac{x - x_{min}}{x_{max} - x_{min}} = g\left(\frac{m - m_{min}}{m_{max} - m_{min}}\right)$$
$$f_y = \frac{y - y_{min}}{y_{max} - y_{min}}$$
$$= h\left(\frac{z - z_{min}}{z_{max} - z_{min}}\right) \qquad (10\text{–}13d)$$

and finally, from Eq. 10–13a, the result

$$h\left(\frac{z - z_{min}}{z_{max} - z_{min}}\right) = \frac{1}{y_{max} - y_{min}} \left\{ f\left[x_{min} + (x_{max} - x_{min}) g\left(\frac{m - m_{min}}{m_{max} - m_{min}}\right)\right] - y_{min}\right\} \quad (10\text{–}13e)$$

This equation appears to be complex; but it is easy to use in practice, since the subscripted values are constants and the functions f, g, h are given by relationships of the form of Eqs. 10–13a and c.

Example 10–3. The heat transferred to the cold fluid in a heat exchanger is given as

$$q = C_p i \, \Delta T \qquad \text{Btu/min}$$

where $C_p = 1$ is the fluid heat capacity in Btu/lb-°F, i is the flow rate in lb/min, and ΔT is the fluid temperature change in °F. The ΔT is measured with a copper-constantan thermocouple and is expected to be in the range of 0–120° F. The i is measured with a head meter and is expected to be in the range of 0–100 lb/min. Write and scale the necessary transmitter and computer equations for pneumatic components with a range of 3–15 psi.

Solution. Assume that q has the range of 0–10,000 Btu/min. The span of each variable is given as

$$f_q = q/10,000 \qquad f_{\Delta T} = \Delta T/120 \qquad f_i = i/100$$

and the heat-transfer equation becomes

$$f_q = 1.20 f_i f_{\Delta T}$$

The signal-variable relationships in terms of fraction of span are

$$f_q = \frac{S_q - 3}{12} \qquad f_{\Delta T} = \frac{S_{\Delta T} - 3}{12} \qquad f_i^2 = \frac{S_i - 3}{12} \text{ (head meter)}$$

where S_q, $S_{\Delta T}$, and S_i are the values of the pneumatic signals within each span. Substitution of these relationships in the heat transfer equation gives the scaled computer equation as

$$S_q = 0.346 \sqrt{S_i - 3} \, (S_{\Delta T} - 3) + 3$$

Notice that it is not necessary to consider such details of the transmitters as the psi/millivolt ratio in the ΔT component.

PROBLEMS

10–1. The useful temperature range of a thermocouple can be extended several thousand degrees beyond its normal temperature range by computing the static temperature from thermocouple step response information (see *Instruments and Control Systems,* **37,** No. 5, pp. 101–3, 1964). The step response of a first-order device is exponential, and the static response can be computed from the initial response data. The system consists of an analog computer, a thermocouple, and a switching device which exposes the thermocouple alternately to a standard coolant and to the high-temperature gas. The thermocouple is a first-order device whose time constant τ varies with the thermocouple and the hot-gas characteristics and must be computed during the measuring operation. Propose an analog computer program for finding the gas temperature from the thermocouple response to high-temperature gas pulses of about 0.1τ-sec. duration. HINT: The gas temperature is given as

$$T_g = \tau \frac{dT}{dt} + T$$

Now, if T_g is constant during the pulse, τ is the value that makes $\tau \dot{T} + T$ constant and T_g is the value of that constant.

10–2. A pumping station supplies water by a pipeline to an industrial plant 20 miles distant. A constant pressure at the far end of the pipeline is maintained by variable-speed pumps. The pumping costs dominate the economics of the water supply, and for this reason excess output pipeline pressures are to be avoided. The prohibitive expense of transmitting the output pressure to the pumping station suggests that the required input pressure be computed at the pumping station and used as the control signal. Write an expression for the pipeline input pressure, and show a computer program for computing it from the measured flow rate.

10-3. What functions do these devices (Fig. P10–3) generate?

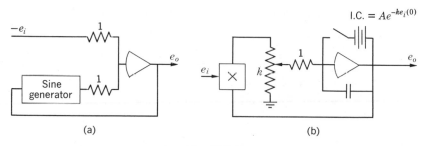

(a)   (b)

Fig. P10-3

10-4. The composition of a ternary mixture can be determined by measurement of two physical properties P_1 and P_2 which are functions of the mixture composition. Write equations which can be used to find the compositions x_1, x_2, and x_3 when the properties are known. Assume a linear property-composition relationship. Then devise an analog computer program that will solve these equations (*ISA Journal*, **8**, (10), 38, [1961]).

10-5. Sketch an analog computer program for computing the masses of two ferroalloy additives to be added to a given batch of steel, B lb, to produce a required alloy steel. The mass fractions of each component (x, y) in the batch are x_b and y_b; in the final alloy, x_a and y_a; and in each ferroalloy, x_f and y_f. Each ferroalloy contains only steel and one other component. Let the masses of the ferroalloys be M_x and M_y.

10-6. Analog logarithmic units are useful computing devices. What computations do the programs shown in Fig. P10–6 perform?

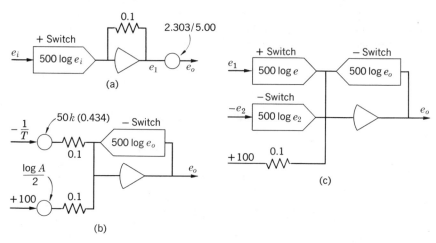

Fig. P10-6

10-7. Accurate gas flow measurements are necessary to eliminate accounting losses in transfer of gases. The gas flow rate Q in standard ft³/hr may be given as

$$Q = KF_g F_c \sqrt{\frac{\Delta h\ p}{T}}$$

where Δh is the differential pressure across the flow orifice, p is the upstream static pressure, T is the absolute temperature, K is the orifice flow constant, F_g is the specific gravity factor, and F_c is the pressure pulsation correction factor. Assume that Δh, p, and T measurements are converted to millivoltages, and sketch a block diagram of a computer to give computed values of Q.

10-8. The heat removal rate from a reactor can be computed by measuring the temperature rise of the cooling fluid going through the reactor heat exchanger and the cooling-fluid flow rate. Then the cooling rate is given as

$$\text{Btu/min} = C_p i\, \Delta T$$

where C_p is the heat capacity of the fluid in Btu/lb-°F, i is the flow rate in lbs/min, and ΔT is the cooling-fluid temperature rise in °F. Sketch the block diagram of a computer which uses the ΔT in millivolts and flow rate as air signal proportional to head (square root must be obtained).

10-9. Suppose that, in the $(1 + K\, \Delta T)$ section of the computer in Fig. 10–13, the differential thermocouple is copper-constantan, the maximum ΔT is 100° F, and the minimum ΔT is zero. If this section produces a pneumatic output range of 3 to 15 psig with 3 psig as the zero output, find the equation for the output as a function of ΔT when $K = 0.004$ per °F.

10-10. Improved fractionator operation will result from use of a feed enthalpy computer. The feed to many fractionators enters at the bubble point or partially vaporized, under which condition the feed temperature is not a good measure of the enthalpy. Initially, the feed is preheated and partially vaporized by heat exchange with the hot bottom product in an economizer heat exchanger. Then the feed is brought to the desired enthalpy by a controlled steam preheater. Sketch the block diagram of a feed enthalpy computer-controller which could be used to control the enthalpy of a feedstream to the fractionator. (*Ind. Eng. Chem.*, **53**, 963, [1961].)

10-11. Write an analog computer program to simulate the physical system described by the equations

$$2\frac{dc}{dt} + c = z$$

$$\frac{d^2 z}{dt^2} + 2\frac{dz}{dt} + 10z = 10$$

when

$$c(0) = 0 \quad z(0) = -10 \quad \dot{z}(0) = 10$$

(a) Find ζ and ω_n for the system. Is time scaling necessary with a computer recorder that can follow a 2-cps signal?

(b) Draw the program, and indicate integrator initial conditions.

10-12. An analog device is needed to instantaneously compute the overall heat-transfer coefficient in a condensing steam–cold oil heat exchanger. The relationships for any consistent set of units are

heat-transfer coefficient: $U = q/A \; \Delta T_{lm}$
heat-transfer rate to oil: $q = i C_p (T_2 - T_1)$

where ΔT_{lm} is the log mean terminal temperature difference between steam and oil, $T_2 - T_1$ is the temperature change in the oil whose flow rate is i and whose heat capacity is C_p, and A is the area of heat-transfer surface. Assuming that thermocouples are used for temperature measurement, that A and C_p are constant, and that the oil flow rate is given as a millivoltage from a strain-gage differential pressure transducer, devise an analog computer to evaluate U, using the instantaneous data from the heat exchanger.

A

Complex Functions and Mapping[*]

The mathematical concept of function defines a relationship of dependence between two or more variables. If a given value of s, by some rule of correspondence, determines a value $G(s)$, then $G(s)$ is a function of s, as symbolically stated in

$$G(s) = f(s)$$

This statement assigns, for each complex number s in the region of definition, the corresponding value of the dependent complex variable $G(s)$. When $s = \sigma + j\omega$, then the corresponding complex number $G(s)$ may be written

$$G(s) = u + jv = f(\sigma + j\omega) \tag{A-1}$$

and the real variables u and v are determined by the pair of real variables σ and ω; so the functional dependence can be extended as

$$u = u(\sigma,\omega) \qquad v = v(\sigma,\omega)$$

When values of s are real, the functional dependence of $G(s)$ can be shown as a graph of $G(s)$ versus s. But when values of s are complex, each value of s involves four quantities—the real and imaginary parts of s and the real and imaginary parts of $G(s)$—which cannot be represented in the usual graphical manner. However, several pictorial representations of functions of a complex variable are possible as described here.

A–1. PLOTS OF MAGNITUDE LOCI AND PHASE-ANGLE LOCI

For each value of s, the function $G(s)$ has a magnitude and phase angle which can be shown on two separate three-dimensional graphs on the s-plane. Thus, on one s-plane, at each value of s, a perpendicular can be erected whose height is equal to the magnitude of $G(s)$, forming a

_____
* Appendix A is supplementary to Chapter 2.

magnitude of $G(s)$ surface. On a second s-plane, at each value of s, a perpendicular can be erected whose height is the angle of $G(s)$, forming an angle of $G(s)$ surface. Since three-dimensional plots are not convenient to manipulate graphically, the information on the surface can be projected onto each s-plane as loci of constant magnitude and of constant phase angle.

Two examples of such plots are shown in Figs. A–1 and A–2. In Fig. A–1, the functional relation is

$$G_1(s) = s + 1 = (\sigma + 1) + j\omega \tag{A-2}$$

or in polar form

$$G_1(s) = [(\sigma + 1)^2 + \omega^2]^{1/2} \angle \tan^{-1} \omega/(\sigma + 1)$$

where the magnitude is:

$$|G_1(s)| = [(\sigma + 1)^2 + \omega^2]^{1/2}$$

and the angle is:

$$\underline{/G_1(s)} = \tan^{-1} \omega/(\sigma + 1)$$

The isometric sketches in Fig. A–1a show the magnitude and phase angle surfaces for $G_1(s)$. Lines of constant ω and constant magnitude are shown on the magnitude surface. The phase-angle surface includes angles from $-180°$ to $+180°$ for values of s inside a circle around the point $s = -1$. Practical working diagrams are obtained by projecting constant-magnitude and phase-angle loci for $G_1(s)$ onto the s-plane as shown in Fig. A–1b. The equations of these loci are found as follows.

For loci of constant magnitude $G_1(s)$, where r is the magnitude,

$$(\sigma + 1)^2 + \omega^2 = r^2$$

For loci of constant phase angle of $G_1(s)$,

$$\omega = (\sigma + 1) \tan \theta_1$$

The constant-magnitude loci are circles of radius equal to the magnitude of $G_1(s)$ with centers at $s = -1$; the constant phase-angle loci are straight lines intersecting at $s = -1$ and having slope of $\tan \theta$. On these plots the point $s = -1 + j0$ has special significance since it is a value of s that makes $G_1(s) = 0$; hence, it is known as a *zero* of $G_1(s)$.

A second example will make these methods of plotting more familiar. In Fig. A–2, the functional relation is

$$G_2(s) = (s + 1)^{-1} = [(\sigma + 1) + j\omega]^{-1} \tag{A-3}$$

and in polar form

$$G_2(s) = [(\sigma + 1)^2 + \omega^2]^{-1/2} \angle \tan^{-1} -\omega/(\sigma + 1)$$

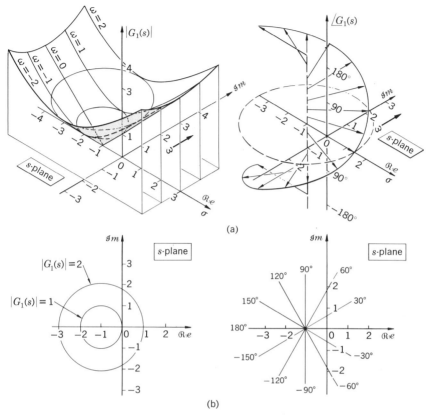

(a)

(b)

Fig. A–1. Two methods of representing $G_1(s) = s + 1$ on the s-plane. (a) Magnitude and phase-angle surfaces $|G_1(s)|\angle\theta$ in space. (b) Projections of magnitude and phase-angle loci of $G_1(s)$ on the s-plane.

The isometric sketches in Fig. A–2a show the magnitude and phase-angle surfaces for $G_2(s)$.   Lines of constant ω and constant magnitude are shown on the magnitude surface.   The phase-angle surface includes angles from $+180°$ to $-180°$ for values of s inside a circle around the point $s = -1$. It is seen that values on the magnitude surface at a given s are reciprocal to those at the same s on the magnitude surface in Fig. A–1a and also that the phase angles are the negative of the phase angles in Fig. A–1a. Projections of constant magnitude and phase-angle loci for $G_2(s)$ onto the s-plane are shown in Fig. A–2b.   The equations for these loci are given.
    For loci of constant magnitude r:

$$(\sigma + 1)^2 + \omega^2 = r^{-2}$$

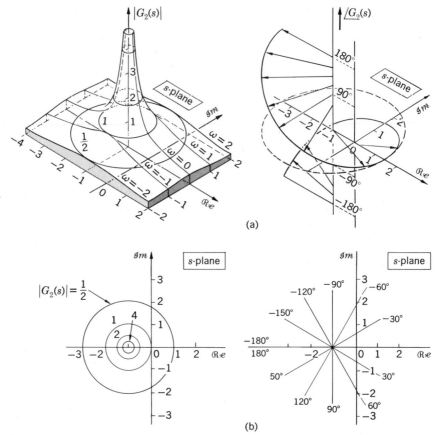

Fig. A–2. Two methods for representing $G_2(s) = (s + 1)^{-1}$ on the s-plane. (a) Magnitude and phase-angle surfaces $|G_2(s)|\angle\theta$ in space. (b) Projections of magnitude and phase-angle loci of $G_2(s)$ on the s-plane.

For loci of constant phase angle:

$$\omega = -(\sigma + 1) \tan \theta_2$$

The magnitude loci are circles of radius equal to the reciprocal of the magnitude of $G_2(s)$ with centers at $s = -1$. The phase-angle loci are straight lines intersecting at $s = -1$ and having slope of $-\tan \theta_2$. The magnitude of $G_2(s)$ at $s = -1 + j0$ is infinite; this value of s is called a *pole* of $G_2(s) = (s + 1)^{-1}$. The function has a *zero* at $s = \infty$ since an infinite value of s gives zero value to the function.

A-2. PLOTS BY TRANSFORMATION FROM s-PLANE TO $G(s)$-PLANE

Another way to show the nature of a function of a complex variable is to use the given function to map an arbitrary set of values of s from the s-plane onto the function plane. Each point in the s-plane determines a point in the $G(s)$-plane by the $G(s)$ transformation, so that the function maps or transforms s-values into $G(s) = u + jv$ values that can be plotted on the $G(s)$-plane.

For experimentally studying the dynamics of process plants, process control engineers use a technique called *frequency response analysis*, which restricts s to values along the imaginary axis ($s = j\omega$). During the frequency response test, as s is varied along the $j\omega$-axis from zero to infinity, the plant response takes on values of $G(j\omega)$ that are characteristic of the

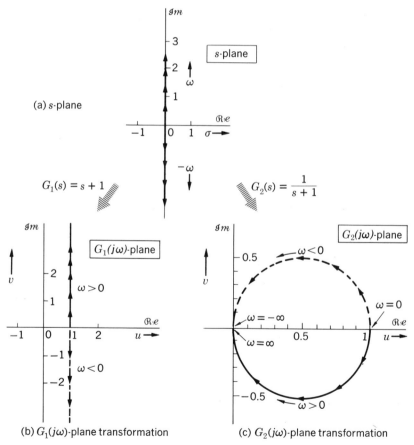

(a) s-plane

$G_1(s) = s + 1$ $G_2(s) = \dfrac{1}{s + 1}$

(b) $G_1(j\omega)$-plane transformation   (c) $G_2(j\omega)$-plane transformation

Fig. A-3. Examples of transformation from $s = j\omega$ to the $G(j\omega)$-plane.

plant unit and the frequency ω. In other words, the frequency response $G(j\omega)$ is the result of mapping $s = j\omega$ values onto the $G(j\omega)$ plane, using the plant transformation $G(s)$. The frequency response of the function $G_1(s)$ is the transformation of $s = j\omega$ onto the $G_1(j\omega)$ plane, thus:

$$G_1(s) = s + 1 \quad \text{becomes} \quad G_1(j\omega) = 1 + j\omega$$

In Fig. A–3a values of $s = j\omega$ are shown on the s-plane, and the transformed values are shown on the $G_1(j\omega)$ plane in Fig. A–3b; from these it is seen that the axis of the imaginaries in the s-plane is translated one unit to the right in the transformation to the $G_1(j\omega)$ plane.

Next, consider the mapping properties of the reciprocal transformation when $s = j\omega$:

$$G_2(s) = (s + 1)^{-1} \quad \text{becomes} \quad G_2(j\omega) = (1 + j\omega)^{-1} = u + jv$$

where $u = (1 + \omega^2)^{-1}$ and $v = -\omega/(1 + \omega^2)$. Elimination of ω in these relationships gives the frequency response function on the $G_2(j\omega)$ plane as

$$v^2 + (u - \tfrac{1}{2})^2 = \tfrac{1}{4}$$

which is a circle as shown on Fig. A–3c. The map for $0 < \omega < \infty$ is the mirror image of the map for $0 > \omega > -\infty$, as seen on the plot.

A–3. PLOTS BY TRANSFORMATION FROM $G(j\omega)$-PLANE TO $G(j\omega)/[1 + G(j\omega)]$-PLANE

The frequency response (see previous article) of an open-loop plant, $G(j\omega)$, is known either from experiment or analysis. The process engineer will want to know the frequency response of the closed-loop system. If a unity feedback loop is combined with $G(j\omega)$, the overall system function called the *closed-loop function* becomes

$$\frac{C(j\omega)}{R(j\omega)} = \frac{G(j\omega)}{1 + G(j\omega)} = M\angle\alpha \tag{A–4a}$$

where $C(j\omega)/R(j\omega)$ is the ratio of the output variable to the input variable (as shown in Chapter 1) and M and α are the magnitude and phase angle of that ratio; so

$$M = \left|\frac{C(j\omega)}{R(j\omega)}\right| = \left|\frac{G(j\omega)}{1 + G(j\omega)}\right| \qquad \angle\alpha = \tan^{-1}\frac{\mathfrak{Im}\ C(j\omega)/R(j\omega)}{\mathfrak{Re}\ C(j\omega)/R(j\omega)} \tag{A–4b}$$

The function $G(j\omega)$ may be known from analysis of or experimentation on a system; it is desired to have a procedure to obtain the closed-loop function $M\angle\alpha$ from the open-loop function $G(j\omega)$. In short, a transformation procedure from the $G(j\omega)$-plane to the $M\angle\alpha$-plane is desired.

For purposes of illustrating the transformation procedures, a function $G(s) = (s + 1)^{-1}$ is assumed for the plant unit and the plots for that function are shown in Fig. A–3c for values of $s = j\omega$ with ω varying from zero to infinity. In Fig. A–4b, $G(j\omega)$, the open-loop frequency response,

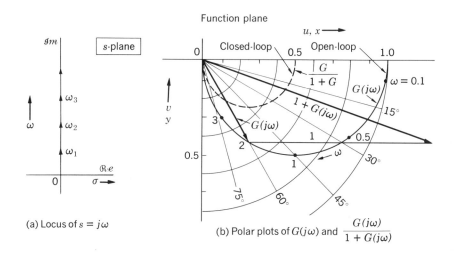

(a) Locus of $s = j\omega$

(b) Polar plots of $G(j\omega)$ and $\dfrac{G(j\omega)}{1 + G(j\omega)}$

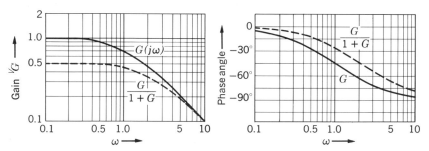

(c) Logarithmic plots (Bode plot) of amplitude ratio and phase angle

Fig. A–4. Open-loop and closed-loop frequency response plots on polar and logarithmic coordinates.

is plotted on polar coordinates (or rectangular coordinates for $G(j\omega) = u + jv$) from the equation with positive ω:

$$G(j\omega) = \frac{1}{1 + j\omega} = u + jv = \frac{1}{\sqrt{1 + \omega^2}} \angle \tan^{-1} - \omega$$

where $u = 1/(1 + \omega^2)$ and $v = -\omega/(1 + \omega^2)$. The complex function $G(j\omega)$ may be plotted on logarithmic coordinates called Bode charts by taking the principal value of the logarithm function as

$$\ln G(j\omega) = \ln |G(j\omega)| + j\angle G(j\omega)$$
$$= -\tfrac{1}{2}\ln(1 + \omega^2) + j\tan^{-1}(-\omega \pm 2\pi k) \qquad k = 0, 1, 2, \ldots$$

Using the principal value ($k = 0$), this equation is sketched as the solid lines on the Bode charts in Fig. A–4c in two parts: the magnitude plot, as $\ln |G(j\omega)|$ versus $\ln \omega$; and the phase angle plot, $\angle G(j\omega)$ versus $\ln \omega$. These two plots clearly show the dependence of $G(j\omega)$ upon the frequency parameter ω and display the same information as the polar plot in Fig. A–4b.

The closed-loop frequency response may be obtained from the open-loop plot in Fig. A–4b by graphically measuring the vectors $G(j\omega)$ and $1 + G(j\omega)$ and forming the ratio $C(j\omega)/R(j\omega)$ as required by Eq. A–4a. In the present case, on substituting $G(j\omega) = (1 + j\omega)^{-1}$, the closed-loop function becomes

$$\frac{C(j\omega)}{R(j\omega)} = \frac{1}{2 + j\omega} = M\angle\alpha = x + jy = \frac{1}{\sqrt{4 + \omega^2}} \angle\tan^{-1} -\omega/2 \quad \text{(A–4c)}$$

and

$$\ln C(j\omega)/R(j\omega) = -\tfrac{1}{2}\ln(4 + \omega^2) + j\angle\tan^{-1} -\omega/2$$

where $x = 2/(4 + \omega^2)$ and $y = -\omega/(4 + \omega^2)$. This equation is shown on polar coordinates as the dashed line in Fig. A–4b and on logarithmic coordinates as the dashed lines in Fig. A–4c.

In general, the closed-loop function $C(j\omega)/R(j\omega)$ may be read graphically from the $G(j\omega)$ polar plot by the superposition of the M and α grid lines shown in Fig. A–5a onto the $G(j\omega)$ plot. These grid lines are computed by writing the complex open-loop function as

$$G(j\omega) = u + jv$$

and then relating the M and α values to u and v as

$$\frac{C(j\omega)}{R(j\omega)} = M\angle\alpha = \frac{G(j\omega)}{1 + G(j\omega)} = \frac{u + jv}{(1 + u) + jv}$$

The magnitude M and the phase angle α are found as

$$M^2 = \frac{u^2 + v^2}{(1 + u)^2 + v^2} \qquad \angle\alpha = \tan^{-1}\frac{v}{u} - \tan^{-1}\frac{v}{1 + u} \quad \text{(A–4d)}$$

The magnitude equation can be rearranged into the normal form of the equation of a circle,

$$v^2 + \left(u + \frac{M^2}{M^2 - 1}\right)^2 = \frac{M^2}{(M^2 - 1)^2}$$

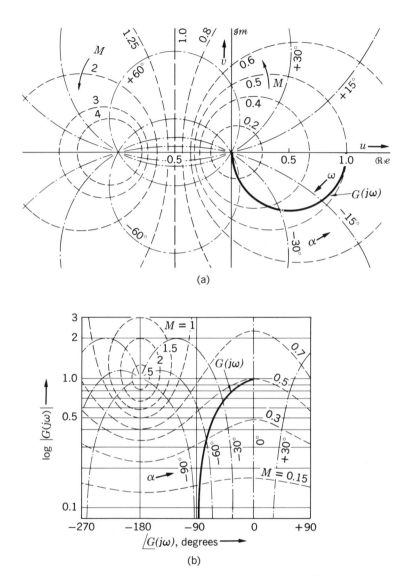

(a)

(b)

Fig. A–5.   Transformation of the open-loop function $G(j\omega)$ to the closed-loop function $M\angle\alpha$ on the complex plane: (a) Superposition of M and α circles on the complex plane; (b) M and α circles on Nichols chart.

whose radius is $|M/(M^2 - 1)|$ and whose center is located at the point $v = 0$, $u = -M^2/(M^2 - 1)$.   A few of these magnitude circles are drawn as dashed lines on Fig. A–5a, from which it is seen that all values of $u >$ -0.5 result in closed-loop magnitudes less than 1 and that as values of u approach -1, the corresponding values of M approach infinity.

The phase-angle equation Eq. A–4d can be simplified by noting that angle α is a difference between two angles and therefore $\tan \alpha$ can be written as

$$\tan \alpha = \frac{\dfrac{v}{u} - \dfrac{v}{1+u}}{1 + \dfrac{v^2}{u(1+u)}} = \frac{v}{u(1+u) + v^2}$$

After rearranging the equation and completing the square by the addition of $\frac{1}{4}(1 + 1/\tan^2 \alpha)$ to both sides of the equation, it is seen that a line of constant angle α is a circle

$$\left(u + \frac{1}{2}\right)^2 + \left(v - \frac{1}{2\tan\alpha}\right)^2 = \frac{1}{4}\left(1 + \frac{1}{\tan^2\alpha}\right)$$

with radius

$$\frac{1}{2}\left(1 + \frac{1}{\tan^2\alpha}\right)^{1/2}$$

and center located at the point $v = 1/(2\tan\alpha)$, $u = -\frac{1}{2}$. The constant angle α lines are shown as dash-dot lines on Fig. A–5a. The function $G(j\omega)$ is plotted on Fig. A–5a as the heavy solid line, and the closed-loop function $G(j\omega)/(1 + G(j\omega))$ can now be read from the intersections of $G(j\omega)$ with the M and α grid of circles. The closed-loop M and α values for $G(j\omega) = 1/(1 + j\omega)$ are plotted as the dashed lines on the Bode plots of Fig. A–4c. The advantage of the M–α grid on the complex plane is that it can be superimposed on the $G(j\omega)$ plot in Fig. A–4b and used to obtain the M and α values directly. The student should verify that the closed-loop plots in Figs. A–4c can be read from Fig. A–5a. Yet another graphical method is available for easily obtaining the closed-loop frequency response from the open-loop values. In Fig. A–5b the open-loop frequency response, $G(j\omega)$, is plotted on log $|G|$ vs. $\angle G$ rectangular coordinates. The relationship for $G(j\omega) = (j\omega + 1)^{-1}$ is given above and drawn as the heavy solid line in Fig. A–5b. The M and α lines (remember: $G(j\omega) = u + jv$) form an overlaid grid from which the closed-loop frequency response can be read for any open-loop frequency response with unity feedback. These transformations are frequently used in the frequency response chapter; see also Appendix D.

These examples show that each complex function $G(s)$ can be interpreted as a mapping of an arbitrary set of s-values into a resultant set of $G(s)$-values in the $G(s)$-plane and that there are many possible graphical representations for $G(s)$.

A–4. OPERATIONS ON COMPLEX FUNCTIONS

Process engineers are chiefly interested in functions of a complex variable that have a unique derivative. Some examples of complex functions are these:

Polynomials:

$$G(s) = a_n s^n + a_{n-1} s^{n-1} + \cdots a_0$$

Exponential:

$$G(s) = e^{as}$$

Logarithmic:

$$G(s) = \log s = \log |s| + j\theta \qquad 0 < \theta < 2\pi \text{ (principal value)}$$

Trigonometric:

$$\sin s = \frac{1}{2j} (e^{js} - e^{-js}) \qquad \cos s = \frac{1}{2} (e^{js} + e^{-js})$$

Limits, continuity, and differentiation of complex functions are defined as for real functions. Thus, the derivative of a complex function is

$$\frac{dG(s)}{ds} = G'(s) = \lim_{\Delta s \to 0} \frac{G(s + \Delta s) - G(s)}{\Delta s} \qquad \text{(A–5a)}$$

when the limit exists uniquely as $\Delta s \to 0$ from any direction in the complex plane. If the derivative is not unique, then it is not possible to differentiate $G(s)$ by means of simple formulas. Most important, however, it is found that most of the ordinary types of functions used to describe physical systems have unique derivatives. A function $G(s)$ is said to be *analytic* in a region in the s-plane if it has a finite continuous derivative at each point in that region and if it is single-valued in that region. The test for analyticity of a function in a region is that the Cauchy-Riemann equations hold in that region. This requirement is

$$\frac{\partial u}{\partial \sigma} = \frac{\partial v}{\partial \omega} \qquad \frac{\partial u}{\partial \omega} = -\frac{\partial v}{\partial \sigma}$$

When $G(s)$ is analytic at the point considered, then the derivative is given as

$$\frac{dG(s)}{ds} = \frac{d(u + jv)}{ds} = G'(s) = \frac{\partial u}{\partial \sigma} + j \frac{\partial v}{\partial \sigma} = \frac{\partial v}{\partial \omega} - j \frac{\partial u}{\partial \omega} \qquad \text{(A–5b)}$$

and the usual differentiation formulas hold. A result of these relationships is that if one part of an analytic function is given, then the other part, and also the function itself, may be found except for an additive constant.

Example A–1. Determine if the function $|s|^2$ is analytic.

Solution. Two methods may be used to show analyticity: either show that the function is single-valued and has a unique derivative in a region of s or show that the Cauchy-Riemann conditions prevail. Using the latter approach, write

$$G(s) = u + jv = |\sigma + j\omega|^2 = [\sqrt{\sigma^2 + \omega^2}]^2 = \sigma^2 + \omega^2$$

from which $u = \sigma^2 + \omega^2$ and $v = 0$. Then $\partial u/\partial \sigma = 2\sigma$ and $\partial v/\partial \omega = 0$, and the only value for which $\partial u/\partial \sigma = \partial v/\partial \omega$ holds is $\sigma = 0$. Likewise, $\partial u/\partial \omega = 2\omega$ and $\partial v/\partial \sigma = 0$, and the only value for which the Cauchy-Riemann condition holds is $\omega = 0$. Therefore, this function is not analytic, since it does not satisfy the Cauchy-Riemann equations.

The definite integral of a complex function is the line integral defined for a continuous path in a stated region, then

$$\begin{aligned} {}_C\!\int_{s_1}^{s_2} G(s) \, ds &= {}_C\!\int_{s_1}^{s_2} (u + jv)(d\sigma + j \, d\omega) \\ &= {}_C\!\int_{s_1}^{s_2} (u \, d\sigma - v \, d\omega) + j {}_C\!\int_{s_1}^{s_2} (v \, d\sigma + u \, d\omega) \end{aligned} \quad \text{(A–6a)}$$

It is necessary to state the entire path C which integration follows, since there is more than one continuous path from s_1 to s_2 in the s-plane. When the path C lies in a region inside which $G(s)$ is analytic, the line integral is independent of the path C and its value can be found in the usual way as

$$\int_{s_1}^{s_2} G(s) \, ds = F(s_2) - F(s_1) \quad \text{(A–6b)}$$

where $F'(s) = G(s)$. When s_1 and s_2 coincide, the value of the integral is zero, so

$$\oint_C G(s) \, ds = 0 \quad \text{(A–6c)}$$

where C is a closed path in a region in the s-plane where $G(s)$ is analytic. This result is known as Cauchy's theorem. In cases where $G(s)$ is not analytic within the region enclosed by the closed curve C, the integral may or may not vanish.

Example A–2. Evaluate the integral of Eq. A–6c for the cases $G_1(s) = s^{-1}$ and $G_2(s) = (s + 1)^{-1}$ when s varies along the closed curve C given as the unit circle $|s| = 2$ with the center at the origin and inclosing the points $s = 0$ and $s = -1$ at which $G_1(s)$ and $G_2(s)$, respectively, are not analytic.

Solution. Values of s on the circle are written as

$$s = 2e^{j\theta} \quad \text{and} \quad ds = 2je^{j\theta} \, d\theta$$

The integral for the function s^{-1} becomes

$$\oint_C G_1(s) \, ds = \int_0^{2\pi} \tfrac{1}{2}e^{-j\theta}(2je^{j\theta}) \, d\theta = \int_0^{2\pi} j \, d\theta = 2\pi j$$

The integral for the function $(s + 1)^{-1}$ becomes

$$\oint_C G_2(s) \, ds = \int_0^{2\pi} \frac{2je^{j\theta}}{2e^{j\theta} + 1} \, d\theta$$

$$= \ln \left(2e^{j\theta} + 1\right) \Big|_0^{2\pi} = \ln \left(2 \cos \theta + 1 + j2 \sin \theta\right) \Big|_0^{2\pi} = 0$$

Some very remarkable formulas, known as *Cauchy integral formulas*, apply when $G(s)$ is analytic in a region of the s-plane and C is a simple closed path in the region. If s_0 is interior to closed path C, then the following formulas apply where the integral is taken in the positive sense around C (counterclockwise):

$$G(s_0) = \frac{1}{2\pi j} \oint_C \frac{G(s) \, ds}{s - s_0}$$

$$\frac{dG(s_0)}{ds} = \frac{1}{2\pi j} \oint_C \frac{G(s) \, ds}{(s - s_0)^2} \qquad (A-7)$$

$$\cdots \cdots \cdots \cdots \cdots$$

$$\frac{d^n G(s_0)}{ds^n} = \frac{n!}{2\pi j} \oint_C \frac{G(s) \, ds}{(s - s_0)^{n+1}}$$

The formulas show that the value of an analytic function and its derivatives at a point s_0 in a region are determined by the values of the function on the boundary of any curve C enclosing the point and lying in the region.

A-5. SINGULARITIES AND RESIDUES OF COMPLEX FUNCTIONS

Recall that a function $G(s)$ is analytic in a region of the s-plane if it is single-valued and has a finite derivative at each point in that region. Points at which a single-valued function $G(s)$ is not analytic are called *singular points*. The singular points of a function of a complex variable determine its behavior throughout the s-plane, and an analytic function having no singularities is a constant. A point where a function becomes infinite is always a singular point, but there can be singularities of other types where the function does not become infinite. The classification depends upon the manner in which the function or a derivative behaves as s approaches the singularity. An isolated singular point is a point interior to a region throughout which the function is analytic except at the point itself. The classification of singularities is discussed below.

Poles. When $G(s)$ is not finite at $s = p$ and when k is the smallest positive integer that makes the product

$$(s - p)^k G(s)$$

analytic at $s = p$, then the function $G(s)$ has a pole at $s = p$, of order k. Poles are the most commonly encountered singularities in linear control theory since all singularities of rational albegraic functions are poles. For example, $G_1(s) = 1/s$ has an isolated singular point (a pole) at $s = 0$ and $G_2(s) = (s + 1)/(s + 2)^2$ has a second-order pole at $s = -2$.

Essential Singularities. An essential singularity is a singular point $s = a$ of $G(s)$ where $G(s)$ is single-valued, its derivative $G'(s)$ does not exist, and where there is no integer k for which

$$\frac{d}{ds}\left[(s - a)^k G(s)\right]$$

exists at $s = a$. It can be shown that, as s approaches an essential singularity a, the function $G(s)$ can be made to approach any finite or infinite value by choosing the manner of approach for $s \to a$. The functions $\sin(1/s)$ and $e^{1/s}$ have an essential singularity at the origin and the function e^{rs} has one at infinity. Fortunately, they are seldom found in functions encountered in process engineering problems.

Branch Points. Branch points occur in multivalued functions and have the characteristic that the value of the function after completely traversing a closed path surrounding the branch point differs from the initial value of the function at that initial point. The functions $\ln s$ and s^k (k not an integer) each have a branch point at $s = 0$. Functions having branch points can be handled by limiting values of s to those for which the function is single-valued, e.g., $\ln s$ is analytic for $0 < \theta < 2\pi$.

Example A–3. Find and classify the singularities of the following functions:

    (a) $(s + a)/[s^2(s + b)(s - c)]$
    (b) $e^{1/s}$

Solution. (a) By inspection, the rational fraction has a second-order pole at $s = 0$, since the function $s^2 G(s)$ is analytic at zero; likewise, it has single poles at $-b$ and $+c$.

(b) The function $e^{1/s}$ can be represented by the series

$$G(s) = e^{1/s} = 1 + \frac{1}{s} + \frac{1}{2!s^2} + \frac{1}{3!s^3} + \cdots$$

from which it can be seen that the function is finite and single-valued at all values of s except $s = 0$. The derivative

$$G'(s) = -\frac{1}{s^2} e^{1/s}$$

exists everywhere except at $s = 0$. Therefore, the function has a singularity at $s = 0$. However the singularity is not a pole, because

$$sG(s) = s + 1 + \frac{1}{2!s} + \frac{1}{3!s^2} + \cdots$$

is not analytic at $s = 0$, and it is not a branch point, because the function is single-valued.   Therefore, the function has an essential singularity at $s = 0$.

Residues.   Every function $G(s)$, at each of its singular points, has a residue given as

$$\text{Res }[G(s);s_0] = \frac{1}{2\pi j} \oint_C G(s)\, ds \qquad (A\text{-}8)$$

where C is any closed curve around s_0 but excluding all other singularities of $G(s)$.   The function $G(s)$ is analytic everywhere on and within C except at $s = s_0$, and integration is in the counterclockwise direction (positive direction).   By Eq. A–6c, when the closed curve C does not enclose a singularity the integral vanishes.   The residue is a property only of the function with respect to the singular point, since its value is the same for all closed paths surrounding s_0 but surrounding no other singular point. The residue of $G(s)$ at $s = s_0$ is also the coefficient of the $(s - s_0)^{-1}$ term in the expansion of $G(s)$ in a series having both negative and positive integral powers of $(s - s_0)$.   If the singularity is a pole of order k at $s = s_0$, this latter identification of the residue as a coefficient in a power series gives an easier method of computing the residue as follows:

$$\text{Rule 1:}\quad \text{Res }[G(s);s_0] = \frac{1}{(k-1)!} \lim_{s \to s_0} \left[\frac{d^{k-1}}{ds^{k-1}} \{(s-s_0)^k G(s)\} \right] \quad (A\text{-}9a)$$

If the order of the pole at $s = s_0$ is not known, the rule may be applied by taking $k = 1, 2, \ldots$ until a finite limit is obtained for the residue. The value of k for which this occurs is the order of the pole.   At a first-order pole, $k = 1$, and the rule becomes:

$$\text{Rule 2:}\qquad \text{Res }[G(s);s_0] = \lim_{s \to s_0} (s-s_0)G(s) \qquad (A\text{-}9b)$$

When $G(s)$ is given as a ratio of two analytic functions $N(s)$ and $D(s)$ as

$$G(s) = \frac{N(s)}{D(s)}$$

and if $N(s_0) \neq 0$ and $D(s)$ has a first-order zero at $s = s_0$ (giving $G(s)$ a first-order pole at s_0), the residue is given as follows:

$$\text{Rule 3:}\qquad \text{Res }[G(s);s_0] = \frac{N(s_0)}{D'(s_0)} \qquad (A\text{-}9c)$$

which does not depend upon factoring $D(s)$.   The computation of a few residues is shown in the next example.

Example A–4.   Compute the residues of each of these functions at each singularity:

   (a) $(s + a)/[s^2(s + b)(s - c)]$
   (b) $(\sin s)^{-1}$
   (c) $s/(s^2 + 1)$

Solution. (a) This rational function has first-order poles at $-b$ and c and a second-order pole at zero. The residues are found as follows:

First-order pole at $-b$. Use rule 2; then

$$\text{Res } [G(s); -b] = \lim_{s \to -b} \frac{s+a}{s^2(s-c)} = \frac{b-a}{b^2(b+c)}$$

First-order pole at c. Use rule 2; then

$$\text{Res } [G(s); c] = \lim_{s \to c} \frac{s+a}{s^2(s+b)} = \frac{c+a}{c^2(c+b)}$$

Second-order pole at zero. Use rule 1; then

$$\text{Res } [G(s); 0] = \frac{d}{ds} \frac{s+a}{(s+b)(s-c)} \bigg|_{s=0}$$
$$= \frac{(s+b)(s-c) - (s+a)(2s+b-c)}{[(s+b)(s-c)]^2} \bigg|_{s=0}$$
$$= \frac{-bc - a(b-c)}{b^2 c^2}$$

(b) The function $(\sin s)^{-1}$ has a first-order pole at zero. Use of rule 1, or its equivalent in this case, rule 2, gives

$$\text{Res } [G(s); 0] = \lim_{s \to 0} \frac{s}{\sin s} = \lim_{s \to 0} \frac{1}{\cos s} = 1$$

using L'Hôpital's rule to find the limit.

(c) The function $s/(s^2 + 1)$ has two first-order poles, located at $+j$ and $-j$. The residues, found by using rule 3, are

$$\text{Res } [G(s); j] = \frac{s}{2s} = \frac{1}{2}$$

$$\text{Res } [G(s); -j] = \frac{s}{2s} = \frac{1}{2}$$

Cauchy's residue theorem states that, if C is a closed curve on and within which the function $G(s)$ is analytic except for a finite number of singular points within C, then the integral taken counterclockwise around curve C is equal to $2\pi j$ times the sum of the residues of $G(s)$ at each singular point within C, thus:

$$\oint_C G(s) \, ds = 2\pi j \sum_{i=1}^{k} \text{Res } [G(s); s_i] \qquad \text{(A–10)}$$

This theorem is useful in the inversion of Laplace transforms, as will be seen.

Argument Principle. The difference between the number of zeros, Z, and the number of poles, P, of $G(s)$ inside a closed curve C is given as

$$Z - P = \frac{1}{2\pi j} \oint_C \frac{G'(s)}{G(s)} \, ds = \frac{1}{2\pi j} \oint_C d \ln G(s) \qquad \text{(A–11)}$$

when $G(s)$ is analytic on the closed curve C and inside except for a finite number of poles within C, and provided $G(s)$ has no zeros on C and only a finite number of zeros within C.

Now $G(s)$ is complex along the curve C and the logarithm function can be written

$$\ln G(s) = \ln |G(s)| + j\angle G(s) \qquad (A\text{--}12)$$

The integration gives

$$\frac{1}{2\pi j} \oint_C d \ln G(s) = \frac{1}{2\pi j} [\ln |G(s)| + j\angle G(s)]_{s_0}^{s_1} = \frac{1}{2\pi} [\angle G(s_1) - \angle G(s_0)]$$

$$Z - P = \frac{1}{2\pi} \Delta_C \theta \qquad (A\text{--}13)$$

where s_0 and s_1 are the arbitrary beginning and end of the closed curve C and $\Delta_C \theta$ is the net change in angle of $G(s)$ about the origin as s moves along curve C. In other words $Z - P$ is the number of encirclements of the origin in the $G(s)$ plane.

This important theorem, called *Cauchy's argument principle*, is illustrated with the following example. Let

$$G(s) = \frac{s + 1}{(s - 1)(s^2 + 2s + 2)}$$

with poles at 1 and $-1 \pm j$ and a zero at -1, as shown on the s-plane in Fig. A–6a. Also shown there is the closed curve, $s = 2e^{j\theta}$, enclosing all

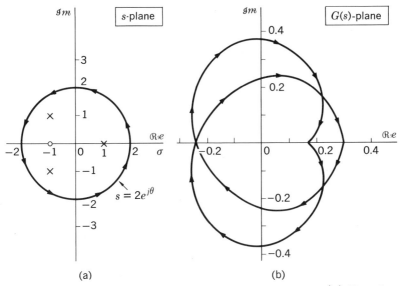

(a)   (b)

Fig. A–6. Illustration of Cauchy's argument principle. (a) The closed curve C on which s moves counterclockwise and the zero-pole map for $G(s)$. (b) Plot of $G(s)$ for $s = 2e^{j\theta}$. The arrows indicate direction of movement.

the poles and zeros of $G(s)$, and along which the point s moves in a counter-clockwise direction (taken as positive direction for angle θ). Now visualize s moving along closed curve C in the positive direction and the corresponding values of $G(s)$ tracing a path on the $G(s)$-plane in Fig. A–6b. When the point s traverses the closed curve C in the s-plane, the point $G(s)$ traces the closed $G(s)$ curve in the $G(s)$-plane. The $G(s)$ trace is in the negative direction and the net change in angle of $G(s)$ is -4π, giving the result

$$Z - P = \frac{1}{2\pi} \Delta_C \theta = \frac{1}{2\pi} (-4\pi) = -2$$

which is in agreement with the observed fact that $G(s)$, in this case, has an excess of poles over zeros of two within the boundary C. The same result is obtained by evaluating the integral along the circle $s = 2e^{j\theta}$:

$$\frac{1}{2\pi j} \oint_C d \ln G(s) = \frac{1}{2\pi j} \left\{ \oint_C d \ln (s+1) - \oint_C d \ln (s-1) \right.$$

$$\left. - \oint_C d \ln (s^2 + 2s + 2) \right\}$$

$$= \frac{1}{2\pi j} \left\{ \oint_C \frac{ds}{s+1} - \oint_C \frac{ds}{s-1} - \oint \frac{ds}{s+1+j} \right.$$

$$\left. - \oint \frac{ds}{s+1-j} \right\}$$

$$= \frac{1}{2\pi j} \{2\pi j - 2\pi j - 2\pi j - 2\pi j\} = -2$$

Since the closed boundary encloses the singularity of each term, the integrals are evaluated by use of Cauchy's residue theorem as given in Eq. A–10.

An important application of this theorem will be to determine the excess of zeros over poles of $G(s)$ in the right-half s-plane by making the boundary C enclose that area. (See Chapter 8.)

B

Liquid-Level Processes[*]

In the case of liquid-level processes and viscous liquid flow, a set of R, C, and L units based upon pressure in feet of fluid and flow in ft³/min is frequently used. Viscous flow results in a linear resistance given as

$$R = \frac{p}{i} \qquad \frac{\text{ft fluid-min}}{\text{ft}^3}$$

where p is the pressure drop across the resistance in feet of fluid and i is the flow rate in ft³/min.

The liquid capacitance of an open tank is defined as

$$C = \frac{d(\text{volume})}{d(\text{pressure})} = A \frac{dp}{dp} = A \qquad \frac{\text{ft}^3}{\text{ft fluid}}$$

where A is the cross-sectional area of the tank in ft², and p is the pressure in ft fluid.

The inertance of a liquid in a pipeline is defined as

$$L = \frac{d(\text{ft fluid})}{\dfrac{di}{dt}} = \frac{l}{gA} \qquad \text{ft fluid-min}^2/\text{ft}^5$$

where l is the pipeline length in ft, A is the cross-sectional area of the pipe in ft², and g is the gravitational acceleration in ft/min².

[*] Appendix B is supplementary to Chapter 3.

C

Analog Computer Magnitude and Time Scaling*

In order to get quantitative results from a computer program it is necessary to fix magnitude and time scale factors relating the process variable to the computer voltages. The magnitude must be scaled to ensure that the computer amplifier outputs remain within the linear range of the amplifier (± 100 volts or ± 10 volts usually). The time must be scaled for several reasons: to minimize computer errors, to save computer time, to stay within frequency range of the amplifiers and recording equipment, and to study the physical phenomena more effectively.

The necessity for time and magnitude scaling is shown by looking at the computer program for the second-order equation with no damping,

$$\frac{1}{\omega_n^2} \ddot{y} + y \ = \ 1 \qquad \dot{y}(0) = y(0) = 0 \qquad \text{(C--1a)}$$

This equation has the solution $y = 1 - \cos \omega_n t$, which is periodic and of frequency ω_n. The derivatives are

$$\dot{y} = \omega_n \sin \omega_n t \qquad \text{(C--1b)}$$
$$\ddot{y} = \omega_n^2 \cos \omega_n t \qquad \text{(C--1c)}$$

If the equivalence between the physical process variable and the computer voltage is one unit of y equals 1 volt, the maximum possible voltages representing the terms on the computer amplifiers are

$$\left.\begin{array}{ll} 0 \le y \le 2 & y_{\max} = 2 \\ -\omega_n \le \dot{y} \le \omega_n & \dot{y}_{\max} = \omega_n \\ -\omega_n^2 \le \ddot{y} \le \omega_n^2 & \ddot{y}_{\max} = \omega_n^2 \end{array}\right\} \qquad \text{(C--2)}$$

If ω_n is large (say, $\omega_n = 100$ rad/sec), some computer amplifiers may overload and also the recording equipment may not be able to follow the

---

* Appendix C is supplementary to Chapter 4.

442

problem solution. If ω_n is small, the computer solution will consume much machine time and computing errors will be increased. To make the best use of the computer, the problem should be scaled so that the computer voltages cover the full range of allowable values, and the problem frequencies are low enough to be followed by the recording equipment.

The types of recording equipment used with analog computers are oscilloscopes (very fast), galvanometer recorders (moderately fast), and servo-driven recorders (slow). Since electronic computer components can handle signals from zero to several thousand cycles per second, the recorder is the slow component in the system and its characteristics may dictate the need for time scaling. A servo recorder of good quality can easily follow frequencies of 1 rad/sec, so it is sometimes stated that 1 rad/sec is an optimum problem frequency. This gives rise to a rule-of-thumb suggestion that time-scale changes should make the coefficients in the differential equation approximately equal.

C-1. TIME SCALING

It is very easy to change the relative magnitude of the coefficients of a differential equation without changing the properties of the solution by making a proportional change in the time scale (independent variable). Let t represent problem time and τ represent machine time, and make the substitution

$$\tau = \beta t \qquad\qquad (C-3a)$$

which requires that

$$\frac{d}{dt} = \frac{d}{d(\tau/\beta)} = \beta \frac{d}{d\tau} \qquad \frac{d^n}{dt^n} = \beta^n \frac{d^n}{d\tau^n} \qquad (C-3b)$$

The scale factor β is the number of computer seconds equal to one second in the problem, so that when $\beta > 1$, the problem is slowed on the machine, and when $\beta < 1$, the problem is speeded up on the machine. Let x be a computer dependent variable (voltage); then

$$\frac{dx}{d\tau} = \frac{dx}{dt} \frac{dt}{d\tau} = \frac{1}{\beta} \frac{dx}{dt}$$

The computer integrates with respect to computer time τ, giving

$$x(\tau) = x(0) + \frac{1}{\beta} \int_0^\tau -\frac{dx}{dt} d\tau \qquad (C-3c)$$

The results of slow and fast time scaling are shown in Fig. C-1. Notice that the initial condition does not change with scale factor β. Thus, a general rule for time scaling may be stated: To obtain a time-scale factor β, computer seconds/problem second, multiply *each* integrator input by $1/\beta$.

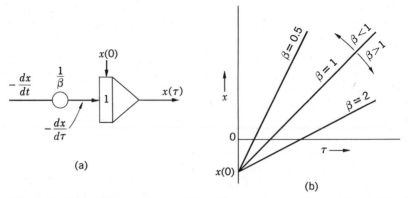

Fig. C–1. Time scaling of computer. The response is for a unit step input, $-dx/dt = -1$, and initial condition $x(0)$. (a) Computer program. (b) Computer response.

Differentiation in real time and in computer time can be represented as

Real time: $s = d/dt$
Computer time: $p = d/d\tau$

so that Laplace-transformed equations can be time-scaled by the substitution

$$s = \beta p$$

From another viewpoint, the capacitor is the only dynamic computer element, and its impedance in both time scales is

$$Z_c = \frac{1}{Cs} = \frac{1}{\beta C p}$$

which shows that C in real time corresponds to βC in computer time. Therefore, when all the capacitors in an analog computer program are changed by the scale factor β, the problem time scale is changed by $1/\beta$. Since the integrator gain is actually $1/RC$, the time change can be effected by changing either R or C so that generally a time change is obtained by multiplying all the integrator gains by the factor $1/\beta$.

C–2. MAGNITUDE SCALING

The analog computer manipulates voltages, whereas a process equation relates physical quantities; therefore it is necessary to select a magnitude scale factor for each dependent variable in the system. If the maximum expected values of each variable and its derivatives are known from experience with the actual physical plant, from inspection of the system equations, or from a wise guess, the magnitude scale factors may be defined as

$$k_i y_{i,\max} = V_{i,\max} \qquad k_i y_i = V_i \qquad \text{(C-4a)}$$

where y_i and $y_{i,\max}$ are any value and the maximum value of the problem variable, respectively; V_i and $V_{i,\max}$ are the corresponding computer voltages; and k_i is the scale factor for that variable. The maximum voltage range $V_{\max}$ of analog computers is usually 10 or 100 volts. Refer to the undamped second-order equation above and assume that the computer $V_{\max}$ is 100 volts; then the indicated scale factors are

$$k_y = 100/2 \quad k_{\dot y} = 100/\omega_n \quad k_{\ddot y} = 100/\omega_n{}^2 \qquad \text{(C-4b)}$$

For safety (in case $y_{i,\max}$ is too small) and convenience the scale factors usually are rounded off to a lesser value than the maximum value.

In terms of the general scale factors k_i and computer time τ, Eq. C-1a becomes

$$\frac{\beta^2}{\omega_n{}^2} \frac{[k_{\ddot y} \ddot y_\tau]}{k_{\ddot y}} + \frac{[k_y y_\tau]}{k_y} = 1$$

and

$$[\beta^2 k_{\ddot y} \ddot y_\tau] = \omega_n{}^2 k_{\ddot y} - \frac{\omega_n{}^2 k_{\ddot y}}{k_y} [k_y y_\tau] \qquad \text{(C-5)}$$

where the bracketed terms represent the respective amplifier output voltages in the computer. The integrator initial conditions $\ddot y_t(0)$, $\dot y_t(0)$, and $y_t(0)$, after time and magnitude scaling, become

$$[\beta^2 k_{\ddot y} \ddot y_\tau(0)] = k_{\ddot y} \ddot y_t(0) \quad [\beta k_{\ddot y} \dot y_\tau(0)] = k_{\ddot y} \dot y_t(0) \quad [k_y y_\tau(0)] = k_y y_t(0)$$

Notice that the time scaling has not changed the initial condition values. The computer program for solving this equation is given in Fig. C-2, where it is noted that the $1/\beta$ time-scale factor occurs in the input of each integrator.

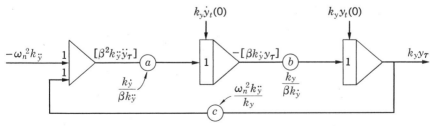

Fig. C-2. Computer program for solving Eq. C-1a with initial conditions and time and magnitude scaling.

Example C–1. Analog simulation of an oscillatory second-order system is requested. The analog computer uses a servo recorder. The equation for the system and its forcing function is

$$2\ddot{x} + 30\dot{x} + 200x = 400 \qquad x(0) = 10 \quad \dot{x}(0) = -20$$

Prepare a properly scaled computer program for the simulation.

Solution. (a) Time scaling. The system equation when rewritten as

$$\ddot{x} + 15\dot{x} + 100x = 200$$

shows that the system natural frequency $\omega_n = \sqrt{100} = 10$ rad/sec is too high for satisfactory use with a servo recorder. Therefore, the problem situation will be slowed by a factor of 5. On substitution of $\tau = 5t$, the time-scaled equation becomes

$$\ddot{y} + 3\dot{y} + 4y = 8$$

where $y(\tau) = x(5t)$. The initial conditions become

$$x(0) = y(0) = 10 \quad \dot{y}(0) = \tfrac{1}{5}\dot{x}(0) = -4$$

(b) Magnitude scaling. Assuming that the computer range is 100 volts and that the maximum values of the variables are as listed in the following table, then a first estimate of magnitude-scale factors is derived from Eq. C–4b, and they are listed as

Variable	Max. value, est.	k
y	10	10
$\dot{y}$	20	5
$\ddot{y}$	40	2.5

After substituting the scale factors k_i and solving for the highest derivative, the working equation for the computer simulation is

$$[2.5\ddot{y}] = 20 - [10y] - 1.5[5\dot{y}]$$

where the bracketed terms are the computer voltages. The computer program is given in Fig. C–3, where it is seen that amplifier 1 sums the signals to give

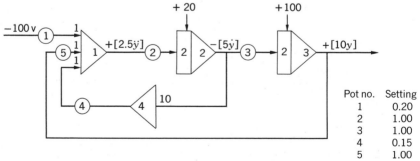

Pot no.	Setting
1	0.20
2	1.00
3	1.00
4	0.15
5	1.00

Fig. C–3. Computer program illustrating time and magnitude scaling.

$+[2.5\ddot{y}]$, amplifier 2 integrates $]2.5\ddot{y}]$ and multiplies by the scale factor ratio $5/2.5$ to give $-[5\dot{y}]$, amplifier 3 integrates $-[5\dot{y}]$ and multiplies by the scale factor ratio $\frac{10}{5}$ to give $+[10y]$, the answer. Amplifier 4 changes the sign of signal $-[5\dot{y}]$ and multiplies by 10, which enables pot 4, set at 0.15, to give the signal $+1.5[5\dot{y}]$.

Observe that the setting of pot 2 multiplied by the gain of amplifier 2 must equal the scale ratio $k_{\dot{y}}/k_{\ddot{y}}$. Likewise, the setting of pot 3 multiplied by the gain of amplifier 3 must equal the scale ratio $k_y/k_{\dot{y}}$. Do not forget that the answer $[10y]$ is both time- and magnitude-scaled.

D

Nichols Chart for Open-Loop-to-
Closed-Loop Transformation[*]

The open-loop-to-closed-loop frequency response transformation is conveniently obtained from a Nichols chart plot and the M and α grid lines, as shown on Fig. A–5b. The open-loop transfer function is

$$G(j\omega) = Ae^{j\phi}$$

where A is the magnitude ratio and ϕ is the phase angle. Then the closed-loop frequency response is obtained as

$$\frac{G(j\omega)}{1 + G(j\omega)} = \frac{A(\cos\phi + j\sin\phi)}{1 + A(\cos\phi + j\sin\phi)} = M\underline{/\alpha}$$

from which

$$M = \left|\frac{G}{1+G}\right| = \frac{1}{\left[\left(\frac{1}{A} + \cos\phi\right)^2 + \sin^2\phi\right]^{1/2}}$$

$$\angle\alpha = \underline{/\frac{G}{1+G}} = \phi - \tan^{-1}\left[\sin\phi\bigg/\left(\frac{1}{A} + \cos\phi\right)\right] = \tan^{-1}\left[\frac{\sin\phi}{A + \cos\phi}\right]$$

Grid lines of constant M and α values given by these equations are shown on the Nichols chart in Fig. D–1. The chart is actual size to fit standard graph paper with a log scale of 2 inches per cycle and an arithmetic scale of 20° per inch.

[*] Appendix D is supplementary to Chapter 8.

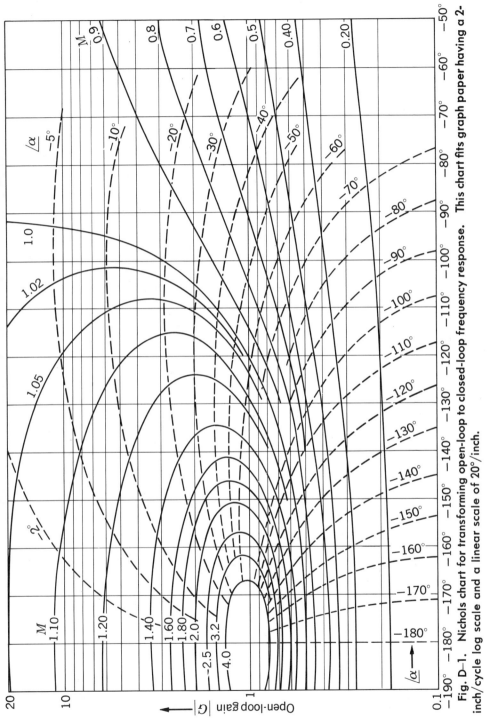

Fig. D-1. Nichols chart for transforming open-loop to closed-loop frequency response. This chart fits graph paper having a 2-inch/cycle log scale and a linear scale of 20°/inch.

449

E

Correlation of Transient and Frequency Response[*]

Both transient response and frequency response of process systems are important. Design and analysis for transient response is accomplished by means of the root locus on the s-plane while the frequency response manipulations are made on the $G(j\omega)$-plane. Since the root-locus plot includes all values of $s = \sigma + j\omega$, the nature of the correlation between the frequency and transient responses is easiest to demonstrate on the s-plane. The exact correlation depends upon the system transfer function. Table E–1 gives frequency loci and root loci for a few simple open-loop transfer functions. The frequency locus is the conformal transformation of the $s = j\omega$ axis on the s-plane into the $G(j\omega)$ plane. The root locus is the contour of all points in the s-plane that make the phase angle of $G(s)$ equal to $-180°$; hence it is the conformal transformation of the negative real axis of $G(j\omega)$ onto the s-plane. This transformation is the basis for a correlation between frequency and transient responses. An especially significant point is the $G(j\omega)$ at $\underline{/-180°}$ marked ω_1 on the diagrams in item 3 of Table E–1. On the root locus it corresponds to onset of instability while on the frequency response plot it denotes instability only if it passes through the $-1 + j0$ point. In addition, the frequency ω_1 is the maximum possible bandwidth of the closed-loop system since the resonant frequency in a minimum phase system is always less than frequency ω_1, of unstable oscillation.

Another correlation between transient and frequency response of systems resides in the relationship between M_p and ζ, and ω_r and ω_d. In Chapter 6 the exact relationships for a second-order system are

$$M_p = \frac{1}{2\zeta \sqrt{1 - \zeta^2}} \qquad 0 < \zeta < 0.707 \qquad (6\text{--}16c)$$

$$\omega_r = \omega_n \sqrt{1 - 2\zeta^2} \qquad (6\text{--}16d)$$

[*] Appendix E is supplementary to Chapter 8.

450

For higher-order systems, the relationships are more involved and not readily obtained without making both the root locus and Bode plots. Because a properly adjusted feedback control system shows the under-damped characteristics of a second-order system (caused by a dominant pair of complex roots) there is always the tendency to relate M_p with ζ, and ω_r with ζ and ω_n for all systems.

The transient and frequency response functions are exactly related through the Fourier transform. In Chapter 4 the frequency response was shown to be related to the impulse response $w(t)$ as

$$G(j\omega) = \int_0^\infty w(t)e^{-j\omega t}\,dt \qquad (E\text{--}1)$$

which is the Fourier transform of the impulse response. For stable systems, the inverse Fourier transform gives the impulse response from the frequency response $G(j\omega)$ as

$$w(t) = \frac{1}{2\pi}\int_{-\infty}^\infty G(j\omega)e^{j\omega t}\,d\omega = \frac{1}{\pi}\int_0^\infty G(j\omega)e^{j\omega t}\,d\omega \qquad (E\text{--}2a)$$

Now $e^{j\omega t}$ can be expanded by Euler's relationship and $G(j\omega)$ can be written in its complex form to give

$$w(t) = \frac{1}{\pi}\int_0^\infty [\Re e\, G(j\omega) + j\,\Im m\, G(j\omega)](\cos \omega t + j \sin \omega t)\,d\omega$$

$$= \frac{1}{\pi}\int_0^\infty [\Re e\, G(j\omega)] \cos \omega t\,d\omega - \frac{1}{\pi}\int_0^\infty [\Im m\, G(j\omega)] \sin \omega t\,d\omega \qquad (E\text{--}2b)$$

Since there is no response for negative time, the fact that $c(-t) = 0$ gives the relationship

$$\int_0^\infty [\Re e\, G(j\omega)] \cos \omega t\,d\omega = -\int_0^\infty [\Im m\, G(j\omega)] \sin \omega t\,d\omega$$

which when combined with Eq. E–2b gives the simple relationship for impulse response from the frequency response as

$$w(t) = \frac{2}{\pi}\int_0^\infty [\Re e\, G(j\omega)] \cos \omega t\,d\omega \qquad (E\text{--}2c)$$

When the integration is difficult to perform, a graphical procedure using straight-line approximations of $\Re e\, G(j\omega)$ can be employed by breaking up the integral into segments. Other time responses can be obtained from the impulse response of Eq. E–2c by the appropriate operations in the time domain; e.g., the step response is the integral of the impulse response.

The closed-loop frequency response of several pole-zero maps whose transient response was discussed in Chapter 7 are sketched in Table E–2. The first system in Table E–2 has a desirable type of frequency response

TABLE E–1
Frequency Loci and Root Loci for Simple Systems

Process System	Nyquist Plot on $G(j\omega)$-Plane	Root Locus on s-Plane
1. $\dfrac{1}{s(\tau s + 1)}$		
2. $\dfrac{\tau_1 s + 1}{s(\tau_2 s + 1)}$		
3. $\dfrac{1}{s(\tau_1 s + 1)(\tau_2 s + 1)}$		
4. $\dfrac{1}{s\left(\dfrac{s^2}{\omega_n^2} + 2\dfrac{\zeta}{\omega_n} s + 1\right)}$		
5. $\dfrac{\tau_3 s + 1}{s(\tau_1 s + 1)(\tau_2 s + 1)}$		
6. $\dfrac{\tau_1 s + 1}{\dfrac{s^2}{\omega_n^2} + \dfrac{2\zeta}{\omega_n} s + 1}$		

which is characterized by a closed loop pole-zero map having a pair of dominant complex poles. The transient response will show an underdamped response. When all the poles are simple, the frequency response has the shape given in case 2. If a simple pole dominates a pair of complex poles as in case 3 the transient response is sluggish (see Fig. 7–11 with

TABLE E-2
Frequency Response Loci for Simple Pole-Zero Maps

Pole-Zero Map on s-Plane	Magnitude Ratio	Phase Angle

$c = 2$ and $b = 0.5$). By experience gained from using the frequency response method, it is known that a minimum in the magnitude ratio as in case 3 results in unsatisfactory transient response. Case 4 shows that the effect of the zero is to lessen the phase angle at low frequency and increase the bandwidth. If the zero is close to the origin, corresponding to large derivative action ($1/\tau_d$ is small), the magnitude ratio will show a high peak and the overshoot in the transient response will be serious. These cases emphasize that the process engineer should examine the closed-loop magnitude ratio and phase angle when fixing an M_p value to be sure that the system transient response will be satisfactory.

F

Frequency Response from Pulse Testing[*]

It might appear that experimental frequency response data are relatively simple to obtain for any type of process system. This may well be so in electrical and mechanical systems. However, in processing systems, not only are there formidable problems in generating sinusoidal signals in processing variables such as compositions, temperatures, and flows but the time constants encountered in processing systems are often so large that experimental frequency response tests are impracticable. For example, it may take hours for a large processing unit to attain steady state at a single frequency. In addition, the manufacturing department of the plant for good economic reasons may limit the time and extent of plant tests in order to minimize the interruption of normal production activities.

Fortunately, pulse testing circumvents most of the usual objections to dynamic plant tests and is a reliable experimental technique when certain conditions are met. Pulse testing, therefore, effectively exchanges experimental difficulties for computational complexities. However, with the common availability of digital computers this is a fair exchange.

Since all responses of a given linear system depend on the same transfer function, differences in responses are due only to differences in the inputs. For any known input the response should be analyzable to yield the transfer function. Pulse testing uses a single known pulse input to excite the system at many frequencies, thereby obtaining the response to many frequencies from a single test. The pulsed system should be at equilibrium initially. The best shape of pulse to use is still under study, although it seems clear that initial and final values should be the same and the shape should be selected for a frequency content that will excite the desired dynamics of the system. The frequency content of a pulse (obtained

[*] Appendix F is supplementary to Chapter 8.

from a Fourier analysis) increases as the pulse width decreases and, generally, it is expected that a pulse width approximately equal to the largest process time constant will have sufficient frequency content to excite the plant in the frequency range of interest.   In general, narrow high pulses are preferable to broad low pulses.

For a mathematical relationship of pulse response to frequency response, consider the input to be a function $m(t)$ and the output to be $c(t)$.   The system transfer function is related to the Laplace transformations of input and output by the defining relationship

$$G(s) = \frac{\mathcal{L}[c(t)]}{\mathcal{L}[m(t)]} = \frac{\int_0^\infty c(t)e^{-st}\,dt}{\int_0^\infty m(t)e^{-st}\,dt}$$

The frequency response of the system becomes

$$G(j\omega) = \frac{\int_0^\infty c(t)e^{-j\omega t}\,dt}{\int_0^\infty m(t)e^{-j\omega t}\,dt}$$

and applying the Euler relationship for $e^{-j\omega t}$, it is

$$G(j\omega) = \frac{\int_0^\infty c(t)[\cos \omega t - j \sin \omega t]\,dt}{\int_0^\infty m(t)[\cos \omega t - j \sin \omega t]\,dt} = \frac{A - jB}{C - jD}$$

where $A = \displaystyle\int_0^\infty c(t) \cos \omega t\,dt$

$B = \displaystyle\int_0^\infty c(t) \sin \omega t\,dt$

$C = \displaystyle\int_0^\infty m(t) \cos \omega t\,dt$

$D = \displaystyle\int_0^\infty m(t) \sin \omega t\,dt$

Finally, the frequency response is computed as

$$G(j\omega) = \frac{AC + BD}{C^2 + D^2} + j\frac{AD - BC}{C^2 + D^2}$$

from which the magnitude ratio and phase angle can readily be obtained as

$$|G(j\omega)| = \{[\mathfrak{Re}\, G(j\omega)]^2 + [\mathfrak{Im}\, G(j\omega)]^2\}^{1/2}$$

$$\angle G(j\omega) = \tan^{-1}\frac{\mathfrak{Im}\, G(j\omega)}{\mathfrak{Re}\, G(j\omega)}$$

The actual computational problem is the evaluation of the integrals A, B, C, and D at a number of different frequencies. In the general case, $m(t)$ and $c(t)$ are graphical recordings of the experimental data and A, B, C, and D must be evaluated by some numerical integration procedure. The details of the numerical integration are beyond the purpose of this text.* However, a FORTRAN program for carrying out the integration and calculating the gain and phase angle directly from experimental pulse test data is listed here.

The following FORTRAN program† is used in the normal manner with the experimental test data listed on data cards added to the program. It is found that normal experimental error becomes increasingly significant in the calculations at higher frequencies and the program will terminate itself when the normal frequency content falls below 0.2. The printout table will list frequency, magnitude ratio, and phase angle. The format of the data cards is readily obtained from the program listing, and the mnemonics for the variables are defined here.

Card (1) **FORMAT** (7F10.4)

>   **OMEGI**—The initial value of ω.
>   **OMEGF**—The final value of ω.
>   **DOMEG**—The logarithmic increment at which ω is to increase. Usually about 0.1 is satisfactory.
>   **DLTX**—Time increment between the points on the input pulse.
>   **DLTY1, DLTY2**—Time increments between points on the output pulse. Two different size increments are possible. The last point for **DLTY1** must be repeated as the first point for **DLTY2** increments.

Card (2) **FORMAT** (7F10.4)

>   **XSS**—Steady-state value of input pulse.
>   **YSS**—Steady-state value of output pulse. These are subtracted from all of the X's and Y's and reduce the data to "displacements from steady-state."

---

* For more information on pulse testing see, W. C. Clements, Jr., and K. B. Schnelle, Jr., "Pulse Testing for Dynamic Analysis," *I&EC Process Design and Development*, **2**, 94–102 (1963).

† This computer program was written by T. M. Pell.

Card (3) **FORMAT** (7I10) must be right justified!

> **MFX**—Number of input points (odd number).
> **MFY1**—Number of output points with **DLTY1** increment (odd number).
> **MFY2**—Number of output points with **DLTY2** increment (odd number).
> **NRUN**—Identification of number of run.

Card (4) (several) **FORMAT** (7F10.4)

> Data for input $x(t)$

Card (5) (several) **FORMAT** (7F10.4)

> Data for output $y(t)$

$X(M)$ and $Y(M)$ are input and output points, respectively. They are to be punched on data cards, 7 points to a card, until all of the data points are given.

```
C     FORTRAN PROGRAM TO CALCULATE FREQUENCY RESPONSE FROM PULSE DATA
      DIMENSION X(100), Y1(100), Y2(100), Z(100)
100   READ INPUT TAPE 5, 1, OMEGI, OMEGF, DOMEG, DLTX, DLTY1, DLTY2
      READ INPUT TAPE 5, 1, XSS, YSS
      READ INPUT TAPE 5, 2, MFX, MFY1, MFY2, NRUN
      READ INPUT TAPE 5, 1, (X(M), M = 1, MFX)
      READ INPUT TAPE 5, 1, (Y1(M), M = 1, MFY1)
      READ INPUT TAPE 5, 1, (Y2(M), M = 1, MFY2)
1     FORMAT (7F10.0)
2     FORMAT (7I10)
      WRITE OUTPUT TAPE 6, 3, NRUN
3     FORMAT (53HO      FREQUENCY RESPONSE FROM PULSE DATA, RUN NUMBER,
     112///)
      DO 101 M = 1, MFX
101   X(M) = X(M) − XSS
      DO 102 M = 1, MFY1
102   Y1(M) = Y1(M) − YSS
      DO 103 M = 1, MFY2
103   Y2(M) = Y2(M) − YSS
      XODD = 0.
      XEVEN = 0.
      I = MFX − 1
      DO 4 M = 2, I, 2
4     XEVEN = XEVEN + X(M)
      J = MFX − 2
      DO 5 M = 3, J, 2
5     XODD = XODD + X(M)
      AIPX = (DLTX/3.)*(X(1) + 4.*XEVEN + 2.*XODD + X(MFX))
9     OMEG = OMEGI
48    JSHXY = 1
10    GO TO (11, 12, 13, 14), JSHXY
```

```
11 DO 20 M = 1, MFX
20 Z(M) = X(M)
   JSHXY = 2
   MF = MFX
   DLT = DLTX
   TTOT = 0.
   GO TO 15
12 DO 21 M = 1, MFY1
21 Z(M) = Y1(M)
   JSHXY = 3
   MF = MFY1
   DLT = DLTY1
   TTOT = 0.
   GO TO 15
13 DO 22 M = 1, MFY2
22 Z(M) = Y2(M)
   JSHXY = 4
   MF = MFY2
   DLT = DLTY2
   CMFY1 = MFY1
   TTOT = DLTY1*(CMFY1 − 1.)
15 CMF = MF
   SODD = 0.5*Z(1)*SINF(OMEG*TTOT) + 0.5*Z(MF)*SINF(OMEG*((CMF − 1.)
  1      *DLT + TTOT))
   K = MF − 2
   DO 16 M = 3, K, 2
   CM = M
16 SODD = SODD + Z(M)*SINF(OMEG*((CM − 1.)*DLT + TTOT))
   SEVEN = 0.
   L = MF − 1
   DO 17 M = 2, L, 2
   CM = M
17 SEVEN = SEVEN + Z(M)*SINF(OMEG*((CM − 1.)*DLT + TTOT))
   CODD = 0.5*Z(1)*COSF(OMEG*TTOT) + 0.5*Z(MF)*COSF(OMEG*((CMF − 1.)
  1      *DLT + TTOT))
   DO 18 M = 3, K, 2
   CM = M
18 CODD = CODD + Z(M)*COSF(OMEG*((CM − 1.)*DLT + TTOT))
   CEVEN = 0.
   DO 19 M = 2, L, 2
   CM = M
19 CEVEN = CEVEN + Z(M)*COSF(OMEG*((CM − 1.)*DLT + TTOT))
   THE = OMEG*DLT
   IF (THE − 0.75) 43, 44, 44
43 ALA = (2.*THE**3.)/45. − (2.*THE**5.)/315. + (2.*THE**7.)/4725.
   BTA = 0.6666667 + (2.*THE**2.)/15. − (4.*THE**4.)/105.
  1      + (2.*THE**6.)/567. − (4.*THE**8.)/22275.
   GMA = 1.3333333 − (2.*THE**2.)/15. + (THE**4.)/270. −
  1       (THE**6.)/11340. + (THE**8.)/997920.
   GO TO 99
44 ALA = 1./THE + (SINF(2.*THE))/(2.*THE**2.) − (2.*(SINF(THE))**2.)
  1      /(THE**3.)
   BTA = 2.*(((COSF(THE)**2.) + 1.)/(THE**2.) − (SINF(2.*THE))
  1      /(THE**3.))
   GMA = 4.*((SINF(THE))/(THE**3.) − (COSF(THE))/(THE**2.))
99 SINTR = DLT*(ALA*(Z(1)*COSF(OMEG*TTOT) − Z(MF)*COSF(OMEG*((CMF −
  1      1.)*DLT + TTOT))) + BTA*SODD + GMA*SEVEN)
   CINTR = DLT*(ALA*(Z(1)*COSF(OMEG*TTOT + 1.5707963) − Z(MF)
```

```
  1      *COSF(OMEG*((CMF - 1.)*DLT + TTOT) + 1.5707963)) +
  2      BTA*CODD + GMA*CEVEN)
   GO TO (30, 30, 31, 32), JSHXY
30 C = CINTR
   D = SINTR
   GO TO 10
31 A1 = CINTR
   B1 = SINTR
   GO TO 10
32 A = CINTR + A1
   B = SINTR + B1
14 E = C**2. + D**2.
   CIMAG = (A*D - B*C)/E
   REAL = (A*C + B*D)/E
   CMR = SQRTF(CIMAG**2. + REAL**2.)
   PHI = ATANF(CIMAG/REAL)
   PHID = 57.29578*PHI
   IF (PHID) 200, 200, 210
200 IF (CIMAG) 220, 220, 201
201 PHID = -180. + PHID
202 GO TO 220
210 IF (CIMAG) 201, 201, 213
213 PHID = -360. + PHID
220 DBMR = (20.0/2.303)*LOGF(CMR)
   CNFC = ABSF((SQRTF(E))/AIPX)
   IF (CNFC - 0.200) 24, 23, 23
24 WRITE OUTPUT TAPE 6, 40
40 FORMAT (61H NORMALIZED FREQUENCY CONTENT BELOW 0.2, PROGRAM DISCON
  1TINUED////)
   GO TO 50
23 WRITE OUTPUT TAPE 6, 41, OMEG, CNFC, CMR, PHID, DBMR
41 FORMAT (6H FREQ = F13.8, 6H NFC = F8.5, 5H MR = F10.5,
  1       8H ANGLE = F12.6, 10H MR(DB) = F11.6)
   COMEG = (LOGF(OMEG))/2.303 + DOMEG
   OMEG = 10.**COMEG
   IF (OMEG - OMEGF) 48, 48, 50
50 GO TO 100
   END
```

G

Analog Computer Simulation of Systems*

The general-purpose analog computer is ideally suited for use as a model for assistance in process control design. Special analog computers may be used as active components in the plant control system. The emphasis here is on computer simulation of the control system for design experimentation. Good simulation practice requires that the computer program be developed in terms of the physical system for maximum human ease in interpreting and altering the computer hardware. To satisfy this criterion, each component of the system should correspond to an isolatable portion of the program with each component parameter represented by one adjustment on the computer. The programmer should work from the component descriptions (differential equation or transfer function) rather than from the overall system description.

As introduced in Chapter 4 and discussed further in Chapter 10, the basic unit of an analog computer is the operational amplifier, whose dynamic characteristics are determined by the input and feedback impedances. A simplified analysis of the amplifier under practical conditions assumes that the grid current and grid voltage are zero. The current summation at the grid gives

$$i_i + i_f = 0 \qquad \text{(G–1)}$$

These currents must be currents into the grid due to input and output voltages; therefore the Z_i and Z_f must be transfer impedances. The driving point impedance is the ratio of voltage to current produced. These concepts are identical for many circuits but the difference is clear for the circuit in Fig. G–1b where the driving point impedance is e_i/i_i and the transfer impedance is e_i/i_r. With this in mind, the operational amplifier

---

* Appendix G is supplementary to Chapter 10.

TABLE G-1
RC Transfer Impedance Functions

Function	Network	Parameters
1. K		$K = R$
2. $\dfrac{1}{Ks}$		$K = C$
3. $\dfrac{\tau s + 1}{Ks}$		$\tau = RC$ $K = C$
4. $\dfrac{K}{\tau s + 1}$		$\tau = RC$ $K = R$
5. $K(\tau s + 1)$		$\tau = RC/2$ $K = 2R$
6. $\dfrac{1}{Ks}\left(\dfrac{\tau_1 s + 1}{\tau_2 s}\right)$		$\tau_1 = R(C_1 + C_2)$ $\tau_2 = RC_2$ $K = C_1$
7. $K\left(\dfrac{a\tau s + 1}{\tau s + 1}\right)$ $a < 1$		$\tau = (R_1 + R_2)C$ $K = R_1$ $a = R_2/(R_1 + R_2)$
8. $K\left(\dfrac{\tau s + 1}{a\tau s + 1}\right)$ $a < 1$		$\tau = \dfrac{R}{2}(C_1 + C_2)$ $K = 2R$ $a = 2C_2/(C_1 + C_2)$
9. $\dfrac{1}{Ks}\left(\dfrac{a\tau s + 1}{\tau s + 1}\right)$ $a < 1$		$\tau = R_2 C$ $K = R_1 C/(R_1 + R_2)$ $a = 2R_1/(R_1 + R_2)$
10. $\dfrac{1}{Ks}\left(\dfrac{\tau s + 1}{a\tau s + 1}\right)$ $a < 1$		$\tau = RC_2$ $K = C_1 + C_2$ $a = C_1/(C_1 + C_2)$

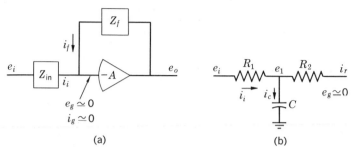

Fig. G–1. (a) Analog computer operational amplifier. (b) Illustration of transfer impedance.

equation is

$$\frac{e_i}{Z_i} + \frac{e_o}{Z_f} = 0 \quad \text{or} \quad e_o = -\frac{Z_f}{Z_i} e_i \quad \text{(G–2)}$$

A table of transfer impedance functions would expedite the programming of transfer functions for analog computers. Such a table is given in Table G–1 and can be built up by circuit analysis as shown below for the RC network in Fig. G–1b.

The current summation at the node whose voltage is $e_1(= R_2 i_r)$ gives

$$i_i = i_c + i_r$$

The currents as given by Ohm's law are substituted in this equation to give

$$\frac{e_i - R_2 i_r}{R_1} = Cs(R_2 i_r) + i_r = (R_2 Cs + 1)i_r$$

and the transfer impedance function is found as

$$Z_i = \frac{e_i}{i_r} = R_1(R_2 Cs + 1) + R_2 = 2R_2\left(\frac{R_1 C}{2} s + 1\right) \quad \text{(G–3)}$$

which is item 5 in Table G–1. Many more complex entries are possible for the table but using them, while making elegant use of the computer equipment, destroys the simple correlation between process system parameters and computer potentiometers that is so helpful to the process control engineer.

The tabulated functions are used by direct substitution into Eq. G–2. For example, the use of items 10 and 5 as feedback and input impedances, respectively, for one operational amplifier simulates the transfer function

$$e_o = -\frac{(\tau s + 1)e_i}{KK_i s(a\tau s + 1)(\tau_i s + 1)}$$

which represents a third-order differential equation. Whenever computing equipment is in short supply, the use of more complex transfer impedances is indicated.

Index

Active elements, 81
Actuating error, 20
Amplifier, operational, 392
  pneumatic, 128
Amplitude ratio, 144, 303
Analog computer, 121, 151, 442
  division, 405
  linear operations, 462
  nonlinear operations, 399
  programming, 151
  scaling, 443
Analogous elements, 85
  capacitance, 108
  inertance, 111
  resistance, 102
Analogous variables, 80
Angle, of asymptotes, 262
  of complex number, 41
Asymptote, Bode plot, 307, 314
  root locus, 261
Automatic control, 4
Automatic reset (PI), 184
Automation, 3

Bandwidth, 241
Basic components, 122
Bellows, 106
Blender, 363
Block diagram, 19, 21
  algebra, 26
  symbols, 22
Bode diagram, 304
  asymptotes, 307
  components in series, 312
  construction, 311
  controllers, 189
  distributed component, 310
  exothermic reaction component, 310
  first-order system, 144, 307
  inverse response component, 310
  limiting values, 314
  second-order system, 238
  transportation lag, 309
Bode stability criterion, 324

Capacitance, 103
  bellows, 106
  electrical, 103
  fluid, 104
  mechanical, 104
  thermal, 107
Cascade control, 289
Cauchy-Riemann equations, 433
Cauchy's argument principle, 439
Cauchy's theorem, 434
Characteristic equation, 214
  roots of, 255
Chemical reactor, 168, 406
Closed loop, 12, 212
  frequency response, 316
  sensitivity, 212
  stability, 215, 321
  system equations, 213
  systems, 12
  transient response, 217, 270
Comparator, 400
Compensation, 280, 332
Complex number, 39
Complex root, 45
Construction, of Bode plot, 311
  of mathematical model, 118
  of root locus, 258
Control system response, 217
  performance criteria, 234
Control terminology, 18
Control valve, 91
Controlled variable, 19
Controller, adjustment, 243
  analog simulation, 203
  calibration, 185
  ideal modes, 181
  mechanism, 192
  selection, 241
  transfer functions, 200
  tuning, 249
Convolution, 63
Convolution integral, 63, 140
Corner frequency, 190, 307

Criteria, Nyquist stability, 322
  root locus, 255
  Routh-Hurwitz, 47
  system performance, 234
Critical damping, 147, 256
Cubic equation, 49

Damped oscillation, 161, 256
Damping ratio, 147, 157, 235
Data processing, 391
  for analog control, 413
  gas chromatograph, 411
Dead time, 161, 383
Decay rate, 235
Decaying exponential, 57
Decibel, 304
Derivative action, 184, 284, 334
Derivative time, 185
Deviation variable, 31
Differential equations, 70
  analog computer solution, 151
  Laplace-transform solution, 64
Diodes, 393, 399
Direct digital control, 349
Distributed-parameter component, 165
Disturbance variable, 8
Division on analog computer, 405
Dominant roots, 258, 280, 293
Doublet function, 74
Dynamic error, 236

Electrical circuits, 119
Energy balance, 119
Enthalpy balance, 412
Electronic controller, 200
Error signal, 19
Exothermic reaction, 168

Feedback control, 15
Feedback dynamics, 222
Feedforward control, 15, 216, 416
  modeling, 352
Final control element, 91
Final-value theorem, 63, 278
First-order system (lag), 133
  analog simulation, 138
  frequency response, 145
  impulse response, 138
  interacting, 172
  step response, 140
Floating control action, 184
Fluid circuits, 119
Fluid manometer, 150
Follower operation, 18, 213
Force balance controller, 198
Forcing function, 71
Forward transfer function, 213

Frequency response, 300
  Bode diagram, 145, 304
  Bode stability criterion, 324
  closed loop, 316, 428, 448
  comparison with root locus, 328
  of components in series, 312
  construction of plots, 311
  of controllers, 188
  definition, 301
  experimental determination, 301
  of first-order component, 146
  Nichols chart, 448
  Nyquist plot, 304
  Nyquist stability criterion, 324
  performance criteria, 237
  from pulse test, 454
  of second-order component, 238
  by substituting $s = j\omega$, 303
  of systems, 311
  Ziegler-Nichols settings, 335
Function generation, 401

Gain, of component, 123
  of operational amplifier, 393
  ultimate, PB_u, 247
Gain margin, 240, 327
  design specification, 330
Gas absorber, optimization of, 360

Heat conduction, 165
Heat exchanger, analysis, 371
  control, 376
  resonance in, 376
Higher-order system, 277
Hydraulic controller, 203

Imaginary roots, 147, 256
Impedance, transfer, 462
Impulse function, 73
Impulse response, 112, 139
  relation to frequency response, 144
Inertance, 108
  electrical, 109
  fluid, 109
  mechanical, 109
  thermal, 110
Initial-value theorem, 63, 278
Input, 6, 71
Integral action, 333
Integral control, 224
Integral time, 184
Integrator, 129
Interacting components, 171, 378
Internal-reflux computer, 414
Inverse Laplace transform, 64
  table of operations, 62
  table of pairs, 56, 57

Inverse response component, 170
  frequency response, 310

Kirchhoff's law, 119

Lag component, 133
Laplace transform, 54
  of functions, 55
  of operations, 58, 62
  inversion of, 64
  in solution of differential equation, 64, 70
  in solution of partial differential equation, 165
Linear equation, 28
Linear system, 28
Linearization, 29
Liquid-level control, 217
Liquid-level dynamics, 135, 171
Load change compensation, 216
Loop gain, 214
Loop transfer function, 213
Lumped-parameter models, 80, 117

Magnitude ratio, 144, 240
Magnitude scaling, 444
Manometer (mercury), 150
Mapping, complex, 423
Mass-spring damper, 149, 159
Material balance, 119
Mechanical circuits, 120, 149
Method of residues, 69
Mixing, 136
Modeling, 118
  for computer control, 351
Multiloop system, 289
Multiplication, 404
  quarter-square, 405
  servomultiplier, 404

Natural frequency, 147, 256
Negative feedback, 15, 214
Newton's law, 120
Nichols chart, 448
Non-interacting stages, 172
Nonlinear computer operations, 399, 404
Nonlinearities, 379
Non-minimum phase components, 309
Non-unity feedback, 222, 320
Nozzle-flapper device, 125
Nyquist plots, 304
Nyquist stability criterion, 322

Objectives of control, 5
Offset, 219
On-off control, 10

Open-loop system, 7
  transfer function, 6, 321
Operational amplifier, 392
Optimizing control modeling, 360
Output, 6
Overdamped system, 147
Overshoot, 157, 235

Padé circuit, 164
Padé polynomials, 162
Partial fraction expansion, 65
Peak attenuation, 157
  quarter-decay, 235, 249
Phase angle, 144
Phase lag, 144
Phase lead, 190
Phase margin, 240, 327
PID controller mechanism, 196
Pneumatic controller, 192
Pneumatic valve, 92
Polar plot (Nyquist), 304
Pole-zero map, 53
Poles, 435
Poles and zeros, 52
Polynomials, 44
  repeated roots, 50
  roots, 48
Potentiometer, 123
Process control computer, 348
Process models, 351
Process system inputs, 71
Proportional band, 183
Proportional component, 123, 183
Proportional control, 217, 281, 336
Proportional controller mechanism, 193
Proportional-derivative control, 231, 284, 338
Proportional-integral control, 227, 283, 338
Proportional-integral-derivative control, 284
Proportional speed floating, 184
Pulse function, 75
Pulse testing, 454
Pump characteristics, 82

Quality control, 363
Quarter-square multiplier, 405

Ramp function, 56, 73
Ramp response, 112
RC circuit, 133
Reaction, chemical, 137
Reactor simulation, 406
Regulator operation, 18, 213
Reset, 184
Residue, 437

Residue theorem, 69, 438
Resistance, 85
    electrical, 87
    fluid, 87
    mechanical, 87
    radiation, 101
    thermal, 100
Resonance in heat exchanger, 376
Resonant frequency, 237, 295, 297
Resonant peak, 237
Response, 6
    of first-order lag, 139
    of ideal controllers, 188
    of process elements, 111
Response time, 11
Rise time, 235
Root locus, 254
    comparison with frequency response,
      297
    dominant roots, 280
    frequency and damping from, 256
    rules for plotting, 260
    step response from, 270
    transportation lag, 291
Roots of polynomials, 45
Routh-Hurwitz criterion, 46
Rules, for block diagrams, 26
    for root loci, 260
    for transfer loci, 311
Rules of thumb, 334

s-plane, 46, 423
Scaling analog computer, 442
Scaling process computer, 416
Second-order system, 146
    analog simulation, 151, 442
    dynamic parameters ζ and ω_n, 147
    frequency response, 308
    impulse response, 154
    step response, 154
    transfer function, 146
Set point, 179, 212
Settling time, 235
Signal, 6, 22
Signal flow diagram, 21
    reduction rules, 26
Single-speed floating control, 184
Singularities, 435
Sinusoidal forced response, 300
Sketching root loci, 258
    transfer loci, 311
Speed of response, 235
Spirule, 265
Spring-mass damper, 159
Steady state, 11
    error, 236

Step function, 55, 72
Step response related to ζ, 159
Step testing, 141
Signal summing, 22
Stability, 215, 322
    Bode criterion, 324
    Nyquist criterion, 322
    Routh-Hurwitz criterion, 46
Superposition, 28, 55
System, 6
Systems engineering, 4

Table of Laplace-transform pairs, 56, 57,
    62
Taylor's series expansion, 29
Test input signals, 72
Thermal circuits, 119
Thermometer dynamics, 137
Third-order system, 49
Three-mode controller, 191
Time constant, 133, 141
Time scaling computer, 443
    Laplace transform, 63
Time to first zero error, 236
Transfer function, 54
Transient response from frequency re-
    sponse, 450
Transportation lag, 161
    computer simulation, 163
    root-locus plot, 291
    transfer function, 162
Two-parameter model, 245

Ultimate period, 247
Unity feedback, 316
Unstable component, 168
Unstable response, 170

Valve, control, 91
Valve characteristic, 92
    equal-percentage, 94
    linear, 94
    linearization, 93

Wheatstone bridge, 397

Zero-pole map, 53
    for controllers, 269
    transient response from, 270
Zeros and poles, 52
Zeros of polynomials, 45
Zero steady-state error, 215
Ziegler-Nichols method, 243, 246, 335